WESTERN FOREST INSECTS

R. L. Furniss
and
V. M. Carolin

Entomologists, Retired
Pacific Northwest Forest and Range Experiment Station
Forest Service

MISCELLANEOUS PUBLICATION NO. 1339

Issued November 1977

This publication supersedes "Insect Enemies of Western Forests,"
Miscellaneous Publication No. 273.

U.S. Department of Agriculture   **Forest Service**

For sale by the Superintendent of Documents, U.S. Government Printing Office
Washington, D.C. 20402
Stock Number 001-000-03618-1
Catalog No. 1.38-1339

PREFACE

This manual concerns itself with insects and related organisms in forests and woodlands of North America, west of the 100th Meridian and north of Mexico. ("Eastern Forest Insects," by Whiteford L. Baker (1972) covers the area east of the 100th Meridian.) The intended primary users are practicing foresters and others responsible for preventing or minimizing insect-caused damage to forests and wood products. Thus, major purposes of the manual are to facilitate recognition of insects and their damage and to provide needed information for determining a course of action. The manual should also be useful to students of forestry and entomology, professional entomologists, extension specialists, forestry technicians, forest owners, forest recreationists, teachers, and others.

This manual supersedes "Insect Enemies of Western Forests," (Misc. Pub. No. 273), by F. Paul Keen, issued in 1938 and last revised in 1952. In this manual the discussion of insects is arranged in taxonomic order rather than by part of the tree affected. The number and kinds of insects and the geographic area covered are greatly increased. Photographs are used as a principal means of identification; no keys, either to the insects or their work, are included. No specific chemicals are mentioned.

Since the last revision of the manual by Keen, literature on technical forest entomology has been expanded greatly. Also, texts, research publications, and materials such as the Forest Pest Leaflets (now being revised and reissued as Forest Insect and Disease Leaflets by the Forest Service) are much more generally available. Thus, an extensive bibliography is included. The literature search was terminated during 1973, but some subsequent articles are cited because of their pertinence.

LIBRARY OF CONGRESS CATALOG CARD NO. 76–600049

ACKNOWLEDGMENTS

The preparation of an up-to-date manual on western forest insects was assigned to the authors in 1967 by Dr. James A. Beal, then director of Forest Insect and Disease Research, Forest Service, U.S. Department of Agriculture. Inspiration and encouragement came from F. Paul Keen, whose "Insect Enemies of Western Forests" served as a classic handbook for 35 years.

Many people contributed in various ways to this manual. Included are the scores of individuals in the Western United States and Canada, whose published observations and findings are compiled and interpreted in this manual. Many, perhaps most, are cited as authors. To the others, our enduring thanks. In response to questionnaires and interviews, foresters and entomologists throughout the West have shaped the direction and coverage of the manual. Reward for their efforts will depend on the usefulness of the finished product.

Scientific names and taxonomic relationships were checked for accuracy by a number of specialists. The initial listing of species in the manual was reviewed by taxonomists in the California Department of Food and Agriculture, namely William R. Bauer, George M. Buxton, Tokuwo Kono, George T. Okumura, Terry N. Seeno, Marius S. Wasbauer, and Richard F. Wilkey, and by specialists in the Insect Identification and Beneficial Insect Introduction Institute, U.S. Department of Agriculture. The latter also provided information on insect distribution, host trees, and characteristics of closely related species. Significant contributions to the listing of species were made by Alan A. Berryman (Washington State University), John A. Schenk (University of Idaho), and several entomologists in the Canadian Forestry Service.

Technical reviews of chapters or parts of chapters were made by a number of Forest Service and Agricultural Research Service entomologists, as well as William F. Barr (University of Idaho), H. H. Keifer (State of California, retired), Gerald W. Krantz (Oregon State University), Gerald N. Lanier (State University of New York), Woodrow W. Middlekauff (University of California), Paul W. Oman (Oregon State University), Jerry A. Powell (University of California), Paul O. Ritcher (Oregon State University), Edward L. Smith (Seattle, Washington), Richard F. Wilkey (California Dept. of Food and Agriculture), and Stephen L. Wood (Brigham Young University). Help with certain technical details was provided by Alan A. Berryman, Donald E. Bright

(Entomology Research Institute, Canada), Leland R. Brown (University of California), Robert I. Gara (University of Washington), Ronald M. Hawthorne (California Dept. of Food and Agriculture), Norman E. Johnson (Weyerhaeuser Company), E. Gorton Linsley (University of California), Hector A. Richmond (Consultant), and Ronald W. Stark (University of Idaho), as well as several Forest Service entomologists.

Photographs and other illustrations were obtained, as credited in the legends, from individuals, previous publications, and from the files of the Canadian Forestry Service and the U.S. Forest Service. (Photographs in the Forest Service central file are designated by F–numbers; in Station files, by EPQ–numbers or others.) Several individuals in both the Canadian and U.S. forestry organizations made a special effort to obtain specific photos. Major credit for taking needed photos goes to Wallace C. Guy, now retired from the Pacific Northwest Forest and Range Experiment Station of the Forest Service.

Preparation of indexes required the patient help of several people on our Station staff, not all of whom were entomologists. The format for the Diagnostic Host Index and the procedures for developing the General Index were devised by Mary Wells (deceased).

We regret that the conscientious and competent assistance provided by certain people on our staff, in completing a myriad of meticulous tasks, cannot be personally acknowledged. Their efforts, however, were basic to the completion of this effort.

CONTENTS

PART II
INSECTS AND ALLIES

PART III
GLOSSARY, LITERATURE CITED, AND INDEXES

LIST OF TABLES

INTRODUCTION

The protection of forests from damage is basic in the practice of forestry. Among the destructive agents, insects rank with fire, diseases, and wind. Many kinds of insects are constantly at work in the forest and cause a steady drain on timber supplies. A relatively few species of insects periodically become epidemic and kill forest trees on extensive areas, causing great economic losses.

Injurious insects may be encountered in every forest operation, from the collection of seed through the planting, growing, and harvesting of trees; in the handling and protection of wood products; and in other forest land management activities. It is hoped that the information assembled in this manual will aid timber owners and foresters in recognizing the work of important western forest insects, in applying suitable control measures, or in adjusting forest practices so as to reduce losses from this source to the lowest possible point.

In this manual, forest insects are considered to be those that inhabit forests and related areas, including urban areas supporting tree growth. The emphasis is upon damaging insects that live in or upon trees, woody plants, and wood products. Beneficial insects, biting insects, and certain others of significance in multiple use of forest land are included by example and by reference to publications specifically concerning them.

HOW TO USE THIS MANUAL

This manual is designed primarily for the individual who has an insect to identify—and an example of its work. He can first leaf through the manual to see whether the insect or something similar to it is illustrated; related species and their pictures are grouped in the text. If the individual is not familiar with insects of his area, he should check table 3 on page 46, and related text to see if the insect is listed as one of the major pests.

A systematic approach is to turn to the host tree, say Douglas-fir, in the Diagnostic Host Index. There, under the part infested, say foliage, several insects will be listed. The next step is to consult the text and tables of species by genus and, by elimination, select the species that best fits the one in hand. Often it will be desirable to consult the text for both the species and its genus.

If the text is not sufficiently informative, the references should be consulted. Literature cited immediately following the name of an insect provides additional information about the insect and frequently lists other pertinent publications. Taxonomic publications usually are referenced after the name of the genus or higher category. References in the body of the text concern details, as when there are differences of opinion among observers.

If a particular insect is suspected and its name is known, the text material can be consulted for verification on the page indicated in the General Index. The page location for the principal text will be italicized.

Scientific names are given for all insects discussed in this manual. Specific names in parentheses are aliases under which additional published information may be found and are not always synonyms in the taxonomic sense. Generic names in brackets are recent synonyms or misapplied names. Common names approved by the Entomological Society of America (Anderson 1975) are used to the extent available. Other common names are from various sources, principally members of the Western Forest Insect Work Conference.

Names of trees and woody plants are as given in "Check List of Native and Naturalized Trees of the United States" (Little 1953), if listed; otherwise, as in "Standardized Plant Names" (Kelsey and Dayton 1942).

The range of insects is given in broad geographic terms or by limits of distribution when the range is very extensive, or by States and provinces when it is more localized. In some cases, insect range is related to that of the principal tree host or hosts.

Most measurements are given both in Metric and English units. A glossary is provided for technical terms that may be unfamiliar to some readers.

Part I
Forest Insects and their Environment

ROLE OF INSECTS IN THE FOREST

The question is frequently asked, "Where did these destructive forest insects come from?" The answer is that most of them have been here a long time. In the shale beds at Florissant, Colo., laid down 35 million years ago, are fossil remains of species in present day genera of roundheaded borers such as *Arhopalus, Leptura, Semanotus,* and *Phymatodes,* and of bark beetles such as *Hylastes, Hylurgops,* and *Leperisinus* (Leng 1920, Linsley 1961). Their role in those ancient days was as it is now, except that they were not competing then with man.

In the course of geologic time, many insects adapted to the forest environment. Bark beetles, roundheaded borers, flatheaded borers, and others became forest dwellers, true forest insects. Each kind of tree became host to many insects, for example, Douglas-fir (Bedard 1938), Jeffrey pine (Lange 1937), pinyon (Little 1943), oak (Brown and Eads 1965a), sequoia (De Leon 1952), and spruce (Brown 1941). Some trees proved more attractive than others. For example, pines and oaks are infested by far more insects and are affected more by them than are redwood and yew. Some insects acquired a major role in the life cycle and structure of extensive forests, such as the **western pine beetle** in ponderosa pine.

When man appeared upon the scene, he affected the forest insect relationships. Inadvertently, he began redistributing the insects such as those in the seeds he carried for food and those that clung to his body and belongings. He even ate some that were plentiful (Bodenheimer 1951). Commerce and travel by horse, ship, train, automobile, and airplane have speeded the process of insect dispersal (see Introduced Insects section). When man began using the forest intensively he came into direct competition with insects. Finally it became necessary to control the most destructive ones.

Most western forest insects are native, and are widely distributed. Their role is complex and ranges from benefactor to killer. The beneficial and innocuous ones are by far the most abundant. The destructive ones receive most attention because they affect man most directly. Their numbers fluctuate widely. Some periodically become epidemic and cause great economic losses over extensive areas. Some are important only locally under certain conditions. Some set the stage for other less aggressive ones. The biological role of insects is covered more fully under Habitat Relationships. Throughout this manual, emphasis is given to the harmful insects because they are the ones prompting action.

LOSSES CAUSED BY INSECTS

Forest insects cause losses by killing trees and by damaging trees and wood products. In western forests, these losses are great in total, varied in character and amount from year to year, and difficult to measure. Tree killing by insects has been and continues to be greatest in mature and overmature forests. As the forests are opened and put under management, opportunities to protect the remaining mature trees against insects are increased. This gain is somewhat offset by an increased need to protect young forests against damage by insects.

The economic impact of insects upon western forests is known only approximately because: (1) Killing by insects, diseases, fire, and other causes is interrelated, hence is difficult to assign by cause; (2) much insect-killed timber is salvaged in various stages of deterioration, hence is not a total loss; (3) reduction of quality, growth rate, and stocking by insects is difficult to measure; and (4) esthetic effects of insect-caused damage cannot be assigned precise monetary values. The most ambitious effort to identify and estimate insect-caused losses in the Western United States was in 1952 (USDA Forest Service 1958). For that year, insect-caused mortality of sawtimber in the Western States, including Alaska, was estimated to be 4.5 billion fbm. Insect-caused growth loss and growth impact for sawtimber was estimated to be 6.9 billion fbm. In 1952, insects also killed or damaged an estimated 2.2 billion fbm of young forest growing stock.

In mature timber of the West, the largest item of insect-caused loss is tree killing by bark beetles (fig. 1). The mortality is of two types—epidemic, that caused by beetle outbreaks, and endemic, that caused year after year by normal infestations. Epidemic mortality is conspicuous and sometimes reaches catastrophic proportions (table 1). The cause is readily identified, so concerted efforts often are made to do something about it through prevention, direct control, or salvage. Endemic mortality is large in total amount but widely scattered and mixed as to cause, hence practical countermeasures are limited to prevention through intensified forest management and to salvage.

Defoliating insects sometimes kill extensive stands of timber.

4

FIGURE 1.—A commercial pine stand in California badly
damaged by bark beetles.

More characteristically, they deform and retard the growth of
the infested trees. Major outbreaks usually occur at rather long
intervals, often affect hundreds of thousands of acres, last a few
years, and then subside rapidly (see tables 1 and 2 on page 6).
Lesser outbreaks occur from time to time causing some damage
locally. Between outbreaks, damage to timber by most defoliators
is nil.

Insect-killed trees increase forest-fire hazard. The foliage and
fine branches of recently killed trees provide flash fuel that often
gets a fire on its way. Conflagrations that defy control often run
through the dead timber and beyond. Long after trees are killed
by insects, they stand as snags inviting lightning to strike and
increasing the cost, difficulty, and danger of fire control. This is
a two-way relationship. Insects set the stage for fire. Fires kill
trees that then breed insects.

Insects also adversely affect wood products, range plants, shelterbelts, and esthetic and recreational values; see the sections
concerning these subjects. For more detailed current information on insect-caused losses and the insects that cause them, the
reader should consult the annual reports by the Forest Insect and
Disease Survey, Canadian Forestry Service, Department of the
Environment, and the annual Forest Insect and Disease Conditions in the United States reports, by the Forest Service.

Table 1.—*Timber mortality due to major outbreaks of forest insects in Western North America*

Insect	Years	States	Timber mortality
			Billion fbm
Coleoptera			
Dendroctonus brevicomis	1921–37	Oreg.	12.6
western pine beetle	1931–37	Calif.	6.0
Dendroctonus ponderosae	1911–35	Idaho and	15.0
mountain pine beetle		Mont.	
Dendroctonus pseudotsugae	1962–64	Oreg. and	3.0
Douglas fir beetle		Wash.	
Dendroctonus rufipennis	1940–51	Colo.	5.0
spruce beetle			
Pseudohylesinus spp.	1947–55	Wash.	0.5
Homoptera			
Adelges piceae	1950–57	Wash.	1.5
balsam woolly aphid			
Lepidoptera			
Lambdina fiscellaria lugubrosa	1918–22	Oreg.	0.5
western hemlock looper			
Neophasia menapia	1893–95	Wash.	1.0
pine butterfly			
Orgyia pseudotsugata	1928–30	Wash.	0.3
Douglas fir tussock moth	1971–74	Idaho, Oreg., and Wash.	1.0

Table 2.—*Acreage infested by some defoliators in major outbreaks in Western North America*

Insect	Years	States and provinces	Acreage infested
			Thousand acres
Acleris gloverana	1948–55	Southeastern Alaska	11,000
western blackheaded budworm	1952–56	British Columbia	2,000
Choristoneura occidentalis	1949–62	Oreg. and Wash.	15,000
western spruce budworm	1951–70	Mont. and northern Idaho	10,000
Coloradia pandora	1937–39	Colo.	100
pandora moth			
Lambdina fiscellaria lugubrosa	1918–22	Oreg.	27
western hemlock looper	1929–32	Wash.	52
Malacosoma disstria	1957–?	Alberta	48,000
forest tent caterpillar			
Neophasia menapia	1893–95	Wash.	150
pine butterfly	1952–54	Idaho	255
Orgyia pseudotsugata	1946–47	Idaho and Oreg.	556
Douglas fir tussock moth	1971–75	Idaho, Oreg., and Wash.	800

RECOGNITION OF INSECTS AND THEIR DAMAGE

A forester should become familiar with the appearance and characteristics of the insects capable of killing or injuring trees and destroying wood products on the area under his care; also, he should recognize and know about some other insects relating to his multiple use responsibilities. The insects he really needs to know are comparatively few. In this manual, predominant emphasis is on the habits, work, and appearance of insects that feed upon trees and shrubs. For more comprehensive information about insects, it is suggested that the reader consult basic texts, such as Brues et al. (1954), Doane et al. (1936), Essig (1926), K. Graham (1963), Graham and Knight (1965), Metcalf and Flint (1962).

The insects most important in forestry are included in seven main groups, or orders, under the class Insecta (Hexapoda). These common orders include the beetles (Coleoptera), butterflies and moths (Lepidoptera), wasps (Hymenoptera), flies (Diptera), scales and aphids (Homoptera), bugs (Hemiptera), and termites (Isoptera). There are a number of other orders of insects less frequently encountered. Some small animals closely related to insects, and sometimes confused with them, also are important in forestry.

Insects are small. This obscures the fact that, as a group, they differ greatly in form and structure. Foresters should carry and use a 10-power hand lens to view insects in the scale referred to in this manual, as a basis for field identification.

Adult insects can be distinguished from other small invertebrate animals by the fact that they have jointed bodies of three parts (head, thorax, and abdomen), breathe through tracheae, and have one pair of antennae and three pairs of legs.

The larva is the life stage most frequently encountered by foresters, but unfortunately it is difficult to distinguish insects in this form by any simple characters. Usually it is sufficient to be able to recognize the larva as one belonging to a certain group. A forester easily acquires the ability to recognize some of the more common species through becoming familiar with their work.

Most insects pass through either three or four stages of development. The beetles, wasps, flies, butterflies, and moths pass through four such stages, and so are said to undergo complete metamorphosis. The adult female lays eggs, from which the larvae, the second stage, develop. The larvae usually are soft-bodied. The larvae of beetles are called grubs; those of moths and butterflies are called caterpillars; those of flies are called maggots; and those of wasp-like insects with four clear wings are called grubs, slugs, or false

7

caterpillars. The larvae feed and grow, the final size which they attain being influenced to some extent by the abundance of food and moisture. As they increase in size they molt or shed their skins several times. The larvae transform to the pupal or resting stage, and the pupae in turn change to the fourth stage, the adult insects. Growth takes place only in the larval stage. Although some adult insects feed, none of them increases in size. Their chief function in life is to mate and produce eggs and thus initiate another life cycle.

Scale insects, aphids, bugs, and termites undergo what is called incomplete metamorphosis; that is, they have only three forms— the egg, the nymph, and the adult. Growth takes place during the nymphal stage, in which the insect has much the form and appearance of the adult but lacks fully developed wings.

Certain insects, such as the termites and ants, have several specialized adult forms. Thus, in addition to the usual stages, there may be workers, soldiers, and secondary sexual forms. Certain scale insects and aphids give birth to living young rather than eggs. Some insects are able to reproduce by means of eggs laid by virgin females, which develop without being fertilized. In some cases, as among some gall midges, larvae are able to give birth to similar larvae without passing through other stages. These are all exceptions to the general rule.

Insects damage trees in any one of several ways. Adults of some species cause injuries by feeding on the leaves, twigs, or tender cambium, or by slitting bark or leaves to deposit eggs. Adult bark beetles do considerable damage in constructing egg tunnels under the bark. Most commonly, however, the damage is done by the larvae or nymphs in their feeding on various parts of the tree. No damage is ever done by the insects while in the egg or pupal stages.

The principal methods of feeding by which insects injure trees are chewing, sucking, and gall forming. The great majority of forest insects belong to the chewing group, and in the larval or the adult stage, or both, these chew and ingest plant material. This group includes the leaf eaters, the cambium miners, and the wood borers. Aphids, scale insects, and bugs suck plant juices by means of slender mouth parts, which they insert into the tender portions of the tree. A group of specialized insects irritate a portion of the tree and thus cause it to form a swelling or gall, which encloses them. The method of feeding has an important bearing on the methods of control.

Before observed damage is charged to insects, other possible causes should be investigated. Often several agents, such as fire, insects, fungi, and physiological injuries, are so closely associated or interrelated that it is difficult to determine the primary cause of the damage. If insects are not the primary cause, little benefit can be expected from efforts to control them.

NATURAL REGULATION OF INSECTS

Physical, nutritional, and biological forces regulate insect populations and account for their ups and downs (Morris 1963). Under normal conditions, these forces counterbalance the enormous reproductive capacity of insects. The relatively few individuals which escape their enemies live and feed on their hosts without doing conspicuous injury. Defoliating insects feed on a few leaves or needles, but the damage is insignificant. Bark beetles kill an occasional tree or breed in down logs and broken tops. The aggregate damage is negligible, and the annual growth which the trees acquire exceeds the drain, so that there is a net increase of volume in the stand. Insect infestations which continue under these conditions are called endemic. This is the normal condition in Nature and it is a hopeless and unwise undertaking to try to exterminate native insects under such conditions. The result of an effort in this direction would be more likely to disrupt the delicate balance than to accomplish the objective.

Under certain conditions, the bonds of natural control may loosen. For example, the beneficial insects or enemies of harmful species may become reduced in numbers; the resistance of the trees may be lowered through drought, fire, or stagnation; large quantities of slash, windthrow, or other breeding material may become available; the supply of favored hosts may be increased as in plantations and on selectively cut areas; or climatic factors may become especially favorable. Under any such conditions the injurious insects often breed rapidly and become widely destructive. Within a few seasons a large proportion of a timber stand may be killed by bark beetles. Such epidemics may continue for years and spread over large areas. Defoliators may suddenly appear in great numbers and, after consuming the foliage of valuable timber on extensive acreages, disappear with equal suddenness. Many factors come into play in bringing about these sudden changes, and it is often difficult to isolate the responsible causes. At their height, extensive outbreaks are difficult to curb and often are beyond the practical limits of artificial control. Prevention is the better approach, when feasible.

FOOD

Forest insects, like other living things, depend upon a supply of suitable food for their existence and well being. Some are so exacting in their food requirements that they exist only on a portion of one species of tree of limited range. Others have a wide variety of hosts and a correspondingly wide distribution.

Insects, such as the defoliators that attack healthy forest trees, usually have an abundant food supply at their disposal, and their numbers are controlled primarily by biological and climatic factors. However, many defoliators are quite selective regarding their food. Most *Neodiprion* sawflies feed only on the old needles of conifers, whereas many budworms feed principally on developing new needles. Food requirements of young larvae often are more critical than older larvae, for example, larvae of the **Douglas fir tussock moth** (Beckwith 1976). When the amount of foliage on an infested area has been drastically reduced, starvation sometimes causes larval mortality directly and reduces the reproductive capacity of the partially starved survivors, as with the **larch sawfly** (Heron 1955).

A great many insects, such as most of the bark beetles, can develop in large numbers only when enough of their food material in a suitable condition for attack is available. Thus the development of certain destructive bark beetle outbreaks is dependent on a supply of overmature, decadent, or weakened trees. For example, destructive epidemics of the **mountain pine beetle** and western pine beetle mostly have been in extensive old-growth forests.

In recent years, the development of artificial diets for insects (fig. 2) has made it possible to mass-rear forest insects in the laboratory, notably the **spruce budworm** (Grisdale 1970, Lyon et al. 1972). This leads to a better understanding of the insects and greatly facilitates the testing of control measures.

F-521894

FIGURE 2.—Plastic dish with chunks of artificial media on which European pine shoot moth (*Rhyacionia buoliana*) larvae are feeding.

CLIMATIC AND ENVIRONMENTAL INFLUENCES

Climate and environment have an important bearing on the abundance, activity, and distribution of insects, both directly and through the host plants (Uvarov 1931, Wellington 1954). Their influence should be taken into account when efforts are made to regulate insect populations artificially, as in control programs.

TEMPERATURE

Insect development, activity, and abundance are directly affected by temperature. In laboratory tests, larvae of the western pine beetle are normally active from 13° to 32° C (55° to 90° F) (Miller 1931), and adults of the **Douglas fir beetle,** from 10° to 34° C (50° to 93° F) (Rudinsky and Vité 1956). Optimum temperatures for Douglas fir beetle adults are 26° to 28° C (79° to 82° F). Temperatures materially higher or lower than optimum for a species limit its activity and extremes cause death. Few insects can withstand temperatures above 49° C (120° F), and this makes possible the control of many species of bark- and wood-boring insects by raising the temperature of their environment to fatal heights; for example, by felling and burning bark beetle-infested trees. Low temperatures are also fatal. In laboratory tests, exposed larvae of the western pine beetle are killed by a temperature of −23° C (−10° F) (Yuill 1941). Extremely cold winters with air temperatures below −29° C (−20° F) have proved fatal to a high percentage of the brood of this and other bark beetles (Keen and Furniss 1937).

Latitude, elevation, and exposure modify temperature and thereby limit the distribution of insect species and govern the number of generations per year. Relatively fewer insects are able to adapt to the extremely low temperatures and short seasons of the far North. Some that do, such as defoliators, develop quickly and overwinter in sheltered situations. Others, such as the **spruce beetle,** require more than one year to mature and have become relatively cold-hardy. In southern latitudes, the kinds of insects are more abundant and their period of activity is much longer, often resulting in the production of several generations per year. In general, native forest insects are adjusted to the temperatures where they live and populations soon recover from the effects of extremes, such as in abnormally cold winters (Keen and Furniss 1937).

MOISTURE AND DROUGHT

Moisture has an important bearing upon the kind, abundance, and behavior of insects. Some insects, such as the **western hem-**

lock looper and others typical of coastal forests, thrive in moist conditions. Some, such as most flatheaded borers and other inhabitants of inland forests, are adjusted to drier conditions. Much insect activity is closely associated with seasonal precipitation. For example, the first fall rains in western Oregon bring out the rain beetles en masse for the annual mating season. Abnormally heavy or prolonged rains often kill large numbers of forest insects, particularly the adults of defoliators, such as western hemlock looper.

Precipitation and evaporation determine the amount of soil moisture available to forest trees. During periods of drought, forests slow down in growth rate and vigor, thus becoming susceptible to fatal attack by insects (Keen 1937). Periods of drought are frequently followed by epidemics of bark beetles (Beal 1943). Moisture deficiency may be short-term and result in recurrent outbreaks, as with the **California fivespined ips** in years of subnormal spring precipitation in the Sierra Nevada of California (Struble 1966). Long-term deficiency may be the basic cause of catastrophic tree killing by insects (fig. 1), as by the western pine beetle and associates during the great drought of the 1920's and 1930's in California, Oregon, and Washington (Keen 1937, Miller and Keen 1960).

LIGHT

Insects respond to light in various ways, depending upon the species, life stage, and period within a life stage. Each forest insect has characteristic reactions to light. Thus, adult flatheaded borers can be depended upon to mate and lay eggs in bright sunshine and the **European pine shoot moth** to choose the dusk of evening for its activities.

In the alternating sequence of day and night, day length has diverse and profound effects upon insects (Beck 1968). In forest entomology, knowledge concerning these effects has greatest practical application in laboratory rearing. By regulating the length of periodic exposure to light, diapause can be broken and insects such as spruce budworms (Grisdale 1970) can be continuously reared in quantity for study and experimentation.

WIND AND AIR CURRENTS

Wind, air currents, and air mass movement directly affect insect dispersal and other activities. It is suspected that air movement accounts in considerable part for the spread of some forest insect outbreaks. In Alberta, adults of the **forest tent caterpillar** have been transported en masse at least 300 miles by a cold air front (Brown 1965). In laboratory tests, *Dendroctonus* beetles cannot make headway flying against air movement of even a few miles per hour. From this it is assumed that wind direction influences their course of flight outdoors. Instances of apparent mass flights with prevailing wind across extensive treeless areas are recorded for the mountain pine beetle and spruce beetle.

Of pressing concern to foresters is the relationship of insects to windbroken and windthrown trees. Such trees often attract bark beetles, some of which attack and breed in the broken and uprooted trees and others attack nearby undamaged trees (Johnson and Pettinger 1961). Extensive windthrow that occurs occasionally in the Douglas-fir region of Oregon and Washington (fig. 3) can be expected to cause outbreaks of the Douglas fir beetle (Greeley et al. 1953). Similarly, windthrow in Engelmann spruce stands leads to outbreaks of the spruce beetle (Massey and Wygant 1954) and windfall in ponderosa pine stands often has stimulated outbreaks of the western pine beetle (Miller and Keen 1960).

SNOW, ICE, AND PARCH BLIGHT

On some areas, young coniferous stands are damaged by recurrent snow and ice storms. The broken trees and tops are favorable

F–521895

FIGURE 3.—Windthrown trees, such as these in western Oregon, are an important source of Douglas fir beetle outbreaks.

breeding material for bark beetles and sometimes cause local outbreaks. Salvage before the beetles emerge and attack healthy trees is the best countermeasure.

Injury to the foliage of conifers, variously known as parch blight, red belt, and winter burn, occurs in well defined elevational zones extensively in the West (Henson 1951). The appearance may be spectacular but is short-lived and seldom, if ever, stimulates an insect outbreak.

LIGHTNING

Trees that are struck by lightning often are attacked and killed by bark beetles and wood borers. For example, lightning-struck ponderosa pine are very susceptible to the western pine beetle (Johnson 1966). During periods of endemic infestation, when the forest generally may be practically beetle-free, lightning-struck trees continue to harbor significant numbers of bark beetles.

FIRE

Trees scorched or killed by forest fires are attractive to many forest insects, which may be attracted from a radius of several miles (Miller and Patterson 1927). Some are attracted while the trees are still smoking (Linsley 1943a). Damage caused by insects augments fire losses in three principal ways. Bark beetles often kill many trees that otherwise might survive (Furniss 1965, Miller and Keen 1960). Such killing occurs principally in the first year or two following a fire. Bark beetles that breed in fire-killed and fire-scorched trees may spread and kill nearby green trees (Furniss 1941). For example, in Douglas-fir stands of western Oregon and Washington, large fires usually trigger outbreaks of the Douglas fir beetle. Boring insects enter the wood of fire-killed trees, causing degrade and, together with fungi, limit the time available for salvage (Kimmey and Furniss 1943).

Fire can be beneficial. Felling and burning bark beetle-infested trees has long been a principal method of direct control (see Insect Prevention and Control). Prescribed burning has been advocated, but not fully tested, as a practical means of thinning dense, young ponderosa pine stands to reduce tree competition and thereby increase resistance to bark beetles (Weaver 1967). Broadcast burning to sanitize the forest by destroying injurious bark beetles in the "underbrush" had many proponents among oldtime woodsmen but is of no proven merit.

MECHANICAL INJURY

Injured trees are much more susceptible to bark beetles and wood-boring insects than are uninjured trees. Somewhat arbi-

14

trarily, mechanical injury is classed as that caused by man and animals. Man-caused injury commonly occurs on logging operations, right-of-way and construction projects, and campgrounds and other intensive use areas. Bears, porcupines, burrowing rodents, and sapsuckers are among the mammals and birds that damage trees sufficiently to make them attractive to insects. Efforts should be made to minimize man-caused injury, especially on selectively logged areas where slash and windthrow sometimes compound the insect attraction.

SLASH

The slash left from the cutting of trees in the forest is a suitable and attractive breeding ground for a great many forest insects, some beneficial and some harmful (Patterson 1927, USDA Bur. Ent. 1927). When slash is freshly produced, the dying inner bark is attractive to many species of bark beetles that commonly breed in standing trees. Usually these bark beetles select the type and size of material in which they normally breed. Thus the limb- and twig-feeding bark beetles go into the smaller pieces of slash, trunk-breeding bark beetles go into the cull logs and butts, and those that normally work at the base of the tree attack the stumps. The abundance of the progeny depends a great deal on the moisture and temperature within the slash and on the requirements of the different species of beetles. The **red turpentine beetle**, which breeds readily in pine stumps, frequently develops in such numbers as to do serious injury to adjacent forest trees. The trunk-breeding pine beetles rarely find suitable conditions in the cull logs and butts, and the progeny which they produce under such circumstances seldom cause any trouble in neighboring forests or to the reserve stand, especially where logging operations are continuous and the logs are promptly harvested. The engraver and twig beetles, which breed in the smaller pieces of slash, frequently emerge in such enormous numbers as to kill patches of young trees and sometimes the tops of older trees.

The wood-boring species that breed in slash must be considered generally beneficial, in that they help to decompose the wood and reduce the slash with its accompanying fire hazard. They may become injurious, however, and to avoid or reduce a possible menace from slash-breeding insects special considerations in slash disposal are frequently necessary. When a logging operation is continuous and a fresh supply of slash is furnished throughout the flight period, the emerging progeny is repeatedly absorbed in the slash and in the logs removed to the mill, and no special precautions need be taken. But if a cutting operation ceases or is intermittent, as in road and powerline developments, then some damage from slash-breeding insects may be expected and should be avoided if possible. Burning the slash is beneficial, provided the large limbs, cull logs, and stumps are included and the burning is done before the insects emerge. In many cases this would mean that the burning would have to be done in midsummer or early in the fall, and this would present a fire hazard. Spreading the slash so that it will receive the direct rays of the sun will kill a high percentage of the insects in the more southern latitudes, where high temperatures can be attained in and under the bark in this way.

SMOKE, SMOG, AND DUST

Smoke, fumes, and dust from smelters and industrial plants have long been observed to be associated with insect outbreaks in nearby forests. Outbreaks also are common along dusty roads. The precise causes in particular situations are largely unresolved. In the case of the **black pineleaf scale**, outbreaks develop when conditions are created that are unfavorable for its principal parasite (Edmunds 1973).

Since the mid-1950's, atmospheric pollution or smog has progressively reduced the vigor of ponderosa pine on some areas in southern California. The effects, at first reported as "X-disease," are attributed to photochemical oxidants and have led to increased killing by bark beetles (Stark et al. 1968).

TREE DISEASES

Close relationships exist between insects and the organisms that cause tree diseases. Trees weakened or killed by root-rotting fungi, such as **Poria root rot**, *Phellinus [Poria] weirii* (Murr.) Gilbertson, **annosus root rot**, *Fomes annosus* (Fr.) Cke., **shoestring root rot**, *Armillaria mellea* (Vahl. ex Fr.) Kummer, and *Phytophthora lateralis* Tucker and J. Milb., often are attacked by bark beetles (Cobb et al. 1974). Some insects, such as the **smaller European elm bark beetle**, carry disease-causing fungi from tree to tree and thus spread diseases (Schreiber and Peacock 1974). Bark beetles, ambrosia beetles, and wood borers introduce staining fungi into the wood of attacked trees and thus degrade it (Prebble and Graham 1957). Some wood borers that mine in sound wood help speed the penetration of wood-rotting fungi in dead and down trees and logs (Basham and Belyea 1960). Some termites, especially **subterranean termites**, are strongly attracted to *Lenzites trabea* Pers. ex Fr., a wood-decaying fungus (Allen et al. 1964).

Damage to the foliage of conifers by some disease organisms resembles damage caused by insects, particularly defoliators, hence must be distinguished in forest pest surveys. Examples are **needle**

16

blight of Douglas-fir, *Rhabdocline pseudotsugae* Syd., **pine needle cast**, *Elytroderma deformans* (Weir) Darker, **larch needle cast**, *Hypodermella laricis* Tubeuf, and **spruce needle rust**, *Chrysomyxa ledicola* (Pk.) Lagerh. Likewise, group killing of conifers by fungi resembles killing by bark beetles; furthermore, diseased trees are likely to be attacked by bark beetles and other insects. Poria root rot and annosus root rot are examples of tree-killing fungi that must be taken into account on insect surveys and in assessing insect control needs.

NATURAL ENEMIES

This section concerns the insects, diseases, nematodes, birds, and mammals that kill harmful insects. Some of these natural enemies can be used in applied control by man (see Biological Control). In general, the species of natural enemies are numerous and the relationships complex, hence treatment in this manual is by example and by reference to more comprehensive, authoritative publications.

ASSOCIATED INSECTS

Many species of insects belonging to different orders and families are beneficial in that they feed on pest species (Clausen 1940). In the forest these beneficial forms are mainly in two large groups: (1) Parasites, which live in, on, or with some particular host insect and gradually consume it, and (2) predators, which feed externally and devour their prey (Thompson 1943). The line of demarcation between a parasite and a predator is not a rigid one. A parasite is usually considered to be one capable of completing its feeding cycle in or on the body of one host, whereas a predator feeds on a succession of individuals, moving freely from one to another.

Most insect parasites belong to the orders Hymenoptera and Diptera, and most forest insects have numerous parasitic enemies. Individual species, especially defoliators, often serve as hosts for a large number of parasites. Some parasites attack and develop in many host species; others are limited to a few hosts or occasionally only one. Even parasites are not immune from attacks of other parasites, called hyperparasites. Parasites attack parasites which may in turn be attacked by other parasites, making parasitism a complex relationship. Hyperparasitism is common and must be guarded against in the introduction of parasites for biological control.

The principal predaceous insects are beetles belonging to the families Cleridae, Trogositidae, Carabidae, and Coccinellidae;

flies, in several families of the Diptera; ants, in the Hymenoptera; lacewing flies and snakeflies, in the order Neuroptera, and several families of true bugs, in the Hemiptera. Often both the immature and adult forms of predaceous insects feed upon their insect hosts. Predators usually attack a greater variety of hosts than do parasites.

In addition to serving as food for insect parasites and predators, tree-killing bark beetles create conditions that are favorable for other associated insects, including secondary bark beetles (Dahlsten 1970, De Leon 1934). Some of the associates live concurrently and peacefully with the bark beetle broods; some linger on long after the bark beetles have flown. The significance in direct control projects is that the primary bark beetle must be distinguished from its associates and determined to be still present, if treatment is to be effective.

INSECT DISEASES

Forest insect populations are regulated in nature to a considerable extent by disease-causing organisms (Stairs 1972). The pathogenic organisms include viruses, rickettsiae, bacteria, fungi, protozoa, and nematodes (Burges and Hussey 1971, Steinhaus 1963b,c). Viruses in particular are known to suppress outbreaks of several economically important forest insects (David 1975, Smith 1967). Viral diseases are suspected of being the principal cause of sudden decline of outbreaks of **gypsy moth,** spruce budworms, **larch bud moth,** western hemlock looper, several species of tent caterpillars, and the **European spruce sawfly.** In western forests, viral diseases cause extensive mortality in Douglas fir tussock moth populations (Wickman et al. 1973a). Two nucleopolyhedrosis viruses (Hughes 1972, Hughes and Addison 1970) and a cytoplasmic polyhedrosis virus (Martignoni et al. 1969) have been identified as the causative agents. Field applications of one of the nucleopolyhedrosis virus and of *Bacillus thuringiensis*, a pathogenic bacterium, by helicopters (Stelzer et al. 1975), have shown that biological control of the Douglas fir tussock moth appears to be near (see Biological Control). To date over 600 species of insects and mites have been reported to have viral diseases (Hughes, 1957, Martignoni and Langston 1959, Martignoni and Iwai 1975). Of these, 76 occur in western forests.

It is highly desirable that foresters and others who observe evidence of possible disease in insect populations promptly report the occurrence to specialists, usually through the regional or State forest insect control organizations. In the Pacific Northwest, the Forestry Sciences Laboratory at Corvallis, Oreg., will accept diseased forest insects for diagnosis.

18

Dead or diseased insects may be found under loose bark sections, in rolled leaves, or in webs. Sometimes, dead insects can be seen attached to leaves or needles by means of fungal growths, dried body fluids, or fecal matter. Frequently, caterpillars which are dying (or have died) of nucleopolyhedrosis are seen hanging from twigs, leaves, or needles by their prolegs (fig. 4). The remains of these larvae may be dry or, if death occurred recently, they may be filled with decomposed and frequently ill-smelling tissues and body fluids.

It is important that the collector of diseased or dead insects provide all the pertinent information relating to the site where the mortality occurred (e.g., the name of the host plant, the extent of the disease outbreak, the abundance of the insect, and the weather conditions). In addition, abnormal movements or abnormal feeding behavior by these insects should be reported.

Ideally, a shipment of specimens for diagnosis would include healthy insects, insects in the early stages of disease, and insects dead of the disease. This is often impractical because of the necessity for getting authorization from Federal and State quarantine agencies for shipment of live insects. For this reason it is recommended that shipments be confined to dead insects. These may be transported without restriction and are usually adequate for diagnosis. Instructions and suggestions for submitting specimens to diagnostic centers, as well as descriptions of diagnostic procedures, have been published by several laboratories (Steinhaus 1963a, Weiser and Briggs 1971). An important precaution is the use of clean, dry glass or plastic vials or powder boxes; specimens should not be placed in alcohol, formalin, or other preservatives. The dry containers with the specimens should be protected from breakage

F–521896

FIGURE 4.—Larva of Douglas fir tussock moth, *Orgyia pseudotsugata*, killed by nucleopolyhedrosis virus.

19

by wrapping them or packing them with a cushiony material. Prompt shipment increases the likelihood of obtaining a diagnosis.

NEMATODES

Nematodes are considered to be one of the major biotic factors affecting bark beetle populations (Massey 1974). Most species of bark beetles have parasitic nematodes, such as species of *Parasitylenchus*, *Contortylenchus*, *Sphaerularia*, and *Allantonema*. Parasitic nematodes live internally in their hosts, sterilizing them in varying degrees but usually not killing them (fig. 5). *Parasitylenchus elongatus* Massey, a species that does kill its host, is recorded as being responsible for the decline of an outbreak of the **fir engraver** in New Mexico (Massey 1964). It is considered possible to use nematodes for biological control of destructive bark beetles, but exploratory efforts with *Neoaplectana* DD–136 against the Douglas fir beetle in Oregon were unsuccessful.

Many species of nematodes are phoretic, that is, they are carried from tree to tree on the bodies of bark beetles. These phoretic nematodes live freely in the bark beetle galleries, not harming the beetles that transport them.

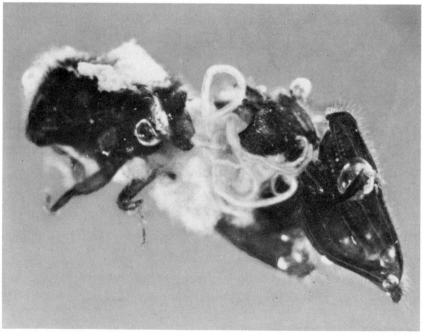

F–521848

FIGURE 5.—*Ips confusus* infected with adults of a nematode, *Contortylenchus elongatus*.

20

BIRDS

Many species of birds feed upon forest insects. Nuthatches, chickadees, creepers, warblers, kinglets, and others search for insects on tree trunks and foliage. Flycatchers, swallows, and nighthawks catch them on the wing. Woodpeckers peck through the bark and feed upon broods of bark- and wood-boring insects. In general, predation by birds is most effective when the insect population is relatively low (Graham and Knight 1965).

Substantial efforts have been made to increase bird populations in forests. In parts of Germany, birdhouse programs have increased the number of insectivorous birds 5 to 10 times (Franz 1961). Similar programs have been conducted in Japan and, to a limited extent, in the State of Washington. These programs are presumed beneficial, but their effectiveness in control of specific forest insects is largely unmeasured.

In western North America, woodpeckers are a conspicuous element in natural control. These industrious birds feed upon and materially reduce broods of bark beetles and other boring insects. Woodpeckers are the most important predators of the spruce beetle, sometimes destroying up to 75 percent of the population (Knight 1958, Massey and Wygant 1954). At times, they are similarly destructive to broods of the western pine beetle (Miller and Keen 1960) (fig. 6). Unfortunately, they also feed upon associated beneficial insects, such as clerids.

MAMMALS

Small mammals feed upon insects that spend part of their life in forest litter and soil, notably sawflies and some Lepidoptera (Buckner 1966). In Manitoba, upward of 70 percent of the brood of the larch sawfly in cocoons may be destroyed by shrews and voles (Buckner 1959). In Oregon and California, rodents, such as ground squirrels and chipmunks, are important in natural control of the pandora moth by feeding upon the pupae (Carolin and Knopf 1968).

SYMBIONTS

Insects live together harmoniously with various organisms (Steinhaus 1947). This relationship is called symbiosis and the participants are symbionts. When the relationship is to mutual advantage, it is spoken of as mutualism (Graham 1967). Examples are the protozoa that live in the intestinal tract of termites and predigest cellulose. Ambrosia beetles transport, colonize, and feed upon ambrosia fungi (Batra 1967; Funk 1965, 1970). Many bark beetles innoculate trees with wood-staining fungi, some of which

F-523528

FIGURE 6.—Bark of ponder-
osa pine riddled by wood-
peckers searching for brood
of the western pine beetle.

aid in overcoming the trees. Roundheaded borers, bark beetles,
and **carpenter ants** are among the insects consistently associated
with yeasts, but in relationships not yet fully known (Callaham
and Shifrine 1960, Graham 1967).

INSECT SURVEYS

Surveys provide the information needed to identify destructive
forest insects, to determine their status from year to year, and to
provide the basis for effective prevention or control of outbreaks.

Survey details are as diverse as the insects surveyed. The basic elements are detection and evaluation (Knight 1967).

Detection of insect outbreaks is a normal and continuing responsibility of the forester who is charged with managing and protecting a particular forest. Primary detection or surveillance should be so planned that all valuable forest types subject to insect outbreaks are examined at least once each year. This work does not need to be intensive, but at least it should disclose whether trees are dying or distressed and, if so, the probable cause and extent of the trouble.

Prompt reporting of the first signs of an outbreak will reduce the cost of suppression. If trees are observed to be dying or the foliage is abnormally sparse or off-color, the trunk, branches, and foliage should be searched for insects or their work. If one kind of insect is found in abundance, that insect is a likely suspect. A prime purpose of this manual is to identify the insect or at least indicate the species it is likely to be.

If the cause of the problem cannot be determined, a specialist should be called in. If insects are found that cannot be identified, samples of the insects and their work should be sent to an entomologist for study (Hall 1952). In the Western United States, forest insects can be submitted to the Forest Service or to State forestry organizations for identification. Information concerning the location and nature of the infestation, the species of tree infested, date of collection, and the sender's name and address should accompany the specimens. Methods of collecting and processing insects for shipment are described by Beirne (1955), Borror and White (1970), and Oman and Cushman (1948).

Forest insect outbreaks often are extensive and affect many ownerships. In recognition of the need for cooperative action to assess and control outbreaks in the United States, the Forest Pest Control Act of 1947 provided the basis for systematic surveys on forest lands of all ownerships (Bongberg 1958). Reports from individual ownerships are incorporated in this detection system. The findings are reported yearly for the Nation and by Forest Service regions. A national forest insect survey also is conducted in Canada (McGugan 1958b). In addition to detecting and appraising outbreaks, the Canadian survey provides information on the identity, biology, and population trend of many insects. Much of the information in this manual has been extracted from the annual reports of the Canadian survey and related publications.

Aerial surveys, supplemented by ground sampling, are the backbone of the cooperative forest insect detection program in the United States. The techniques are illustrated in reports on the blowdown and bark beetle survey of 1952 in Oregon and Washington (Greeley et al. 1953) and the **balsam woolly aphid** survey of 1957 in Washington (Pope 1958). Aerial photographs are used at times to estimate damage both in the United States (Wear et al. 1966) and in Canada (Murtha 1972).

When direct control is under consideration, intensive surveys are made to determine the biological status of the insect and the trend of infestation, and to evaluate the probable economic impact. A thorough knowledge of the insect and a reliable system of sampling are required. Through research and experience, sampling procedures have been developed for such insects as the **western spruce budworm** (Carolin and Coulter 1972, McKnight 1970), Douglas fir tussock moth (Mason 1970), larch sawfly (Ives and Prentice 1958), and the **lodgepole needleminer** (Stevens and Stark 1962).

INSECT PREVENTION AND CONTROL

When an insect outbreak has been identified as critical, alternative courses of action have to be considered and the costs and benefits of each carefully weighed (Eaton 1962, Hurtig 1964, Leuschner and Newton 1974, Newport 1962, Vaux 1954). Always there are elements of uncertainty. What will the insect do next? How much damage will it cause if left unchecked? How much timber can be salvaged if extensive killing occurs? The degree of acceptable risk differs by ownership, and many ownerships are likely to be involved. A decision whether to control or not to control must be reached.

Measures to prevent or control outbreaks of insects that damage forests are along two main lines: (1) Direct or remedial measures to curb outbreaks in progress by killing insects or protecting foliage, and (2) silvicultural, biological, and other measures to utilize and reinforce natural control for long-term protection. These measures are not equally practical or available for use against all insects.

In the 1952 edition of the manual by Keen, methods for controlling bark beetles were described in considerable detail. At that time, direct control, principally by felling and burning infested trees (fig. 7) or by treating them with chemical sprays, was still in wide use. These methods remain useful in some cases; however, they are so well known that redescription here is unnecessary. For historical purposes, they are thoroughly documented by Miller and Keen (1960). Now, the principal approach to bark beetle control is through forest management practices to prevent outbreaks.

24

FIGURE 7.   Burning lodgepole pine in decks as a method of treating
bark beetle-infested trees of small diameter.

During the past 30 years or so, aerial spraying with insecticides
has been developed to the point that extensive defoliator outbreaks can be effectively and economically controlled, for example,
the western spruce budworm (Whiteside 1958), the Douglas fir
tussock moth (Johnson and Ross 1967), and the hemlock looper
(Bullard et al. 1964). There are two basic approaches in aerial
spraying: (1) Single applications sufficient to achieve a high
degree of control and avoid repeat spraying, and (2) repeated
light applications to protect infested trees until natural control
takes over. The former applies principally to areas where spraying
to natural barriers is possible; the latter to extensive, unbroken
forests. The aim in either case is to apply the minimum overall
amount of insecticide required for effective protection. Spraying
by helicopter permits precise application of the spray material and
minimum contamination of streams and lakes (fig. 8). The major
problem is to choose chemicals that will control the pest insects
with minimum adverse side effects.

Much attention is being given to the development of prevention
measures. Though promising, most of them still are in develop-
mental stages. Forest management practices aimed at bark beetles
are the principal prevention measures in actual use, and even they
are not yet fully perfected.

FIGURE 8.—Helicopter applying spray for control of
western hemlock looper in coastal forest.

PREVENTION THROUGH FOREST MANAGEMENT

When timber stands are brought under management, it becomes
possible to regulate conditions so as to make forests less vulnerable to insect attack; or if insect damage does occur, to salvage the
timber without undue loss (Cornelius 1955). The aim is to minimize insect-caused losses throughout the rotation period of a
forest, taking into account the primary uses and the costs. This
task requires a thorough understanding of the factors contributing to insect abundance and the resistance of forest stands
(Craighead 1941, Keen 1950).

The field of silvicultural control offers almost unlimited possibilities. In older forests, much can be done to lessen insect damage
by avoiding injury to the trees from forest fires and other weakening influences; by keeping forests in a healthful condition
through disposal of windfalls, slash, and other insect-breeding
material; and by selective cutting operations to regulate composition and density and to remove the trees most susceptible to insect
attack. In plantations, consideration should be given to the selec-

tion of the site, to the planting of species and varieties of trees best adapted to it, and to proper spacing. These are just a few of the possible ways in which insect activity can be modified through silvicultural practices.

In overmature virgin forests of ponderosa pine, bark beetles attack certain trees or groups of trees scattered through the stand (Person 1928). A study of the types of trees selected has shown that in general the more slowly growing ones, the codominants and intermediates in the stand, and the older age classes are selected in preference to the thrifty, dominant, young trees (Keen 1936). It also has been found that trees currently in poor health are of highest risk to western pine beetle attack (Salman and Bongberg 1942), and that beetle control can be obtained over a period of many years through sanitation-salvage logging, in which the high-risk trees, constituting usually from 15 to 25 percent of the stand, are removed and utilized. Cutting priority should be areas of greatest hazard (Johnson 1949). Instead of cutting heavily on small logging units, forest managers are favoring a light selective system whereby large areas are opened up so that insect-killed and high-risk trees can be quickly harvested and stands improved in both growth and insect resistance (Orr 1942, 1945).

Stand composition is closely related to the amount and severity of insect attack. In mixed coniferous forests of the West, serious outbreaks are not frequent. Conversion of such forests to a single species generally would increase the risk of insect-caused damage. Mature forests comprised principally of one tree species are most subject to extensive outbreaks. In fact, insects are a principal means whereby some tree species are naturally renewed as extensive even-aged forests. Examples are outbreaks of the spruce beetle in spruce forests of the North and elsewhere, mountain pine beetle in lodgepole pine throughout the West, and western hemlock looper in coastal hemlock. The lesson to be learned from Nature is not that pure stands should be converted to abnormal mixtures, but that they should be managed so as to short-circuit the insects and beat them to the harvest. This is a complex undertaking, but it can be accomplished as in the positive system of management developed to reduce losses of lodgepole pine caused by the mountain pine beetle in British Columbia (Safranyik et al. 1974).

Under intensive forest management with shortened rotations, insect pests of young trees are increasingly important. To some extent, young forests solve pest problems of old forests. At the same time they introduce and magnify other insect problems. Per-acre investment in the timber crop increases and with it the need for adequate protection against insect-caused losses.

Stand density has an important bearing on temperature and moisture conditions and often must be regulated so as to improve growth rates and discourage the attacks of certain insects. For example, thinning of dense, young stands of ponderosa pine may be necessary to reduce competition and prevent outbreaks of the mountain pine beetle (Sartwell and Stevens 1975).

Prevention through silviculture and management becomes increasingly important when new plantations are established. Sites must be selected that are adapted to the growing of trees, or growth will be so poor and the trees so weak that insects will have a fertile field for their activities. Likewise, strains of trees that are adapted to the site should be chosen because they grow best, hence are least likely to be damaged or killed by insects. Drainage, the mixture of species, and the spacing of the trees also must be given special consideration.

SALVAGE

Salvage logging is a standard forest management practice, the primary purpose of which is to utilize dead and severely damaged trees that otherwise would be a total loss. Sometimes salvage is undertaken to destroy bark beetles in trees killed by fire, wind, insects, diseases, and other causes and thus prevent spread to green trees (fig. 9). Salvage of the wood fiber is a race with time and the rate of deterioration (Engelhardt 1957, Kimmey and Furniss 1943, Mielke 1950, Richmond and Lejeune 1945, Shea et al. 1962, Wickman 1965, Wright and Harvey 1967, Wright et al. 1956). The race is even tighter when the objective is beetle control. Salvage is most practical on well-roaded areas; however, aerial logging now opens possibilities not available until recently (see also discussion of sanitation-salvage logging in the section, Prevention Through Forest Management). Market conditions strongly affect salvage. When the demand for wood products is brisk, relatively more dead, down, and infested timber can be harvested and sold.

When beetle-infested trees occur in catastrophic numbers on extensive unroaded areas, time runs out and the beetles fly long before control through salvage can be completed (Hagenstein and Furniss 1956), as was experienced in the 1962 blowdown in western Oregon and Washington. Even when the beetle-infested trees are relatively concentrated, many of them are unmerchantable because of small size and rapid development of checks and blue stain. Logging of such trees has to be subsidized to achieve fully effective control of bark beetles through salvage. Economic salvage of the wood fiber of beetle-killed trees ranges from a year

28

FIGURE 9.—Early method of controlling bark beetle infestations in ponderosa pine by felling infested trees and utilizing wood.

or so for such species as lodgepole pine, white pine, Engelmann spruce, and white fir, to many years for more durable species such as Douglas-fir.

CHEMICAL CONTROL

Chemicals are an effective and economical means for meeting emergencies created by insect pest outbreaks. They can materially increase forest yields by keeping insect-caused losses to a minimum. They must be used carefully to insure against unintended detrimental effects upon fish, wildlife, livestock, human beings, and other elements of the environment.

Fortunately, foresters do not have to apply chemical insecticides routinely. Most of the time natural controls are sufficient to keep insect impacts within acceptable limits. At such times the insects are considered to be endemic. Occasionally insects increase greatly and cause extensive killing or serious loss of grown trees. Then they are considered to be epidemic and sometimes are in need of direct control. At present, insecticides are the only proven means for immediate control of outbreaks of some of the most destructive defoliators.

Policies pertaining to chemical control are going through a period of rapid change and adjustment. Hence no specific recommendations regarding chemical control are made in this manual. U.S. Department of Agriculture publications (USDA 1972) and those of various States, e.g., Oregon (Capizzi and Robinson 1975) and Washington (Washington State University 1971), give detailed and current recommendations on treatment schedules, materials, application rates, and procedures. In North America, chemicals are most commonly applied in spray form. See Potts (1958) for equipment and Hurtig (1964) for control guidelines.

If chemical control is decided upon, the work must be done under the provisions of applicable Federal and State regulations. This may be relatively simple, as in the case of spraying a small Christmas tree plantation with a registered material used in a registered way. Such a project would not require a complicated review before being approved. At the other end of the scale would be an extensive project using unconventional materials and methods; this would necessitate a lengthy and complex full-scale review. The key elements are the size of the job and the materials and methods used. Larger jobs are coordinated and conducted almost exclusively by Federal and State agencies. The organization and conduct of a chemical control project differ in detail according to the insect and the particular outbreak, but there are basic principles that apply to all, as outlined by the National Academy of Sciences (1962).

BIOLOGICAL CONTROL

Biological control (Balch 1960, Beirne 1962, Buckner 1966, Clausen 1958, deBach 1964, Doutt 1967, Dowden 1959, Sweetman 1958), as defined here, is the applied use of natural enemies to reduce damage by forest insects. The objective is to achieve more lasting protection and decrease the need for chemical insecticides. The three avenues of approach are: (1) To apply disease-causing organisms and other natural enemies for direct control, (2) to encourage established natural enemies, and (3) to introduce and colonize natural enemies from other areas. Biological control measures have great potential, but they are difficult to develop and evaluate, and each must be custom tailored to the pest species to be controlled. As yet, practical application in western forests is limited.

Most of the major forest insect pests in western forests are native (table 3, page 46) and have a full complement of natural enemies including diseases. Efforts are being made to use some of these enemies directly to control outbreaks, much as in chemical control (Burges and Hussey 1971). In the case of disease-causing organisms, development, testing, and clearance for use is a long and difficult process. Aerial application of mass-produced virus to speed up natural epizootics in Douglas fir tussock moth populations appears to be on the verge of practical use (Stelzer et al. 1975). Viruses have been applied experimentally and appear promising for control of other forest defoliators, including sawflies and tent caterpillars. Aerial application of *Bacillus thuringiensis* likewise is promising for control of the tussock moth and also for the spruce budworm (Smirnoff 1974), but early field trials were ineffective against some other insects, including the western hemlock looper (Carolin and Thompson 1967). It is considered possible to use nematodes for biological control of bark beetles, but exploratory efforts so far have not been successful. Mass production and release of native insect parasites and predators for direct control at present is a theoretical possibility (Berryman 1967, Struble 1942b).

Chemical and physical control measures can be scheduled and applied in ways to protect particular kinds of insect parasites and predators (see Integrated Control section). Chemical spraying against early instars of the western hemlock looper will kill fewer tachinid parasites than will late spraying. On fell-and-burn operations against the western pine beetle, clerids can be protected by leaving the stump unburned. Insectivorous birds can be increased by developing nesting sites for them. Silvicultural practices to encourage the long-term effectiveness of natural enemies is a little-explored possibility.

Another possibility is the introduction of insect parasites or predators to control native forest insects. To do this, it is first necessary to find an insect not already present within the infested area that will prey upon the harmful species. Even though such an enemy may be found, there are many complex factors that will influence the success of the introduction and its ultimate effectiveness. The life history of the new enemy must synchronize with that of its host if it is to be on hand at the proper time for attack. If a parasite has more generations annually than the host, other insects must be present for it to attack at other periods during the season. The parasite must be capable of wide distribution and have a greater reproductive capacity than that of its host. Moreover, its ability to adapt itself to the change in climatic conditions in its new environment may be an important factor in determining its ability to succeed (Force 1967). So far, no introduction of a foreign parasite or predator has been outstandingly successful in the control of any of our native forest insects.

In western forests, parasites and predators have been introduced mostly to control injurious insects accidentally introduced without their natural enemies (Dowden 1962, McGugan and Coppel 1962). Effective control of the **satin moth** in British Columbia, Washington, and Oregon by introduced insect parasites is an example of success (Jones et al. 1938, Lejeune and Silver 1961). Several insect predators of the balsam woolly aphid have been established in the Pacific Northwest, but it is questionable whether they accounted for the subsequent decline of this introduced pest (Mitchell 1965). The larch sawfly and **larch casebearer** are other introduced forest insects against which biological control has been attempted in the West by introduced insect parasites.

EXOTIC CONTROL

Broadly, the control measures grouped in this section are biological, and they are so considered by some specialists. They are set apart as being potential measures not yet used to protect forests from insects. In relation to practical application, they range from imminent use of pheromones to the remote possibility of introducing lethal genes into pest populations. These sophisticated concepts of control are a natural outgrowth of earlier efforts that theorized 101 ways to kill bark beetle broods and produced a few practical ways. In addition to the two measures already mentioned, today's theoretical possibilities include the use of hormone growth regulators, sterilized males, antibiotics, resistant host trees, and others. Kilgore and Doutt (1967) discuss many of these potential control measures; Birch (1974) discusses pheromones; Gerhold et al. (1964) discuss the breeding of insect-resistant trees; and Knipling (1960) discusses ways to use insect species to destroy their own kind.

Pheromones that strongly influence the behavior of the Douglas fir beetle, mountain pine beetle, western pine beetle, California fivespined ips. European pine shoot moth, Douglas fir tussock moth, western spruce budworm, and gypsy moth have been identified and commercially produced. These materials are being used experimentally for surveys and control. Control is being approached in two ways through pheromones that attract and concentrate the target pest for subsequent destruction (Pitman 1971, Vité 1970), and through pheromones that repel the pest (Furniss et al. 1974).

It has long been observed that individual trees and types of trees within a species differ in susceptibility to insect attack (Austin et al. 1945, Keen 1943). This observation led to the sanitation-salvage type of timber harvesting to reduce losses caused by bark beetles (see Prevention Through Forest Management section). It also suggested the possibility of selecting, breeding, and planting insect-resistant trees to obtain long-lasting protection against insects (Beal 1957, Roth 1970). In California, a Jeffrey pine X Coulter pine hybrid has been found to resist attack by the **pine reproduction weevil,** but it has not been extensively used. For information on the art and status of breeding pest-resistant trees, see Gerhold et al. (1964) and Søegaard (1964). The mass production and release of sterilized males, which has been highly successful against the **screwworm,** a pest of cattle in the South, has been explored as a measure to eradicate the European pine shoot moth from the West. Before its technical feasibility could be determined, it was ruled out on cost. Cost alone seemingly blocks use of this method against any forest insect currently present in the West.

INTEGRATED CONTROL

Integrated control is a system that utilizes all suitable techniques to reduce pest populations and maintain them at levels below those causing economic injury (Smith and van den Bosch 1967, van den Bosch and Stern 1962). In forestry the ultimate would be a combination of silvicultural, biological, chemical, and other preventive and remedial control measures. The techniques are being developed and tested individually, but no complete regime of integrated control of insect pests has yet been applied in western forests. A principal problem is to determine what specific measures are needed on particular areas. Fortunately, natural control can be depended upon to do an adequate job of protection most of the time. Emergency measures, such as aerial spraying, are available to meet most urgent needs.

HABITAT RELATIONSHIPS

This section focuses first on insects in relation to various parts of a tree, then on insects in other special relationships. It is a general sorting of the insects likely to be encountered by a forester and is intended as an aid in identification. For this purpose, the user should be aware that many insects infest more than one part of a tree. The general sorting also provides a birds-eye view of the role of insects treated in Part II of this manual.

INSECTS AFFECTING FLOWERS AND SEEDS

Regeneration of forests, whether by natural or artificial means, starts with flowers and seeds. Tree seed production is erratic from year to year due to physiological, climatic, and biotic factors.

Insects are among the more important biotic factors. In some years insects destroy practically all the seeds of certain tree species in certain localities. Insect-caused damage increases the cost of harvesting and processing tree seeds. Damage by insects is especially important in seed orchards, genetics studies, and the collection of seeds from premium quality trees. Such damage can also seriously affect the natural reestablishment of the forest on burned or cutover lands where timing of seeding may be highly critical.

Destruction of seeds may be caused by insects that attack the buds, flowers, or immature cones, as well as by those that attack the seeds themselves. Insects such as thrips and sawflies feed on pollen. Others feed upon the flowers causing wilting, blighting, and premature dropping of the parts affected. The fruit or cones developing after insect attack may be deformed or "wormy," riddled by the borings of various grubs, caterpillars, or maggots. In many cases the cones show no damage, but the seeds are infested with the small white larvae of seed chalcids. Even the old, hard, dry cones of certain pines are often mined by wood borers. The insects that affect seed production in these various ways belong to a number of different orders and families; some work only in cones or seeds, whereas others work also in the bark or cambium of succulent growing shoots, stems, and twigs, or even in dry wood.

Knowledge of the presence of seed-infesting insects will help a forester to avoid the disappointment and loss attendant on the collecting, handling, and sowing of insect-damaged seeds. In certain situations, Douglas-fir trees can be treated with insecticides to protect the seeds from damage by cone midges and the **Douglas fir cone moth** (USDA 1972).

Some of the more important insects affecting the flowers and seeds of forest trees are discussed in this manual. For more information, the comprehensive bulletin by Keen (1958) on cone and seed insects of western forest trees, the informative publication by Hedlin (1974) on cone and seed insects of British Columbia, and the bibliography by Barcia and Merkel (1972) should be consulted.

INSECTS AFFECTING FOLIAGE

No other part of a forest tree provides nourishment to such a host of insects as do the leaves. Hundreds of insect species feed on them in one way or another. Some mine within the needles, some skeletonize the leaves, and others eat the entire leaf tissue or suck the juices. Caterpillars (Lepidoptera) and sawflies (Hymenoptera) are the most damaging of the insects that consume the foliage. Aphids, scales, bugs, beetles, and leaf-mining fly larvae are among the other commonly encountered defoliators. The insects that feed upon foliage are primary in that they attack healthy, vigorous trees as readily as undernourished, weakened ones. Sixteen of the 31 major pests listed in table 3 (page 46) are defoliators.

Trees can withstand a great deal of feeding on the leaves without being seriously affected, and some such insect work is going on more or less constantly. If the feeding is heavy, the growth of the tree is retarded. If a high proportion of the leaf surface is destroyed, the tree may die. The damage done to the forest by defoliators is difficult to estimate since a large part of it involves only a loss of increment and not the death of the trees. When defoliators become epidemic, their ability to destroy timber, especially coniferous timber, over large areas in a short time places them among the most destructive forest insects.

The extent to which a tree may be injured by defoliation will depend upon the tree species, whether the tree is evergreen or deciduous, its position within the stand, its general health, the insect species involved, and the time of year when the defoliation occurs (Kinghorn 1954). Dominant trees are more resistant than their suppressed neighbors, and vigorous trees have a better chance of surviving attacks than those weakened from one cause or another. Since evergreens cannot replace their leaves as readily as deciduous trees, they are much more seriously injured by defoliation than those that normally shed their leaves each year. One year of severe defoliation may be enough to kill such trees as white fir, hemlock, and ponderosa pine. Oaks, aspen, and alder, on the other hand, can usually withstand several seasons of defoliation without fatal injury.

Defoliators, unlike bark beetles, usually show little preference for weakened individual trees. Their feeding is more influenced by the condition of the foliage—whether it is new or old, tough or tender—and by its position on a tree. Usually defoliating insects show no particular choice as to the age or size of tree they attack, and young trees in the forest may be fed on by almost any leaf-feeding form. However, some of the young trees in the stand are actually avoided by defoliating insects. This has been observed in hemlock looper outbreaks where heavy defoliations ceased when stands of young growth were reached. On the other hand, sometimes young trees are fed on in preference to older trees. This has been noted in some outbreaks of the Douglas fir tussock moth. Also, small trees may be fed on because of their closeness to the ground or their more tender succulent growth. For instance, young, low-growing pines have been seriously damaged by invasions of **Mormon crickets** and grasshoppers which, when in epidemic numbers, chew all green foliage within reach.

Outbreaks of defoliators are characteristically sporadic. For many years the forester may not observe a single specimen of some important leaf-feeding insect, and then without warning, a sudden outbreak may occur and the forest may be swarming with millions of caterpillars that devour everything in their path. Some defoliators, like the tent caterpillars, appear nearly every year at widely separated points in the forest. Others, such as the **pine butterfly** and **pandora moth,** appear in major outbreaks at long intervals of time. Typically, outbreaks go through a cycle of variable length and intensity. First there is a gradual buildup from the normal level of the insect population. During this stage the insect multiplies, but the effects of feeding are inconspicuous. Next the buildup accelerates and defoliation appears. Then at the peak of an outbreak, defoliation becomes extensive and may be very destructive. Finally, there is an abrupt decline and return to normal. This natural decline usually is brought about by disease, parasitic insects, or climatic conditions. Among the principal defoliators in the West, the duration of outbreaks ranges from a few to many years, even within species (table 2, page 6).

Outbreaks of leaf feeders do not always result in the death of the defoliated trees. For instance, large areas of hemlock forest in Washington, Canada, and Alaska have been severely defoliated by the **western blackheaded budworm** for 2 or more years in succession, and yet most of the trees have recovered. On the other hand, outbreaks of the hemlock looper, the pine butterfly, the Douglas fir tussock moth, and even one outbreak of the blackheaded budworm on Vancouver Island, British Columbia, have caused the death of hundreds of thousand board feet of standing timber, with a high percentage of the stand killed over thousands of acres.

Prevention of defoliator outbreaks in the West through forest management practices is largely unproven theory. Manipulating the mixture of tree species and breaking up the age classes offer promise with some species.

The aim in applied control of native forest defoliators is not to attempt eradication but to protect forests from severe damage, either by preventing the buildup of epidemics by "catching them while they are small" or by reducing populations at the peak of epidemics to prevent heavy, concentrated feeding, which would be fatal to the trees. In the protection of ornamental, park, and shade trees, rather intensive spray programs are justified in order to prevent damage. In protecting large timber stands, aerial spraying is now available as an effective weapon in defoliator control. The most difficult problem involved is one of deciding when an outbreak may become sufficiently damaging to justify the expense of spraying, for most outbreaks subside of their own accord without reaching the stage of inflicting severe forest damage. Since young caterpillars are more easily killed by poison than older ones, provided they can be reached, early application of control measures is highly desirable. Spraying against the early stages has the further advantage of reducing the loss of foliage in the year of treatment.

INSECTS AFFECTING BUDS AND SHOOTS

Injury to leaf buds and terminal and lateral shoots is caused by insects of a number of different groups, such as caterpillars, weevils, bark beetles, midges, aphids, and scale insects (see Diagnostic Host Index). Some of these insects also infest cones and branches; others also feed upon foliage and are ranked as defoliators. By far the most important ones are the budworms, such as the western spruce budworm and blackheaded budworm, that feed in buds and on shoots during their early life and later feed on the expanded foliage. Budworms infest and sometimes kill trees of all ages.

The larvae of some moths, such as the European pine shoot moth and **western pine tip moth,** are destructive by feeding in and killing the developing shoots of conifers, especially pines. The seriousness of this type of damage is shown in the Sand-hill plantations of the Nebraska National Forest (Van Haverbeke et al. 1971). Two species of pine tip moths, which were of little importance in their native habitat, found their way into these isolated plantations of ponderosa pine. In the new environment, freed from their native parasites, they repeatedly infested, deformed, and stunted the planted trees.

The insects that start life as budworms and end as defoliators continue to be widely destructive in both young and mature forests. Their control is the same as for defoliators generally. Many of the insects that spend their lives as shoot miners are increasingly important in young forests by slowing growth and reducing quality (Stoszek 1973). Practical prevention and control measures for most of these insects are yet to be developed.

INSECTS AFFECTING TWIGS
AND BRANCHES

As a habitat group, the insects that infest twigs and branches are a mixed lot. Some of them also infest cones and shoots; others also infest the bole, particularly on small trees. Because of this mixed situation, a forester seeking to identify an insect found on a twig or branch, should check these other groups in the Diagnostic Host Index.

Weevils often damage the terminals of young conifers. The three most important genera are *Pissodes, Cylindrocopturus*, and *Magdalis*. Among these, the **white pine weevil** is the most important. It is one of the major forest insect pests in the West. The larvae of this species kill the terminals of pines and spruces by feeding under the bark (Stevenson 1967, Wright 1970). The resulting injury deforms infested trees and slows their growth. As a result of this type of injury, planting of Sitka spruce is much reduced in coastal Oregon and Washington. Close planting minimizes damage somewhat. Chemical control has not been attempted in the West because of the cost and the many-year period the trees are subject to attack. The pine reproduction weevil is a pest of planted pines in California (Stevens 1965). It deforms and kills young trees growing under stress conditions by mining beneath the bark of the branches and main stem.

A multitude of bark beetles, borers, cambium miners, twig girdlers, aphids, scales, and other insects feed in and on twigs and branches (see Diagnostic Host Index). Quite a number of these insects are pests of ornamentals. Few cause measurable damage to forest trees; among the latter are aphids, scales, mealybugs, and pitch midges. The balsam woolly aphid is a major forest pest that kills trees slowly by infesting the twigs and branches, or quickly by infesting the bole (Mitchell 1966). It also causes gouting in the tree crown and sometimes on the bole. Most of the twig- and branch-infesting bark beetles and borers that flock into dead or injured trees are of no major consequence in forest management. Tree-killing ips are an exception in that some breed in larger branches as well as in the main stem.

INSECTS AFFECTING BOLES

The bole is the province of some of the most destructive forest insects, notably bark beetles such as species of *Dendroctonus, Ips, Scolytus*, and *Pseudohylesinus*. Twelve of the 31 most important forest insects in the West infest the bole (table 3, page 46). Many different species and families of insects are represented among those that select the cambium region of the main trunk of trees as a suitable place to feed. They bore through the bark and feed in the inner layers of bark and outer layers of wood. As feeding progresses, the channels of some species penetrate deeply into the wood. Some bole-infesting insects, such as the balsam woolly aphid, settle on the bark and suck the juices of the tree through drill-like mouth parts.

A few of the mining insects are capable of attacking healthy trees. By far the greatest number attack only unhealthy, weakened, dying, or dead trees because they cannot resist the flow of sap or resin which, in the normal tree, serves as an effective defense. At times, when a tree's resistance is low, even normally secondary species may kill trees if they attack in sufficient numbers.

It is easy to recognize the work of bark-feeding insects. Often a close inspection of the trunk of an infested tree will reveal boring dust in the crevices of the bark or pitch exuding from small holes in the bark. Positive evidence of infestation can be obtained by removing a small chip of bark and determining whether the phloem is fresh and white or discolored and is mined by insects. If mines are found, a larger piece of bark can be removed, and the species responsible for the damage usually can be identified by the character of its work.

A few species of inner-bark miners, such as the pitch moths, may work in the phloem from the edge of wounds without threatening the life of the tree, and no attempt need be made to control such species under forest conditions. Nor is it necessary to attempt any control of the vast number of inner-bark-feeding insects that confine their attack to weakened, sickly, or felled trees. Only species capable of attacking and killing living trees and some that bore into sound wood (see Insects Affecting Wood and Wood Products, page 41) need cause any concern, and fortunately the number of such species is limited. It is not difficult for the forester to learn to recognize the comparatively few phloem-mining insects that are aggressive killers of the trees in his region.

INSECTS AFFECTING ROOTS

One end of a tree grows in the ground; the other in the air. Both ends are affected by insects. The larvae of some bark beetles and weevils feed under the bark of the root crown and larger roots, much as other species do in the bole above ground. White grubs, seedcorn maggots, cutworms, carpenter ants, aphids, and symphylans feed externally on the roots and below-ground portions of the stem. Not being readily observed, the insects that affect roots have not been much studied and the amount of damage they cause is not well documented except in nurseries.

INSECTS INFESTING GALLS

Many kinds of insects cause galls on forest trees. Galls occur on all parts of a tree, most abundantly on the foliage and least often on the roots. For comprehensive coverage of this fascinating subject, the reader is referred to Felt (1940) and Mani (1964). Numerous gall-forming insects are included in this manual (see Diagnostic Host Index). Some representative examples are the balsam woolly aphid that causes gouting on twigs of true firs; spruce gall aphids that cause conelike galls on twigs of spruce; and gall midges, gall wasps, aphids, and sawflies that cause various galls on the foliage, buds, and branches of forest trees. Gall wasps are by far the most numerous in species. Gall midges are next most abundant. Oaks outrank all other trees as hosts for gall-forming insects. Pines, junipers, willows, and poplars also host many kinds of gall formers.

Numerous insects obtain food and shelter in galls caused by other insects and by fungi. For example, 137 species of insects were recorded from cankers (galls) caused by **comandra blister rust**, *Cronartium comandrae* Pk., on lodgepole pine in Alberta (Powell 1971).

INSECTS IN THE SOIL

As a group, soil-inhabiting insects and related organisms are important to the well-being of forest trees (Burges and Raw 1967). Few species have been studied individually in relation to the management of western forests, hence foresters give little attention to them.

Insects and relatives, ranging from termites and wood borers to springtails and mites, are beneficial by decomposing fallen trees and litter, thus returning nutrients to the soil through excreta and their own dead bodies. Insects in the soil help mix organic matter in the upper layers. As decomposers and soil improvers, insects are important principally because of their great numbers and total volume rather than as individual species. Undoubtedly the number and activities of insects in the soil vary during the life of a stand. As yet, positive means of increasing their beneficial effects have not been developed and put into forest management practice.

Numerous insects such as sawflies and Lepidoptera that feed on above-ground portions of a tree, spend an inactive part of their life in forest soil and litter. There they are sheltered from cold, heat, dryness, and control efforts by man. Still they are sought out and fed upon by insect parasites and predators, many of which also spend part of their life in the soil.

INSECTS AFFECTING WOOD
AND WOOD PRODUCTS

Insects take a heavy toll of crude and finished forest products (Chamberlin 1953, Hickin 1963). This loss has been variously estimated at 1 to 5 percent of the annual cut. The principal damage to forest products is caused by insects that feed on or bore into the wood. A great deal of this damage occurs after trees have been killed or felled and before utilization. Green and seasoned lumber and even the final utilized products are fed on by insects.

After a tree has been killed by fire, insects, or other causes, or felled by wind, snow, or cutting, it becomes particularly attractive to and is deteriorated by a large variety of insects (Kimmey and Furniss 1943, Shea and Johnson 1962, Shea et al. 1962, Wright and Harvey 1967). Ambrosia beetles find the dying wood with fermenting sap an especially suitable medium for the growth of their fungi. Horntail wasps settle on freshly felled trees, sometimes before the woodsmen have finished cutting them into logs, and on fire-killed trees before the fire is out, and insert their long slender ovipositors deeply into the wood to lay their eggs. Many of the flatheaded and roundheaded borers, weevils, and larvae of carpenter moths and clear wing moths are wood boring in habit. The larvae usually feed for a time in the cambium layer and then penetrate the wood. In short, so many different species of wood-boring insects mine in killed or felled trees that it is important that such timber be promptly removed from the woods to avoid heavy damage.

After lumber has been kiln dried it becomes reasonably safe from insect attack. There are, however, a few important groups which still persist in their attacks unless the wood is properly handled. The seasoned sapwood of hardwoods is particularly susceptible to damage by powderpost beetles and must be carefully managed in the lumberyard or in storage to avoid becoming infested. Even after timbers are in place they are subject to attack by powderpost beetles, carpenter ants, roundheaded borers, flatheaded borers, and termites unless precautions are taken to provide proper insulation from the ground or protection is secured through the impregnation of the wood with creosote or other chemicals. Logs rafted or stored for long in seawater are subject to damage by various non-insect marine borers (Hunt 1926).

As has been indicated, the control of insects injurious to forest products is largely a matter of prevention of damage through cutting at the proper season, prompt removal of logs, poles, and other unseasoned products from the woods, proper handling in the mills, and certain precautions in utilization. Logs that are to be used for poles or in rustic work should be peeled before wood borers have an opportunity to enter the wood. Chemical measures for prevention and control vary with the kind of insect and with changes in approved insecticide recommendations.

INSECTS AFFECTING FOREST NURSERIES AND PLANTINGS

A forest nurseryman must guard against insect enemies of young trees, as well as against damping-off, rodents, heat injury, and unfavorable soil conditions. Young seedlings in seed and transplant beds are frequently damaged by root-feeding insects, which are able to inflict more injury at this stage than later when trees have become established and have developed larger root systems. The stems of young seedlings may be attacked above ground by cutworms, grasshoppers, leafhoppers, aphids, and various bark-chewing beetles; and the leaves may be fed upon by caterpillars, sawflies, and various scales, aphids, and bugs.

In western forest nurseries, white grubs, root weevils, seedcorn maggots, cutworms, symphylans, grasshoppers, and aphids are some of the pests that have been troublesome. Damage by root-feeding insects is most likely on newly broken ground previously covered by sod. Most western forest nurseries are not seriously troubled by insect pests.

Although the control of insect pests in forest nurseries is sometimes difficult, the nurseryman can use measures that would be impractical under forest conditions. Most root-feeding insects can be controlled by applying a soil fumigant or by using poisoned baits, but much can be done to avoid injury through regulating cultural methods. Transplant beds that have become heavily infested should be plowed and allowed to remain fallow for at least a year. If they are cultivated often enough to prevent the growth of weeds, most of the insects will have been starved out in a year's time, and the beds can be used again for a period without serious injury to transplants. Leaf-feeding insects usually are easily controlled by the use of sprays.

Young trees in forest and Christmas tree plantings and in seed orchards are subject to the same wide variety of insects that feed upon natural regeneration (Browne 1968). However, planted trees seem to be more susceptible to insect-caused damage, perhaps because of lesser vigor of such trees. The economic damage is more serious, too, because of the high cost of establishing plantations. Some of the insects that give most trouble are white

42

grubs, weevils, shoot moths, bark beetles, pitch midges, carpenter ants, scales, and aphids.

The basic step in protecting plantations against insects is to strive for maximum vigor by minimizing competition by brush and grass and avoiding adverse planting sites. For example, planting ponderosa pine on hardscrabble is an invitation to insects to cause trouble. Of course, cultural and harvesting practices in nearby stands should not be such as to increase damaging insects that likely would spread and invade plantations. Because values are higher and the threat of insect-caused damage is greater in plantations, direct control by chemicals is more frequently warranted than in natural stands of similar age. Acre for acre, seed orchards approach agricultural crops in value and in the need for protection against insects.

INSECTS AFFECTING RANGE PLANTS

Grasses, forbs, and shrubs furnish food for livestock and wildlife on forest-related ranges and thus are within the province of foresters. As with trees, range plants are fed upon by many kinds of insects (Furniss 1972a). A few of these insects are known to cause serious damage. At times in some localities, an insect outbreak will so seriously deplete a key plant, such as bitterbrush, that livestock have to be moved elsewhere. The effects may carry over and reduce the available food for several years. Probably of greater importance than outbreaks is the continuous drain caused by the general feeding of numerous kinds of insects. Direct control is seldom applied because of the low per-acre value of the affected range.

The reader interested in range insects is referred to a recent publication concerning those on browse plants in the Northwest (Furniss and Barr 1975). A few insects likely to be encountered by foresters are included in the present manual; for example, tent caterpillars, other defoliators, and grass bugs of known destructiveness; grasshoppers that sometimes damage young pines; and various other insects that feed on broad-leaved trees and shrubs used as browse by livestock and game animals.

INSECTS AFFECTING ESTHETIC
AND RECREATIONAL VALUES

Insects that attack trees in commercial forests also attack trees grown for esthetic and other special purposes in parks, suburban developments, urban plantings, and shelterbelts. Sometimes the impact is similar; sometimes quite different. A forest devastated by a bark beetle outbreak is reduced in value both for timber production and for most recreational use. A few ornamental trees, or even one, may warrant considerable expense to protect, whereas the continuous loss of a small number of trees in a commercial forest is normal and warrants only salvage, if anything.

Foresters are increasingly called upon to identify insects that attack shade and ornamental trees and to recommend measures to control them. Numerous insects included in this manual are significant only as pests of woody ornamentals. There is a need for a comprehensive manual on western insects that affect trees in ornamental plantings and on recreational areas. For the present, the need is partially met by Herrick (1935), Schuh and Mote (1948), and Weigel and Baumhofer (1948).

Intensive use and misuse in campgrounds and other forested areas weaken trees and call for special measures to protect the trees from insect attack. Rotation of campgrounds, protective barriers on and around individual trees, or direct control measures sometimes are warranted to protect such trees (Wagener 1963).

Insect-killed trees are part of the natural process by which forests are regenerated, hence they are a recurrent part of the scene in wilderness areas. The skeletons of beetle-killed trees even have a stark beauty worthy of preserving, but, when whole forests are killed, the impact within a reserve may be greater than is generally acceptable. In addition, infestation is likely to spread and cause damage to surrounding commercial forests. The forest management challenge is to permit natural processes to run their course within limits that will not cause undue harm.

Insects that bite and otherwise are objectionable to man and animals on forest recreation areas are increasingly important. A basic source of information concerning such insects is Herms's Medical Entomology (James and Harwood 1969). Aquatic Insects of California (Usinger et al. 1963) provides much information concerning the insect fauna of forest streams and lakes.

INSECTS AFFECTING SHELTERBELTS

Trees and shrubs are planted extensively in the Great Plains and other unforested areas of the West, such as portions of the Great Basin and the Columbia River Basin, to protect crops, livestock, and wildlife; to shelter dwellings against wind and snow; and to enhance the landscape. Shelterbelt plantings often suffer from drought, wind, and adverse soils and consequently are vulnerable to attacks by insects. Many kinds of insects feed upon and damage trees in shelterbelts. The profusely illustrated key by Stein and Kennedy (1972) serves to identify the species likely to be encountered in this special situation.

MAJOR FOREST INSECT PESTS

Major pests are defined as those that seriously damage forests and forest products or that affect forest management decisions and practices on extensive areas. On a particular area, they are the insects that forest managers should know and take into account. Somewhat more than 30 species qualify for this classification according to a Westwide sampling of opinion of foresters and entomologists (table 3). This list approximates one developed in Canada by Davidson and Prentice (1967). A few species are ranked as major pests principally because of dramatic outbreaks rather than great damage.

Numerous others might have been included on the basis of their causing significant though often localized damage. In a list published 45 years ago, Craighead and Middleton (1930) took this broader approach. Today in the West, these next lower order pests would include some beetles of the genera *Conophthorus*, *Cylindrocopturus*, *Dryocoetes*, *Lyctus*, *Melanophila*, *Monochamus*, and *Tetropium*; moths such as *Epinotia*, *Eucosma*, and *Galenara*; some *Matsucoccus* scales; an aphid of the genus *Elatobium*; and from time to time, other insects.

The listing of major pests by broadly defined regions (table 3) is to indicate to a forester in a particular State or Province insects for which he should be especially alert. For this purpose, the Northern Region consists of the interior, spruce-hardwood forests of Alaska and Northern Canada. The Pacific Coast Region comprises the fir-hemlock forests of southeastern Alaska, western British Columbia, western Washington and Oregon, and north coastal California. The remaining two regions are dominated by pine and mixed conifer forests from the Cascade Mountains and the Sierra Nevada to the eastern slopes of the Rockies, and from Southern Canada to Mexico. East to West, they are divided by an imaginary line from southern Colorado, Utah, and Nevada, to central California.

Table 3 reveals that northern and Pacific coast forests have fewer and generally different major insect pests than other forests of the West. Several species occur in two or more regions. To qualify as a major pest in a particular region, an insect must seriously affect one or more important species of trees. The spruce beetle, *Dendroctonus rufipennis*, is a major pest in all regions. The **striped ambrosia beetle**, *Trypodendron lineatum*, occurs in all regions but is economically important only in the northern portion of the Pacific Coast Region. The western spruce budworm, *Choristoneura occidentalis*, and the mountain pine beetle, *Dendroctonus ponderosae*, rank as the two most destructive species in the

Table 3.—*Major forest insect pests in regions of Western North America*

Insect	Region and principal forest trees			
	Northern (spruce, aspen, and birch)	Pacific Coast (Douglas-fir, true fir, and hemlock)	Rocky Mountain and Inter-mountain (pines and mixed conifers)	California and South-western (pines and mixed conifers)
Coleoptera				
Dendroctonus adjunctus				X
Dendroctonus brevicomis			X	X
Dendroctonus jeffreyi				X
Dendroctonus ponderosae			X	X
Dendroctonus pseudotsugae		X	X	X
Dendroctonus rufipennis	X	X	X	X
Ips pini			X	X
Ips spp.	X		X	X
Pissodes strobi		X	X	
Pseudohylesinus spp.		X		
Scolytus ventralis			X	X
Trypodendron lineatum		X		
Hymenoptera				
Neodiprion spp.		X	X	X
Pristiphora erichsonii	X		X	
Isoptera				
Reticulitermes spp.		X	X	X
Lepidoptera				
Acleris gloverana		X		
Adelges piceae		X		
Choristoneura conflictana	X			
Choristoneura occidentalis			X	X
Coleophora laricella			X	
Coleotechnites spp.			X	X
Coloradia pandora			X	X
Ectropis crepuscularia		X		
Lambdina fiscellaria lugubrosa		X		
Malacosoma spp.	X		X	X
Melanolophia imitata		X		
Neophasia menapia			X	
Operophtera bruceata	X			
Orgyia pseudotsugata			X	X
Rheumaptera hastata	X			
Rhyacionia spp.			X	X

West, although neither is significant in the Pacific coast and Northern Regions. Pines, spruces, and firs have the greatest number of major insect pests; redwood has none (see Diagnostic Host Index).

INTRODUCED INSECTS

Foreign forest insects known to be established in the West number upward of 70 (table 4, page 48). Most of them were accidentally introduced. Four of them now rank as major pests—balsam woolly aphid, larch casebearer, larch sawfly, and European pine shoot moth (table 3). Several others are presently or potentially damaging to forest trees or forest products. Seventeen of the numerous species introduced for biological control of pest insects and weeds of significance to foresters are reported to be successfully colonized. Some insects, notably sawflies having a northerly distribution, are native both in North America and Eurasia. Although these "natives" have been here a very long time, the introduction of special strains can complicate control, as with the larch sawfly.

Quarantines are the principal means for keeping forest insect pests out of the United States. The Federal quarantine system is based upon the Plant Quarantine Act of 1912 and related legislation. Few destructive forest insects have become established since quarantines were established and enforced. Most recent insect immigrants in the West are species that became established long ago in the East and spread from there, for example, Japanese beetle, gypsy moth, European pine shoot moth, and smaller European elm bark beetle.

Despite the proven effectiveness of quarantines, modern commerce and travel provide abundant opportunities for invasion by destructive forest insects. Many notorious pests of Europe, such as the **pine processionary,** *Thaumetopoea pityocampa* Schiffermüller, are continuous threats. To back up the quarantine program, surveys enlisting the help of foresters, entomologists, and others concerned with forests throughout the West, are needed to detect foreign insect invaders while eradication is feasible (Popham and Hall 1958).

Table 4.—*Insects introduced from other continents and
now established in Western North America*

Insect	Origin	Plant or animal host
Coleoptera (accidentally introduced):		
Anobium punctatum **furniture beetle**	Europe	Wood products
Cryptorhynchus lapathi **poplar-and-willow borer**	Europe	*Salix* and *Populus*
Lyctus brunneus **old world lyctus beetle**	Europe (Cosmopolitan)	Wood products
Lyctus linearis **European lyctus beetle**	Europe (Cosmopolitan)	Wood products
Nacerdes melanura **wharf borer**	Europe	Wood products
Otiorhynchus ovatus **strawberry root weevil**	Europe	Seedling conifers
Otiorhynchus rugosostriatus **rough strawberry root weevil**	Europe	Seedling conifers
Otiorhynchus sulcatus **black vine weevil**	Europe	Seedling conifers
Popillia japonica **Japanese beetle**	Japan	Broad-leaved trees and many ornamentals
Pyrrhalta luteola **elm leaf beetle**	Europe	*Ulmus*
Saperda populnea	Europe	*Populus*
Scolytus multistriatus **smaller European elm bark beetle**	Europe	*Ulmus*
Scolytus rugulosus **shothole borer**	Europe	Broad-leaved trees
Stegobium paniceum **drugstore beetle**	Cosmopolitan	Wood products
Tenebroides mauritanicus **cadelle**	Cosmopolitan	Wood products
Xestobium rufovillosum **deathwatch beetle**	Europe	Wood products
Xyleborus dispar **European shothole borer**	Europe	Broad-leaved trees
Coleoptera (intentionally introduced):		
Apion fuscirostre	Europe	Gorse, *Ulex europaeus*
Apion ulicis **gorse weevil**	Europe	Gorse
Chrysolina hyperici	Europe via Australia	Klamath weed, *Hypericum perforatum*
Chrysolina quadrigemina **Klamathweed beetle**	Europe via Australia	Klamath weed, *Hypericum perforatum*
Laricobius erichsonii	Europe	*Adelges piceae*
Scymnus impexus	Europe	*Adelges piceae*

Insect	Origin	Plant or animal host
Diptera (accidentally introduced):		
Hylemya platura	Europe	Seedling conifers
seedcorn maggot		
Phytomyza ilicis	Europe	*Ilex*
holly leafminer		
Diptera (intentionally introduced):		
Aphidoletes thompsoni	Europe	*Adelges piceae*
Compsilura concinnata	Europe	*Porthetria dispar* and other Lepidoptera
Cremifania nigrocellulata	Europe	*Adelges piceae*
Leucopis obscura	Europe	*Adelges piceae*
Hemiptera (none introduced)		
Homoptera (accidentally introduced):		
Adelges abietis	Europe	*Picea*
Eastern spruce gall aphid		
Adelges nüsslini (= *nordmaneanae*)	Europe	*Picea* and *Abies*
Adelges piceae	Europe	*Abies*
balsam woolly aphid		
Adelges strobilobius (= *laricis*)	Europe	*Picea* and *Larix*
larch woolly aphid		
Asterolecanium minus	Europe	*Quercus*
Cinara tujafilina	Europe	Cupressini
Dialeurodes chittendeni	Asia	*Rhododendron*
rhododendron whitefly		
Elatobium abietinum	Europe	*Picea*
spruce aphid		
Eriosoma ulmi	Europe	*Ulmus*
European elm leafcurl aphid		
Euceraphis punctipennis	Europe	*Betula*
European birch aphid		
Gossyparia spuria	Europe	*Ulmus*
European elm scale		
Lecanium corni	Europe	Broad-leaved trees
European fruit lecanium		
Lepidosaphes ulmi	Europe	Broad-leaved trees
oystershell scale		
Periphyllus californiensis	Asia	*Acer*
Periphyllus lyropictus	Europe	*Acer platanoides* and other *Acer*
Periphyllus testudinacea	Europe	*Acer*
Physokermes piceae	Europe	*Picea*
spruce bud scale		
Pineus strobi	Europe	*Pinus*
pine bark aphid		
Quadraspidiotus perniciosus	Asia	Broad-leaved trees
San Jose scale		
Schizolachnus pineti	Europe	*Pinus*

49

Insect	Origin	Plant or animal host
Hymenoptera (accidentally introduced):		
Eriocampa ovata	Europe	*Alnus*
alder woolly sawfly		
Fenusa pusilla	Europe	*Betula*
birch leafminer		
Pristiphora erichsonii	Europe	*Larix*
larch sawfly		
Profenusa thomsoni	Eurasia	*Betula*
amber-marked birch leafminer		
Trichiocampus viminalis	Europe	*Populus* and *Salix*
Hymenoptera (intentionally introduced):		
Agathis pumila	Europe	*Coleophora laricella*
Apanteles solitarius	Europe	*Stilpnotia salicis*
Chrysocharis laricinellae	Europe	*Coleophora laricella*
Mesoleius tenthredinis	Europe	*Pristiphora erichsonii*
Meteorus versicolor	Europe	*Stilpnotia salicis*
Lepidoptera (accidentally introduced):		
Aethes rutilana	Europe	*Juniperus*
pale juniper webworm		
Archips rosanus	Europe	Broad-leaved trees
Caloptilia negundella	Europe	*Acer*
boxelder leafroller		
Caloptilia syringella	Europe	Lilac and *Fraxinus*
lilac leafminer		
Cnephasia longana	Europe	*Pseudotsuga* and broad-
omnivorous leaftier		leaved trees
Coleophora laricella	Europe	*Larix*
larch casebearer		
Dichomeris marginella	Europe	*Juniperus*
juniper webworm		
Homadaula anisocentra	Unknown	*Albizzia* and *Gleditsia*
mimosa webworm		
Ocnerostoma piniariellum	Europe	*Pinus*
Pandemis cerasana	Europe	Broad-leaved trees
Porthetria dispar	Europe	Broad-leaved trees
gypsy moth		
Rhyacionia buoliana	Europe	*Pinus*
European pine shoot moth		
Spilonota ocellana	Europe	*Quercus* and other
eyespotted bud moth		broad-leaved trees
Stilpnotia salicis	Europe	*Populus* and *Salix*
satin moth		
Lepidoptera (intentionally introduced):		
Leucoptera spartifoliella	Europe	Scotch broom,
		Cytisus scoparius
Tyria jacobaeae	Europe	Tansy ragwort,
cinnabar moth		*Senecio jacobaea*

Part II
Insects and Allies

The chapters in Part II deal with approximately 1,400 species of insects and related organisms occurring commonly in western forests, intermixed rangelands, forest nurseries, plantings of ornamental trees, and wood in use. These insects are considered to be the ones most likely to be seen by foresters and other users of the forest. Information on them is from publications (see Literature Cited). The figures, chosen to illustrate important species and species representative of groups, are closely associated with the text to which they refer.

Phyla represented are Mollusca, which includes the shipworms, and Arthropoda, which includes the crustaceans, symphylans, spiders, and mites, in addition to the insects. The chapters are arranged systematically, beginning with the more primitive organisms in the evolutionary scale and ending with the more advanced ones. The arrangement is as approved by the Entomological Society of America (Anderson 1975), except that the Diptera are placed below the Hymenoptera.

Within the chapters, the major groups such as suborders and superfamilies are arranged systematically, but within these groups the families are arranged alphabetically. Within the families, the arrangement is usually alphabetical, but sometimes important species are presented first so that less important species may be readily compared with them on the basis of structure or life cycle.

Wood structures, boats, and logs in salt water are subject to serious damage by marine borers belonging to the classes Gastropoda (Mollusca) and Crustacea (Arthropoda) (Clapp and Kenk 1963). These animals are briefly discussed here primarily to open the literature concerning them, which is extensive but little known to foresters.

CLASS GASTROPODA

FAMILY TEREDINIDAE—SHIPWORMS OR PILEWORMS

These wood-boring mollusks (Bramhall 1966, Turner 1966) are related to oysters, clams, and mussels. They have wormlike bodies, small shells at the burrowing end, and siphons and pallets at the outer end. The siphons draw in fresh sea water for oxygen and food and discharge the used water and waste products. The pallets are plates of shell used to close the burrows. The burrows are lined with a hard, white, calcareous material that renders logs unfit for lumber. Shipworms invade new wood during the brief larval period when they are free-swimming. The entrance hole is so small that the damage often is not detected until the interior of the wood is riddled and useless (fig. 10).

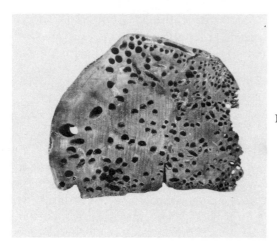

F–519930

FIGURE 10.—Cross section of log honeycombed by shipworms, mollusks in the family Teredinidae.

There are many kinds of shipworms, particularly in the warmer seas and oceans. On the Pacific coast, *Bankia setacea* (Tryon) and *Teredo navalis* L. are abundant. *B. setacea* is larger and more important in northern waters. It attains a length of 60 cm (24 inches) and a diameter of about 20 mm (0.8 inch), and has a segmented pallet. *T. navalis* at maturity is 10 to 15 cm long, about 10 mm in diameter, and has a nonsegmented pallet. The life cycle and habits of *T. navalis* are discussed and illustrated by Lane (1961).

Wooden structures and boats can be treated with preservatives or protective coverings to prevent damage by shipworms. Logs that must be put in saltwater should remain there only a short time because they can be severely damaged in a few months by shipworms.

CLASS CRUSTACEA

This very large class of arthropods consists of mostly aquatic and predominantly marine animals, but some are terrestrial. The order Isopoda (Hatch 1947) contains a few species of interest to the forester.

FAMILY ARMADILLIDIIDAE—SOWBUGS OR PILLBUGS

These grayish, rounded little animals with flexible segments frequent damp or wet places, often feeding on tender young plants. Sometimes they are a nuisance in damp basements. The **dooryard sowbug**, *Porcellio laevis* Koch, and the **common pillbug**, *Armadillidium vulgare* (Latreille), are examples. None is a forest pest.

FAMILY LIMNORIIDAE

The **gribble**, *Limnoria lignorum* Rathke (Bramhall 1966, Hunt 1926) is a representative of this group on the Pacific coast. It is about 6 mm long and resembles the common pillbug to which it is related. *L. lignorum* swims or crawls about at will. It feeds first on the softer outer portions of the wood of pilings, progressing inward as wave action and its feeding erode the wood surface. It attacks in great numbers. Destruction by it progresses most rapidly at low tide level. Prevention of damage is the same as for shipworms.

CLASS SYMPHYLA

Symphylans (Michelbacher 1949) are white, soft-bodied, centipedelike animals, less than 10 mm long, with long, many-segmented antennae and 12 pairs of legs when fully developed (fig. 11). They live in moist soil, often abundantly in forest soil, and feed principally on plant material. Some damage agricultural crops. One is potentially damaging in forest tree nurseries.

FAMILY SCUTIGERELLIDAE

The **garden symphylan**, *Scutigerella immaculata* (Newport) (Berry and Robinson 1974, Michelbacher 1938) feeds on the roots of various vegetable crops and is especially damaging in Pacific Coast States. It has killed broad-leaved tree seedlings in a forest

COURTESY OREGON STATE UNIVERSITY

FIGURE 11.—Adult garden symphylan (*Scutigerella immaculata*), 5.8 mm long.

nursery in western Oregon but is not reported to feed upon conifers. Populations run to many millions per acre and are greatest in moist soils high in organic content. *S. immaculata* shuns light and moves rapidly through natural crevices in the soil. Control is difficult and expensive. Deep and thorough cultivation helps to minimize damage.

CLASS ARACHNIDA

The class Arachnida consists of 11 subclasses, including spiders, mites and ticks, scorpions, pseudoscorpions, daddylonglegs, and related forms. They differ from insects in lacking antennae, true jaws, or compound eyes and in having four pairs of legs, only two body regions, and unique respiratory and reproductive systems.

SUBCLASS ARANAE—SPIDERS

Spiders feed largely on insects and are generally considered to be beneficial. In the West, the **black widow spider,** *Latrodectus mactans* (F.), other species of *Latrodectus,* and the **brown recluse,** *Loxosceles reclusa* Gertsch and Muliak, are venomous to man.

Spiders feed on many forest insects, but there have been few efforts to measure their effectiveness in controlling pest insects (Loughton et al. 1963). Dahlsten (1967) observed several species of spiders feeding on *Neodiprion* larvae. Carolin and Honing (1972) reported spiders as important predators of the western spruce budworm (fig. 12). Jennings and Pase (1975) observed and identified spiders feeding on adults of *Ips pini,* and Jennings (1975) recorded an oxyopid spider feeding on late instar larvae of *Rhyacionia neomexicana.*

Keys for the identification of the more common spiders of the United States are given by Kaston and Kaston (1953). Spiders

F-505849

FIGURE 12.—Jumping spider (family Attidae) feeding on western spruce budworm larva.

of the Americas are catalogued by Petrunkevitch (1911). The biology, behavior, and peculiarities of spiders are discussed by Comstock (1948) and Gertsch (1949).

SUBCLASS ACARI—MITES AND TICKS

The Acari (Baker and Wharton 1952) are a large and diverse subclass of small arthropods. Classification is complex and unsettled. The classification by Krantz (1970), as amended in correspondence, is adopted in this manual. It recognizes three orders, of which two contain species of interest to foresters.

The great majority of mites are small, wingless, generally eight-legged creatures that resemble spiders, but differ in that the leg-bearing portion of the body is broadly joined to the after portion, rather than being joined by a narrow stalk. Some of the many mite species suck the juices from the leaves and tender stems of trees causing damage similar to that of insects. Some prey upon or are variously associated with forest insects, especially bark beetles (Lindquist 1969a, Lindquist 1970, Moser and Roton 1971); mites that are carried on the body of insects but do not feed on them are said to be phoretic. Some contribute importantly to the nutrient cycle in forest soils by decomposing litter and mixing organic matter (Burges and Raw 1967). Others are pests of man and animals. As pests on trees, mites are more important on ornamental plantings than on forest trees. In general, the biology and role of mites in the forest has been little studied and only a small fraction of the species has been named.

ORDER PARASITIFORMES

This order contains three suborders of which two are included in this manual.

SUBORDER MESOSTIGMATA

The species in this large suborder (Krantz 1970) are predators and parasites. They usually have hardened shields or plates above and below. In the forest, some are predators and associates of bark beetles; others prey upon phytophagous mites.

FAMILY CERCOMEGISTIDAE

Cercoleipus coelonotus Kinn is associated with species of *Ips*. It feeds primarily on nematodes, occasionally on other mites, *Ips* eggs, and fungi (Kinn 1971).

FAMILY DIGAMASELLIDAE

The Digamasellidae (Hurlbutt 1967, Lindquist 1975) are oval, smooth, flattened, predatory mites often associated with insects, especially bark beetles. *Dendrolaelaps* [*Digamasellus*] *quadrisetus* (Berlese) occurs extensively in North America and Europe in association with *Ips, Dendroctonus, Orthotomicus,* and *Hylastes.* In California it preys upon the brood of *Ips paraconfusus* and upon nematodes and fungi (Kinn 1967). This mite is carried from tree to tree by its host adult, often on the declivity or under the elytra.

FAMILY PHYTOSEIIDAE

Mites of the Phytoseiidae (Chant 1959) prey upon and are considered to be important in natural control of phytophagous mites. Species of *Typhlodromus* are predators of *Oligonychus ununguis* (Fellin 1968, Johnson 1958).

FAMILY SCHIZOGYNIIDAE

Choriachus reginus Kinn (Kinn 1966) is associated with *Pseudohylesinus sericeus, Phloeosinus punctatus,* and *P. sequoiae* in California and is suspected of preying upon these bark beetles.

FAMILY UROPODIDAE

A species of *Trichouropoda,* formerly known as *Uropoda fallax* Vitzhum, is carried from tree to tree attached to the declivity and under surfaces of *Ips.* This and related species are believed to feed on fungi in beetle galleries.

SUBORDER METASTIGMATA

Ticks (Krantz 1970) are very large, specialized mites. They are external parasites that feed principally on the blood of mammals, birds, and reptiles. There are three families, one of which is of concern to western foresters.

FAMILY IXODIDAE—HARDBACKED TICKS

This family (James and Harwood 1969) contains numerous ticks that feed upon and transmit diseases to man and other animals. The **Rocky Mountain wood tick**, *Dermacentor andersoni* Stiles (Cooley 1932) (fig. 13), occurs extensively in the Western States and Provinces. It transmits Rocky Mountain spotted fever, Colorado tick fever, and other diseases to man, especially in springtime in open woodland areas where wild animal populations are disease reservoirs. Foresters and others in such areas should take precautions to avoid ticks becoming attached. If ticks become attached they should be removed promptly.

ORDER ACARIFORMES

This order contains four suborders, all of which are included in this manual.

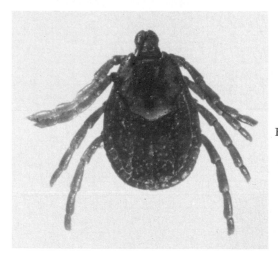

F–521898

FIGURE 13.—Adult of Rocky
Mountain wood tick (*Dermacentor andersoni*), 3.5
mm long.

SUBORDER PROSTIGMATA

This very large suborder (Krantz 1970) contains many of the
mites that damage trees.

FAMILY ERIOPHYIDAE

The **eriophyid mites** are considered by some specialists to be a
superfamily (Lindquist 1974). In this manual they are treated as
one large family (Krantz 1970).

These mites are tiny, elongate, four-legged, translucent creatures that average about 0.2 mm in length. The legs are far forward and the abdomen has many narrow transverse rings.
Through a hand lens, these mites appear only as specks. Microscopic examination of slide-mounted specimens is necessary for
specific determination. Eriophyid mites feed on perennial plants
with few exceptions and are highly selective as to hosts, seldom
attacking species in more than one genus. They have two nymphal
instars, the second instar producing the adult after a resting
period. Under optimum conditions, development from egg to adult
takes 10 days to 2 weeks. Keifer (1952) lists many species on
coniferous and broad-leaved trees in California. Some are significant pests.

Numerous species of *Eriophyes* [*Aceria*] attack a wide variety
of plants, including broad-leaved trees. They feed on leaves, buds,
stems, flowers, and fruit; many of them cause galls. *E. parapopuli*
Keifer (fig. 14) causes woody galls around the buds of various
poplars, including aspen, throughout the West. It stunts tree
growth and in Alberta is rated as a major pest of farm shelterbelts. *E. neoessigi* Keifer causes pendant galls in the catkins of

57

FIGURE 14.—Woody gall caused by *Eriophyes parapopuli* on buds of trembling aspen.

poplars, including aspen, from Alberta to California. The **purple erineum maple mite**, *E. calaceris* (Keifer), causes dense, magenta-colored, hairlike growths on the underside of leaves of *Acer glabrum.*

Species of *Phytoptus* feed on various plants including broad-leaved trees and shrubs. The **alder gall mite**, *P. laevis* Nalepa, is a holarctic species that causes beadlike galls on leaves of *Alnus.*

Mites of the genus *Platyphytoptus* (Keifer 1952) live on pine needles, usually within the needle sheath. *P. sabinianae* Keifer occurs on *Pinus ponderosa, P. radiata, P. sabiniana,* and other pines in California.

Trisetacus contains several species that feed on foliage, buds, and twigs of conifers, usually causing galls. *T. alborum* Keifer induces lateral growths with multiple buds on sugar pine in California.

Trisetacus campnodus Keifer and Saunders (Keifer and Saunders 1972) seriously damages *Pinus sylvestris* in Christmas tree plantations in Washington. It feeds principally within the needle fascicle, causing yellowing, stunting, and twisting of the needles. It is closely related to *T. grosmanni* and *T. pseudotsugae.*

Trisetacus ehmanni Keifer (Keifer 1963) has been confused with the **pine bud mite**, *T. pini* (Nalepa), which causes twig galls on Scotch pine in Europe. *T. ehmanni* (fig. 15A) occurs in California on ponderosa, Jeffrey, Monterey, lodgepole, digger, and knobcone pines. It feeds within the needle sheath on the current year's needles, twisting and shortening them and causing them to turn yellow and drop prematurely. On repeatedly attacked trees, the twigs may become twisted (fig. 15B). This species or a closely related one heavily attacks and weakens young trees in plantations in southern Oregon.

A

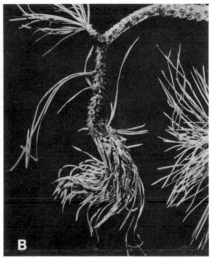

FIGURE 15.—A pine bud mite, *Trisetacus ehmanni*: *A*, Adult female (greatly enlarged); *B*, shoot damage on ponderosa pine.

Trisetacus grosmanni Keifer is reported to damage the buds of young Sitka spruce in British Columbia.

The **Douglas fir bud mite**, *Trisetacus pseudotsugae* Keifer (Keifer 1965), causes big-bud of Douglas-fir from seedling size to mature trees in coastal Oregon and California (fig. 16). It stunts and deforms seedlings (Lavender et al. 1967).

The **juniper berry mite**, *Trisetacus quadrisetus* (Thomas), attacks and destroys the berries of junipers, including *Juniperus californica*, *J. occidentalis*, and *J. scopulorum* (Morgan and Hedlin 1960). It is a holarctic species recorded in California, Oregon, and British Columbia.

FAMILY TENUIPALPIDAE—FALSE SPIDER MITES

The **false spider mites** (Pritchard and Baker 1958) are small, frequently reddish, phytophagous mites that resemble the Tetranychidae. Some are pests of ornamentals and agricultural crops. Some feed on forest trees, but none is rated a forest pest.

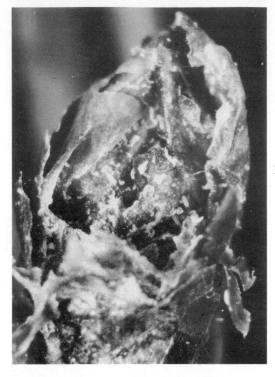

F–521900

FIGURE 16.—Abnormal bud of Douglas-fir, with eggs and larvae of *Trisetacus pseudotsugae* under bud scales.

The genus *Pentamerismus* is holarctic on conifers except the Pinaceae. *P. erythreus* (Ewing) (Pritchard and Baker 1958) is a small red species common on *Chamaecyparis, Cupressus, Juniperus, Libocedrus,* and *Thuja.* It occurs extensively in Western States, including California, Arizona, Nevada, Oregon, Washington, and Idaho.

FAMILY TETRANYCHIDAE—SPIDER MITES

The **spider mites** (Tuttle and Baker 1968) are tiny greenish, yellowish, orange, or reddish creatures, often with black or dark pigmented patterns. They feed on many kinds of plants including deciduous trees and shrubs and some conifers. At times they are serious pests on shade and ornamental trees, especially under hot, dry conditions. Only the spruce spider mite is reported to cause serious damage in the forest. Spider mites feed by sucking plant juices from the leaves with their needlelike mouth parts, thus causing spotting, fading, yellowing, silvering, browning, and premature fall of leaves. Heavy infestations may be detected by the webbing, eggs, cast skins, and the activity of the mites. Spraying of ornamentals sometimes is necessary, but the right spray must be used because some chemicals aggravate mite infestations.

Eotetranychus weldoni (Ewing) (Tuttle and Baker 1968) has been found in Arizona on *Salix* and *Populus*. It also occurs in California, Oregon, Colorado, and Wyoming.

Eurytetranychus admes Pritchard and Baker occurs in California, Oregon, and Utah. *Juniperus* and *Libocedrus decurrens* are hosts.

Some species of *Oligonychus* (Tuttle and Baker 1968) feed on foliage of conifers; others, on broad-leaved trees. They frequently damage ornamentals. One species occasionally becomes epidemic in the forest.

The **spruce spider mite**, *Oligonychus ununguis* (Jacobi) feeds on the foliage (fig. 17) and is a pest of conifers throughout the world. Species of *Abies, Chamaecyparis, Juniperus, Picea, Pinus, Pseudotsuga, Sequoia, Thuja,* and *Tsuga* are among the hosts. The spruce spider mite is a common pest of ornamentals and sometimes becomes epidemic in the forest. It thrives under hot, dry conditions and especially when its natural enemies and the vigor of the host tree are at low ebb.

The largest outbreak of spruce spider mite on record affected 800,000 acres of Douglas-fir in Montana in 1957 following aerial spraying with DDT to control western spruce budworm. It was theorized that the outbreak resulted from killing natural enemies, perhaps mites such as *Typhlodromus*. Since mite outbreaks did not occur on numerous similarly-sprayed areas in Montana and

COURTESY CANADIAN FORESTRY SERVICE

FIGURE 17. — Webbing and cast skins of spruce spider mite (*Oligonychus ununguis*) on Douglas-fir.

61

other parts of the West, the exact role of insecticides in affecting forest mite populations remains to be determined.

The generalized biology of the spruce spider mite is given by Doidge and Marshall (1971) and Johnson (1958). In British Columbia there are up to seven generations annually. Outbreaks in the forest normally develop and subside in 1 year. Effects have not been determined quantitatively.

In California, *Oligonychus subnudus* (McGregor) and *O. milleri* (McGregor) cause severe chlorosis of needles of Monterey pines grown as ornamentals or as Christmas trees (Koehler and Frankie 1968). These mites also occur in Arizona.

The **sycamore spider mite**, *O. platani* (McGregor) (Brown and Eads 1965b) is an injurious pest of sycamore and loquat in California and Arizona. It also feeds on oaks and chinkapin. On sycamore it feeds on the upper surface of the leaf. The adult females are greenish with black pigmented patterns. Ten to 12 generations per year are reported.

Platytetranychus libocedri (McGregor) (Tuttle and Baker 1968) is common on *Pinus* and also occurs on *Cupressus*, *Juniperus*, *Thuja*, and *Tamarix*. It has been recorded from Arizona, California, Oregon, Utah, and Texas.

The **twospotted spider mite**, *Tetranychus urticae* Koch (Tuttle and Baker 1968), often referred to in the literature as *T. telarius* (L.), is a cosmopolitan web-spinning species that attacks many kinds of plants including broad-leaved trees and shrubs. Under hot, dry conditions it may cause defoliation. There are several generations annually.

SUBORDER HETEROSTIGMATA

This group of small soft-bodied mites with minute mouth parts should be considered a suborder rather than a subdivision of the Prostigmata (Krantz in correspondence). Some species prey upon or are associated with forest insects, especially bark beetles.

FAMILY ACAROPHAENACIDAE

Paracarophoenax ipidarius (Redikorzev) (Kinn 1971) probably is parasitic on *Ips paraconfusus*.

FAMILY PYEMOTIDAE—PYEMOTID MITES

The **pyemotid mites** are a very specialized group in which the abdomen of pregnant females becomes greatly distended (fig. 18). Females may give birth to eggs, larvae, or sexually mature adults. Males are tiny and scarcely visible. One or more species in this family sometimes becomes established in laboratory colonies of insects and makes rearings difficult.

F-521901

FIGURE 18. — Pregnant females of a pyemotid mite on a bark beetle (greatly enlarged).

Some pyemotids prey upon immature Coleoptera, Lepidoptera, Hymenoptera, Diptera, and Homoptera (Cross 1975). Others are fungivorous and many of these are associated with bark beetles (Cross and Moser 1975).

Species of *Pyemotes* [*Pediculoides*] (Cross 1965, Cross and Moser 1975) prey upon broods of bark beetles, wood borers, various other beetles, and some Lepidoptera. *P. scolyti* (Oudemans) preys upon the brood of nearly all *Scolytus*, including *multistriatus* and *ventralis*, and is transported by the adult host.

FAMILY TARSONEMIDAE—TARSONEMID MITES

The Tarsonemidae (Beer 1954) feed upon plants, fungi, and insects. Some prey upon or are associated with bark beetles.

The species of *Iponemus* (Lindquist 1969b) are parasites of eggs of *Ips* and other ipine bark beetles. Their role in natural control has not been determined, but their abundance indicates that they may be important. *I. truncatus* (Ewing) (Boss and Thatcher 1970) (fig. 19), feeds on *Ips pini* and other *Ips* from coast to coast. *Iponemus confusus* (Lindquist and Bedard) feeds upon *Ips paraconfusus* and other five-spined *Ips*. Its biology is described by Lindquist and Bedard (1961).

Tarsonemus is a large genus of mites of varied habits. Some are associated with bark beetles but are not believed to be parasitic on them. *T. ips* Lindquist is associated with *Ips* and its near relatives

63

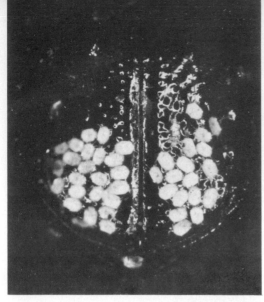

COURTESY AGRICULTURE CANADA

FIGURE 19.—Elytral declivity of *Ips pini* with about 40 females of *Iponemus truncatus* (greatly enlarged).

in North America and Europe and may feed on *Ceratocystis minor* (Moser and Roton 1971). *T. endophloeus* Lindquist is associated with *Dendroctonus ponderosae* and *D. jeffreyi*.

SUBORDER ASTIGMATA

This suborder (Krantz 1970) contains numerous slow-moving, soft-bodied mites of varied habits. Several are of interest to foresters.

FAMILY ANOETIDAE

Species of Anoetidae are found in highly organic, wet situations (Krantz 1970). Some are associated with bark beetles and their galleries (Woodring and Moser 1970). At least two species are known to be phoretic on western bark beetles. One occurs on *Scolytus unispinosus* and the other on various species of *Dendroctonus*, *Orthotomicus*, *Pityokteines*, *Pityophthorus*, and *Ips*. A species of *Bonomoia* is phoretic on *Dendroctonus brevicomis* and *Scolytus ventralis* in California.

FAMILY HEMISARCOPTIDAE

The Hemisarcoptidae contains several species of tiny, soft-bodied mites of which *Hemisarcoptes malus* (Shimer) feeds on various scales, particularly *Lepidosaphes ulmi*.

FAMILY SAPROGLYPHIDAE

Calvolia furnissi Woodring (Woodring 1966) develops in galleries of *Dendroctonus pseudotsugae*.

SUBORDER CRYPTOSTIGMATA

The mites in this suborder (Kevan 1962, Krantz 1970) sometimes are called "beetle mites" because most are hard-shelled and somewhat resemble tiny beetles. An example is *Platynothrus* sp., family Camisiidae (fig. 20) but there are hundreds of genera and thousands of species. Some are important in the decomposition of wood and litter and in the mixing of organic matter in forest soils (Burges and Raw 1967). The biology and exact role of most species are unknown.

F–521902

FIGURE 20.—A "beetle mite," *Platynothrus* sp., a typical decomposer, 0.8 mm long.

CLASS INSECTA (HEXAPODA)

Insects are the largest class in the phylum Arthropoda. Along with other arthropods, they have an external skeleton covered with a horny substance, a segmented body, paired appendages on some of the segments, and bilateral symmetry. They are distinctive from other arthropods by having three body regions—head, thorax, and abdomen. Insect adults and often larvae have a single pair of antennae on the head and three pairs of legs on the thorax. Adults of some groups are unwinged but most bear two pairs of wings on the thorax. Adults and nymphal stages usually have one pair of compound eyes and simple eyes as well.

ORDER THYSANURA—BRISTLETAILS

The **bristletails** (Smith 1970a, Metcalf and Flint 1962) are wingless, scale-covered, streamlined insects with long antennae and three taillike appendages. They shun light. The **silverfish**, *Lepisma saccharina* L., family Lepismatidae, is a household pest and the best known example. Related silverfish often are found under the bark of dead trees, particularly in pine forests. Several species of *Machilis* and *Mesomachilus*, family Machilidae, live in forest litter.

They are nocturnal and feed upon lichens, algae, molds, and decaying matter, hence are innocuous in the forest. Adults often congregate on bark of the lower bole.

ORDER COLLEMBOLA—SPRINGTAILS

The **springtails** (Maynard 1951, Scott 1961) are tiny, wingless insects, most of which jump by means of a springlike appendage attached to the abdomen, hence their common name. They are among the most numerous arthropods in soil (Kevan 1962) and are believed to contribute importantly to the nutrient cycle in forest soils (Burges and Raw 1967). Most of the soil-inhabiting species are white, blind, and less than 1 mm long. Many species live on the bark of living trees and under loose bark on dead and down trees. Springtails generally require a moist environment. They feed principally upon algae, lichens, and fungi and upon decomposing plant and animal material. A few are agricultural pests. None is reported as damaging forest trees. There are two suborders. The Arthropleona are elongate and their body is segmented (fig. 21). The Symphypleona (Richards 1968) are globular and their bodies are unsegmented.

F–521903

FIGURE 21.—A springtail in the suborder Arthropleona, 1.5 mm long.

ORDER PLECOPTERA—STONEFLIES

The **stoneflies** (Jewett 1963) are a small order of aquatic insects. The nymphs usually develop in running water and are important food for trout and other fish. The adults have narrow front wings and wide hind wings with many fine veins. At rest, the wings are folded back horizontally, giving the insect a long slender appearance. A few species in the family Taeniopterygidae (Nemouridae) feed on the buds and foliage of trees. *Taenionema* [*Brachyptera*] *pacifica* (Banks), a black-bodied species about 12 mm long, damages fruit trees in Washington and also feeds on the foliage of alder, elm, and wild cherry (Newcomer 1918). Other species feed on willow and maple.

ORDER DICTYOPTERA—COCKROACHES AND MANTIDS

The **cockroaches** and **mantids**, long considered as part of the Orthoptera, are placed in the order Dictyoptera together with the termites by McKittrick (1964). In this manual, the order Isoptera is retained for the termites.

SUBORDER BLATTARIA—COCKROACHES

Cockroaches are notorious as household pests. One little-known species feeds upon wood.

FAMILY CRYPTOCERCIDAE

This family links the cockroaches with primitive termites (McKittrick 1965). It contains one species.

Cryptocercus punctulatus Scudder is a wingless, leathery, chestnut-brown, wood-feeding, noneconomic cockroach that occurs in California, Oregon, and Washington (fig. 22). Adults are 20 to 27 mm long and 9 to 13 mm wide. In southern Oregon it lives in and feeds upon very rotten, moist logs of Douglas-fir. The life cycle is 6 to 7 years.

F-521904

FIGURE 22.—Adult of *Cryptocercus punctulatus*, a wood-feeding cockroach, 25 mm long.

ORDER ORTHOPTERA—GRASSHOPPERS AND ALLIES

The order Orthoptera (Brues et al. 1954, Helfer 1963) contains grasshoppers, crickets, katydids, walkingsticks, and others. Many species are destructive pests of agricultural crops. Some feed on trees, occasionally causing significant damage locally. Representatives of two suborders are included in this manual.

SUBORDER SALTATORIA

Representatives of two of the three families discussed in this suborder occasionally spread from rangelands and damage shelterbelts, tree seed orchards, forest plantations, and fringe-type forests. Chemical control sometimes is necessary to halt these invasions.

FAMILY ACRIDIDAE—SHORTHORN GRASSHOPPERS

The antennae of members of this family are much shorter than the body. Eggs are laid in cemented, podlike masses in the ground. Counts of these pods are made to forecast abundance and need for control.

Many kinds of **shorthorn grasshoppers** (Thompson and Buxton 1964) inhabit western ranges. During outbreaks some of them migrate into contiguous forests and damage trees by eating the foliage and tender shoots. For example, *Bradynotes obesa opima* Scudder, a short-winged species, in 1968 damaged 4,200 acres of pine plantations in northern California, killing nearly all trees on 800 acres and requiring chemical control. Lesser outbreaks of this grasshopper in 1970 again had to be controlled. Hosts and distribution of other species recorded as damaging conifers in recent years are:

Species	Place and Year	Crop Attacked
Camnula pellucida (Scudder), **clearwinged grasshopper**	Southern Wash., 1969	Young ponderosa pine
Melanoplus devastator Scudder, **devastating grasshopper**	Southwestern Oreg., 1970	Young Douglas-fir
Melanoplus sanguinipes (F.), **migratory grasshopper**	Central Calif., 1964	Young ponderosa pine
Oedaleonotus enigma (Scudder), **valley grasshopper**	Northern Calif., 1973	Pine plantations and tree-breeding orchards
Oedaleonotus tenuipennis (Scudder)	Southern Calif., 1970	Pine plantations

FAMILY GRYLLIDAE—CRICKETS

In this family only the **tree crickets** (Walker 1962) affect forest trees; none is a forest pest. The **snowy tree cricket**, *Oecanthus fultoni* Walker, is an example. It is transcontinental. The adults are greenish white and have long, slender antennae and long hind legs. Forewings of the males are paddle-shaped and lie horizontally over the abdomen. This species lives in the crown of orchard trees and open-grown forest trees such as Garry oak and Oregon ash. The eggs are laid in slits in small branches where they overwinter. There is one generation annually.

FAMILY TETTIGONIIDAE—LONGHORN GRASSHOPPERS AND KATYDIDS

The members of this family have long antennae, often longer than the body. The eggs are laid singly or in rows, usually on vegetation.

The **Mormon cricket**, *Anabrus simplex* Haldeman (Wakeland 1959) occurs in dryland areas of Western States and Provinces, excepting most of California, Arizona, and New Mexico. Two other species of *Anabrus* are similar in appearance and habits. Since pioneer days, *A. simplex* has been a major pest of agricultural crops. During heavy migrations, it occasionally invades and damages fringe-type ponderosa pine. Invasions are soon over and the only evidence is the tattered remains of the chewed foliage and small branches (fig. 23). Damage of this type has occurred in Oregon. The adults are yellow, green, brown, or black, wingless, heavy-bodied insects 35 to 45 mm long.

SUBORDER PHASMIDA—WALKINGSTICKS

The **walkingsticks** and allies are large, generally slender and twiglike, sometimes leaflike, mainly tropical, plant-feeding insects. They are few and of little consequence in western forests.

FAMILY PHASMATIDAE—WALKINGSTICKS

The **walkingstick**, *Diapheromera femorata* (Say) (Wilson 1964) (fig. 24), is primarily an eastern insect but ranges into New Mexico and Arizona. It is a defoliator of hardwoods. The adult is wingless, about 60 to 80 mm long, and twiglike in shape and color. Outbreaks tend to be local. The eggs are black, laid singly, and literally rain down during heavy outbreaks.

ORDER ISOPTERA—TERMITES

Termites (Ebeling 1968; Kofoid et al. 1934; Krishna 1966; Snyder 1949a, 1956, 1961; Weesner 1965) are a large and destructive group of insects which feed upon cellulose, principally in

F–521905

FIGURE 23. — Needles and twigs of young ponderosa pine damaged by the Mormon cricket (*Anabrus simplex*).

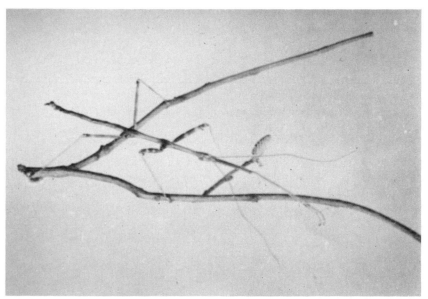

F–504382

FIGURE 24.—Adult male walkingstick (*Diapheromera femorata*) on twig.

wood. Often they mine so extensively that only a paper-thin outer shell of wood remains. In the forest, they commonly occur in felled trees, in snags, and in stumps or other sections of dead or decaying wood. Insofar as they reduce forest debris they are beneficial, but some are very destructive to buildings, telephone poles, fences, furniture, and other wood products. Rarely they injure or kill trees. The group as a whole is most abundant and most destructive in the Tropics, and in the United States causes most damage in the warmer southern latitudes. Numerous species are found in the Southwest and southern California. Only a few range into the Pacific Northwest and Northern Rocky Mountain Region. Four families contain species that may be encountered by western foresters. All species presently found in the West are native.

Termites live in colonies in wood or in the ground and expose themselves to light only when in the winged adult stage (Snyder 1949b). Colonies consist of several forms or castes, such as workers, soldiers, primary and secondary reproductives, and nymphs. Termites, sometimes called "white ants," are frequently confused with true ants but are quite different in appearance and habits. Unwinged termites are soft, whitish, and broad-waisted in contrast to ants, which are tough-surfaced, brownish to black, and narrow-waisted. Winged termites usually are brownish to black, as are ants, but differ in being broad rather than narrow-waisted and in having all four wings of similar size and shape rather than dissimilar (fig. 25). Their excavations in wood are hollow, completely enclosed, more or less longitudinal cavities, in which some species deposit small pellets of excrement. Drywood termites often expel the pellets through surface openings, but no termites expel boring dust as do carpenter ants and some other wood borers.

Prevention is the best approach to termite control. In the case of ground-inhabiting termites, prevention measures consist of

FIGURE 25.—Example of winged termite, showing uniformly broad body and similarity in size of forewings and hindwings; body 8 mm long.

71

isolating wood from contact with the ground and in using wood treated with termite-repellent chemicals. When wood is found to be infested by insects, the first step is to determine whether they are termites or other insects. If termites are present it is recommended that the reader consult one or more of the many publications on control of these insects (Ebeling 1968, Johnston et al. 1972, Snyder 1966). Control measures should be thoroughly applied and should include structural changes to prevent reinfestation when feasible.

FAMILY HODOTERMITIDAE

In the West, the Hodotermitidae contains one genus, *Zootermopsis* (Castle 1934), with three species. They are the largest of the western termites. Known as **dampwood termites,** they live in damp, usually rotten wood, and do not require contact with the ground. Often they colonize in houses and other structures made of wood. They cause some damage but their presence is more significant as an indicator of rot. Insecticides will kill them, but will not solve the basic rot problem. Untreated wood should be kept off the ground to prevent it from becoming damp, and structural changes should be made to eliminate excessive moisture which causes the rot and attracts the termites.

Zootermopsis colonies contain reproductives, soldiers, and nymphs (fig. 26). The nymphs are dirty white, 3 to about 15 mm long and resemble the worker caste of more highly evolved termites. The fully developed soldiers are light brown, 10 to 20 mm long and have a large head armed with a pair of long, black, toothed mandibles. Winged reproductives (fig. 26A) are light cinnamon-brown and have dark brown, heavily veined, leathery wings about 25 mm long, which are readily shed. In northern California and western Oregon and Washington, where *Zootermopsis* is most abundant, the winged forms commonly take flight on warm sultry evenings in August, September, and October to mate and found new colonies.

The **Pacific dampwood termite**, *Zootermopsis angusticollis* (Hagen) (Castle 1934, Goulding and Every 1964), ranges from southern British Columbia through Oregon, Washington, and California into Mexico. It is the common dampwood termite of coastal forests where it sooner or later colonizes most dead and down trees and untreated wood products in contact with the ground.

Z. nevadensis (Hagen) (Castle 1934) ranges from southern British Columbia to central California and eastward into Montana. In general it occurs in cooler, drier, and higher areas than does *Z. angusticollis* which it closely resembles in appearance and

72

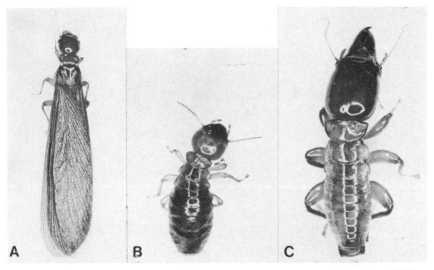

FIGURE 26.—Pacific dampwood termite (*Zootermopsis angusticollis*): *A*, Winged reproductive, body 10 mm long; *B*, nymph, 8 mm long; *C*, soldier, 18 mm long.

habits. *Z. nevadensis* is somewhat smaller and darker in the winged stage.

Z. laticeps (Banks) (Castle 1934) is a little-known species that occurs in southern Arizona and New Mexico.

FAMILY KALOTERMITIDAE

The species of Kalotermitidae (Ebeling 1968, Light 1934b, Weesner 1965), with one exception, live in wood and as a group are known as **drywood termites.** They are generally larger than subterranean termites and smaller than dampwood termites. Typical drywood termites attack and live in sound dry wood above ground, hence prevention and control measures differ from those for subterranean termites (Snyder 1966). Structural methods of preventing attacks by drywood termites are relatively less effective, thus direct control by chemicals is more frequently needed.

Incisitermes [*Kalotermes*] (Light 1934b) is a sizeable genus of typical drywood termites. Several species occur in the Southern United States. In the West, the principal one is the **western drywood termite**, *I. minor* (Hagen) (Ebeling 1968, Harvey 1934). It occurs in California, Arizona, and Mexico. This termite attacks sound dry wood such as the dead branches of trees, the upper portions of buildings, and furniture. Colonies are small and consist of reproductives, soldiers, and immature forms (nymphs), but no true worker caste (fig. 27A, B). Fecal pellets (fig. 27C) sifting

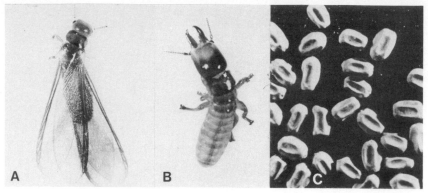

FIGURE 27.—Western drywood termite (*Incisitermes minor*) : *A*, Winged reproductive, length to wing tips, 18 mm; *B*, soldier, 14 mm long; *C*, fecal pellets.

down from infested wood and the swarming of winged forms are the usual signs of attack. Flight occurs at temperatures above 80° F on sunny days in September and October in southern California. The body of the winged adult is black and the head, reddish brown. The third segment of the antenna of the soldier is about as long as the next four segments combined.

Marginitermes hubbardi (Banks) (Light 1934c, Weesner 1965) occurs in Arizona, southern California, and southward in Mexico. It is a typical drywood termite with habits similar to *Incisitermes minor* and causes similar damage to buildings and wood products. The body of the winged adult is yellowish. The third segment of the antenna of the soldier is nearly as long as the other segments combined.

Paraneotermes contains one species, *P. simplicicornis* (Banks) (Light 1934d). This termite, in contrast to other Kalotermitidae, lives in the ground much as do subterranean termites. It occurs in desert areas from southern California to Texas and southward in Mexico. The body of the winged adult is dark brown. The third segment of the antenna of the soldier is about the same length as the fourth. *P. simplicicornis* normally mines and feeds in the dead roots, lower stems, and fallen branches of desert trees and shrubs such as mesquite. At times it damages untreated poles and posts by mining them just below ground line. It also is recorded as damaging living trees.

FAMILY RHINOTERMITIDAE

Rhinotermitidae (Ebeling 1968, Weesner 1965) contains the **subterranean termites** which are the termites that cause greatest damage in the West. Three genera are of principal concern. Subterranean termites develop and maintain their colonies in the ground, but often feed above ground by extending their galleries in wood or by building earthen tubes over obstructions to shield themselves from desiccation and light. Their galleries are open except for some chambers plastered with a mixture of excrement and uneaten particles of wood. Prior to structural failure of infested wood, the principal signs of attack by subterranean termites are the earthen tubes and the seasonal swarming of winged reproductives.

Reticulitermes (Ebeling 1968) contains several species, two of which are widely destructive to man-made structures in the West. They feed principally on the springwood and leave the harder summerwood in ribbons (fig. 28).

The **western subterranean termite**, *Reticulitermes hesperus* Banks (Pickens 1934a) is the major termite pest from southern British Columbia through Washington and Oregon to central California. Colonies consist of workers, reproductives, and soldiers (fig. 29). The workers are grayish white and are about 5 mm long when full grown. The soldiers are of similar color, somewhat longer, and have larger heads and more prominent mandibles. The winged adults are slender, cylindrical, dark brown to black, and about 4 mm long, exclusive of the wings which are translucent and of equal length. Following the first heavy rains in fall, the winged forms emerge en masse, mate, shed their wings, and found new colonies. Once established, a colony may continue to develop for years and attain a population of several hundred thousand. This termite often builds earthenlike tubes over concrete foundations to get to wood above but must retain contact through them to the

F–521907

FIGURE 28.—Cross section of wood damaged by western subterranean termite (*Reticulitermes hesperus*), showing preference for springwood.

FIGURE 29.—Western subterranean termite (*Reticulitermes hesperus*): *A*, Winged reproductive, length to wing tips, 10 mm; *B*, soldier, 7 mm long; *C*, worker, 5 mm long.

ground (fig. 30). Damage can best be prevented by a combination of structural and chemical means (Ebeling 1968, Johnston 1965, Johnston et al. 1972).

The **aridland subterranean termite**, *Reticulitermes tibialis* Banks (Pickens 1934b) occurs in California, the Great Basin, and the southern Rocky Mountain States. Its appearance, habits, potential for causing damage, and control are similar to *R. hesperus*. The ranges of these two species overlap only slightly. Physically, they differ most markedly in that the head of the soldier of *R. tibialis* is short, broad, and dark colored in contrast to the long, narrow, and pale head of *R. hesperus*.

Coptotermes (Light and Pickens 1934) is a tropical genus, one species of which has become established in the United States.

The **Formosan subterranean termite**, *Coptotermes formosanus* Shiraki (Baker 1972) is a destructive oriental species introduced into Hawaii, Texas, Louisiana, and South Carolina. It is a potential invader of the warmer portions of the Pacific coast. Compared with *Reticulitermes*, *C. formosanus* is somewhat larger in all stages; the head of the soldier is oval rather than oblong and rectangular; the wings are hairy rather than hairless; and flight is at night rather than in the daytime. *C. formosanus* builds an earthenlike nest, usually in the ground, and requires a high level of moisture.

Heterotermes is a tropical genus, one species of which ranges northward into the Southwestern United States. The habits are similar to those of *Coptotermes*.

COURTESY WALTER EBELING (1968)

FIGURE 30.—Earthenlike tubes built over cement foundation by western subterranean termite (*Reticulitermes hesperus*).

Heterotermes aureus (Snyder) (Pickens and Light 1934) occurs in southern California and Arizona, causing considerable economic loss. It resembles species of *Reticulitermes* but the winged adults are pale rather than black.

FAMILY TERMITIDAE

The Termitidae (Light 1934a, Weesner 1965) is a large family worldwide. In the United States it consists principally of ground-dwelling termites of the genus *Amitermes*, which occur in the Southwest. They cause little damage to wood. Their earthen tubes often cover desert vegetation, including range grasses.

ORDER PSOCOPTERA (CORRODENTIA)— BOOKLICE AND PSOCIDS

This order (Chapman 1930), sometimes called Corrodentia, contains small insects of no economic significance in the forest. Of the several families, species in the Amphipsocidae and Psocidae are most likely to be encountered by foresters. These insects live principally on the bark, branches, and foliage of trees, hence sometimes are known as bark lice. They feed upon lichens and fungi. The adults resemble aphids in form and size (fig. 31A). Some lay eggs on foliage (fig. 31B).

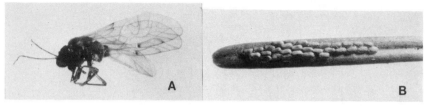

F–521908, F–521909

FIGURE 31.—A psocid, *Teliapsocus conterminus* (Walsh): *A*, Adult, after oviposition; *B*, egg mass laid on grand fir needle.

ORDER THYSANOPTERA—THRIPS

Thrips (Lewis 1973) are minute, slender, generally active insects. The adults have two pairs of slender, nearly veinless, similar-sized wings fringed with long hairs, or are wingless. The tarsi are one- or two-jointed and end in an inflatable sac. Some thrips feed on fungi or fungus spores; many are plant-feeders; and others are predaceous. Some are pests of agricultural crops; some transmit plant diseases. Many occur on forest trees and in forest litter, but their role in the forest is little known. None in North America is recorded as a serious forest pest.

Thrips are divided into two suborders. The Tubulifera (Cott 1956) contains one family, the **tubular thrips,** Phlaeothripidae. On both sexes the terminal abdominal segments are tubelike. The ovipositor is lacking. The wings at rest overlap. The Terebrantia (Bailey 1957) contains four families of which only the **narrowwinged thrips,** Thripidae, are of concern to foresters. The females have a sawlike ovipositor. The wings at rest lie parallel.

FAMILY PHLAEOTHRIPIDAE—TUBULAR THRIPS

In the Eastern United States and Canada *Gnophothrips fuscus* (Morgan) feeds in the staminate cones of pine. It materially reduces pollen production in slash pine seed orchards (De Barr 1969). No species in this family is reported as damaging in western forests.

FAMILY THRIPIDAE—NARROWWINGED THRIPS

The **western flower thrips,** *Frankliniella occidentalis* (Pergande) (fig. 32), occurs throughout the Western States and northward in British Columbia to Alaska and feeds in the flowers of many

F–521910

FIGURE 32.—Nymph of thrips, *Frankliniella occidentalis*, which damages buds and flowers of bitterbrush and other range shrubs, 1.3 mm long.

kinds of plants (Bryan and Smith 1956). It is common on mature staminate cones of pinyon and apparently feeds on the pollen (Little 1943). It also occurs on *Pseudotsuga* and *Abies* in California. In Idaho it feeds on the stamens and pistils of bitterbrush, an important browse plant (Ferguson et al. 1963). *F. occidentalis* has several generations annually. *F. hawksworthi* O'Neill is believed to be the chief pollinator of dwarf mistletoe of ponderosa pine, *Arceuthobium vaginatum* Engelm. (Hawksworth 1961).

The American species of *Oxythrips* are associated with conifers, especially pines, and are presumed harmless to their hosts. *O. pinicola* Hood occurs in flowers of *Pinus edulis* in Colorado. It also occurs in Oregon (Hood 1937). *O. coloradensis* Hood occurs in flowers of *Pinus ponderosa* in Colorado (Hood 1937).

Taeniothrips is a large genus which includes the **pear thrips,** *T. inconsequens* (Uzel), an introduced species now present in California, Oregon, Washington, and British Columbia. In Europe the **larch thrips,** *T. laricivorus* (Kratochvil and Farsky), at times causes serious damage to the shoots of European larch. *T. pini* (Uzel) has been collected on blue spruce in Colorado (O'Neill and Bigelow 1964).

Thrips madronii Moulton (Bailey 1957) occurs on numerous trees and shrubs including madrone, California-laurel, western dogwood, ceanothus, manzanita, and rhododendron. It occurs in British Columbia, Oregon, California, and Utah.

ORDER HEMIPTERA—TRUE BUGS

The **true bugs** pass through five nymphal stages that progressively more and more resemble the adults. The front wings of the adults are thicker and stiffer at the base than toward the outer end (fig. 33). Some are flightless, notably **bed bugs.** All have piercing-sucking mouth parts and many give off a strong odor. Many feed on plant fluids. Some transmit diseases to plants and animals, including man. Some are beneficial in that they prey upon pest insects or feed upon weeds. Few are important in forestry.

Van Duzee (1917) catalogued the Hemiptera of North America. Torre-Bueno (1939, 1940, 1941, 1946) provided keys for identification of species in many families. There are two suborders; only one is included in this manual.

F–521911

FIGURE 33.—Wing characteristics of an adult true bug, as shown in a species of *Tropidosteptes*, 6 mm long.

SUBORDER GYMNOCERATA— LONG–HORNED BUGS

Only the **long-horned bugs** are important in forestry. The following superfamily arrangement is by natural relationship according to Borror and De Long (1954).

SUPERFAMILY CIMICOIDEA

FAMILY ANTHOCORIDAE—FLOWER BUGS OR MINUTE PIRATE BUGS

The Anthocoridae are small to minute, flattened, generally elongate, brownish to black, predaceous bugs. The nymphs are brown to bright red. The adults and nymphs both feed on mites, aphids, and many other small insects, often on conifers (Anderson 1962). *Acompocoris lepidus* (Van Duzee) is an occasional predator on the balsam woolly aphid in Oregon (Mitchell 1962). There are nine species of *Lyctocoris* in North America most of which occur in the West often associated with and presumed predaceous upon the eggs and larvae of *Dendroctonus, Ips,* and other subcortical insects in conifers (Kelton 1967). There are five species of *Tetraphleps* in the West (Kelton 1966). *T. latipennis* Van Duzee, which preys upon *Adelges cooleyi,* is reported to be the most abundant anthocorid on conifers in the Pacific Northwest. It occurs on *Abies, Pseudotsuga, Picea, Pinus,* and *Larix.*

FAMILY MIRIDAE—PLANT BUGS

The **plant bugs** (Knight 1968) are a large family of small to medium-sized, fragile, elongate-oval bugs. When their wings are folded the hind portion bends downward. Many are destructive pests of agricultural crops. Many others occur on forest trees such as pine, spruce, juniper, oak, and poplar, but their role there is not recorded. More western species of Miridae are recorded on *Pinus monophylla* than on any other plant. Some mirids prey on other insects.

The **black grass bug,** *Labops hesperius* Uhler, is one of several plant bugs that damage wheatgrasses on western ranges (USDA 1966a,b). It has been reported in Colorado, Idaho, Montana, Nebraska, New Mexico, Oregon, South Dakota, Utah, Washington, Wyoming, Alberta, British Columbia, and Yukon Territory. Epidemic infestations occurred on reseeded ranges in New Mexico from 1962 to 1966 and in southern Utah from 1965 to 1969. Heavy feeding drains away the green color, causing the grass to become brown and dry and preventing seed formation. Forage is reduced, particularly in pure stands of grass where grass bug populations are greatest (Jensen 1971). The adult is fast moving, about 6 mm long, and dull black except for a pale streak along the edge of the wing covers. Presumably there is one generation annually and the eggs overwinter. Aerial spraying has been done on forest-related ranges in Utah and New Mexico.

Plant bugs of the genus *Tropidosteptes* [*Neoborus*] feed on the leaves, twigs, flowers, and seeds of ash causing heavily infested trees to appear scorched. Sometimes defoliation is complete. *T. illitus* (Van Duzee) is the worst pest of ornamental ash, principally *Fraxinus velutina,* in California (Usinger 1945). *T. pacificus* (Van Duzee) causes similar damage to *Fraxinus latifolia* in Oregon and California. Both are small brownish-yellow bugs. *T. illitus* has one generation annually; *T. pacificus* has two. Eggs are laid in twigs of the current season. They overwinter and hatch early in the spring. Control is applied against the nymphs.

SUPERFAMILY REDUVIOIDEA

FAMILY REDUVIIDAE—ASSASSIN BUGS

The **assassin bugs** are medium- to large-sized, generally oval, narrow-headed bugs with a curved rigid beak and often with spiny front legs. Many prey upon other insects. Some prey upon forest insect pests but do not exert significant control (Readio 1927).

SUPERFAMILY TINGIDOIDEA

FAMILY TINGIDAE—LACE BUGS

Lace bugs (Drake and Ruhoff 1965, Metcalf and Flint 1962) are small, very flat bugs with lacelike wing covers and often with broad extensions on the sides of the thorax (fig. 34). The nymphs are spiny. Lace bugs feed on the under surface of leaves of plants other than conifers. They are inconsequential in commercial forests, but some are pests of ornamental trees.

Several species of *Corythucha* feed on broad-leaved trees, occasionally causing yellowing or browning of foliage under forest

COURTESY BROWN AND EADS (1965b)

FIGURE 34.—Adult western sycamore lace bug (*Corythucha confraterna*), 3 mm long.

conditions. The **western sycamore lace bug,** *C. confraterna* Gibson, occurs in California and Arizona. It is sporadically epidemic on sycamore in southern California (Brown and Eads 1965b). Heavily infested trees appear brownish as a result of feeding by the nymphs on the under surface of the leaves. Adults are 3 mm long and white with a brown spot near the middle of the wing covers. The nymphs are contrastingly black and white. Hosts and distribution of some of the other 30 to 50 tree-infesting western species are:

Species	Hosts	Distribution
C. arcuata (Say), **oak lace bug**	*Quercus* primarily	Colo., Utah, and Ariz.
C. ciliata (Say), **sycamore lace bug**	*Platanus* primarily	Colo. and N. Mex.
C. elegans Drake	*Salix* primarily, also *Populus*	British Columbia to Saskatchewan and Colo.
C. padi Drake	*Prunus demissa* primarily, also *Alnus* and others	British Columbia and extensively in Western States
C. pergandei Heidemann, **alder lace bug**	*Alnus* primarily, also *Betula* and others	N. Mex., Ariz., Calif., and British Columbia
C. salicata Gibson, **western willow lace bug**	*Salix* and *Populus*	British Columbia, Wash., Oreg., Calif., Idaho, and Utah

Leptoypha differs from other common lace bugs by being brown, compact, and without lacy lateral lobes. The **Arizona ash lace bug,** *L. minor* McAtee, is the commonest species in California and also occurs in Arizona (Usinger 1946). It attacks *Fraxinus velutina* and *F. latifolia* causing the leaves to turn whitish. The nymphs live on the underside of the leaves and their cast skins and black fecal deposits adhere long after the insect has left. The adults hibernate by clinging to the bark. Eggs are partially imbedded in the underside of the leaves. There are four or five generations annually and the population gradually builds up until late summer. Three other species feed on ash in the West.

SUPERFAMILY COREOIDEA

FAMILY RHOPALIDAE (CORIZIDAE)

The **boxelder bug,** *Leptocoris trivittatus* (Say) (Tinker 1952, Wollerman 1971b), is principally an eastern species but occurs westward into Alberta, Montana, Utah, and Arizona. It feeds on the female or seed-bearing boxelder, the seeds being its preferred food. Bigleaf maple and ash are occasional hosts. Until the seeds begin to form, the bugs are on the ground feeding on low vegetation and old seeds. There are two generations annually. The adults overwinter, often crawling into houses and being a nuisance. Damage to trees is insignificant. The adult bug is about 12 mm long and brownish black with narrow red lines on the upper surface (fig. 35). The abdomen under the wings is bright red. The **western boxelder bug**, *L. rubrolineatus* Barber, is similar in appearance and habits. It ranges from British Columbia south to California and east to Texas. In Oregon, maple is the principal host.

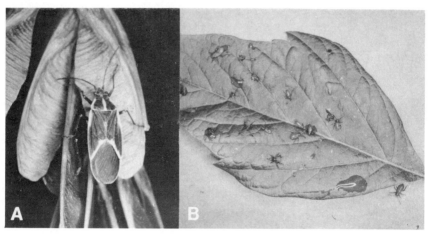

F-508519, F-508517

FIGURE 35.—Boxelder bug (*Leptocoris trivittatus*): *A*, Adult, 12 mm long, on seed of boxelder; *B*, nymphs on leaf, 3 to 5 mm long.

FAMILY COREIDAE—COREID BUGS

The **western conifer seed bug**, *Leptoglossus occidentalis* Heidemann (Koerber 1963, Krugman and Koerber 1969) is a **leaf-footed bug**, so named because of the broad flat tibia of the hind legs. It occurs from British Columbia and Alberta to Mexico and from Colorado to the Pacific coast. It feeds upon and damages the seed of Douglas-fir, ponderosa pine, other pines, and incense-cedar. The adults are 15 to 18 mm long and reddish brown to dark gray (fig. 36). The barrel-shaped eggs are deposited in rows on the needles. The adults overwinter, sometimes invading houses. In northern California there is one generation annually.

84

F-521912

FIGURE 36.—Adult female of *Leptoglossus occidentalis*, 18 mm long.

SUPERFAMILY ARADOIDEA

FAMILY ARADIDAE—FLAT BUGS

Aradus (Parshley 1921) contains many western species. These very flat, intricately sculptured, brown to black bugs usually are found under bark of dead trees and on fungus fruiting bodies. Most are known or presumed to feed upon fungi.

The **pine flat bug**, *A. cinnamomeus* Panzer (fig. 37), is an

F-521913

FIGURE 37.—Adult of the pine flat bug (*Aradus cinnamomeus*), 4 mm long.

85

exception. Its range is holarctic. In western North America it has been reported from British Columbia, Alberta, Washington, Oregon, California, and Colorado. It is common on the branches of ponderosa pine. Its biology and habits are unreported in North America. In eastern Europe it is considered to be a significant pest of pine, especially young trees growing under adverse conditions.

SUPERFAMILY SCUTELLEROIDEA

FAMILY PENTATOMIDAE—STINK BUGS

The **stink bugs** (Metcalf and Flint 1962) are medium- to large-sized, shield-shaped, bugs with a conspicuously large scutellum. The usual colors are greens, browns, and yellows and often match the plant surfaces on which the bugs rest. They give off a strong acrid odor when disturbed. The eggs are laid in multiple rows and often have a fringe of spines around the lid through which the nymph emerges (Esselbaugh 1946). Most are plant feeders but some prey upon other insects. None is a forest pest.

The **rough plant bugs**, *Brochymena* (Ruckes 1946), frequent trees and shrubs where they prey on other insects and sometimes damage fruit. They are shield-shaped, dappled gray bugs, 12 to 15 mm long, with dark markings on the membrane of the wing covers. They are of interest to foresters principally because of their large size and frequent occurrence in winter under loose bark of insect-killed conifers. *B. affinis* Van Duzee occurs from British Columbia to California to Colorado.

Several species of *Chlorochroa* occur in the Western States and Provinces. They feed on many kinds of plants and damage grain, forage, and truck crops extensively. The adults are green, shield-shaped, chunky bugs about 15 mm long. They hibernate under litter on the ground and occasionally invade houses.

The **Say stink bug**, *Chlorochroa sayi* Stål, damages the seed of bitterbrush in Idaho (Ferguson et al. 1963). The **conchuela**, *C. ligata* (Say), and *C. uhleri* Stål cause similar damage in California.

Dendrocoris pini Montandon (Essig 1926) is a pale yellow bug, 5 to 6 mm long, which feeds on singleleaf pinyon in California. It also occurs in Arizona, Utah, Colorado, and Texas.

Soldier bugs of the genus *Podisus* prey upon hairless caterpillars and some other insects, including forest pests (Essig 1926). Because of their indiscriminate feeding, they are not very effective in controlling economic insect pests. The **spined soldier bug**, *P. maculiventris* (Say), said to be the most useful of the

86

predaceous Hemiptera, occurs extensively in the West (Clausen 1940). It has two generations annually. The first stage nymph feeds on plant juices. Later stages prey upon cankerworms, California oakworm, cutworms, and other insects. *P. serieventris* Uhler, occurring in Colorado, Montana, British Columbia, and Alberta, is a smaller species with similar habits. In eastern Canada it preys upon larvae and pupae of *Acleris variana* (Prebble 1933).

ORDER HOMOPTERA—APHIDS, LEAFHOPPERS, PLANTHOPPERS, SCALE INSECTS, AND ALLIES

The Homoptera (Metcalf et al. 1927–71) are a large and diverse order of insects allied to the Hemiptera. Metamorphosis is gradual, that is, after each molt the immature stages increasingly resemble the adult. Except for the cicadas, most species are small. All feed on the sap of plants. Many, particularly among the scales and aphids, are pests of forest and ornamental trees. None is beneficial. At least one, *Adelges piceae,* is a major forest pest in the West.

The suborder Auchenorhynchi, **free beaks,** contains the cicadas, spittlebugs, treehoppers, and leafhoppers. Sometimes these groups are considered to be superfamilies—Cicadoidea, Cercopoidea, Membracoidea, and Cicadelloidea respectively. The Sternorhynchi, **fused beaks,** contains the psyllids, aphids, scales, whiteflies, and mealybugs. This suborder is much the more important in forestry.

SUBORDER AUCHENORHYNCHI, FREE BEAKS
SUPERFAMILY CICADOIDEA

In this manual, this superfamily is considered to contain one family, Cicadidae (Simons 1954). Some authorities divide it into the Cicadidae and Timbicinidae (Metcalf et al. 1927–71).

FAMILY CICADIDAE—CICADAS

There are upward of 150 species of **cicadas** in the United States, somewhat fewer than half of them in the West (Simons 1954). They are medium to large insects. The adult has a chunky body, broad head with bulging compound eyes, large proboscis tucked underneath, and transparent, many-veined wings that are held tentlike in repose (fig. 38). The spiny, humped nymph has conspicuously enlarged clawlike front legs for burrowing (fig. 39A).

The adults lay eggs in slits in twigs of various trees and shrubs. Upon hatching, the young drop to the ground, burrow in, and

COURTESY E. S. ROSS

FIGURE 38.—Adult of cicada, *Platypedia areolata* (Uhler), 30 mm long.

feed upon the roots of plants. When mature they crawl to the surface where they transform into adults. The life cycle of the western species is presumed to range from 2 to 5 years. In Nevada in 1962, cicadas (*Okanagana* sp.) were reported to have caused extensive damage to pinyon being grown for Christmas trees. Generally cicadas are not significant forest pests. No practical control measures are recorded.

The **Apache cicada**, *Diceroprocta apache* (Davis) (Brown and Eads 1966), lays its eggs in twigs and small branches of elm in southern California (fig. 39B). The branches may die. Associated slime flux aggravates the damage, especially in arid areas.

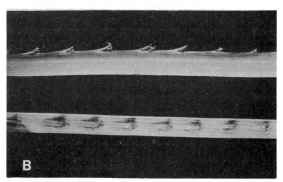

COURTESY BROWN AND EADS (1966)

FIGURE 39.—Apache cicada (*Diceroprocta apache*): A, Nymph, 15 mm long; B, egg-laying punctures, each about 2.5 mm long, in date stem.

Okanagana, comprising some 36 species, is predominantly western. *O. utahensis* Davis and *O. vanduzeei* Distant are widely distributed in the Great Basin. *O. rimosa* (Say) is transcontinental.

Platypedia with about 20 species is entirely western. *P. minor* Uhler is abundant in California where it oviposits in twigs of oak, willow, madrone, and other trees. It also occurs in Nevada and Colorado. *P. balli* Davis is reported to oviposit in oak in Arizona and *P. bernardinoensis* Davis in ponderosa pine in New Mexico.

SUPERFAMILY CERCOPOIDEA

This manual follows the common practice of lumping the superfamily Cercopoidea into one family, the Cercopidae (Doering 1930). Some authorities divide them into four families (Brues et al. 1954).

FAMILY CERCOPIDAE—SPITTLEBUGS

The **spittlebugs** (Doering 1930) are readily recognized by the spittlelike froth that surrounds the nymphs as they feed. The adults are inconspicuous, often brownish insects that jump and fly readily when disturbed. Most of them feed on succulent vegetation. Some feed on forest trees and two of them are serious pests of pine in the Eastern United States.

About a dozen species of *Aphrophora* (Metcalf et al. 1927-71, Severin 1950, Walley 1928) occur in western North America, several of them on conifers. In some species the nymphs leave the trees and feed on understory shrubs, but the adults return to feed and oviposit. Some are vectors of virus-caused diseases of agricultural crops but apparently they do not transmit such diseases to trees. None causes significant damage in western forests.

Aphrophora canadensis Walley (Kelson 1964) is similar to but somewhat smaller than *A. permutata* with which it occurs in mixture in California. *A. canadensis* also is reported in British Columbia. The abdominal segments of fifth-instar nymphs of *A. permutata* are predominantly brown while those of *A. canadensis* are white above except for the last three segments which are black. *A. canadensis* completes its entire life cycle on pine. The nymphs settle on the needles, at the bases of the needles, and on green cones. Needle cast and twig killing that has been attributed to *A. permutata* presumably is caused by *A. canadensis*.

The **western pine spittlebug**, *Aphrophora permutata* Uhler (Kelson 1964), occurs extensively in the Western States and in Alberta and British Columbia. The adults occur on pine, Douglas-fir, hemlock, spruce, and fir. In California on Monterey pine, the adults feed on the underside of twigs, preferably second-year growth, and cause no significant damage. The adults (fig. 40A) are robust, mottled brown, heavily punctured, and about 10 mm

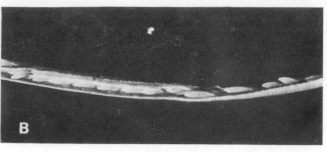

FIGURE 40.—Examples of spittlebug: *A, Aphrophora* adult, 8 mm long, from lodgepole pine; *B, A. permutata* eggs on pine needles.

long. The eggs (fig. 40B) are partially inserted in rows in pine needles in June and July. They hatch in February and March. The first-instar nymphs drop from the pine and feed on many kinds of herbs and shrubs. There are five nymphal instars. The adults appear in May and remain through September. There is one generation annually in central coastal California. *A. permutata* is one of many vectors of Pierce's virus disease of grapevines.

The **Saratoga spittlebug**, *Aphrophora saratogensis* (Fitch) (MacAloney and Wilson 1971), a serious pest in red pine and jack pine plantations in the East, has been recorded in British Columbia and California.

Clastoptera species are smaller and more globose than *Aphrophora* species (Doering 1928). More than 20 species of *Clastoptera* occur in western North America. Among the prevalent western species, the **dogwood spittlebug**, *C. proteus* Fitch, and *C. testacea* Fitch feed on pines, *C. juniperina* Ball feeds on juniper, and the **alder spittlebug**, *C. obtusa* (Say) feeds on alder and other broad-leaved plants. From 1963 to 1965 an unidentified *Clastoptera* caused conspicuous yellowing and twig killing of juniper in Utah and Nevada.

SUPERFAMILY MEMBRACOIDEA

The Membracidae predominate in this superfamily (Metcalf et al. 1927–71).

FAMILY MEMBRACIDAE—TREEHOPPERS

Numerous species of **treehoppers** (Metcalf et al. 1927–71) occur in the West. They are sap suckers. Many live on trees but none is a forest pest. The adults somewhat resemble adult spittlebugs, except that the thorax extends back over the abdomen and often projects forward also (fig. 41). They hop and fly quickly when disturbed.

COURTESY BROWN AND EADS (1965a)

FIGURE 41. — Unidentified species of oak treehopper on holly oak: *A*, Adult, 6 mm long; *B*, nymphs, 3.5 mm long.

The **oak treehopper,** *Platycotis vittata* (F.) (Essig 1926, Brown and Eads 1965a), is transcontinental. It feeds on the twigs of many kinds of oaks and is a minor pest on ornamentals. The eggs are laid in slits in the twigs, causing damage similar to but less conspicuous than that of cicadas. Adults are olive green to bronze with red dots, 10 mm long, densely punctured, and with or without an anterior pronotal horn. The nymphs are black with yellow and red markings. They feed gregariously.

SUPERFAMILY CICADELLOIDEA

This superfamily is considered to be one family, the Cicadellidae, by Oman (1949). Metcalf et al. (1927–71) divide them into 17 families.

FAMILY CICADELLIDAE—LEAFHOPPERS

There are more than two thousand species of **leafhoppers** (Beirne 1956, Essig 1926, Oman 1949) in the United States and Canada. Many occur on western trees and shrubs but cause no recorded economic damage. Some are serious pests in agriculture, principally as carriers of diseases. One transmits a tree disease. All are plant feeders that suck out the juices. The nymphs of a species usually feed on few species of plants; the adults on many. Leafhoppers are typically slender, delicate, boat-shaped insects,

91

mostly 3 to 10 mm long. They are usually various shades of brown, green, or yellow, frequently with contrasting markings. Their hind tibiae have numerous spines in longitudinal rows. They jump and fly readily when disturbed.

Colladonus (Nielson 1957) contains nearly 70 species, most of which are western. Generally they are yellowish brown and about 5 mm long. Several are vectors of plant viruses. Some occur on forest trees but fortunately none of them is implicated as a vector of a tree disease. *C. tahotus* Ball (fig. 42), the adult of which feeds on the needles of *Pinus ponderosa,* is recorded from Colorado, Arizona, California, Oregon, Washington, Idaho, and British Columbia. *C. ponderosus* Ball and *C. beameri* (Ball) feed on pine in Arizona, and *C. cachellus* Ball feeds on *Juniperus californica* in California.

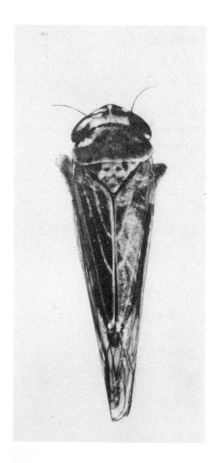

FIGURE 42.—Adult of a leafhopper, *Colladonus tahotus,* 5 mm long.

The **rose leafhopper,** *Edwardsiana* [*Typhlocyba*] *rosae* (L.), occurs extensively in western North America and in many other parts of the world (Metcalf et al. 1927–71). Rose and apple are preferred hosts, but cottonwood, elm, maple, oak, and many other plants are fed upon. The adults are 3.5 mm long. Adults and nymphs are slender and yellowish white. They feed on the under-side of leaves causing them to become mottled and to drop prema-turely. There are two generations annually. This pest of orna-mentals is readily controlled by spraying.

The genus *Koebelia* (Oman 1971) contains four species, all of which live on *Pinus* in western North America. None is recorded as a forest pest. *K. californica* Baker is the most generally dis-tributed, occurring from southern California to southern British Columbia and eastward to Idaho. *Pinus contorta* and *P. radiata* are hosts. The adults are 5.5 to 7.0 mm long, mottled brown and gray, and have numerous tubercles on the forewings.

The **whitebanded elm leafhopper,** *Scaphoideus luteolus* Van Duzee (Nielson 1968), is the only known vector of phloem necrosis of American and winged elm in the south central United States. The adults are about 5 mm long, golden brown with a few irregu-lar ivory spots on the elytra. This insect apparently does not occur west of Kansas and Nebraska, a fact that may limit the westward spread of the disease.

SUBORDER—STERNORHYNCHI, FUSED BEAKS

SUPERFAMILY PSYLLOIDEA

This superfamily contains one family, the Psyllidae.

FAMILY PSYLLIDAE—JUMPING PLANTLICE OR PSYLLIDS

There are about 150 North American species of **jumping plant-lice** or **psyllids** (Essig 1926, Kitching 1971, Tuthill 1943), many of which occur on western trees and shrubs. Adult psyllids resemble cicadas, but are about the size of aphids. Contrasted with aphids, they have stouter legs adapted for jumping, and tougher bodies. The nymphs are flat with conspicuously large wing pads. Like the aphids, they are plant feeders. Some cause leaf galls. Two cause systemic diseases that are serious in agriculture. None is rated as a forest pest.

Several species of *Pachypsylla* cause blisterlike and nipple-shaped galls on the leaves of *Celtis*.

In the West there are numerous species of *Psylla*. *P. americana* Crawford is one of several species that feed on willow. The adults overwinter and in the spring feed on the woody twigs and lay eggs in the catkins and expanding leaves on which the nymphs feed.

Upon completing development in late spring they leave the willows and often are collected on pine where at least some overwinter. Apparently there is one generation annually. *P. alni* (L.) occurs on alder from Arizona north into British Columbia and Alberta.

SUPERFAMILY APHIDOIDEA

This superfamily consists principally of the Aphididae and the Phylloxeridae.

FAMILY APHIDIDAE—APHIDS OR PLANTLICE

Aphids or **plantlice** are small, soft-bodied, generally gregarious insects. They range from almost colorless to green, yellow, or black. A pair of tubelike, truncate, or porelike structures (cornicles) on the upper side of the fifth or sixth abdominal segments of most aphids is an identifying character. Adults may be wingless, or may have four clear or cloudy wings with few veins. The front pair is considerably larger. Specimens must be mounted on slides and examined by microscope for specific identification. The mounting procedure is described by Essig (1948). Aphids of Colorado and adjacent areas are described, illustrated, and keyed by Palmer (1952). The aphids and their hosts in British Columbia are listed by Forbes et al. (1973).

Typically, aphids have several generations annually, mostly parthenogenetic. The last seasonal generation usually is sexual. Most species overwinter in the egg stage. Some species require two kinds of plant hosts.

Aphids have piercing mouth parts through which they feed on the sap of plants, attacking foliage, buds, flowers, fruit, twigs, and roots. They secrete honeydew which attracts ants and other insects, and is a fertile growth medium for sooty mold. Many aphids are serious pests of agricultural crops, some by transmitting virus diseases. Numerous species of aphids attack forest trees but few are known to be economically important. Some are significant pests of ornamental trees. Aphid populations fluctuate widely and quickly. The effects of parasites, predators, and pathogens are reviewed by Hagen and van den Bosch (1968).

The **common birch aphid,** *Calaphis betulaecolens* (Fitch) (Essig 1926) is a large green species that feeds on the leaves of various birches countrywide. It resembles *Euceraphis punctipennis* and, like it, is a pest on ornamentals.

Chaitophorus (Richards 1972) contains 32 species in North America, about half of them in the West. They resemble *Periphyllus* but feed only on *Populus* and *Salix*. Sometimes they severely infest ornamentals, but they are not recorded as forest pests.

The **poplar leaf aphid,** *Chaitophorus populicola* Thomas, is a cloudy-winged species that occurs in all the Western Provinces, Colorado, and Utah. It feeds on the apical twigs and developing leaves of native poplars, sometimes causing noticeable leaf drop in aspen stands.

The **giant conifer aphids,** *Cinara,* are long-legged, dark-colored aphids that are naked or are lightly covered with powdery wax. They range in length from about 2 to 5 mm. There are about 175 species in the world, mostly in North America, many in the West. Feeding sites, location of eggs, and species of host tree are useful aids in identification. Bradley (1961) developed a key to the species in Canada and listed the species of the world and their hosts.

All *Cinara* feed on conifers, mostly on twigs and branches but also on the trunk and roots. Most species are restricted to a single genus of tree; many attack only one species. None has an alternate host. Most *Cinara* feed gregariously, often in large groups (fig. 43). A few are solitary. Heavy infestations cause yellowing of the foliage and reduce tree growth, especially on young trees. The copious flow of honeydew often causes sooty unsightly mold to develop on the foliage. *Cinara* commonly are tended by *Formica, Camponotus,* and other ants which sometimes contribute to the damage by chewing on the trees.

F–521916

FIGURE 43.—Colony of giant conifer aphids (*Cinara* sp.) and an attending carpenter ant (*Camponotus* sp.) on Douglas-fir; aphids, up to 3.0 mm long.

There are several generations annually. Winter is spent in the egg stage on needles and bark. In the summer generations, except the last one, females give birth to living young.

Cinara are seldom recorded in survey reports, hence information on their distribution, abundance, and effects is scant. *C. pseudotaxifoliae* Palmer, attended by *Formica* and *Camponotus*, has caused reduced growth of young Douglas-firs in western Washington by feeding on the stem and root crown (Johnson 1965). *Cinara tujafilina* (Del Guercio) is a European species that has become a pest of ornamental *Thuja, Cupressus,* and *Chamaecyparis* in southern California (Brown and Eads 1967). It feeds both on the stems and roots. The **bow-legged fir aphid,** *Cinara curvipes* (Patch) occurs in California, Oregon, Colorado, and Utah and is reported to attack several species of fir, Engelmann spruce, and deodar cedar. On the latter it is an important pest of ornamentals in California. Some other representative species of *Cinara* and their varied hosts are:

Species	Hosts
C. coloradensis (Gillette)	*Picea engelmannii, P. pungens,* and *P. sitchensis*
C. fornacula Hottes green spruce aphid	*Picea pungens, P. engelmannii, P. glauca,* and *P. mariana*
C. laricifoliae (Wilson)	*Larix occidentalis*
C. occidentalis (Davidson)	*Abies lasiocarpa, A. concolor,* and *A. grandis*
C. oregonensis (Wilson)	*Pinus contorta* and *P. ponderosa* (cones)
C. pergandei (Wilson)	*Pinus contorta* and *P. banksiana*
C. ponderosae (Williams)	*Pinus ponderosa*
C. sabinae (Gillette and Palmer)	*Juniperus scopulorum*
C. tsugae Bradley	*Tsuga heterophylla*

The **painted maple aphid,** *Drepanaphis acerifoliae* (Thomas) feeds on the leaves of various maples extensively in the West. The wing veins are dusky margined. Terminal abdominal segments of the unwinged adult are elongate.

The **spruce aphid,** *Elatobium abietinum* (Walker), previously placed in *Neomyzaphis,* feeds almost exclusively on spruce, but has been recorded on pine and Douglas-fir. It is presumed to be native to Europe (Bejer-Petersen 1962). In North America it occurs from Alaska to California on Sitka spruce (Holms and Ruth 1968). Extensive killing of spruce along the Pacific coast has been attributed to sporadic outbreaks of this aphid, but more recent indications are that it is only one of the causes contributing to the killing. The aphid is a serious pest of ornamental spruce. Its biology and natural control have been studied in detail in Europe (Scheller 1963), but not in North America.

In western North America only the parthenogenetic form is known. Adults (fig. 44A,B) are 1 to 1.5 mm long, olive green, and predominantly wingless. The nymphs (fig. 44C) are lighter green. There are several generations annually. Populations reach a peak during late winter and early spring and practically disappear in summer.

The spruce aphid feeds gregariously, sucking sap from the old needles. It is seldom seen because of its small size, needlelike color, and early feeding habit. The lower and more shaded portions of the crown are most subject to injury. On heavily infested trees practically all the old foliage fades slightly, then drops before the new needles begin to expand. The new needles are not fed upon appreciably by the aphid until the next year. Epidemics in the forest are sporadic and short-term. Damage to ornamentals seems to occur more frequently. Starvation and predation are rated as effective natural controls in Europe (Hussey 1952). Chemical control to be effective must be applied in March and April.

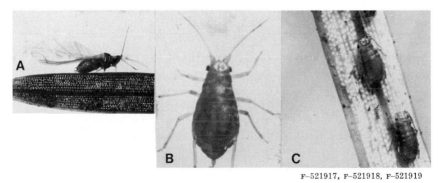

F–521917, F–521918, F–521919

FIGURE 44.—Spruce aphid (*Elatobium abietinum*): *A*, Winged adult, 1.5 mm long; *B*, wingless adult, 1.25 mm long; *C*, nymphs, 1 mm long, feeding on Sitka spruce needle.

Several **woolly aphids** of the genus *Eriosoma* feed on elm and alternately on other hosts, sucking sap from leaves (fig. 45), twigs, trunks, or roots. They are pests on ornamental elms, secreting honeydew and weakening heavily attacked trees. The eulophid parasite, *Aphelinus mali* (Haldeman), effectively controls *E. lanigerum* in British Columbia. The western *Eriosoma* (Baker and Davidson 1916, 1917; Essig 1926; Palmer 1952) are listed in table 5.

97

F–500798

FIGURE 45.—Woolly elm aphid (*Eriosoma americanum*) damage indicated by leaf curl on American elm. Note lady beetle feeding on aphids.

Table 5.—*Hosts, habits, and distribution of western species of* Eriosoma

Species	Habit and winter host	Habit and summer host	Distribution
E. americanum (Riley) **woolly elm aphid**	Curls leaves of *Ulmus americana*	Infests roots, lower trunk, and leaves of *Amelanchier*	Extensively in the West
E. crataegi (Oestlund)	Infests leaves and twigs of *Ulmus*	Infests stems of *Crataegus*	Colo.
E. lanigerum (Hausmann) **woolly apple aphid**	Causes leaf-cluster galls on *Ulmus*	Forms galls on branches, trunk, and roots of *Malus* and other Rosaceae	Extensively in the West
E. pyricola Baker and Davidson **woolly pear aphid**	Causes spiral gall on leaves of *Ulmus americana*	Infests small roots of *Pyrus*	Wash. to Calif.
E. rileyi (Thomas) **woolly elm bark aphid**	Infests trunk and roots of *Ulmus americana*	None	Colo. to N. Mex.
E. ulmi (L.) **European elm leafcurl aphid**	Curls leaves of *Ulmus*	*Ribes*	British Columbia, Oreg., Colo.

Essigella, with 20 species, is predominantly western (Hottes 1957). All feed on needles of conifers, principally pine. The **Monterey pine aphid**, *E. californica* (Essig), attacks *Pinus ponderosa, P. radiata*, and *P. coulteri* in California (Brown and Eads 1967). It is light green, slender, about 1.5 mm long, and has relatively long legs. It moves rapidly and often feeds alone rather than in colonies. *E. gillettei* Hottes, one of several species confused in the literature with *E. californica*, occurs in California, Oregon, and Colorado, and attacks *Pinus ponderosa, P. contorta, P. radiata*, and *P. albicaulis*. *E. pergandei* Hottes occurs on *Abies concolor* and *E. wilsoni* Hottes on *Pseudotsuga menziesii*.

The **European birch aphid**, *Euceraphis punctipennis* (Zetterstedt) (= *betulae* (Koch)) (Essig 1926), is a large green and black species with a powdery wax covering which distinguishes it from *Calaphis betulaecolens*. In the West *E. punctipennis* ranges from British Columbia to California to Colorado. It feeds on the underside of the leaves and produces honeydew in quantity, thus being a pest on ornamentals.

The **giant willow aphid**, *Lachnus salignus* (Gmelin), is a grayish-black species that resembles *Cinara* but attacks only willow. It occurs on the bark in large colonies in Colorado, Utah, and New Mexico.

The **balsam twig aphid**, *Mindarus abietinus* Koch, is a transcontinental species that occurs extensively and abundantly in the Pacific coast and Rocky Mountain regions of the United States and Canada. In the West it is reported on *Abies concolor, A. amabilis, A. grandis, A. lasiocarpa*, and *Picea pungens*. It is greenish yellow, powdery, winged or wingless, and 1.0 to 2.0 mm long. It feeds on the developing new needles and twigs causing them to twist (fig. 46). Needle drop, stunting, and twig distortion makes trees valueless as Christmas trees for 2 to 3 years following attack (Dawson 1971, Saunders 1969). It has several generations annually. In western Washington it becomes most abundant in June and July and then apparently disappears from fir.

The species of *Pemphigus* live in true galls on the leaves and twigs of *Populus* as winter host. Presumably all have alternate herbaceous hosts. The **poplar petiolegall aphid**, *P. populitransversus* Riley, forms a spherical, green gall with a transverse slit on the petiole of poplar leaves and also is a root-infesting pest of cruciferous crops. The **sugarbeet root aphid**, *P. populivenae* Fitch, forms an elongate gall on the midvein on the upper side of poplar leaves and attacks the roots of sugar beets. Harper (1959)

COURTESY CANADIAN FORESTRY SERVICE, F–521920

FIGURE 46.—Balsam twig aphid (*Mindarus abietinus*) on grand fir: *A*, Needles of current year's growth deformed by feeding aphids; *B*, waxy wool, nymphs and adults on the foliage.

keys the species in Alberta and Palmer (1952) the ones in Colorado.

Aphids of the genus *Periphyllus* (Richards 1972) feed on the leaves of *Acer* and are pests of ornamentals. They are green to brown, 2 to 3 mm long, and most forms have abundant spinelike hairs. The life cycle is complex, involving up to 17 different forms, as in *P. californiensis* (Shinji), an oriental species despite its name. Essig and Abernathy (1952) discuss the biology and taxonomy of the species, including the following which occur in the West:

Species	Hosts	Distribution
P. americanus (Baker), **American maple aphid**	*Acer* spp. including *glabrum*	Idaho and Utah
P. brevispinosus Gillette and Palmer, **Colorado maple aphid**	*Acer glabrum*	Colo., Utah, Idaho, British Columbia, and Alberta
P. californiensis (Shinji), **California maple aphid**	*Acer* spp.	Calif., north to British Columbia
P. lyropictus (Kessler), **Norway maple aphid**	*Acer platanoides* and *Acer* spp.	British Columbia to Calif., Colo., and Utah

Species	Hosts	Distribution
P. *negundinis* (Thomas), boxelder aphid	*Acer negundo*	Saskatchewan, Alberta, British Columbia, Wash., Calif., Colo., and other Western States
P. *testudinacea* (Fernie), European maple aphid	*Acer* spp. including *macrophyllum*	Alaska and British Columbia to Calif.

Species of *Prociphilus* feed on corky roots of conifers and usually are attended by ants (Smith 1969). On their primary hosts, broad-leaved trees and shrubs, they form false galls, mostly on leaves, in which all forms live together. All are covered with white cottony wax. *P. americanus* (Walker) is a large species that feeds on roots of noble fir reproduction in Oregon (Zak 1965) and also is reported on Douglas-fir. Ash is its primary host.

Pterocallis alni (De Geer) is a greenish-yellow aphid that occurs widely in Europe and North America on alder (Richards 1965), feeding on the tender, terminal shoots. In British Columbia it attacks *Alnus rubra*.

Rhizomaria [*Pemphigus*] *piceae* (Hartig) feeds on mycorrhizae of second-growth Douglas-fir in western Oregon (Zak 1965) and has been collected on spruce in Colorado and Utah. The aphids, mostly wingless, feed in small colonies and are covered with cottony wax (fig. 47). The same, or a closely related species, feeds

F–521921

FIGURE 47.—Wingless aphids, probably *Rhizomaria piceae*, feeding on mycorrhizae; aphids, 1.75 mm long.

101

on mycorrhizae of western hemlock and Sitka spruce in Oregon.

There are five species of *Schizolachnus* in the West (Hottes 1956). All feed on needles of pine. None is a significant forest pest. The best known is the **woolly pine needle aphid,** *S. piniradiatae* (Davidson), which occurs from coast to coast and from British Columbia to New Mexico (Grobler 1962). *Pinus ponderosa, P. radiata,* and *P. contorta* are attacked. The shiny black eggs are in clusters of four, end to end on the needles. The aphids are dark green, long-legged, and covered with cottony wax. They line up on the needles single file, all headed in one direction. There are several generations annually. *S. pineti* (F.) is an introduced species reported on ornamental pines in California and Oregon.

Several species of *Tuberculatus* attack oaks in the West, feeding on the underside of leaves. *T. columbiae* Richards on *Quercus garryana* in British Columbia is an example (Richards 1965).

FAMILY PHYLLOXERIDAE (CHERMIDAE)—GALL APHIDS AND BARK APHIDS

The **gall aphids** and **bark aphids** (Annand 1928, Carter 1971), at times known as Chermidae and Adelgidae, contains *Adelges* [*Chermes*] and *Pineus*. They attack conifers only. *Adelges* has five pairs of abdominal spiracles; *Pineus* has four pairs. The genera and species are very similar in appearance and sometimes occur in mixture. They can be positively identified only by microscopic examination. On spruce, *Adelges* causes cone-shaped galls on the twigs. On other hosts, *Adelges* and *Pineus* occur as white, cottony tufts on the bark of the trunk, branches, twigs, needles, and cones, the location varying with the insect species. Hosts, part of the tree affected, and distribution as they apply to the West, are listed in table 6. *Adelges piceae* (Ratzeburg) is a major forest pest. Several other species are economically damaging, especially on ornamentals and on young forest trees.

The life cycle is complex (fig. 48). For some species there are up to six kinds of egg-laying adults. The sexual form, if present, always develops on spruce which is considered to be the primary host. The asexual forms feed upon *Abies, Larix, Pinus, Pseudotsuga,* and *Tsuga* which are secondary hosts. Some species alternate between host trees; others live only on the primary or upon the secondary host.

In general, control by spraying is best accomplished when directed against the immature stages, particularly in spring.

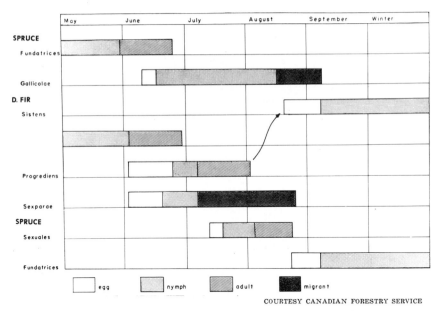

FIGURE 48.—Diagram of a generalized life history of *Adelges cooleyi*.

The **eastern spruce gall aphid,** *Adelges abietis* (L.), was introduced from Europe into eastern North America. It now occurs on both native and ornamental spruce in Saskatchewan and British Columbia.

The **Cooley spruce gall aphid,** *Adelges cooleyi* (Gillette) (Chrystal 1916, Cumming 1959), is the most prevalent of the phylloxerids that cause cone-shaped galls on spruce twigs in the West. This insect also has become widely established in eastern North America and in Europe. The galls are of little importance under normal forest conditions. On seedlings and saplings in nurseries and plantations and on ornamental trees, they are of consequence because they kill the tips of branches and tend to stunt and deform the trees. The galls are from 12 to 75 mm long, light green to dark purple, and are formed by the growing together of the basal portion of the needles so as to form chambers between the base of the needles and the stem (fig. 49A). These chambers, which are separate, usually contain from 3 to 30 small wingless aphids covered with a white waxy coating and also a very few winged ones. The galls turn brown, dry, and hard after the insects have escaped, and they may persist for many years.

On Douglas-fir, the alternate host, *A. cooleyi* settles on the new needles, new shoots, and developing cones where white cottony tufts mark its presence (fig. 49B). The infested needles become twisted and yellowish. Severe infestations on poor sites cause

103

Table 6.—Adelges *and* Pineus *species: Hosts, parts attacked, and distribution in Western North America*

Insect	Primary host [1]	Secondary host [2] and parts attacked		Distribution
Adelges abietis	*Picea engelmannii* P. glauca			British Columbia and Saskatchewan
A. cooleyi	*Picea engelmannii* P. sitchensis P. pungens P. glauca P. breweriana	*Pseudotsuga menziesii*	Needles and cones	Alberta, British Columbia, Wash., Oreg., Calif., Idaho, Mont., Wyo., Colo., Utah, and Alaska
A. lariciatus	*Picea glauca* P. mariana P. pungens	*Larix laricina* L. lyalli	Buds and cones	Alberta and Saskatchewan
A. nüsslini	*Picea* (in Europe)	*Abies nordmanniana* A. procera	Bole, branches, twigs, and needles	British Columbia and Calif.
A. oregonensis		*Larix occidentalis*	Twigs and needles	British Columbia, Wash., Oreg., and Mont.
A. piceae		*Abies amabilis* A. grandis A. lasiocarpa and others	Bole, branches, twigs, and buds	British Columbia, Wash., and Oreg.
A. strobilobius	*Picea mariana*	*Larix* (in Europe)	Needles and twigs	Alberta
A. tsugae		*Tsuga heterophylla*	Bole, branches, and twigs	British Columbia, Wash., Oreg., and Calif.

Insect	Primary host [1]	Secondary host [2] and parts attacked		Distri-bution
Pineus *abietinus*		*Abies amabilis* *A. grandis* *A. lasiocarpa*	Bole and branches	British Columbia and Wash.
P. *börneri*		*Pinus radiata*	Bole, branches, and twigs	Calif.
P. *boycei*	*Picea engelmannii*			Mont. and Oreg.
P. *coloradensis*		*Pinus contorta* *P. edulis* *P. lambertiana* *P. monophylla* *P. monticola* *P. ponderosa* *P. jeffreyi*	Needles and twigs	Wash., Oreg., Calif., and Colo.
P. *pinifoliae*	*Picea engelmannii* *P. sitchensis* *P. pungens*	*Pinus monticola*	Twigs and needles	British Columbia, Wash., Oreg., Calif., Idaho, Mont., and Colo.
P. *similis*	*Picea engelmannii* *P. pungens* *P. mariana* *P. glauca*			British Columbia, Oreg., Colo., Alberta, Utah, and Saskatch-ewan
P. *strobi*		*Pinus*	Bole, branches, and twigs	Calif., on orna-mentals

[1] Hosts (*Picea* species) on which sexual forms of these insects occur, forming cone-shaped galls on twigs; western hosts except as indicated.

[2] Hosts on which asexual forms occur; cottony tufts are the usual evidence of attack.

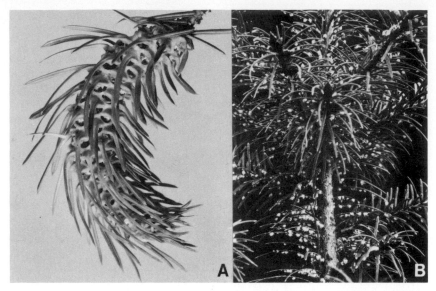

F-521922, F-521923

FIGURE 49.—Cooley spruce gall aphid (*Adelges cooleyi*): *A*, Fresh gall on Sitka spruce; *B*, cottony masses on Douglas-fir needles.

heavy shedding of foliage. Some clones of Douglas-fir apparently are more resistant than others. The discoloration and shedding can be very damaging on Christmas tree areas, necessitating control.

The entire life cycle requires 2 years. There are six stages in addition to the eggs and crawlers when both host trees are present. In Alberta and Saskatchewan an abbreviated parthenogenetic cycle is completed in 1 year entirely on the needles of spruce (Cumming 1962b). A parthenogenetic cycle of two generations annually is common on the needles of Douglas-fir where spruce is scarce or absent. Cone galls on spruce are formed only where Douglas-fir is present.

Control of *A. cooleyi*, either on spruce or Douglas-fir, may be obtained by spraying early in the spring.

Adelges lariciatus (Patch) (Cumming 1968) is an eastern species that extends westward into Alberta. On spruce it forms a globular gall that usually only partly surrounds the twig which sometimes continues to grow beyond the gall. On larch it attacks the buds and cones.

Adelges nüsslini (Börner), known also as *A. nordmannianae* (Eckstein) (Carter 1971), is a European species very similar to *A. piceae* but differing in that it develops both on fir and spruce.

A. nüsslini has been recorded on ornamentals in British Columbia and California.

The **western larch woolly aphid,** *Adelges oregonensis* Annand, feeds on the twigs and base of the needles of western larch. No primary host is recorded. Young, open-grown trees seem to be preferred and at times are heavily attacked. The white woolly masses on the twigs resemble those of *A. tsugae.*

The **balsam woolly aphid,** *Adelges piceae* (Ratzeburg) (Mitchell et al. 1970), is a European species that has become widely established in North America where it is highly destructive to several species of true fir. In the West it is a major forest pest, having killed and damaged Pacific silver fir, subalpine fir, and grand fir extensively in Oregon and Washington, both in commercial forests and on recreation areas. During the late 1950's an outbreak in southwestern Washington killed an estimated 1.5 billion fbm of timber, much of which could not be salvaged (Johnson et al. 1963). This insect also poses a threat in British Columbia where it occurs both in the forest and in ornamental plantings.

A. piceae (fig. 50) feeds on the stem, branches, and twigs. During feeding it injects a salivary substance into the tree which causes calluses and gall-like formations on the twigs and branches. On the bole, dense red rings similar to compression wood are formed. Bole infestations may be very heavy and are easily detected by the white wool (fig. 50D). Such infestations usually kill the tree in a few years. Branch and twig infestations often cause gouting which progressively weakens a tree over a long period of years.

There are two to four generations per year in the West, all on true fir. Distribution apparently is mostly by wind during the crawler stage. All individuals are females, hence it only takes one to form a new colony.

A large-scale effort has been made to control this insect by importing and colonizing its insect predators. Five species have become established but have not given economic control (Mitchell 1965). A beetle, *Laricobius erichsonii,* and a midge, *Aphidoletes thompsoni,* appear to be the most effective. Chemical control by spraying is possible on ornamentals but impractical in the forest.

The **larch woolly aphid,** *Adelges strobilobius* (Kaltenbach), known also as *A. laricis* Vallot (Carter 1971), is a European species now established westward into Alberta in North America. On spruce it causes small globular terminal galls. On larch it feeds on the twigs and needles.

The **hemlock woolly aphid,** *Adelges tsugae* Annand, known also as *A. funitecta* (Dreyfus) (Carter 1971) (fig. 51), appears as

F–521924, F–521925, F–521926, F–521927

FIGURE 50.—Balsam woolly aphid (*Adelges piceae*): *A*, Heavy infestation of crawlers on terminal shoot of grand fir; *B*, gouting of twigs on grand fir; *C*, cottony masses surrounding aphids, greatly magnified; *D*, bole infestation on subalpine fir.

white, cottony tufts on the bark and on the twigs among the needles of western hemlock. It is of little consequence in the forest but seriously weakens and sometimes kills ornamental trees.

Pineus abietinus Underwood and Balch (Johnson 1959) attacks the bole and branches of *Abies amabilis, A. grandis,* and *A. lasiocarpa* in British Columbia and Washington without causing appreciable damage. It closely resembles the balsam woolly aphid but does not cause gouting. The wax secretions of the first-instar larva of *P. abietinus* are threadlike and those of *Adelges piceae* are ribbonlike.

Pineus boycei Annand causes galls on Engelmann spruce similar to those of *P. pinifoliae*. The needles with enlarged bases are

F–521928

FIGURE 51.—Hemlock woolly aphid (*Adelges tsugae*) in cottony masses on western hemlock twig.

pressed closely against the twigs and form intercommunicating chambers in which about 15 nymphs are found. The alternate host is not known.

Pineus coloradensis (Gillette) feeds on the needles and twigs of many western pines. The white, waxy secretions, similar to those of *Adelges tsugae,* often are conspicuous on young ponderosa and lodgepole pines. The foliage of heavily attacked trees becomes yellowish and presumably growth is retarded. Quantitative studies of the effects are not recorded.

The **pine leaf chermid,** *Pineus pinifoliae* (Fitch) (Balch and Underwood 1950, Dimond and Bishop 1968), is transcontinental. On spruce it forms loose, terminal, cone-shaped galls somewhat similar to those of *Adelges cooleyi,* except that the poorly-formed chambers are intercommunicating and contain only one or two young in each chamber, and when the insects emerge the galls flare open and the scales drop from the twigs. These galls are unimportant except on ornamentals where they may be considered unsightly. *P. pinifoliae* may weaken and even kill western white pine seedlings to the extent that control measures are needed. On western white pine it is easily recognized by the whit-

109

ish-gray, waxy secretion that develops on the bark and needles. The attacked foliage is apt to be sparse and stunted; the needles fall prematurely, and the fascicles or bundle sheaths are left protruding from the limbs as short spurs. The adults appear as little, hemispherical, brown scales 1.5 mm in diameter with a fringe of white hairs. Hazard to pine stands can be decreased by reducing the amount of spruce.

The biology of the widely distributed but infrequently observed *Pineus similis* (Gillette) is recorded by Cumming (1962a).

The **pine bark aphid**, *Pineus strobi* (Hartig), and *P. börneri* Annand also occur in the West.

SUPERFAMILY ALEYRODOIDEA

This superfamily contains one family, the Aleyrodidae.

FAMILY ALEYRODIDAE—WHITEFLIES

Whiteflies (Essig 1926) are related to aphids and scale insects. Generally they are about 1 mm long. The adults are winged and covered with a snowy white powder. The nymphs resemble scale insects but do not have a separate shell-like covering. They are naked or covered with waxy material and secrete honeydew which becomes blackened by mold. They feed on leaves and are principally greenhouse and garden pests. A few attack trees and shrubs. None is a forest pest.

The **crown whitefly**, *Aleuroplatus coronatus* (Quaintance) (Brown and Eads 1965a), feeds on oaks and tanoak in California (fig. 52). It prefers coast live oak. The immature forms are about 1 mm long, black, and crowned with broad, white, waxy plates. They feed on the lower surface of leaves, sometimes causing them to fall prematurely. On warm days from February to April the white, flying adults may be so abundant as to resemble a snow flurry. There is one brood annually. The crown whitefly is a pest of ornamentals and sometimes is a nuisance in flight. Spraying shortly before emergence or just after egg-laying is recommended for control.

The **rhododendron whitefly**, *Dialeurodes chittendeni* Laing (Latta 1937), is an introduced pest of ornamental rhododendrons in western Washington and British Columbia. It feeds on the under surface of the leaves, causing them to become mottled. An associated sooty mold contributes to the damage. There is one generation annually. Second- and third-instar larvae overwinter. Spraying in the fall before frost is recommended. The underside of the leaves must be thoroughly wet by the spray.

The **greenhouse whitefly**, *Trialeurodes vaporariorum* (Westwood) (Russell 1948), is a troublesome pest in greenhouses and

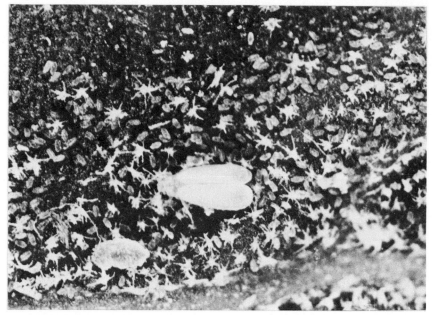

FIGURE 52.—Crown whitefly (*Aleuroplatus coronatus*) on lower leaf surface of coast live oak: Eggs and adult, latter 1.1 mm long.

gardens, attacking a wide range of plants including madrone, ash, manzanita, and ceanothus. It is not a forest pest.

SUPERFAMILY COCCOIDEA

This superfamily (Ferris 1937–61) consists of the scale insects, including the mealybugs. The **scales** are one of the most abundant and variable groups of sap-sucking enemies of plants. They cause great damage to agricultural plants. Seven families of scales contain species of significance in western forestry. A few are important pests. The young are small, inconspicuous, and mobile, but after they become attached to a plant they often lose the power of locomotion. Most of them develop a waxy or shell-like covering and remain fixed in one position until they die. The female causes practically all the injury to plants. The adult males usually have wings, eyes, antennae, and legs, but no functional mouth parts and so cannot feed. Males live only a short time and are rarely seen.

As a rule, scales are most abundant on trees growing under adverse conditions or in situations unfavorable to their natural enemies. Chemical sprays give effective control on ornamentals but rarely are they needed in the forest.

111

FAMILY ASTEROLECANIIDAE—PIT SCALES

The body covering of the **pit scales** is membranous. Adult females have no legs. Some species feed in pits formed by swelling of plant tissue around them, hence their common name.

Asterolecanium contains about 150 species in the world (Russell 1941). Three species attacking oak have been introduced into California from Europe. The most abundant and damaging of these is *A. minus* Lindinger which attacks *Quercus lobata, Q. douglasii, Q. agrifolia,* and *Q. kelloggi* (Pritchard and Beer 1950). It can seriously weaken a tree by killing twigs and branches. Such killing shows up in late summer.

There is one generation a year. Emergence of the crawlers begins in late April and continues until late September. Pits are formed where they settle and feed. Males are unknown. Chemical control is effective from late April until early June (Koehler 1964).

FAMILY COCCIDAE—SOFT SCALES

The Coccidae are soft, convex, generally spherical scales that settle on twigs and branches and sometimes the leaves. Frequently troublesome on ornamental trees and shrubs, they are minor pests in the forest.

The **European fruit lecanium**, *Lecanium* [*Eulecanium*] *corni* Bouché, occurs throughout the United States and in southern Canada. It is an economic pest of fruit trees and also attacks many broad-leaved forest and ornamental trees such as alder, elm, maple, poplar, and willow. It has many shapes, sizes, and colors. Typically the mature female is hemispherical, smooth, shiny brown, 3 to 5 mm long, and often is clustered in large numbers on small branches. There is one generation a year. The chalcid parasite, *Blastothrix sericea* (Dalman), introduced in 1928 from England, is reported to have controlled *L. corni* effectively in British Columbia (Turnbull and Chant 1961).

The **Monterey pine scale**, *Physokermes insignicola* (Craw) (Brown and Eads 1967, Burke 1937), attacks Monterey pine and other pines in California. Young trees are most seriously affected. *P. insignicola* resembles *Toumeyella pinicola* in appearance and habits. The adult females are semiglobular, brown to black, smooth, and 4 to 6 mm in diameter. The young settle first on the needles. Later the females attach themselves to the twigs between the bases of the needles and complete development there. Heavy deposits of honeydew and sooty fungus often obscure them.

The **spruce bud scale**, *Physokermes piceae* (Schrank), (Fenton 1917) is a European species first reported in the Eastern United States in 1906. It now attacks spruce westward to Alberta and the Northwest Territories and has been recorded in California.

Pine also is a recorded host. Lower branches may be killed by it. The adult female is semiglobular, brown, 1.5 to 3 mm long, and closely resembles a bud. The young settle on the needles. In the spring the females migrate to the twigs and complete development there. They produce abundant honeydew. There is one generation a year.

The **cottony maple scale,** *Pulvinaria innumerabilis* (Rathvon) (Essig 1926, Weigel and Baumhofer 1948), occurs throughout the United States and Southern Canada on broad-leaved trees and shrubs, including maple, alder, elm, poplar, willow, and many others. It is a pest of ornamentals. Honeydew and sooty fungus accompany heavy infestations. The winter is spent as partly grown, oval, flat, generally brown scales on twigs and branches. In the spring an elongate white cottony egg sac two or three times the length of the scale is produced. Length overall, including the egg sac, is 5 to 6 mm. Most of the young settle on the leaves until fall when they migrate back to the twigs. There is one generation a year.

The **cottony camellia scale,** *Pulvinaria floccifera* (Westwood), of similar appearance and habits, is a pest of holly and camellia.

Two species of *Toumeyella* sometimes are troublesome pests of ornamental pines in the West, but they generally are of less concern in the forest.

The **pine tortoise scale,** *Toumeyella numismaticum* (Pettit and McDaniel) (Wilson 1971a), is primarily eastern, but it ranges into Nebraska, the Dakotas, and Manitoba. It attacks jack pine, Scotch pine, and red pine but apparently not ponderosa pine. Heaviest damage occurs on seedlings and young saplings, although pole stands are sometimes severely attacked. Heavy attack kills branches or entire trees. Trees may die in one or two seasons of heavy attack.

The immature females are wrinkled and dark brown to black. When mature, they are reddish brown, oval and convex, and about 6 mm long. Males are winged. A sooty mold is associated with heavy infestations. The crawler stage is dispersed largely by wind. The crawlers of both sexes settle upon the twigs and develop there, often in conspicuous clusters. There are one or two generations per year depending upon temperatures.

The **irregular pine scale,** *Toumeyella pinicola* Ferris, (Kattoulas and Koehler 1965), is the most damaging scale on ornamental pines in coastal California. It attacks *Pinus radiata, P. muricata, P. attenuata,* and some exotic species. Severely infested trees make little growth and young trees may be killed by repeated heavy infestation.

The irregular pine scale has one generation a year. The insect overwinters as partially grown female nymphs. The females each produce upward of 1,000 young. The orange-yellow crawlers hatch from February to May. Female-producing crawlers settle upon the twigs at the base of the needle fascicles. Most of the male-producing crawlers settle upon the needles. The adult female is hemispherical, wrinkled, and gray to brown (fig. 53A). The male is elongate oval, rather flattened with a raised central ridge, shining, and semitransparent (fig. 53B). Large concentrations of the scale are usually covered with honeydew and sooty mold and frequently are attended by ants.

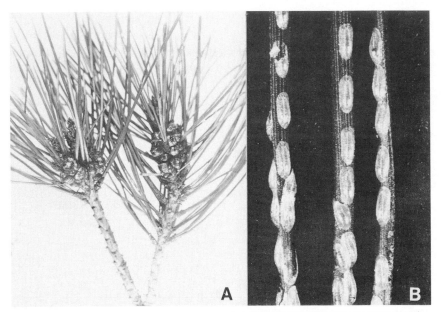

EPQ–6002, COURTESY BROWN AND EADS (1967)

FIGURE 53.—Irregular pine scale (*Toumeyella pinicola*) on Monterey pine: *A*, Female scales, 3 mm long, on twigs; *B*, male cocoons, 2 mm long, on needles.

The **tuliptree scale,** *Toumeyella liriodendri* (Gmelin) (Donley and Burns 1971), is a serious pest of *Liriodendron tulipifera* and also attacks *Magnolia* and other trees in Eastern States. It has been introduced into California on ornamentals.

FAMILY DIASPIDIDAE—ARMORED SCALES

Several of the **armored scales** (McKenzie 1956) attack western forest trees and woody plants. A few cause significant damage but none is a major pest. The adult males are winged; the females wingless. The females cause most of the damage and are the form usually seen. The body of the adult female usually lies between a thin, delicate lower scale and a thick, hard upper scale. The armored scales vary greatly in shape, surface character, and color.

The **redwood scale**, *Aonidia shastae* (Coleman) (McKenzie 1956), feeds on the foliage of *Sequoia sempervirens, S. gigantea, Libocedrus decurrens, Cupressus,* and *Juniperus.* It is recorded in California and Utah. The cone-shaped adult female scale is about 1 mm in diameter and resembles a droplet of hardened pitch on cypress foliage. Damage is inconsequential.

The **juniper scale**, *Carulaspis juniperi* (Bouché) (Brown and Eads 1967, Weigel and Baumhofer 1948), also known as *Diaspis carueli* (Targioni-Tozzetti), is a European species now distributed throughout the United States and Southern Canada. It feeds upon *Juniperus, Chamaecyparis, Cryptomeria, Cupressus, Libocedrus,* and *Thuja.* It attacks the leaves, twigs, branches, and cones, causing the foliage to become sickly yellow, and sometimes it kills branches, and even entire trees. Sooty black mold often is present. The female scale is round, convex, grayish white with an off-center yellowish nipple, and about 1 mm in diameter (fig. 54). The male is smaller and narrow with a ridge down the center. There is one generation a year. Control is most effective against the crawlers in spring.

The **pine needle scale**, *Chionaspis* [*Phenacaspis*] *pinifoliae* (Fitch) (Cumming 1953) (fig. 55), occurs widely in North America, often in mixture with *Nuculaspis californica.* Often distributed on planting stock, it is dispersed locally in the crawler stage by wind. In the West it attacks all species of pine and sometimes Douglas-fir, spruce, and cedar. Frequently a pest of ornamentals, and trees in shelterbelts, this scale sometimes is a forest pest. Small trees, saplings, and poles, especially along dusty roads, are often so heavily infested that the foliage appears white. Sometimes it kills trees but more often weakens them and slows their growth.

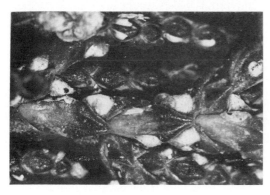

COURTESY BROWN AND EADS (1967)

Figure 54. — Juniper scale *(Carulaspis juniperi)* adult females, 1 mm long, and smaller males, some partially hidden by leaflets, on a juniper twig.

F–521929

FIGURE 55.—Pine needle scales
(*Chionaspis pinifoliae*), 2.0
to 2.5 mm long, on ponderosa pine needles.

At Tahoe, California, a severe infestation developed on 1,200 acres of pine following spraying to control mosquitoes.

Eggs are rusty brown. The scale covering the adult, wingless, dark orange females is white, 2.5 mm long, elongate oval, and with yellowish apical exuviae. The armored covering of the male is about one-third as long as that of the female. Adult males are winged. There is one generation annually in Alberta and perhaps two in California. Eggs laid in the fall overwinter under the female scale and hatch in the spring. Spraying is most effective when directed against the crawlers.

Diaspidiotus ehrhorni (Coleman) (McKenzie 1956) occurs on the bark of white fir, Douglas-fir, incense cedar, digger pine, and Parry pine in California, causing no appreciable damage. The mature female scale is about 1 mm in diameter, gray, flat, circular, and with an off-center nipple. The male is more oval.

The **oystershell scale**, *Lepidosaphes ulmi* (L.) (Griswold 1925, Quaintance and Sasscer 1916), presumably of European origin, now occurs throughout temperate North America. Principally a shade tree and orchard pest, this scale attacks many kinds of trees and shrubs including aspen, birch, maple, poplar, sycamore, and willow, but not conifers. It feeds primarily on the twigs, branches, and thin-barked stems and prefers shady conditions.

116

Heavily attacked trees are weakened and sometimes killed. The scales, resembling tiny oystershells, often mass together (fig. 56). They are gray to purplish brown and attain a length of 3 mm. Practically all are females. Typically there is one generation annually, but there may be two. The young appear in May and June. Chemical sprays are most effective when applied against the crawlers. The predaceous mite, *Hemisarcoptes malus* (Shimer), introduced from Eastern Canada is reported to reduce the abundance of oystershell scale on native vegetation in British Columbia (Turnbull and Chant 1961).

The **black araucaria scale,** *Lindingaspis rossi* (Maskell) (Mc-Kenzie 1956), is a pest of ornamentals, *Sequoia sempervirens*, and *Araucaria* in California. It feeds on the needles causing them to turn yellow. The round to oval female is about 2 mm in diameter, rather flat, and has a central point of white wax. The male is smaller and more oval. The color is light to dark brown.

The **black pineleaf scale,** *Nuculaspis* [*Aspidiotus*] *californica* (Coleman), (Edmunds 1973, Struble and Johnson 1964) is widely distributed in North America. It often is associated with the pine needle scale. In the West its principal hosts are ponderosa, Jeffrey, sugar, Monterey, and digger pines. It also attacks Douglas-fir. Sustained heavy infestation for several years progressively weakens and kills trees of all sizes. Seriously affected trees have

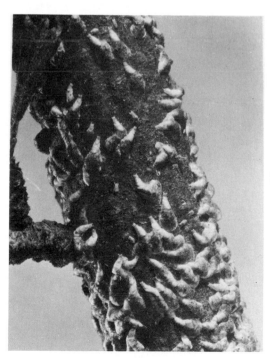

F–521930

FIGURE 56.—Oystershell scale (*Lepidosaphes ulmi*), 2.5 to 3.0 mm long, on bitterbrush twig.

sparse, short foliage at the tips of the twigs (fig. 57A). Individual needles are blotchy yellowish green and often are encrusted with scales. Outbreaks are commonly associated with industrial fumes, smog, dust, and spray drift. These conditions are presumed to reduce the effectiveness of insect parasites, especially the chalcid, *Prospaltella* near *aurantii* (Howard), and predators. Notable outbreaks have occurred at Penticton, British Columbia; Spokane and Cashmere, Washington; The Dalles, Oregon, and in many parts of California.

N. californica feeds only on the needles. The insect is bright yellow. The scale that covers the mature female is about 2 mm long, yellowish brown to black, broadly oval in outline, broadly conical in profile, and has a central nipple (fig. 57B). The male scale is smaller and generally darker. Females outnumber males 10 to 1. In northern Washington there is one generation annually; in southern California two or three. The minute yellow eggs are laid in masses under the scales in spring and early summer. The crawlers soon settle and develop the scalelike covering. Spraying is most effective when directed against the crawlers.

The *Protodiaspis* scales (McKenzie 1956) are small scales that usually occur in cracks of the bark of oaks, though some are exposed. *P. agrifoliae* Essig occurs on the twigs and imbedded in the leaf hairs of *Quercus agrifolia* in California. The armor of the female is light gray to blackish and has terminal exuviae. Damage is inconsequential.

The **San Jose scale**, *Quadraspidiotus* [*Aspidiotus*] *perniciosus* (Comstock) (Weigel and Baumhofer 1948), is presumed to have

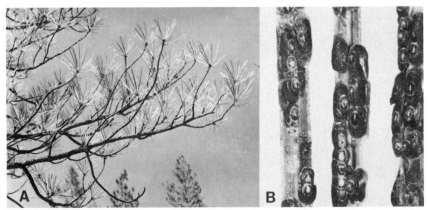

F–506705, COURTESY BROWN AND EADS (1967)

FIGURE 57.—Black pineleaf scale (*Nuculaspis californica*): *A*, Sparse short foliage resulting from persistent infestations; *B*, mature and nearly mature scales up to 1.75 mm long.

been introduced from China. It is widely distributed in the West and is an important pest of apple and other fruit trees. It attacks many other trees and shrubs including alder, birch, cherry, elm, maple, poplar, and willow. It attacks the twigs, branches, and stems, often in numbers sufficient to cause branch killing and to create a problem on ornamentals. There are two to six generations annually. The adult female scale is gray, circular, slightly convex with a nipple near the center, and about 1.5 mm in diameter. The male scale is smaller and more oval. Control is by dormant spray or by spraying against the crawlers in early summer.

The **Kellogg scale**, *Stramenaspis kelloggi* (Coleman) (McKenzie 1956), is the only species in this genus. It occurs on the needles of *Pseudotsuga menziesii,* and several species of *Abies* and *Pinus* in California. The armor is elongate but readily distinguishable by its straw color from *Chionaspis pinifoliae* which occurs on the same hosts.

FAMILY ERIOCOCCIDAE

The **European elm scale**, *Gossyparia [Eriococcus] spuria* (Modeer) (Herbert 1924), is a serious pest of ornamental elms in many parts of the country, particularly in the West. It was introduced from Europe. Heavy infestation causes premature yellowing and shedding of leaves and killing of twigs and branches. Small trees may be killed. Associated honeydew and black mold also are a nuisance.

The immature forms and the white male cocoons resemble mealybugs. Females predominate. Adult females are wingless and dark reddish brown with a conspicuous fringe of white cottony wax along the sides (fig. 58). Adult males may be winged and have a pair of long waxy filaments at the tail end or may have only small wing pads and no filaments. Adult females feed on branches. First- and second-stage larvae feed on leaves. The second-stage larvae overwinter on the small branches. There is one generation

COURTESY BROWN AND EADS (1966)

FIGURE 58.—European elm scale (*Gossyparia spuria*) mature females, about 3 mm long, with attending ants on Chinese elm.

119

a year. Egg laying is from late May into August. Dormant sprays may be applied before the leaf buds swell. Sprays against the young crawlers are applied in midsummer.

FAMILY KERMIDAE

The Kermidae (Ferris 1937–61) is a little-known family of scales recognizable chiefly by not having characters that other related groups have.

About a dozen species of *Kermes* (Brown and Eads 1965a, Ferris 1937–61) attack the twigs of western oaks. They are inconsequential even on ornamentals. Because of their appearance they are something of a curiosity. At maturity the females swell greatly, becoming globular and resembling cynipid galls. *Kermes cockerelli* Ehrhorn on *Quercus lobata* in north central California and *K. nigropunctatus* Ehrhorn and Cockerell on *Q. agrifolia* in southern California are representative species.

FAMILY MARGARODIDAE—MARGARODID SCALES

The family Margarodidae contains several important enemies of forest trees. These scales are seldom seen, hence field identification is largely based on damage, host, and distribution. Some are evidenced by white waxy secretions and by associated black mold.

Matsucoccus scales (Morrison 1939) attack only pine. They cause tip killing, branch "flagging," stunting, and needle injury. The flagging on white pines resembles the effects of white pine blister rust, hence complicates blister rust surveys. Some *Matsucoccus* predispose pines to attack by bark bettles.

Matsucoccus larvae and adults are small, oval, yellow to brown, inconspicuous insects (fig. 59) which are extremely difficult to detect because they push themselves beneath the sheath of needle fascicles or bury themselves in crevices of the bark of twigs and branches, taking on the color of their environment. Ten species of these scales occur in the West. Their habits, hosts, and distribution are summarized in table 7.

The **piñon needle scale,** *Matsucoccus acalyptus* Herbert (McCambridge 1974), is damaging to pinyon, singleleaf pinyon, and foxtail pine in the Southwestern United States. Serious outbreaks have occurred in Mesa Verde and Grand Canyon National Parks. Repeated infestation on large pinyon trees weakens them and subjects them to killing by *Ips confusus*. Small trees may be killed outright or seriously weakened as the foliage becomes thin and needle length is drastically reduced.

The adult females are motile but wingless. Males are winged. Mating (fig. 60A) occurs early in April. The yellow eggs are laid in masses held together by white cottony webbing. The egg masses are concentrated around the root collar, in the crotches of large branches, and along the undersides of large branches (fig. 60B). The first-stage crawlers migrate to and settle down upon the needles formed the previous year. In very heavy infestations they also feed on new foliage. The second stage formed in late August or early September is without legs. By October the second-stage larva, still attached to the needle, resembles a small black bean 1.5 mm long (fig. 60C). The winter is spent in that stage.

The **ponderosa pine twig scale**, *Matsucoccus bisetosus* Morrison (McKenzie 1942b), is rated as the most damaging of this group of scales in California. It feeds in twig axils, on twigs and branches, and on the trunks of trees of all ages. Heavily infested trees are characterized by twig killing and by needles that are short, pale, and reduced in numbers. Such trees apparently are susceptible to bark beetle attack. The motile adult female scales and winged males emerge early in the spring. The females settle singly under bark scales, secrete wax, and lay eggs. The first-stage larvae

Table 7.—*Hosts and distribution of western species of* Matsucoccus

Species by habit group	Hosts	Distribution
On needles:		
M. acalyptus Herbert **piñon needle scale**	*Pinus edulis, P. monophylla, P. aristata, P. lambertiana,* and *P. balfouriana*	Calif., Ariz., N. Mex., Utah, Colo., Nev., and Idaho
Within needle sheath, at base of needle bundle:		
M. degeneratus Morrison	*Pinus ponderosa*	Ariz.
M. fasciculensis Herbert **needle fascicle scale**	*Pinus ponderosa, P. jeffreyi,* and *P. sabiniana*	Calif. and Oreg.
M. secretus Morrison	*Pinus ponderosa*	Calif., Nev., Ariz., N. Mex., and Colo.
On bark at base of needle bundles; in axils of twigs and branches; and on small branches in bark crevices:		
M. eduli Morrison	*Pinus edulis*	Ariz.
M. monophyllae McKenzie	*Pinus edulis* and *P. monophylla*	Calif.
M. paucicicatrices Morrison **sugar pine scale**	*Pinus lambertiana, P. monticola,* and *P. flexilis*	Calif., Oreg., Mont., and Wyo.
M. vexillorum Morrison **Prescott scale**	*Pinus ponderosa*	Calif., Nev., Ariz., N. Mex., and Colo.
On twigs in bark crevices and under thick bark:		
M. bisetosus Morrison **ponderosa pine twig scale**	*Pinus ponderosa, P. jeffreyi, P. contorta, P. sabiniana,* and *P. radiata*	Calif., Oreg., and Colo.
M. californicus Morrison	*Pinus ponderosa* and *P. jeffreyi*	Calif. and Ariz.

have legs. In midsummer they transform into legless pre-adults which overwinter under bark scales. The life cycle is completed in 1 year.

The **Prescott scale**, *Matsucoccus vexillorum* Morrison (McKenzie et al. 1948), is considered to be the primary cause of so-called twig blight which was epidemic in Arizona and New Mexico in

F–521931

FIGURE 59.—*Matsucoccus* larva, about 1.5 mm long, on bark of ponderosa pine branch.

F–521932, F–522461, F–521933

FIGURE 60.—Piñon needle scale (*Matsucoccus acalyptus*) on pinyon pine: *A*, Winged male, 1.5 mm long, mating with sessile female; *B*, egg masses clustered at base of tree; *C*, early instar larvae, 1.0 to 1.5 mm long, on needles.

1933 and 1934. Since then, outbreaks have been sporadic and local. Tree killing by *M. vexillorum* has been insignificant and has occurred primarily among seedlings and saplings. The motile adult males and females emerge early in the spring. The females settle on twigs, mainly at the nodes of branches, where they lay

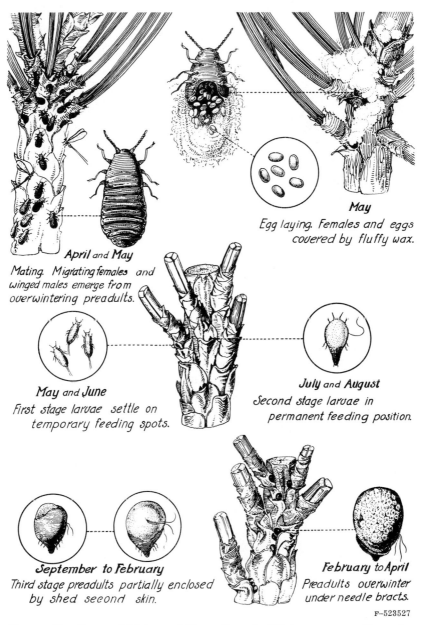

May
Egg laying. Females and eggs covered by fluffy wax.

April and **May**
Mating. Migrating females and winged males emerge from overwintering preadults.

May and **June**
First stage larvae settle on temporary feeding spots.

July and **August**
Second stage larvae in permanent feeding position.

September to **February**
Third stage preadults partially enclosed by shed second skin.

February to **April**
Preadults overwinter under needle bracts.

F–523527

FIGURE 61.—Seasonal history of Prescott scale (*Matsucoccus vexillorum*).

eggs, covering them with a fluffy white wax. Two stages of larvae develop late in the spring and in the summer; they feed beneath scales at the base of needles and in cracks and crevices of twigs, particularly around the first and second nodes. During the fall the third or pre-adult stage develops and then overwinters under needle bracts as purplish, prune-shaped bodies. The life cycle is completed in 1 year (fig. 61).

Three other genera of margarodid scales (Florence 1917, McKenzie 1942a) attack forest trees in the West. They are seldom seen and are not economic pests. Hosts and distribution of species by habit group are as follows:

Species by Habit Group	Hosts	Distribution
In cells deep beneath bark of branches and trunk:		
Desmococcus captivus McKenzie	*Pinus monophylla*	Calif.
D. sedentarius McKenzie	*Pinus edulis* and *P. monophylla*	Ariz.
Under bark scales or in cracks on trunk and limbs:		
Pityococcus ferrisi McKenzie	*Pinus lambertiana, P. monticola, P. flexilis,* and *P. edulis*	Calif., Ariz., N. Mex., Tex., Utah, and Colo.
P. rugulosus McKenzie	*Pinus edulis*	Ariz.
In crevices in bark of branches and trunk:		
Xylococculus betulae (Pergande)	*Alnus* and *Betula*	Calif., Oreg., and Wash.
X. macrocarpae (Coleman)	*Cupressus macrocarpa,* and *Libocedrus decurrens*	Calif.

The **sycamore scale**, *Stomacoccus platani* Ferris (Brown and Eads 1965b), occurs on native and introduced sycamores in central and southern California. This small scale is a pest of ornamental trees distorting the leaves and causing them to drop prematurely. It feeds on the under surface of the leaves, on leaf buds, and on the tender bark of twigs and branches. Eggs are laid in masses of cottony wax in bark crevices and under bark plates. There are three to five generations per year. Midwinter, when all the scales are in the first or second instar, is the best time to spray.

FAMILY PSEUDOCOCCIDAE—MEALYBUGS

Mealybugs (McKenzie 1967), are slow-moving insects which, in the adult female stage, are elongate-oval, soft, distinctly segmented, and usually covered with a mealy or cottony wax secretion. They feed upon plant fluids. The adult males usually are winged and do not feed. Many mealybugs attack forest trees and woody plants, but in general they are much less damaging than those in agriculture. They have been little studied in forestry.

Dysmicoccus (McKenzie 1967, Miller and McKenzie 1973), closely related to *Pseudococcus,* contains 30 species in North America. Several attack forest trees in the West. The **cypress mealybug,** *D. ryani* (Coquillett), is an example. It occurs on the foliage of *Cupressus macrocarpa, Thuja, Juniperus,* and *Araucaria* in California. The adult female is 2 to 3 mm long with short marginal wax filaments. The eggs are laid in a loose mass of white waxy filaments. The **Monterey pine mealybug,** *D. aciculus* Ferris, feeds on the twigs at the base of the needle fascicles of Monterey pine. It has one generation annually.

The **cypress bark mealybug,** *Ehrhornia cupressi* (Ehrhorn) (Herbert 1920, McKenzie 1967), is the only species in this genus. It occurs in California and Oregon on *Libocedrus decurrens* from which host it is presumed to have been spread by man to *Cupressus macrocarpa,* other ornamental *Cupressus,* and *Juniperus californicus.* It is a serious pest of ornamental Monterey cypress, but is unimportant in the forest. The female is 1 to 2 mm long, broadly oval, and pale pink to bright red. It occurs beneath bark flakes on the trunk and branches and is imbedded in a white waxy secretion. White cottony wax protruding from bark cracks and on twigs is evidence of infestation. There is one generation a year.

There are 20 species of *Pseudococcus* (McKenzie 1967), several of which feed on western forest trees. *P. obscurus* Essig is widely distributed in the United States and Canada. In California it is recorded on many plants including *Pinus, Picea, Chamaecyparis, Salix, Platanus,* and other trees but principally ornamental shrubs and perennials. It may occur on any part of a plant including the roots. The female is 2.5 to 5 mm long, with slender well-defined wax filaments along the body margin, becoming progressively longer to the rear. The light gray body is lightly covered with a thin powdery wax. Several other species of *Pseudococcus* occur on *Juniperus* and *Cupressus.*

Five of the 24 North American species of *Puto* (McKenzie 1967) feed on western conifers. The females are soft, oval, wingless creatures usually covered on the dorsal surfaces and on sides with a white waxy secretion. The adult males of the conifer-infesting, western species are winged. The white, felted cocoons of the males are a distinguishing character.

The **fir mealybug,** *Puto cupressi* (Coleman) (McKenzie 1967), is recorded in California, Oregon, Washington, Idaho, British Columbia, and Alberta and has many hosts, including *Cupressus macrocarpa, Sequoia sempervirens, Abies concolor, A. lasiocarpa, Pinus albicaulis, P. contorta, P. radiata, P. torreyana, Picea engelmannii,* and *Pseudotsuga menziesii.* It occurs in mixed stands and apparently is most damaging to true firs, hence the common name. Populations may persist in fluctuating intensity in local areas for years. Outbreaks have been recorded on the Payette and Nezperce National Forests in Idaho and near Princeton, British Columbia.

On heavily infested subalpine fir, the foliage becomes stunted, sickly, and covered with a black mold. Tumorlike swellings develop on the bole, branches, and twigs. Branches in the upper portions of the crown die first. Small trees may be killed and others reduced in growth. The damage could be confused with that of *Adelges piceae*, thus complicating surveys. Examination of currently infested twigs reveals white felt-like cocoons of the males. The adult males are winged. Fluffy masses of white waxy threads cover the females and the clusters of eggs (fig. 62). The adult females are 3 to 5 mm long. The biology is not recorded. Control in the forest has not been attempted.

The **pine bark mealybug**, *Puto laticribellum* McKenzie (McKenzie 1967), is known only from California on *Pinus ponderosa, P. jeffreyi*, and *Libocedrus decurrens*. It infests the cracks of bark on the main bole. Biology and economic significance are not recorded. *Puto pricei* McKenzie occurs on *Pinus albicaulis* and the **Douglas fir mealybug**, *P. profusus* McKenzie on *Pseudotsuga menziesii* and *Abies* in California.

The **spruce mealybug**, *Puto sandini* Washburn (Washburn 1965), attacks *Picea engelmannii* at high elevations in Utah. An epidemic discovered in 1939 on the Fishlake National Forest was still present in 1970. A larger infestation discovered in 1953 on the Dixie National Forest covered more than 60,000 acres in 1970. Mortality of reproduction through pole size trees was prevalent in these epidemics. Growth reduction and deformity was common in surviving trees. First evidence of attack is likely to be heavy sap flow from branches during the second and third year of feeding by the mealybug. Conspicuous yellowing of needles on branches scattered throughout the tree occurs in the third feeding season. Male pupal cases and sooty black mold on the limbs and twigs are useful indicators of infestation. The adult females

F–521934

FIGURE 62. — Fir mealybug (*Puto cupressi*) eggs, male cocoons, and wax-encrusted females, 3 to 5 mm long, on subalpine fir twig stunted by mealybug feeding.

are grayish, oval, about 4.5 mm long, and covered dorsally by a white waxy secretion which is fringelike along the sides (fig. 63). They feed on the twigs among the needles. The adult males are winged.

F–521935

FIGURE 63. — Spruce mealybug (*Puto sandini*) male cocoons and adult females, 4 to 5 mm long, on Engelmann spruce.

P. sandini has a 4-year life cycle. The females give birth to living young under bark flakes on the main bole in late August and early September. The crawlers alternately feed on the needles in the summer and overwinter in the duff until they mature the fourth year. The females form a transparent pupal case behind bark flakes. The males form conspicuous, white, cottony, elliptical pupal cases open at the posterior end, found usually among the branches. No practical control measures are known.

There are 24 species of *Spilococcus* (McKenzie 1967, Miller and McKenzie 1973), four of which feed on western forest trees. The **redwood mealybug**, *S. sequoiae* (Coleman), feeds on the foliage of *Sequoia sempervirens, Cupressus macrocarpa,* and other *Cupressus* in California. Its long, white egg sac is a distinguishing character.

ORDER NEUROPTERA

This small order (Essig 1926) sometimes is known as the **nervewinged insects** because of the network of fine veins in the wings of most species. There are three suborders, two of which are commonly encountered in the forest. The larvae and in some species, the adults, are predaceous. The larvae are hairy or spiny, tapered at both ends, and have large, often sickle-shaped mandibles.

SUBORDER RAPHIDIODEA

This suborder consists of two families, one of which contains species that prey on various insect pests. The importance of the forest-dwelling species in natural control of forest pests has not been determined.

FAMILY RAPHIDIIDAE—SNAKEFLIES

The **snakeflies** (Carpenter 1936) are common but little-studied inhabitants of forests and woodlands west of the Rocky Mountains. The adults (fig. 64A), resembling miniature winged serpents, occur on the foliage, branches, and trunks of pines, firs, and other trees. The slender, agile larvae (fig. 64B) move quickly

FIGURE 64.—Snakefly, *Agulla* sp.: *A*, Adult, 20 mm long; *B*, larva, 12 mm long.

forward or backward. They develop on or under bark in association with their insect prey. Both larvae and adults are predaceous.

Agulla, with 20 species, is the predominant genus in this family in North America. The biology has been studied principally under orchard conditions (Wolgum and McGregor 1959). The adult of *Agulla occidentis* Carpenter has been observed feeding on mature larvae and pupae of the Modoc budworm, *Choristoneura viridis.*

SUBORDER PLANIPENNIA

This suborder comprises several families, two of which contain some species that prey upon forest insects.

FAMILY CHRYSOPIDAE—GREEN LACEWINGS

The **green lacewings** (Bickley and McLeod 1956, Smith 1922) consist of several genera. *Chrysopa* is typical and most likely to be encountered. The adults usually are bright green insects about 15 to 20 mm long to the wingtips, and have gauzelike wings and golden eyes. *Chrysopa* contains about 50 species in North America, many of them in the West. The **common green lacewing,** *C. carnea* Stephens (= *californica* Coquillett) (Toschi 1965) has been mass-reared for biological control of agricultural pests in California and has been observed on Douglas-fir foliage in Oregon. *C. quadripunctata* Burmeister (Mitchell 1962) is a minor predator of the balsam woolly aphid (fig. 65). In some species of *Chrysopa*

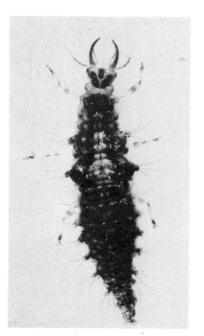

F–521937

FIGURE 65.—Larva of a green lacewing, *Chrysopa quadripunctata,* 6 mm long.

both larvae and adults are predaceous, in others, only the larvae. Aphids and other small soft-bodied insects are the prey.

FAMILY HEMEROBIIDAE—BROWN LACEWINGS

Adult **brown lacewings** (Carpenter 1940) (fig. 66) are similar to green lacewings but are smaller and brownish. The larvae prey upon aphids, mealybugs, and other small insects. *Hemerobius neadelphus* Gurney commonly feeds upon the balsam woolly aphid (Mitchell 1962).

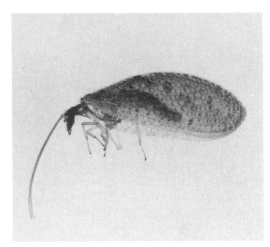

F–521938

FIGURE 66.—Adult of a brown lacewing, *Hemerobius neadelphus*, 8 mm long.

ORDER LEPIDOPTERA—BUTTERFLIES, MOTHS, AND SKIPPERS

The Lepidoptera (Dominick et al. 1971, McDunnough 1938, 1939) are a large group of insects, consisting of more than 10,000 species in North America. Butterflies and skippers fly during the day; most moths fly at night. The larvae, usually called caterpillars, feed mostly on plants, especially on the foliage. Many species feed on trees (McGugan 1958; Prentice 1962, 1963, 1965) and some are among the most destructive forest pests. The number and importance of these pests is increasing as forestry becomes more intensive.

Four suborders are now recognized (Common 1971). The Zeugloptera, Dachnonypha, and Monotrysia consist of a few small families of moths, the adults of which have generalized kinds of mouth parts, female sex systems, and wing venation. Only the Monotrysia is represented in this manual. The fourth suborder, Ditrysia, contains the butterflies and skippers and most of the moths, and is characterized by separate mating and oviposition openings in the female, and wings of dissimilar venation. The Lepidoptera discussed in this manual fall into 14 superfamilies

130

which are presented in a sequence progressing from more primitive to more specialized superfamilies.

SUBORDER MONOTRYSIA

SUPERFAMILY HEPIALOIDEA

This is a small superfamily of primitive moths (Forbes 1923). Adults are large to very large and have rudimentary mouth parts. Larvae bore in roots and stems. The family Hepialidae contains most of the species.

FAMILY HEPIALIDAE

The **ghost moth,** *Sthenopis quadriguttatus* Grote, occurs in British Columbia and Alberta. The larvae bore in roots of aspen, cottonwood, and willow, causing no commercial damage to forest trees. The large-bodied, swift-flying adults fly in the evening.

SUPERFAMILY INCURVARIOIDEA

This superfamily consists of a few families of very small moths. One family, the Heliozelidae, is represented in this manual.

FAMILY HELIOZELIDAE—SHIELD BEARERS

The Heliozelidae are tiny narrow-winged moths, the larvae of which form pupal cells cut from leaves in which they mine.

The **madrone shield bearer,** *Coptodisca arbutiella* Busck, mines the leaves of madrone from California to British Columbia. Within the small mines, the mature larvae form elliptical cases out of the upper and lower leaf surfaces, in which to pupate. The cases drop out, leaving holes as though cut by a paper punch (fig. 67). An undescribed species of *Coptodisca* of similar habits is a pest of ornamental *Populus fremontii* in southern California (Brown and Eads 1969).

FIGURE 67.—Elliptical holes cut in a madrone leaf by the madrone shield bearer (*Coptodisca arbutiella*).

SUBORDER DITRYSIA

SUPERFAMILY COSSOIDEA

This superfamily consists of one family.

FAMILY COSSIDAE—CARPENTERWORM MOTHS

Larvae of the **carpenterworm moths** (Barnes and McDunnough 1911) make burrows in the trunks or large limbs of living trees similar to those of wood-boring beetles. Adults have long spindle-shaped bodies and lightly banded or spotted translucent wings. They fly at night and deposit their eggs on the bark of trees or in old carpenterworm exit holes. Less than 50 species occur in North America; most infest deciduous trees.

Acossus consists of probably four species, all of which range into the West. At least three of them are found on *Populus*.

The **aspen carpenterworm**, *Acossus populi* (Walker), infests cottonwoods and poplars in the Western States, Southern Canada, and the Northern States. It is common but its life cycle and damage have been little studied. The larvae are cream colored, shiny, and hairless (fig. 68), and 35 to 40 mm long. Their tunneling in the bole of trembling aspen sometimes causes infested trees to snap off.

The genus *Givira* has several species, most of which occur in the Southwest.

The **pine carpenterworm**, *Givira lotta* Barnes and McDunnough (Essig 1926), is recorded only from Arizona and Colorado, but probably occurs throughout the Southwest. Its whitish larva, about 30 mm in length, mines the rough outer bark at the base of trunks of ponderosa pine. The adult is gray, marked with brown, and has a wingspread of about 30 mm.

Prionoxystus is represented in North America by two species, both of which are common pests in the East. One of them ranges to the west coast.

The **carpenterworm**, *Prionoxystus robiniae* (Peck) (Hay and Morris 1970, Solomon and Hay 1974), is distributed throughout the United States and southeastern Canada. Its preferred hosts vary with the forest region. In California, *Quercus*, particularly *agrifolia*, and *Ulmus* are preferred hosts, and in the Rocky Mountains, species of *Populus* are preferred. Other common hosts are *Fraxinus*, *Acer*, *Robinia*, *Salix*, and fruit trees. The carpenterworm will attack both small and large trees, and limbs as well as trunks. It particularly infests open-growing trees, whether in the forest, in windbreaks, or planted for shade. Lumber cut from infested trees is degraded by the large feeding tunnels and by stain and wood decay radiating from the tunnels.

F–521939

FIGURE 68.—Larva of the aspen carpenterworm (*Acossus populi*), 30 mm long, in its tunnel.

The adult is a large grayish moth (fig. 69A) which appears in early summer. Females are half again as large as males and have a wingspread of 75 mm. The wings are uniformly mottled with gray and brown scales, and the male has a yellowish to orange spot on its hindwing. Females deposit ovoid, olive-brown eggs, each about 2.4 mm long, in groups of two to six in bark crevices, under lichens, and near wounds and scars. The small larvae first make shallow, irregular tunnels in the inner and outer bark. Larvae then penetrate the sapwood, each making an upward-slanting tunnel, and later extend the tunnel vertically into the heartwood (fig. 69B). Completion of feeding takes usually 3 years, and results in a tunnel 150 to 225 mm long and about 15 mm wide. The mature larva has a shiny brown head and a greenish-white body, and reaches a length of 65 to 75 mm. It pupates in the tunnel and the pupa wriggles to the mouth of the tunnel just prior to moth emergence.

FIGURE 69.—The carpenterworm (*Prionoxystus robiniae*): *A*, Female adult, 32 mm long; *B*, tunnels in heartwood.

The most important natural control factors appear to be birds, particularly woodpeckers. No satisfactory control has been developed for the carpenterworm under forest conditions.

SUPERFAMILY TINEOIDEA

The Tineoidea includes a number of families of mostly small or very small moths. The **clothes moths** are well-known examples. Larval feeding habits in this group vary considerably. Four families have species of minor importance in western forestry.

FAMILY GRACILLARIIDAE—LEAFBLOTCH MINERS

The **leafblotch miners,** Gracillariidae (Needham et al. 1928), are the most abundant of the leaf-mining Lepidoptera. Many feed on broad-leaved trees and shrubs. Some damage ornamentals. None is a serious forest pest. The small larvae are very flat. Most species mine leaves; a few mine bark. The larger larvae are more cylindrical and many feed as leafrollers. The adults are tiny narrow-winged moths often clothed with glistening scales.

The **boxelder leafroller,** *Caloptilia* [*Gracillaria*] *negundella* Chambers, is a European species now widely established on boxelder in North America. In the West it occurs in Colorado, Manitoba, Saskatchewan, and Alberta. There are two generations annually.

The **lilac leafminer,** *Caloptilia* [*Gracillaria*] *syringella* (F.) (Schuh and Mote 1948), is a European species now a pest of lilac

134

in Oregon, Washington, and British Columbia. The mining causes the leaves to turn brown and unsightly. Privet and ash also are attacked. There are two generations per year.

Cameraria [*Lithocolletis*] *agrifoliella* (Braun) mines the upper surface of leaves on *Quercus* (Brown and Eads 1965a).

Lithocolletis [*Phyllonorycter*] (Braun 1908) is the largest genus of leafminers. Many species mine leaves of broad-leaved forest and shade trees. The larvae of some are cylindrical; others are flattened (fig. 70). Practically all pupate in the larval mine. The adults are tiny moths. Their forewings are elongate and yellowish with white cross bars and diagonal markings. Wingspread is 5 to 10 mm.

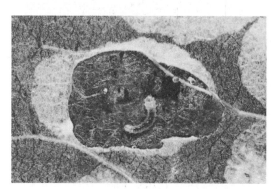

COURTESY BROWN AND EADS (1969)

FIGURE 70.—*Lithocolletis* larva, 4.8 mm long, in blotch mine on underside of poplar leaf.

The **aspen blotchminer,** *Lithocolletis tremuloidiella* Braun, is a representative species. The larvae construct irregularly shaped mines between the lower layers of the leaf. Adults appear in August. During heavy infestations nearly all the leaves on the lower parts of the trees are attacked, but infestation seldom extends above 15 m (50 ft). This damage results in premature shedding of the foliage. This species has been reported from California, Idaho, Utah, British Columbia, and Alberta and probably has a more extended range.

Some other species of *Lithocolletis* commonly encountered in western trees are:

Species	Host	Leaf surface mined
L. alnicolella Walsingham	Alnus	upper
L. apicinigrella Braun	Salix	lower
L. arbutusella Braun	Arbutus	—
L. felinelle (Heinrich)	Platanus	lower
L. incanella Walsingham	Alnus	both
L. salicifoliella Chambers	Salix and Populus	lower
L. umbellulariae Walsingham	Umbellularia	—

Several species of *Marmara* mine the inner bark of young twigs of conifers and broad-leaved trees. Two species mine leaves. The mines of all are long, narrow, and very shallow. *M. arbutiella* Busck mines the leaves and twigs of madrone throughout its range. Unidentified species mine the bark of *Pseudotsuga menziesii, Tsuga heterophylla,* and *Pinus monticola* in the West (Fitzgerald and Simeone 1971).

The **aspen leafminer,** *Phyllocnistis populiella* Chambers (Condrashoff 1964), is a transcontinental species that apparently is universal on trembling aspen in the West. Periodically it becomes epidemic, especially in Wyoming, Idaho, Alberta, and British Columbia. Heavy repeated attacks reduce tree growth and are reported to kill trees. There is one generation annually. Adults overwinter. The labyrinthine galleries are formed just under the cuticle on both leaf surfaces (fig. 71). Other species of *Phyllocnistis* attack other species of *Populus*.

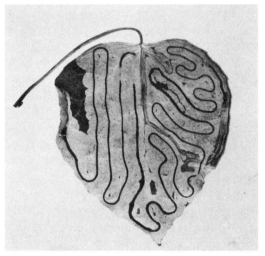

EPQ-6778

FIGURE 71.—Winding gallery of the aspen leafminer (*Phyllocnistis populiella*) in aspen leaf.

FAMILY LYONETIIDAE

The Lyonetiidae (Needham et al. 1928) contain numerous species of small narrow-winged moths. The larvae are leafminers when young. Most species become leaf skeletonizers when older. Pupae are formed in elongate ribbed cocoons on the foliage and branches. *Bucculatrix* is the largest genus.

The **oak ribbedcase maker,** *Bucculatrix albertiella* Busck (Brown and Eads 1965a, Opler 1974) is a pest of coast live oak and other oaks in California. The larvae are cylindrical throughout life. Only the first-instar larva mines the leaves. The cocoon is white, longitudinally ribbed, and about 6 mm long. The adults have a wingspread of 8 mm and the wings are widely fringed. Presumably there are one or two broods annually.

The **birch skeletonizer,** *Bucculatrix canadensisella* Chambers, (Baker 1972) is a transcontinental species. In the West it occurs principally in Canada but also in the Northern States. It feeds on various birches, periodically becoming extensively epidemic. The moth has a wingspread of 10 mm. It is bright brown and the forewings are crossed with three diagonal silvery bars. The head is white. The larva is 6 mm long, green, and slender; it feeds on the lower surface of the leaf.

The larvae of *Lyonetia* are leafminers throughout life. An undesignated species in this genus occurs extensively on willows in British Columbia and Alberta. *L. candida* Braun mines the leaves of native rhododendrons in California, Oregon, and Washington.

Leucoptera is similar to *Lyonetia* in larval habits. An undesignated species is a blotchminer of cottonwood leaves in interior British Columbia.

FAMILY PSYCHIDAE—BAGWORM MOTHS

The **bagworm moths** (Davis 1964) in the West are principally encountered on trees and shrubs of the Southwestern States. None is a forest pest. The larvae spend their entire lives in portable silken bags (fig. 72) covered with pieces of twigs or leaves or particles of soil. The females are flightless. *Oiketicus* and *Thyridopteryx* are representative genera. The **bagworm,** *T. ephemeraeformis* (Haworth) (Wollerman 1971a), is a pest of ornamental shrubs in Eastern States. It ranges westward through Texas into southeastern New Mexico. *Thuja* and *Juniperus* are preferred hosts. Other conifers and many broad-leaved trees are attacked.

F–521058

Figure 72.—Larval cases, 20 to 25 mm long, of a bagworm moth, *Thyridopteryx ephemeraeformis*, on juniper.

FAMILY TINEIDAE—CLOTHES MOTHS

The **clothes moths** are small, generally drab moths. The larvae of three species are household pests by feeding on wool and other animal products. In the forest many species feed upon wood-

137

rotting fungi (Powell 1967). *Elatobia fuliginosella* (Zeller) (=*martinella* (Walker)) has been implicated in damage by pitch moths to a ponderosa pine plantation in California (USDA Forest Service 1967).

SUPERFAMILY YPONOMEUTOIDEA

Larvae of the Yponomeutoidea have a wide range of feeding habits. A few feed openly, some web leaves, others mine leaves, buds, or twigs, and in one family they bore into stems. Four families are represented in this manual.

FAMILY GLYPHIPTERIGIDAE

The Glyphipterigidae is a small family closely related to the Tortricidae.

Hilarographa regalis (Walsingham) is one of several moths reported as damaging pine plantations in California. Its biology is unreported.

The **mimosa webworm,** *Homadaula anisocentra* Meyrick (= *albizzae* Clark) (Wester and St. George 1947) is an introduced pest of ornamental *Albizzia* and *Gleditsia*. Active in Eastern States since 1940, it appeared in central California about 1962 and is now established there despite efforts to eradicate it. The young larvae web the leaves together and feed on them gregariously. Larger larvae feed separately. Leaves are eaten on one side. The remaining tissue soon dies, giving the tree a scorched appearance. There are two or more generations annually. Larvae overwinter in the soil or in other protected places. The mature larva is pale gray to dark brown with five longitudinal white stripes and is about 12 mm long. The forewings are mouse gray with black spots. Wingspread is 12 mm.

FAMILY PLUTELLIDAE

The Plutellidae is a small family of small moths several species of which feed on the leaves of trees. None is a forest pest.

Abebaea cervella Walsingham (= *subsylvella* Walsingham) is a leafroller of oaks, particularly live oak in California and Garry oak in British Columbia.

FAMILY SESIIDAE (AEGERIIDAE)—CLEARWING MOTHS

The **clearwing moths** (Engelhardt 1946, MacKay 1968) are a well-defined family of moderate size. Species in several genera bore in the roots, trunks, and branches of trees and shrubs. A few are pests on trees, especially ornamentals. The adults often resemble bees or wasps. They have narrow interlocking wings that usually are transparent and unscaled in part, especially the hind pair. The larvae are naked and ivory white, except for brownish markings on the thorax.

The **cottonwood crown borer**, *Aegeria tibialis pacifica* (Hy. Edwards) (Engelhardt 1946), occurs in the Rocky Mountain and Pacific Coast States, British Columbia, and Alberta. The larvae bore in the root crown area of poplars and willows, sometimes causing considerable damage to ornamentals.

Paranthrene (MacKay 1968) contains several species that feed principally on poplar, willow, and oak.

The **locust clearwing**, *Paranthrene robiniae* (Hy. Edwards), (Engelhardt 1946), bores in the trunks and large branches of poplars and willows in the Western States and Provinces. It is a pest of ornamentals.

The **ash borer**, *Podosesia syringae fraxini* (Lugger), is injurious to young ash trees in ornamental and protective plantings in Colorado, Montana, North and South Dakota, Manitoba, and Saskatchewan. The adult resembles a *Polistes* wasp.

Synanthedon [*Ramosia*, *Thamnosphecia*] (MacKay 1968) contains 20 or more species that feed on a variety of trees, shrubs, and herbs.

Synanthedon americana (Beutenmuller) bores shallow winding channels in the wood under the bark of the trunk of alder from California to British Columbia, Montana, and Utah.

The **western sycamore borer**, *Synanthedon resplendens* (Hy. Edwards) (Brown and Eads 1965a, 1965b), is a pest of ornamental sycamore and oak in California. It occurs eastward to New Mexico. The larvae bore in and under the bark of the main bole up to about 9 m (30 ft). The adults are blue black with yellow markings and a prominent brush of long hairs at the end of the abdomen. The mature larva is 18 mm long. There is one generation annually.

Vespamima (Engelhardt 1946) contains three species all of which feed in conifers. Two are western. These species are now being transferred to *Synanthedon*.

The **sequoia pitch moth**, *Vespamima sequoiae* (Hy. Edwards), occurs from California to British Columbia, Idaho, and Montana. *Pinus ponderosa*, *P. contorta*, *P. radiata*, *P. lambertiana*, and various other species of pines are attacked, also Douglas-fir. Despite its name, it evidently does not feed on *Sequoia*. It is a significant pest of ornamentals and, among the clearwing moths, it comes the closest to being an economic pest in the forest (Weidman and Robbins 1947). The larvae bore in the cambium region causing masses of pitch to form (fig. 73A, B) and often seriously damaging young trees. The pitch masses contribute to the fire hazard (Powers and Sundahl 1973). Attacks are most commonly made

F–521940, F–521941

FIGURE 73.—Sequoia pitch moth (*Vespamima sequoiae*): *A*, Pitch masses on bole of ponderosa pine; *B*, larva boring in cambium region.

around injuries and at junctions of limbs and bole. Repeated attacks over a period of years are common and result in greatest damage. Adults are black with yellow markings much like a wasp. Mature larvae are 25 to 30 mm long. The life cycle requires 2 years.

The **Douglas fir pitch moth**, *Vespamima novaroensis* (Hy. Edwards), is similar to *V. sequoiae* in appearance, distribution, and habits. It differs from the latter in having an orange-banded rather than yellow-banded abdomen in the adult stage. Hosts are *Pseudotsuga menziesii, Picea sitchensis, P. engelmannii, Pinus ponderosa,* and *P. contorta.*

FAMILY YPONOMEUTIDAE—ERMINE MOTHS

The members of this family are usually small, often strikingly-marked moths. Three genera contain species of some importance, all of which mine conifer needles, fascicle sheaths, twigs, or buds.

Argyresthia (Freeman 1972), with upward of 50 species, feeds in the leaves, buds, and twigs of conifers and broad-leaved trees. Several are pests of ornamental conifers. The adults generally have narrow, yellowish, strongly fringed wings ranging from 6 to 14 mm from tip to tip. At rest, the adults appear to be standing on their heads. The **cypress tipminer**, *A. cupressella* Walsingham, is discussed as a pest of ornamentals by Brown and Eads (1967). The white paperlike cocoons (fig. 74) among the leaflets of cypresses, junipers, and arborvitae aid in identifying this species. A biology of the **Monterey pine needleminer**, *A. pilatella* Braun,

COURTESY BROWN AND EADS (1967)

FIGURE 74.—White paperlike cocoon, 3.5 mm long, of the cypress tipminer (*Argyresthia cupressella*), on *Thuja*.

is given in detail and its stages are described by Jessen (1964). The principal species of *Argyresthia* in western conifers are:

Species	Host and Part Attacked	Distribution
A. arceuthobiella Busck	*Libocedrus decurrens* Twigs and leaflets	Oreg.
A. columbia Freeman	*Larix occidentalis* Twigs	British Columbia
A. cupressella Walsingham	*Cupressus, Juniperus, Thuja,* and *Sequoia* Twigs	Calif., Oreg., and Wash.
A. flexilis Freeman	*Pinus flexilis* Needles	Mont.
A. franciscella Busck	*Cupressus* Twigs	Calif.
A. laricella Kearfott	*Larix laricina* Twigs	British Columbia and transcontinental
A. libocedrella Busck	*Libocedrus decurrens,* and *Chamaecyparis lawsoniana* Twigs and leaflets	Oreg.

141

A. *picea* Freeman	*Picea glauca* Buds	Yukon Territory
A. *pilatella* Braun	*Pinus radiata* Needles	Calif.
A. *pseudotsuga* Freeman	*Pseudotsuga menziesii* Twigs	British Columbia
A. *trifasciae* Braun	*Cupressus* Twigs	Calif.
A. *tsuga* Freeman	*Tsuga heterophylla* Twigs	British Columbia

Ocnerostoma piniariellum Zeller (Harris 1958) is a European species that occurs in British Columbia and Montana. It mines needles of *Pinus monticola* and *P. contorta*. The immature larva is golden brown; the mature is pale green. Adults are white with an 11 to 13 mm wingspread.

The **pine needle sheathminer**, *Zelleria haimbachi* Busck (Stevens 1959), is a transcontinental species recorded in the West in California, Oregon, Washington, British Columbia, Nebraska, Colorado, and Arizona. It attacks many species and hybrids of two- and three-needle pines. *Pinus ponderosa* and *P. jeffreyi* are favorites. Abundant at times, the sheathminer has caused appreciable damage at the Institute of Forest Genetics, Placerville, California, and in plantations elsewhere in California and Oregon. The adults are silvery white with a wingspread of 12 mm (fig. 75A). The forewings are light yellow with a white band length-

F–521942, F–498340, F–521943

FIGURE 75.—Pine needle sheathminer (*Zelleria haimbachi*): *A*, Adult, 8 mm long; *B*, needle-mining larva, 1.5 mm long; *C*, needle damage on new shoots.

wise through the center. First-instar larvae are elongate and bright orange (fig. 75B). Later ones are tan with two dull orange lines along the back.

Eggs are laid on current needles from early summer until midsummer. The first-instar larva is a needleminer and spends the the winter in that stage. In the spring, the larvae emerge from the needles and migrate to the base of the needle cluster where they feed within the sheath, severing the needles, causing them to droop, die, and shed prematurely (fig. 75C). Each larva kills 6 to 10 clusters of needles in this fashion. There is one generation annually.

SUPERFAMILY TORTRICOIDEA

These are small, often drab moths. Most species are placed in two large closely-related families. Larvae are naked and usually inconspicuous. They either bore into plant parts or feed from silken shelters in rolled leaves. Pupae have movable segments on the abdomen and wriggle actively when disturbed. Many species cause economic damage in the forest. Some are very destructive.

FAMILY OLETHREUTIDAE—OLETHREUTID MOTHS

The Olethreutidae (Heinrich 1923, 1926; MacKay 1959) is a large family of small- to medium-sized moths, closely related to the Tortricidae, and sometimes considered as part of that family. Among foresters, the olethreutids are generally known as twig- and tipminers because of prevalent feeding habits of the larvae. Others feed on or in foliage, in cones and seeds, or in stems. Some species are among the most damaging insect pests of young coniferous trees.

The **Douglas fir cone moth**, *Barbara colfaxiana* (Kearfott) ranges from California to British Columbia, Montana, and Colorado, seriously damaging the cones of Douglas-fir and true firs. Heinrich (1923) treated three varieties, one of which, *siskiyouana*, is now known to be a member of the genus *Eucosma*, and the other two are not yet verified biologically. The yellowish-white caterpillars mine through scales and seeds, making a tortuous resinous tunnel and an opening at the surface through which resin and larval castings exude (fig. 76A). The pupae overwinter near the axis of the cone in a papery, resin-coated cocoon among the resin-matted scales. Some pupae remain in diapause 1 to 3 years. The adults, which are gray moths with a wingspread of about 15 to 20 mm and with speckled forewings (fig. 76B), emerge in the spring and lay their eggs on the young tender budding cones. Hedlin (1960) and Keen (1958) report the biology in detail.

The genus *Epinotia* (Heinrich 1923) contains some 60 species, many of which feed on broad-leaved trees and shrubs; several, including at least one serious forest pest, feed on conifers.

Epinotia albangulana (Walsingham) is a little-known solitary leafroller on *Alnus rubra* from California to British Columbia and Idaho. The larvae also feed in the catkins.

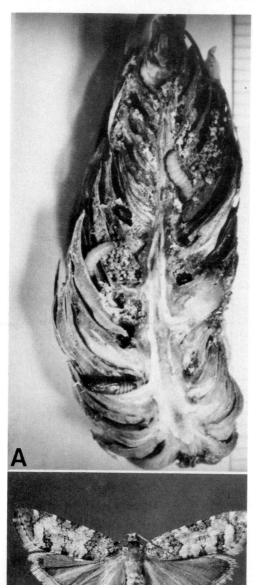

FIGURE 76.—The Douglas fir cone moth (*Barbara colfaxiana*): *A*, Larvae feeding in Douglas-fir cone; *B*, adult, 20 mm wingspread.

Epinotia criddleana (Kearfott) (Kusch 1967) is a solitary leafroller principally on trembling aspen but also on willow and oak. It occurs in Alberta, Saskatchewan, and eastward. There is one generation annually. The eggs, laid in short rows on the twigs, overwinter. The mature larva is yellowish, about 12 mm long, and resembles that of *Pseudexentera oregonana*.

Epinotia hopkinsana (Kearfott) ranges from California to British Columbia. It attacks the terminal shoots, foliage buds, and cones of Sitka spruce, true fir, and Bishop's pine, and the cones of Monterey pine. The wingspread is 16 to 19 mm. The forewings are mottled with brown and green scales, some of them in raised tufts. Mature larvae are dirty white to purplish and are 8 to 10 mm long. The variety *cupressi* Heinrich is darker in the adult stage and larger in the larval stage. It feeds on foliage, in the cones, and under the bark of limbs of Monterey cypress in California.

The **white fir needleminer,** *Epinotia meritana* Heinrich (Washburn and McGregor 1974), mines the needles of true fir, principally *Abies concolor* and *A. magnifica*. It occurs from New Mexico and Colorado to California and British Columbia. Outbreaks of several years each occurred in the 1940's, 1950's, and 1960's on white fir in Bryce Canyon National Park (McGregor and Washburn 1968). Other outbreaks have occurred on white fir in Arizona. In 1965 and 1966 an outbreak occurred on red fir in the central Sierra Nevada of California (Struble 1968). Repeated defoliation by this insect causes extensive branch killing, deterioration of tree crowns, and increased susceptibility to *Scolytus*. The forewings of the adult (fig. 77A) are dusty gray, alternately banded with black scales and are fringed behind with long gray scales. Wingspread is 10 to 11 mm. The mature larva is about 8 mm long, yellowish green to cream colored, and has a brownish-black head and prothoracic shield (fig. 77B). The pupa is dark brown and about 5.5 mm long. It protrudes from the hole in the mined needle prior to much emergence (fig. 77C). In California on red fir Struble (1968) reported a 2-year cycle and overlapping generations in contrast with one generation per year in Utah. He also found that each larva mined fewer needles and did not web the needles together in contrast with findings in Utah.

The **cypress leaftier,** *Epinotia subviridis* Heinrich (Brown and Eads 1967) is a significant pest of ornamental *Cupressus* and to a less degree *Thuja* and *Juniperus*. It is distributed from southern California north through Oregon and Washington into British Columbia, often occuring with *Argyresthia cupressella*. The larvae form cocoonlike feeding shelters in which are incorporated gnawed leaves and twigs. Heavy infestations cause attacked trees to turn brown early in the spring. The mature larvae are blackish pink

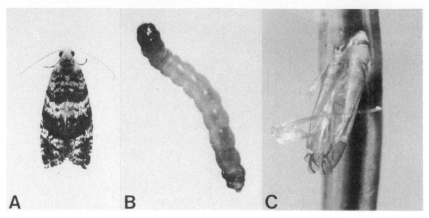

F–522304, F–521717, F–521944

FIGURE 77.—White fir needleminer (*Epinotia meritana*): *A*, Adult, wing-spread 10 mm; *B*, larva, 6.5 mm long; *C*, pupal case, 5.5 mm long, protruding from mined needle.

and about 10 mm long. Wingspread is about 20 mm. The fore-wings are checkerboarded.

The **hemlock needleminer**, *Epinotia tsugana* Freeman (Collis 1970), apparently prefers western hemlock and mountain hemlock but also attacks Sitka spruce and Pacific silver fir. It is recorded only in British Columbia. An outbreak occurred in 1965–66 on some 46,000 acres on Vancouver Island. The larvae are brown with a black head and attain a length of 7 mm. The adults are steel gray with a wingspread of 8 to 10 mm. The larvae mine in needles of all ages. Most of the damage occurs in March and April. Adults emerge in June and July.

Several of the many species of *Eucosma* (Heinrich 1923) feed on conifers in the West. The larvae of one of these conifer-infesting species bore through the pith of growing shoots; the others live in cones (Powell 1968).

Eucosma bobana Kearfott occurs from central and southern California to Colorado, New Mexico, and western Texas. It attacks the cones of *Pinus monophylla* and *P. edulis* and probably *P. flexilis* and *P. aristata*. Forewings are tan with squarish dark-reddish to blackish-brown markings.

Eucosma ponderosa Powell occurs in California, Oregon, and western Nevada. It develops in cones of *Pinus ponderosa* and *P. jeffreyi*. Wing markings are similar to *E. bobana* with which it was long confused.

The **lodgepole cone moth**, *Eucosma rescissoriana* Heinrich, ranges from southern Alberta through Idaho, Washington, and Oregon to central California. It is highly destructive to cones and seeds of *Pinus monticola* (Ollieu and Schenk 1966) and also attacks *P. contorta* and possibly other pines. Wing markings are similar to *E. bobana*. There is one generation per year. In Idaho, eggs are laid in June on second-year cones. Pupae overwinter, presumably in the duff.

Eucosma siskiyouana Kearfott, formerly considered a variety of *Barbara colfaxiana*, feeds in cones of *Abies*.

The **western pineshoot borer**, *Eucosma sonomana* Kearfott (Stoszek 1973), is recorded from Arizona, California, Oregon, British Columbia, Colorado, and Montana, evidently following the range of its principal host, ponderosa pine. It also feeds on lodgepole pine and Engelmann spruce. On young open-grown ponderosa pine, it is a significant pest that until recently has been overlooked and underrated. The larvae bore down through the center of the terminal shoots, stunting and sometimes killing them (fig. 78A). Tree height is significantly retarded and excessive branching may result (fig. 78B). The adult, which has coppery-red forewings marked with two bright gray transverse bands and a wingspread of 16 to 22 mm, lays eggs on the elongating shoots in spring. The larvae bore into the shoots and leave scant evidence of attack before they vacate the shoots in late spring, dropping to the ground to pupate.

The **spruce tip moth**, *Griselda radicana* (Heinrich) (Blais 1961, Powell 1964a), is a transcontinental species occurring in the West from California to British Columbia to Manitoba. It is common on spruce, Douglas-fir, and true firs, and occasionally feeds on other

F-521945, F-521946

FIGURE 78.—Damage to ponderosa pine terminals by the western pineshoot borer (*Eucosma sonomana*): *A*, Larval burrow in pith; *B*, stunted terminal.

147

conifers. It feeds in the opening buds much as does the spruce budworm with which it often occurs. No economically important outbreak of *G. radicana* is recorded. The forewings are ashy gray with rusty markings. Wingspread is 13 to 15 mm. The first- and second-instar larvae resemble *Zeiraphera*. The eggs are laid singly at the base of the needles where they overwinter.

Hedulia (Heinrich 1923) contains one species, *H. injectiva* Heinrich (Keen 1958). It is destructive to the seeds of Jeffrey pine and also infests ponderosa pine. It is similar in appearance and habits to *Laspeyresia piperana* which is more abundant in cones of ponderosa pine. These insects are presumed to hybridize.

Several species of *Laspeyresia* (Heinrich 1926) feed on forest trees, some attack cones (Keen 1958), and others feed in the bark of the trunk and branches. One species does both. The following are among the economic species in the West:

Species	Hosts	Distribution
CONE FEEDERS		
L. bracteatana (Fernald), **fir seed moth**	Principally *Abies*, also *Pseudotsuga menziesii* and *Picea sitchensis*	Calif. to British Columbia, and Colo.
L. cupressana (Kearfott), **cypress bark moth**	*Cupressus macrocarpa* and other *Cupressus*	Calif.
L. miscitata Heinrich	*Pinus ponderosa* and *P. jeffreyi*	Calif. to British Columbia, and Colo.
L. piperana (Kearfott), **ponderosa pine seed moth**	*Pinus ponderosa* and *P. jeffreyi*	Calif. to British Columbia, and Colo.
L. youngana (Kearfott), **spruce seed moth**	*Picea engelmannii, P. sitchensis, P. glauca* and other *Picea*	Alaska, Western provinces, Oreg., Mont., and Colo.
CAMBIUM FEEDERS		
L. cupressana (Kearfott), **cypress bark moth**	*Cupressus, Chamaecyparis, Libocedrus, Thuja, Juniperus,* and *Sequoia*	Calif.
L. inopiosa Heinrich	*Pinus contorta*	Idaho
L. laricana Busck	*Larix occidentalis* and *Pseudotsuga menziesii*	Mont.
L. leucobasis Busck	*Larix occidentalis* and *Picea engelmannii*	Mont.
L. populana Busck	*Populus trichocarpa* and *P. tremuloides*	Mont. and Alberta
L. pseudotsugae Evans	*Pseudotsuga menziesii*	British Columbia

The **cypress bark moth**, *Laspeyresia cupressana* (Kearfott) (Frankie and Koehler 1971), is a small dark brown moth with transverse silver and gray bands on the forewings. Wing expanse is 12 to 15 mm. The caterpillars are a grayish white. *Cupressus macrocarpa* is the principal host. On *Cupressus*, the larvae bore in cones, branch nodes, and injured areas on branches and trunk, often leaving accumulations of granular reddish frass. Only the branches and trunks of other hosts are attacked. In cones it feeds principally on the scales. As a pest, it is secondary to the tree-killing bark disease *Coryneum cardinale* Wagener with which it frequently occurs; it is suspected of transmitting this disease (Wagener 1939). It has two generations annually.

The **ponderosa pine seed moth**, *Laspeyresia piperana* (Kearfott) (Hedlin 1967), is presumed to occur throughout the range of its hosts, ponderosa pine and Jeffrey pine. It sometimes heavily reduces crops of ponderosa pine seeds, thus increasing costs of collections. The dirty-white caterpillars are 9 to 14 mm long when full grown. They burrow through the central axis of the cones and enter the seeds through the point of attachment (fig. 79). Pupation takes place in the pith. The moths have a wingspread of 16 to 20 mm, and range in color from gray to black. There is one generation annually but some larvae remain in diapause 1 or more years.

Another pine seed moth, *L. miscitata* Heinrich (Koerber 1967), occurs in California and Oregon in cones of ponderosa pine and Jeffrey pine. It is similar to *L. piperana* in appearance and habits, and within its range is similarly destructive to seed crops.

The **spruce seed moth**, *L. youngana* (Kearfott), commonly infests cones of spruces throughout the West. Its larvae burrow

F–521947

FIGURE 79.—Larvae of the ponderosa pine seed moth (*Laspeyresia piperana*) boring through axis of cones and feeding on seeds.

through cone scales near the cone axis (fig. 80), destroying both scales and seeds.

FIGURE 80.—Larva of seed moth, probably *Laspeyresia youngana*, feeding in Engelmann spruce cone.

The larvae of *Laspeyresia pseudotsugae* Evans (Evans 1969) construct meandering galleries in the phloem of the bole of young open-grown Douglas-fir (fig. 81A) in British Columbia and Montana. Effect on tree growth is nil. Third-instar larvae overwinter and adults (fig. 81B), appear the following May or June. There is one generation annually.

The **filbertworm**, *Melissopus latiferreanus* (Walsingham), is a transcontinental species. It occurs extensively in the Western States and British Columbia in oak acorns and galls (Keen 1958). It also attacks the fruit of *Castanopsis*, *Lithocarpus*, *Prunus*, and many other hosts and has become an important pest of cultivated filberts (Dohanian 1940). Color of the adult is variable but generally brownish with shining coppery transverse bands. The larvae are whitish with red heads and measure up to 15 mm. In the Pacific Northwest there is one, and a partial second, generation a year. The larvae hibernate in cocoons beneath or on the surface of the ground, or in the damaged host (fig. 82). Emergence of adults seems to be synchronized with the formation of nuts or acorns.

Larvae of the **pitch nodule moths**, genus *Petrova* (Heinrich 1923), bore into both the new and old growth of pine stems, twigs, and branches. Their work is characterized by a nodule or round dirty lump of pitch and frass, which is formed at the point of attack (fig. 83). They do not attack the buds but usually work

FIGURE 81.—*Laspeyresia pseudotsugae*: *A*, Larval mine in bark of Douglas-fir; *B*, adult, wingspread 14 mm.

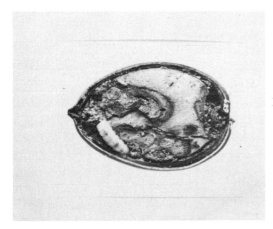

EPQ–7697

FIGURE 82.—Larvae of the filbertworm (*Melissopus latiferreanus*) in a California black oak acorn.

FIGURE 83.—Pitch nodule and frass on limb of lodgepole pine, indicating attack by a pitch nodule moth, *Petrova* species.

151

at nodes or whorls of branches and pupate within the pitch nodule. Trees are seldom, if ever, girdled by the larval channels but they may be so badly weakened that the tops are broken by wind or snow. As a group, the pitch nodule moths are minor pests of young trees. The moths are speckled with brown, yellow, or gray markings and have a wing expanse ranging from about 15 to 25 mm. The following are western species:

Species	Hosts	Distribution
P. albicapitana (Busck), northern pitch twig moth	Pinus contorta and P. banksiana	Western Provinces, Idaho, Mont., Wash., and east to Atlantic coast
P. albicapitana arizonensis (Heinrich), piñon pitch nodule moth	Pinus edulis	Ariz., Utah, and Colo.
P. burkeana (Kearfott), spruce pitch nodule moth	Picea sitchensis and P. engelmannii	Wash. and Mont.
P. edemoidana (Dyar)	Pinus ponderosa	Ariz., Calif., and New Mex.
P. luculentana (Heinrich)	Pinus ponderosa	Colo.
P. metallica (Busck), metallic pitch nodule moth	Pinus contorta and P. ponderosa	British Columbia, Alberta, Mont., and Calif.
P. monophylliana (Kearfott)	Pinus monophylla	Calif.
P. picicolana (Dyar)	Abies lasiocarpa and A. grandis	Wash., Idaho, British Columbia, and Calif.
P. sabiniana (Kearfott)	Pinus sabiniana	Calif.

The **northern pitch twig moth**, *Petrova albicapitana* (Busck) (Turnock 1953), feeds on lodgepole pine and has a 2-year life cycle in Manitoba and Saskatchewan. Most larval feeding occurs in the sapwood of the main stem and is indicated by a pitch mass at the base of a branch (fig. 84). The **piñon pitch nodule moth**, *P. albicapitana arizonensis* (Heinrich) was extensively epidemic in 1964 and 1965 on pinyon in Utah, reducing the nut crop and rendering attacked trees unfit for Christmas trees.

Proteoteras (Heinrich 1923) is a small genus the species of which resemble *Epinotia*.

Proteoteras aesculana Riley (Keen 1958) is a transcontinental species that occurs widely in the West. Larvae bore into seeds, seed stalks, and terminal twigs of *Acer macrophyllum* and other maples. Forewings of the adults are olive green. Larvae overwinter in cocoons in the soil.

The **boxelder twig borer**, *Proteoteras willingana* (Kearfott) (Peterson 1958), is a pest of boxelder grown in shelterbelts and as shade trees in the Great Plains, especially in Saskatchewan,

152

COURTESY CANADIAN FORESTRY SERVICE

FIGURE 84.—Pitch nodule of the northern pitch twig moth (*Petrova albicapitana*) on stem of lodgepole pine.

Alberta, and North Dakota. The larvae destroy dormant buds in the fall and early spring and then burrow in the developing shoots, causing spindle-shaped galls. Repeated attacks cause excessive branching. Forewings of the adult are grayish brown with darker streaks. Larvae are yellowish white with brown to almost black heads. Larvae, mostly fourth-instar, spend the winter in cocoons in hollowed-out, dormant leaf buds. There is one generation annually.

Pseudexentera oregonana (Walsingham) (Wong and Melvin 1967) is a solitary leafroller on trembling aspen in Oregon, British Columbia, Alberta, and Saskatchewan. It is a common but less important defoliator than *Choristoneura conflictana* and *Malacosoma*. There is one generation annually. Pupae overwinter in the soil. Eggs are laid early in the spring. Larvae feed on new foliage and complete development by late May.

Pseudexentera habrosana (Heinrich) (Powell 1961) feeds on the new foliage of *Quercus agrifolia* in California.

Species of *Rhyacionia* (Heinrich 1923) are the best known of the **pine tip moths.** They cause damage by mining in the buds and shoots of young pines, especially in plantations, even-aged natural stands, and ornamental plantings. Attacked trees are deformed

153

and their growth is retarded but they are seldom killed. Trees from seedling size up to a height of about 7.5 m (25 ft) are most susceptible to injury. Several species are native in the West and one has been introduced from Europe. The wings are strongly fringed, especially the hind pair which also is notably duller and less varied in color. The mature larvae are naked and vary from yellowish to brown.

The **European pine shoot moth**, *Rhyacionia buoliana* (Schiffermüller) (Miller 1967b, Miller et al. 1970), is a much studied insect of European origin. Strenuous efforts have been made to control it and prevent its spread since its discovery in 1914 in New York State. In eastern North America it has been a pest of pine plantations. It deforms trees (fig. 85), and reduces their rate of growth, thus lowering productivity. Through the movement of nursery stock, it is now established in British Columbia, Washington, and Oregon, chiefly on ornamentals in the Douglas-fir region.

F–521949

FIGURE 85.—Deformity of Scotch pine leader caused by feeding of European pine shoot moth (*Rhyacionia buoliana*).

R. buoliana attacks many kinds of pines. In the West, ornamental Mugho, Scotch, Japanese red, and lodgepole pines are heavily attacked, and naturally-growing lodgepole and ponderosa pines have been shown susceptible to damage. In much of the pine region, low winter temperatures and light snow cover will restrict establishment and survival of this shoot moth. However, pine stands in southern Oregon and northern California are expected to be highly susceptible to damage (Daterman and Carolin 1973).

There is one generation annually. The yellowish, disk-shaped eggs (fig. 86A) are laid in midsummer on the twigs, buds, and needles. The small larva spins a small web coated with resin between the needle sheath and twig and then mines the base of the needles. Later it bores into a bud, causing formation of a crust of dried pitch (fig. 86B). The partially-grown, dark brown larva overwinters either in the mined bud or under the pitch. The spring-feeding larva (fig. 86C) mines another bud and then the bases of elongating shoots. The pupa (fig. 86D) is formed in a mined shoot and protrudes from the shoot just prior to moth emergence. The adult flies at dusk. It has orange forewings marked with irregular silvery lines and gray hindwings (fig. 86E). Wingspread is 15 to 20 mm.

The **western pine tip moth,** *Rhyacionia bushnelli* (Busck), closely resembles the **Nantucket pine tip moth,** *R. frustrana* (Comstock) (Miller 1967a), which has been recently introduced into California where it damages ornamental Monterey pine. *R. bushnelli* occurs naturally on young ponderosa pines in Montana, the Dakotas, and Nebraska. It also occurs in New Mexico and Arizona, presumably by introduction. Introduced between 1902 and 1909 into the plantations of the Nebraska National Forest, it has seriously stunted and deformed the ponderosa pine there. It has also spread extensively in shelterbelt plantings of ponderosa pine in the Central Plains States where it is a serious deterrent to planting of this tree. Various other pines, native and introduced, also are attacked.

The adult moths have a wingspread of 10 to 15 mm. The head, body, and appendages are covered with gray scales, except the forewings which are mottled yellowish gray and reddish brown. The larvae are yellowish with black heads and when fully grown are 9 to 12 mm long. A single generation occurs in the Black Hills, the moths flying late in May and early in June to lay their eggs on the pine needles, buds, and shoots, and the larvae feeding during June and July. In Nebraska two generations develop annually, the moths flying in April and May and again late in June and early in July. The winter is passed in the pupal stage in cocoons spun by the larvae in the litter or soil. Experimentally, a systemic insecticide applied to the soil in the spring has protected young ponderosa pines from damage by the western pine tip moth for two growing seasons (Van Haverbeke et al. 1971).

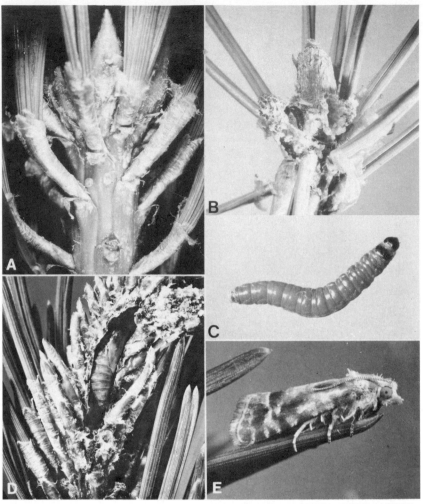

F–521950, F–521951, F–521952, F–521953, F–521954

FIGURE 86.—Life stages of European pine shoot moth (*Rhyacionia buoliana*):
A, Eggs on pine twig, each 1.0 mm long; B, mined bud with larva under
pitch; C, overwintering larva, 6 mm long; D, pupa, 9 mm long, in mine in
new shoot; E, adult, 9 mm long.

Rhyacionia montana (Busck), recorded from *Pinus contorta* in
Montana (Heinrich 1923) is doubtfully distinct from *R. zozana*.

The **southwestern pine tip moth**, *Rhyacionia neomexicana*
(Dyar) (Jennings 1975), distorts and kills terminals of young
ponderosa pine in Arizona, New Mexico, Colorado, the Dakotas,
and Nebraska. From 1966 to 1971 some 100,000 acres in Arizona
were infested by this insect. Naturally grown and planted trees
both were attacked. Recently planted seedlings on poor sites were

most seriously damaged. Growth loss is not considered serious enough to justify the cost of present direct control measures. The moths measure about 20 to 25 mm in wingspread. The base of the front wings is dark gray and the outer third is reddish orange usually with two horizontal black lines. The reddish larvae, when full grown, are 12 to 15 mm long. There is one generation annually. The moth flight ranges from March in Arizona to the latter part of May and early in June in the Black Hills of South Dakota. The full-grown larvae leave the tips during July and early August and spin cocoons, usually in the bark crevices on the base of the tree below the litter. Here they transform to pupae and pass the remainder of the season and the winter. Infested tips can be identified, after the larvae leave, by the dead, partially developed needles toward the apex of the shoot and by the fact that this part of the shoot, and usually the buds, have been riddled by the larval burrows and crumble readily when dry.

The **Monterey pine tip moth**, *Rhyacionia pasadenana* (Kearfott) (Koehler and Tauber 1964b), attacks *Pinus radiata, P. muricata,* and *P. contorta* along the coast of California. Principally it is a pest of ornamentals. There is one generation annually. The yellowish-orange larvae feed first on needles within the needle sheath and then mine in the buds and new shoots, causing a pitch exudation and ultimately killing them. Pupation is within the mined shoots. Pupae overwinter.

Rhyacionia subcervinana (Walsingham) is a little-known species reported from California, Oregon, and British Columbia. In California, the larvae mine the needles of *Pinus jeffreyi,* then tie them together in a tube which is cut off well above the needle sheath. Pupation is within the stub of the tube.

The **ponderosa pine tip moth**, *Rhyacionia zozana* (Kearfott) (Stevens 1966, 1971), is a pest of young ponderosa pine in California, Oregon, and Washington (fig. 87). It also attacks Jeffrey, lodgepole, sugar, digger, and other pines. Generally not seriously destructive, it is most damaging to open-grown seedlings and saplings less than 2 m (6 ft) tall. Repeated heavy attacks retard growth and predispose trees to attacks by other insects, such as *Cylindrocopturus.* In 1962 and 1963 it seriously damaged grafted pines in a seed orchard in Placerville, Calif.

The adults have a wing expanse of 20 mm. The forewings are irregularly banded gray and white on the inner two-thirds and are brick red on the outer third. The hindwings are grayish brown. The larvae are orange and attain a length of 12 to 15 mm. The pupae are formed in tough, brownish cocoons usually fastened near the base of the tree. There is one generation annually. The pupae overwinter.

157

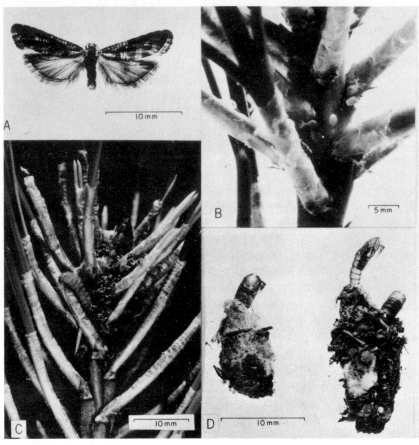

FIGURE 87.—Ponderosa pine tip moth (*Rhyacionia zozana*) : *A*, adult, 20 mm wingspread; *B*, eggs, each 1.0 mm long, on new shoot; *C*, mature larva, 12 mm long, on infested shoot; *D*, pupal cases protruding from masses of cocoons.

In North America, *Sciaphila* contains one species, the **aspen leaftier**, *S. duplex* (Walsingham). A transcontinental species, it occurs in the Western Provinces, Wyoming, Utah, Idaho, Nevada, and California. *Populus tremuloides* is the preferred host. From 1961 to 1966 an outbreak occurred in Utah, Wyoming, and Idaho, reaching a peak of 250,000 acres (McGregor 1967). The small larvae first skeletonize a portion of a new leaf, then roll and tie it (fig. 88). As the larvae grow, they tie more and more leaves together into a nest in which they feed. There is one generation per year. The larvae overwinter in silken hibernacula in bark crevices.

The **eyespotted bud moth**, *Spilonota ocellana* (Denis and Schiffermüller), an import from Europe, is primarily an orchard

FIGURE 88.—Skeletonizing and rolling of trembling aspen leaf by the aspen leaftier (*Sciaphila duplex*).

pest but also occurs on oak and other woodland, broad-leaved trees. At maturity, the larvae are 12 mm long and reddish brown. They feed first in buds; later they tie the leaves together. In the West this species occurs in Montana, Idaho, Oregon, Washington, and British Columbia.

Taniva (Heinrich 1923) contains one species, the **spruce needle-miner**, *T. albolineana* (Kearfott) (Cumming 1954). It is a transcontinental species that occurs extensively in the Western States and Provinces on various kinds of spruce, including Engelmann, white, blue, and Sitka. It is a pest of ornamentals but is seldom seen in the forest.

The forewings are dark brown with three grayish bands. Wingspread is 11 to 15 mm. The eggs are pale yellow, round, ridged, and flattened. They are laid in May and June in single rows of 2 to 12 overlapping eggs on the underside of needles of the preceding year. The young larvae cut a hole near the base of a needle and mine the interior, usually one larva per needle. The hollowed needles are held to the twig in a funnel-shaped web. Frass collects in the web and from 4 to 20 larvae may feed together in one web mass (fig. 89). Feeding is suspended by October. The larvae overwinter in hibernacula in the frass and resume feeding in spring.

F-521955

FIGURE 89.—Spruce needle-miner (*Taniva albolineana*) larval nest and mined needles.

The full-grown larva is light green with a brown head and is about 8 mm long. One generation per year is typical, perhaps universal.

Seven species of *Zeiraphera* feed upon western conifers, according to Mutuura and Freeman (1966) who described and keyed the adults. These closely related, similar appearing native species are now considered distinct from *Z. ratzeburgiana* (Saxeson) and *Z. griseana* (Hübner), the latter also known as *Z. diniana* (Guenée), two European species erroneously recorded as introduced from Europe. The taxonomic confusion of the past led to many confusing survey records. Confusion persists regarding the species on spruce and true fir. The biology of the western *Zeiraphera* is not recorded in detail. The adults are inconspicuous, mottled, grayish to brownish moths, with a wingspread of about 10 to 20 mm (fig. 90A). Larvae are dirty white to pale yellow and up to 14 mm long, and have dark brown heads (fig. 90B).

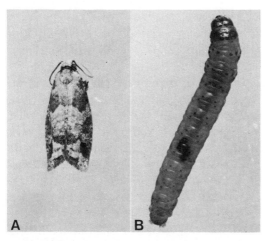

F-521956, F-521957

FIGURE 90.—*Zeiraphera* species: *A*, Adult reared from Douglas-fir, wing length 6 mm; *B*, larva, 9 mm long, from Sitka spruce bud.

The following species are known to occur in the West:

Species	Hosts	Distribution
Z. canadensis Mutuura and Freeman	Picea glauca and P. sitchensis	Transcontinental in Canada and Northern U.S.
Z. destitutana (Walker)	Picea glauca, P. mariana, P. engelmannii, Abies lasiocarpa, and A. amabilis	Nova Scotia to British Columbia
Z. fortunana (Kearfott)	Picea glauca and P. engelmannii	Nova Scotia to British Columbia
Z. hesperiana Mutuura and Freeman	Pseudotsuga menziesii	British Columbia and Oregon
Z. improbana (Walker)	Larix laricina, L. occidentalis, and Abies concolor	Transcontinental in Southern Canada and Northern U.S.
Z. pacifica Freeman	Picea sitchensis	British Columbia and Wash.
Z. vancouverana McDunnough	Picea sitchensis and P. engelmannii	Vancouver Island, B.C.

Periodically the **larch bud moth**, *Z. improbana* (Walker), becomes epidemic on *Larix occidentalis* in British Columbia, Washington, Idaho, and Montana. In 1966 in Montana, 518,000 acres were infested (Tunnock 1967). Such outbreaks are conspicuous but their effect upon the trees has not been considered serious and has not been measured.

Along the Pacific coast, the **spruce bud moth**, *Z. canadensis* Mutuura and Freeman and two other species of *Zeiraphera* feed on Sitka spruce. Condrashoff (1966b) reported *Z. pacifica* Freeman as stunting and deforming young spruce trees on the Queen Charlotte Islands, B.C. The habits of the three species on Sitka spruce are believed very similar. Each young caterpillar enters an opening bud and feeds on the tender new needles, webbing them together to form a shelter under the bud cap (fig. 91). As the twigs elongate, the partially eaten needles die and cause the trees to appear reddish brown early in the season. The dead needles drop off by midseason leaving little evidence of the feeding. There is one generation annually.

FAMILY PHALONIIDAE

This is a small family of little importance in forestry. The **pale juniper webworm**, *Aethes* [*Phalonia*] *rutilana* (Hübner) (Freeman 1967a) is an introduced species that occurs in British Columbia and Alberta. It mines and webs the needles of *Juniperus*.

161

FIGURE 91.—Webbed bud caps on Sitka spruce, indicating presence of *Zeiraphera* larvae.

An unidentified species of *Phalonia* (Brown and Eads 1969) mines the buds and tender twigs of *Populus fremontii* in southern California.

Commophila [*Henricus*] *fuscodorsana* Kearfott (Keen 1958) occurs from California to British Columbia. The larvae are reddish green and mine in cones of *Picea, Pseudotsuga, Sequoia, Abies,* and *Larix. C. macrocarpana* Walsingham mines cones of *Cupressus macrocarpa* in California. The larvae are greenish, greenish red, purplish, or reddish brown. Their presence is marked by webbing and frass outside the infested cones.

FAMILY TORTRICIDAE—LEAFROLLER MOTHS

The Tortricidae (Freeman 1958, MacKay 1962, Powell 1964b) is a large family of small- to medium-sized, often drab moths, sometimes considered to include the Olethreutidae. Many species feed upon the foliage of forest trees; some are highly destructive pests of western forests. The larvae usually feed individually, often in webbed shelters consisting of rolled leaves or of needles tied together. When disturbed, the larvae of many species wriggle and often drop suspended by a thread.

Acleris (Powell 1964b) contains about 50 species in North America, about 30 of which occur in the West predominantly as incidental feeders on broad-leaved forest trees (Prentice 1965). One species is a major pest of western conifers.

The **western blackheaded budworm**, *Acleris gloverana* (Walsingham) (Powell 1962a, Schmiege and Crosby 1970), now considered distinct from the eastern *A. variana* (Fernald), is an important defoliator in western North America. It ranges from northern California to western Montana and northward into the Yukon and Northwest Territories in Canada and into southeastern Alaska. Hosts include *Tsuga heterophylla, T. mertensiana, Picea sitchensis, P. engelmannii, P. glauca,* various *Abies,* and *Pseudotsuga menziesii.* In coastal forests this budworm often causes extensive defoliation of western hemlock Sitka spruce and true firs, and trees of all ages may be killed, top-killed, or severely weakened. Extensive outbreaks occurred during the 1940's and 1950's in southwest British Columbia, notably on Vancouver Island and the Queen Charlotte Islands, and during 1948–55 in southeastern Alaska. These outbreaks involved millions of acres and resulted in considerable tree mortality. Flareups have occurred in interior forests, sometimes over wide areas, but have subsided without causing appreciable damage.

The adult is a small gray moth having a wingspread of about 18 mm and a variable wing pattern (fig. 92). The variation in wing coloration is an excellent example of polymorphism; the many color forms look different but actually are one species. The forewing is usually dappled with brown, black, orange, and white with a faint to strong band across the wing; but some have a longitudinal yellow, orange, or white stripe down the wing. Hindwings are a uniform gray or brownish gray. The egg is yellow, oval, and flattened and about 0.8 mm long (fig. 93A). The young larva is pale yellow or pale yellow green and has a black head.

F–521959

FIGURE 92.—Western blackheaded budworm (*Acleris gloverana*) adults, showing some common variations in color pattern.

The mature larva (fig. 93B) is green with a brown head and 12 to 16 mm long. The pupa is brown with a greenish tinge and about 9–10 mm long (fig. 93C).

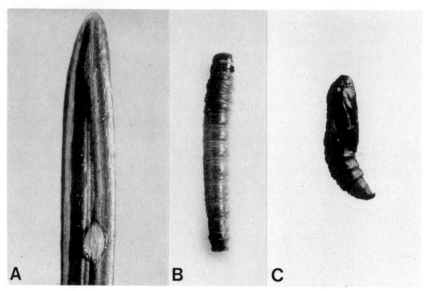

FIGURE 93.—Western blackheaded budworm (*Acleris gloverana*): *A*, Egg, 0.8 mm long, on underside of hemlock needle; *B*, larva, 12 mm long; *C*, pupa, 9 mm long.

The moths fly in late summer and deposit eggs singly on the underside of needles, mostly on the upper branches. Eggs over-winter and hatch the following spring. The young larvae bore into the opening buds, each often destroying two or three buds. When half-grown, larvae leave the expanding buds and construct a loose shelter by clipping needles and silking them together. From this shelter the larvae feed on new foliage, or on old foliage if the new foliage has been consumed. Larvae complete their develop-ment between mid-July and mid-August, and pupate in their feed-ing shelters or amongst debris on the branches. Larvae of the blackheaded budworm are wasteful feeders, rarely consuming whole needles. The dead partially consumed needles turn reddish brown, causing heavily defoliated trees to have a scorched appear-ance.

The blackheaded budworm does a little feeding every year, but the damage is scarcely noticeable. It can build up rapidly. In British Columbia its populations increase greatly after 1 or 2 years of below average precipitation during July and August (Silver 1960). In outbreak areas, budworm populations usually build up for 2 or 3 years, remain at a high level for 2 or 3 years, and then decrease, often abruptly. Factors contributing to the end of outbreaks include starvation, insect parasites, insect diseases (Graham 1954), high temperatures during the early feeding period, inclement weather during late larval feeding and during the adult flight period, and effects of sliding snow and ice on eggs. Direct control is sometimes needed to prevent serious economic damage.

Adoxophyes negundana McDunnough is an uncommon, solitary leafroller on boxelder in Manitoba, Saskatchewan, and Alberta.

Archippus (Freeman 1958) contains six North American species that closely resemble *Archips*. Mostly they feed on northern conifers but are of little significance.

Archippus alberta (McDunnough) is a transcontinental species that feeds principally on back spruce. It is common in Saskatchewan. *A. packardianus* (Fernald) also is a transcontinental species in Canada. It webs the needles of spruce and other conifers. *A. tsuganus* Powell (Powell 1962b) is a little-known species on hemlock in coastal British Columbia.

Archips (Freeman 1958) is closely related to *Archippus* and *Choristoneura*. About 10 species of *Archips* feed on the foliage of forest trees in the West, but none is a significant forest pest.

The **fruittree leafroller,** *Archips argyrospilus* (Walker) (Powell 1964b), is a transcontinental species that occurs extensively in the West. It is a damaging pest on orchard trees and at times is troublesome on ornamental trees, especially oaks (Brown and Eads 1965a). Birch, aspen, willow, and many other broad-leaved trees are fed upon. The adult is brownish with dark brown or gray hindwings. Eggs are laid in flat masses on tree limbs and trunks where they overwinter. There is one generation per year.

The **uglynest caterpillar,** *Archips cerasivoranus* (Fitch) (Powell 1964b), occurs from coast to coast. In the West it is most prevalent in Canada and adjoining States to the south. Wild cherry is the preferred host. In some areas the dense, frass-filled nests in hedgerows and along roads and streams are a common phenomenon of mid-summer (fig. 94). These nests contrast with the more gauzelike nests of the fall webworm that often occur in similar situations. The adults are bright orange with yellow hindwings and have a wingspread of 19 to 24 mm. Mature larvae are yellowish green with black heads. They feed and pupate in the nests. Eggs overwinter.

Archips negundanus (Dyar) (Parker and Moyer 1972) skeletonizes and rolls the leaves of boxelders, sometimes completely defoliating attacked trees. This pest of ornamentals occurs in Nebraska, Utah, Idaho, Washington, Manitoba, Saskatchewan, and

F–521963

FIGURE 94.—Larvae of ugly-nest caterpillar (*Archips cerasivoranus*), 18 mm long, feeding in frass-filled nest on cherry.

British Columbia. Eggs overwinter in bark crevices. There is one generation annually.

Archips rosanus (L.) is an introduced species. In the West it occurs uncommonly in Oregon, Washington, and British Columbia. Alder, willow, and oak are among its principal hosts.

Argyrotaenia (Powell 1964b) contains more than 40 species in North America. Several feed on foliage of western conifers and at least one is a significant forest pest. The adults resemble *Choristoneura* but are smaller.

The **orange tortrix**, *Argyrotaenia citrana* (Fernald) (Lange 1936, Powell 1964b), feeds on a large number and variety of plants including several agricultural crops in California, Oregon, and Washington. In California it is a minor pest on ornamental *Pinus radiata*, first mining within the needle sheath, later feeding more extensively on the current needles which are webbed together. On Monterey pine there are two or more generations annually. The adults vary in color. Usually the forewing is orange brown with a dark median cross band. The mature larvae are green with colorless tubercles bearing setae.

Argyrotaenia dorsalana (Dyar) (Powell 1964b) occurs in small numbers on *Pseudotsuga menziesii, Picea engelmannii, Abies concolor*, and *Larix occidentalis*. It ranges from California to British Columbia, Colorado, and New Mexico. The forewing is straw yellow. The full-grown larva is grass green with pale brown head and prothoracic shield and is 15 to 17 mm long.

Argyrotaenia occultana Freeman (Prentice 1965) is transcontinental in Canada. The larva feeds singly on foliage of white spruce, lodgepole pine, and other conifers, not causing appreciable damage. The forewing of the adult is grayish with traces of reddish-brown banding.

Argyrotaenia provana (Kearfott) occurs extensively in the Western States and British Columbia. The larva closely resembles that of *A. dorsalana* and sometimes is associated with it on *Pseudotsuga menziesii* and *Abies concolor*.

The **lodgepole needletier,** *Argyrotaenia tabulana* Freeman (Burke 1932), is principally a western species occurring in Montana, Wyoming, Idaho, Washington, British Columbia, Alberta, and Saskatchewan. *Pinus monticola, P. contorta, P. banksiana, P. albicaulis, P. ponderosa, Pseudotsuga menziesii,* and *Tsuga heterophylla* are recorded western hosts. In the literature this insect has often been recorded as *A. pinatubana* (Kearfott), an eastern species. Usually *A. tabulana* is not particularly destructive, but from 1921 to 1925, feeding along with the lodgepole sawfly (*Neodiprion burkei* Middleton), it killed trees over a large area of immature lodgepole pine near West Yellowstone, in Montana. From 1961 to 1965 this moth, or a similar one, and associated defoliators were epidemic on young lodgepole in southern Idaho and western Wyoming, and caused stunting and deformity but no mortality.

The forewing of the adult is mottled brownish gray (fig. 95A) with a wing expanse of 13 to 17 mm. In Montana, flat, oval, greenish eggs are laid during the latter part of June and early in July in groups of 2 to 30 on the concave side of lodgepole pine needles. These eggs hatch in 7 to 10 days. The young larva mines a needle of the current growth, lining the inside with a papery, white, closely-woven web to form a tube. Later, it binds several other needles to the original one so as to form a new and larger tube (fig. 95B) also lined with a papery, white web and having an opening at each end. Feeding takes place within the tube, and as

F–521964, COURTESY CANADIAN FORESTRY SERVICE

FIGURE 95.—Lodgepole needletier (*Argyrotaenia tabulana*): *A*, Adults, 8 mm long, on pine needles; *B*, larval feeding tubes on whitebark pine.

the caterpillar becomes larger the tube is extended farther down the needles, often to the base. During the latter part of August the mature caterpillar, which is dark green and about 12 mm long, drops to the ground litter on a silken thread and spins a loosely-woven cocoon. Here it pupates and passes the winter. The adult emerges the following May or June, to complete one annual generation. The work of the pine needletier is recognized by the silk-lined tubes, which may consist of as many as 16 needles webbed together, and which, as a result of the feeding, turn brown and die.

The genus *Choristoneura* [*Archips*] (Powell 1964b) contains about a dozen described species in North America of interest in forestry. They feed on the foliage of trees, mostly conifers, and two of them are among the most destructive forest insect pests (table 8). The species on fir and spruce can now be identified (Freeman 1967b) but questions remain concerning the forms on pine.

The **western spruce budworm**, *Choristoneura occidentalis* Freeman (Carolin and Honing 1972b), is the most destructive forest defoliator in Western North America. Until recently, this species and several near relatives were considered to be strains of *C. fumiferana* (Freeman 1967b), hence much information concerning them was published under that name (McKnight 1968). *C. occidentalis* occurs principally on Douglas-fir and true firs in the Pacific Coast States, British Columbia, and the Rocky Mountain States.

The first recorded outbreak of the western spruce budworm was in 1909 on southern Vancouver Island, B.C. Two outbreaks in Idaho in 1922 established this budworm as a serious enemy of forests in the Western United States. Since then numerous outbreaks have developed and large-scale efforts have been made to control them by aerial spraying. Some outbreaks flare up and subside naturally in a few years. Others persist a long time; for example, an epidemic in the northern Rocky Mountains has been in progress more than 20 years.

The budworm larvae feed principally in buds and on foliage of the current year. Sustained heavy attack causes nearly complete defoliation in 4 to 5 years. Epidemics cause decreased growth, tree deformity, top killing, and ultimate death of trees on extensive areas. In the northern Rocky Mountains budworm larvae also damage the cones and seeds of western larch and Douglas-fir.

The adults predominantly are mottled orange brown and have a wingspread of 22 to 28 mm (fig. 96A). The eggs are light green and are laid in masses shinglelike on the underside of needles (fig. 96B). Newly-hatched larvae are light green with brown heads. Full-grown larvae are 25 to 32 mm long, with brownish

Table 8.—*Principal hosts and distribution of* Choristoneura *species that occur in western forests*

Species	Principal hosts	Distribution
C. *biennis* Freeman **2-year budworm**	*Abies lasiocarpa, Picea engelmannii,* and *P. glauca*	Alberta, British Columbia, and Yukon Territory
C. *conflictana* (Walker) **large aspen tortrix**	*Populus tremuloides*	Transcontinental and N. Mex. to Alaska
C. *fumiferana* (Clemens) **spruce budworm**	*Abies* and *Picea*	Eastern States and Provinces to British Columbia and Yukon Territory
C. *houstonana* (Groté)	*Juniperus californicus, J. occidentalis,* and other *Juniperus* species	Western Kans. and Tex., Colo., N. Mex., Ariz., and Calif.
C. *lambertiana* (Busck) complex **sugar pine tortrix**	*Pinus contorta, P. flexilis, P. lambertiana,* and *P. ponderosa*	Calif., Oreg., Idaho, Alberta, Mont., Wyo., and Colo.
C. *occidentalis* Freeman **western spruce budworm**	*Pseudotsuga menziesii, Abies concolor, A. grandis, A. lasiocarpa, Larix occidentalis, Picea engelmannii, P. glauca,* and *P. pungens*	British Columbia, Wash., Oreg., N. Calif., Idaho, Mont., Wyo., Colo., Ariz., and N. Mex.
C. *orae* Freeman	*Abies amabilis* and *Picea sitchensis*	Northern coast of British Columbia
C. *pinus* Freeman **jack pine budworm**	*Pinus banksiana*	Eastern States and Provinces to Manitoba and Saskatchewan
C. *rosaceana* (Harris) **obliquebanded leafroller**	*Betula, Populus, Salix,* and other broad-leaved trees	Transcontinental; southwestern States to British Columbia and Alberta
C. *subretiniana* Obraztsov	*Pinus contorta* and *P. ponderosa*	Calif. and Oreg.
C. *viridis* Freeman **Modoc budworm**	*Abies concolor*	Northeastern Calif. to southcentral Oreg.

head and body and prominent ivory-colored spots (fig. 96C). Pupae are 12 to 16 mm long, broad at the head end but tapering rapidly toward the tail (fig. 96D).

Eggs are laid in July and August. They hatch in about 10 days. The larvae do not feed but spin silken shelters among lichens and under bark scales in which they hibernate. The next spring they mine old needles until the buds swell. Then they bore into the buds and feed upon the expanding needles. Later they loosely web the growing tips and feed upon the new needles (fig. 97).

Parasites, predators, adverse weather, and starvation tend to hold the budworm in check and to control outbreaks naturally. Some 40 species of insect parasites feed upon the budworm and 10 or so of these exert significant control (Carolin and Coulter 1959). When outbreaks develop despite natural checks and widespread destruction is threatened, aerial spraying may become necessary. Because of the large and diverse areas involved, the right chemical must be selected and properly applied to control the budworm yet prevent damage to other resources (USDA 1972).

The **2-year budworm**, *Choristoneura biennis* Freeman (Harris 1963), is a subalpine species in British Columbia, Alberta, and Yukon Territory and presumably occurs in adjoining States. In

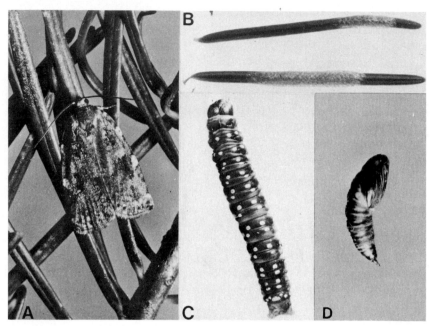

F–494229, F–494225, F–494231, F–494233

FIGURE 96.—Life stages of the western spruce budworm (*Choristoneura occidentalis*): *A*, Adult, 11 mm long; *B*, egg masses; *C*, mature larva, 28 mm long; *D*, pupa, 14 mm long.

F–521965

FIGURE 97.—Feeding shelter of western spruce budworm (*Choristoneura occidentalis*) on Douglas-fir.

British Columbia eggs are laid in even-numbered years and the larvae overwinter in the second instar. In odd-numbered years they develop to the fourth instar and again overwinter. The following year they feed on both new and old needles and complete their 2-year life cycle. The adults are darker and slightly larger than those of *C. occidentalis*.

The **large aspen tortrix**, *Choristoneura conflictana* (Walker) (Prentice 1955, Beckwith 1973), occurs from the Atlantic to the Pacific and from Alaska to California, Arizona, and New Mexico along with its principal host, *Populus tremuloides*. When epidemic, it also feeds on other associated broad-leaved trees. Epidemics have occurred sporadically in extensive stands of trembling aspen in the Western Provinces. During 1966-68, a large outbreak occurred in interior Alaska. Outbreaks characteristically last 2 or 3 years. Trees may be completely defoliated for a year or two but normally recover with only growth loss.

The moths have a wingspread of 25 to 35 mm. The forewing is grayish with basal, middle, and outer brownish patches (fig. 98A). The large larvae are gray green to nearly black. The pale green eggs are laid in large flat masses usually on the upper surface of aspen leaves in June and July (fig. 98B). Second-instar larvae overwinter in white silken hibernacula in bark crevices and other out-of-the-way places. In the spring the larvae mine the buds, sometimes causing complete defoliation before the buds open. Later stage larvae (fig. 98C) roll the leaves into shelters within which they feed and then pupate (fig. 98D). The aspen tortrix is host to numerous insect parasites among which a tachinid fly, *Omotoma fumiferanae,* and an ichneumon, a species of *Glypta*, are common. Starvation of larvae is considered a likely cause of decline of outbreaks.

The **spruce budworm**, *Choristoneura fumiferana* (Clemens) (Bean and Mott 1972, Morris 1963), is highly destructive in northern spruce-fir forests of the Eastern United States and Canada. It extends westward into Yukon Territory and perhaps Alaska. The adults are predominantly gray and slightly smaller than those of *occidentalis*. Mature larvae have a black head. Feeding habits and most features of the life cycle are similar to those of *occidentalis*.

Choristoneura houstonana (Groté) (Heinrichs and Thompson 1968, Powell 1964b) occurs extensively on western junipers in the States of the Southwest and Great Basin, but causes little damage. The larvae feed inconspicuously in silken tubes among the foliage. The mottled yellowish-tan moths fly in June and July.

The **sugar pine tortrix**, *Choristoneura lambertiana* (Busck) (Powell 1964b), is an enigma comparable to that of the *fumiferana* complex before the species in it were sorted (Freeman 1967b).

F-521966, F-523525, F-523526, F-521967

FIGURE 98.—Large aspen tortrix (*Choristoneura conflictana*): *A*, Adult, 14 mm long; *B*, egg mass—black eggs are parasitized by *Trichogramma minutum*; *C*, large larva, 30 mm long; *D*, rolled aspen leaves.

Several forms of *Choristoneura* that feed on western pines have been described as species but more commonly they are considered to be forms of *C. lambertiana*. One of these top-killed lodgepole pine extensively in Idaho, 1965–66, and in Montana, 1967–68 (McGregor 1970). The first-instar larvae of this form overwinter in silken hibernacula in crevices in the bole and branches. In spring, when new shoot development is nearly complete, the larvae mine the needle sheaths and staminate cones. Numbering one to five per shoot, the larvae web the needles into feeding shelters (fig. 99). Pupae are formed among the webbed needles. Adults fly in July and August. At times *C. lambertiana* is destructive to the new buds and pollen bodies of sugar pine.

The **jack pine budworm**, *Choristoneura pinus* Freeman (Batzer and Millers 1970), is an eastern species that extends westward on its principal host, jack pine, into Manitoba and Saskatchewan, where it was extensively epidemic in 1965. It occurs on lodgepole pine in Saskatchewan, but in the United States, records of it on that tree probably refer to *C. lambertiana*. The adults are rust colored, never gray, and are smaller than the spruce budworm.

The **obliquebanded leafroller**, *Choristoneura rosaceana* (Harris) (Powell 1964b), is a transcontinental species that is prevalent in

172

EPQ–7690

FIGURE 99.—Feeding habit and damage of the sugar pine tortrix (*Choristoneura lambertiana*).

the West at low elevations except the arid Southwest. It feeds on a wide variety of broad-leaved trees and is a pest in orchards and on ornamentals, but causes no significant damage in the forest. Two generations per year are usual; in colder areas there is only one. The adults are brownish red with a darker, oblique band across the center of the forewing. The mature larvae are dark green with a brown or black head. They are solitary leaf-rollers.

Choristoneura subretiniana Obraztsov, sometimes considered to be a subspecies of *C. lambertiana*, feeds on cones and staminate flowers of lodgepole pine in California (Stark and Borden 1965). In the second instar in spring it is a needle sheathminer. Report-edly this insect was responsible for extensive defoliation of the new needles on open-grown ponderosa pine in central Oregon.

The **Modoc budworm**, *Choristoneura viridis* Freeman (Freeman 1967b), reaches peak abundance in the Warner Mountains of California and Oregon. Outbreaks occur sporadically but so far have caused no great damage. Long confused with the western spruce budworm, it differs in that the adults are smaller and lighter colored, and the mature larvae and pupae are green rather than brown. Feeding habits are similar to those of *occidentalis*; details of the life history are unreported. A change in the specific name is pending.

The **omnivorous leaftier**, *Cnephasia longana* (Haworth) (Edwards and Mote 1936), is a European insect long established as a pest of agricultural crops from California to British Columbia. It attacks a wide range of broad-leaved herbs, shrubs, and trees and also damages the new growth of conifers. In 1969 it damaged a plantation of Douglas-fir Christmas trees in Oregon.

173

Pandemis is a small genus, the larvae of which are solitary leafrollers on hardwoods. *P. canadana* Kearfott (Prentice 1965) is a transcontinental species that is prevalent in Alberta, Saskatchewan, and Manitoba. It feeds on many trees, especially aspen, willow, birch, and poplar.

Pandemis cerasana (Hübner) (Evans 1970) is a Eurasian species that feeds on a wide variety of broad-leaved trees and shrubs. It is now established in British Columbia where its principal host is *Quercus garryana*. The larvae feed mostly on the small leaves, at times causing considerable defoliation. The mature larvae are shiny, pale pea green, and are about 15 mm long. The adults have a wingspread of 14 to 23 mm. The forewings are squarish and yellowish with a dark band diagonally across the middle.

Parapandemis borealis Freeman, a conifer-feeding species known previously only from Eastern Canada, has been found in small numbers on *Abies concolor* in northeastern California.

SUPERFAMILY GELECHIOIDEA

This is a large superfamily of generally small moths. The larvae have a wide range of feeding habits. Those on forest and shade trees mostly mine leaves, buds, or fruit. A few feed externally, webbing leaves together.

FAMILY BLASTOBASIDAE

The Blastobasidae is a little-known family of small moths with long antennae. The larvae of several species feed in the cones and nuts of trees. The pink to reddish-brown larva of *Holocera augusti* Heinrich (Keen 1958) mines in the cones of *Pseudotsuga menziesii* from California to British Columbia. Its role is not established. Other species of *Holocera* feed in the fruiting structures of *Pinus, Cupressus,* and *Acer* in the West. Most are probably secondary feeders in previous infestation sites of other insects.

FAMILY COLEOPHORIDAE—CASEBEARER MOTHS

Larvae of the **casebearer moths** start life as leafminers. Later they live and feed in caselike or tubelike shelters. *Coleophora,* containing nearly 100 species, is the lone genus. Only one species is significant in western forests.

The **larch casebearer,** *Coleophora laricella* (Hübner) (Denton and Tunnock 1972), is a European insect that became established in New England prior to 1886. In the West it was discovered in 1957 in northern Idaho on western larch. It now occurs on that tree in Montana, Idaho, Oregon, Washington, and British Columbia.

The principal damage is caused by the fourth-instar larvae feeding on new foliage in early spring. Heavily infested trees become reddened as though scorched. Later in the season they regain their normal appearance as the dead needles are replaced by a second crop. Repeated deterioration for several years materially reduces diameter growth and weakens trees so that they deteriorate and may die from other causes (Tunnock et al. 1969).

The adults are tiny, silvery-brown moths with narrow fringed wings that fold along the body when at rest (fig. 100A). The eggs are laid singly on needles from late May until early July (fig. 100B). The larvae feed first as needleminers. Then they line with silk and cut off a portion of hollowed-out needle. From then on they live, feed, and pupate in this case (fig. 100C). They overwinter as third-instar larvae in their cases attached to winter buds on twigs (fig. 100D). There is one generation annually.

Control of the larch casebearer by aerial spraying is still experimental. The braconid, *Agathis pumila*, a larval parasite, has been extensively colonized in the West in an attempt at biological control (page 458). Other parasite species also are being introduced.

FAMILY ETHMIIDAE

The Ethmiidae is a small family of small moths, mostly in the genus *Ethmia*. *E. discostrigella* (Chambers) (Furniss and Barr 1975) is a defoliator of species of *Cercocarpus*, mountain-mahogany. Outbreaks of this insect occasionally deplete winter ranges for big game in Oregon and probably other areas. Its range is from Oregon to California, western Texas, and Colorado. The mottled grayish or blackish larvae attain a length of nearly 20 mm. The pupae overwinter.

FAMILY GELECHIIDAE—GELECHIID MOTHS

The Gelechiidae is a large family of small moths with narrow forewings and broadly-fringed hindwings. Most feed on or in foliage, many on forest trees. A few are destructive forest pests.

Anacampsis [*Compsolechia*] *niveopulvella* (Chambers) (Prentice 1965) is a transcontinental species that rolls and ties the leaves of *Populus*, principally *P. tremuloides*. In Alberta and Yukon Territory it is common but apparently causes little damage. The adults are gray with black dots and have a wingspread of 12 mm.

The **sagebrush defoliator**, *Aroga websteri* Clarke (Hall 1965), periodically defoliates and kills sagebrush over extensive areas

175

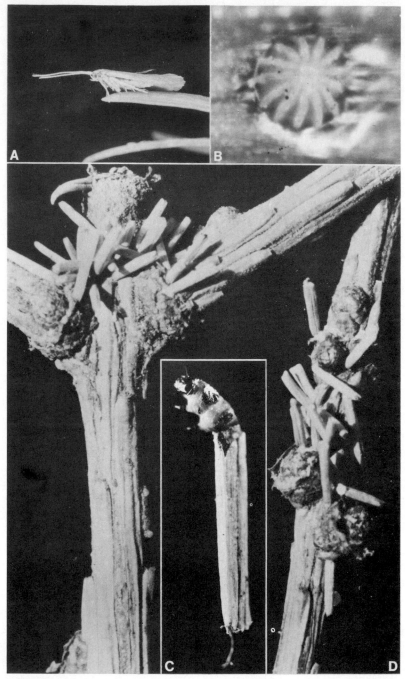

F-509460, F-509462, F-520754, F-509463

FIGURE 100.—Larch casebearer (*Coleophora laricella*) : *A*, Adult, 4.5 mm long; *B*, egg, 0.3 mm long, on needle; *C*, mature larva in case, 5 to 6 mm long; *D*, overwintering cases, 2.5 to 3.5 mm long, attached to western larch twigs.

of western rangeland. One such outbreak occurred in parts of California, Oregon, and Nevada in 1962–64.

Most species of *Chionodes* are leafminers in broad-leaved trees and shrubs. Three species develop in conifers. The adults resemble *Coleotechnites* but are more broad-winged and usually more colorful. *C. retiniella* (Barnes and Busck) occurs in British Columbia, Washington, California, and Nevada and mines needles of *Pinus ponderosa* (Freeman 1960). *C. sabinianae* Powell mines staminate cones of *Pinus sabiniana* in California (Burdick and Powell 1960). *C. periculella* (Busck) occurs in California, Oregon, and Colorado and mines in the seed cones of *Pinus ponderosa, P. edulis* and *Pseudotsuga menziesii* (Keen 1958). Some other species feed on oaks.

Coleotechnites [*Eucordylea, Evagora, Pulicalvaria, Recurvaria*] (Freeman 1960, 1967a; Hodges 1965) contains about 30 species of small, narrow-winged, mottled, generally grayish moths of very similar appearance. The larvae are leafminers. Those that mine the foliage of conifers (fig. 101) are most numerous and are of principal concern to foresters. Two named species and at least two unnamed ones are economic forest pests. The following species occur in the West:

Species	Hosts	Distribution
C. ardes (Freeman)	Pinus contorta	Mont.
C. biopes (Freeman)	Pinus contorta	Saskatchewan
C. canusella (Freeman)	Pinus contorta	British Columbia and Wash.
C. condignella (Busck)	Pinus ponderosa	Ariz.
C. florae (Freeman)	Pinus contorta	Mont., Alberta, and Saskatchewan
C. granti (Freeman)	Abies	British Columbia
C. juniperella (Kearfott)	Juniperus occidentalis	
C. lewisi (Freeman)	Pinus flexilis	Alberta
C. milleri (Busck)	Pinus contorta	Calif.
C. moreonella (Heinrich)	Pinus ponderosa	Colo., Utah, and Oreg.
C. occidentis (Freeman)	Juniperus	British Columbia
C. piceaella (Kearfott)	Picea	Colo. and Alberta
C. pinella (Busck)	Pinus ponderosa	Colo.
C. stanfordia (Keifer)	Cupressus macrocarpa	Calif.
C. starki (Freeman)	Pinus contorta	Mont., British Columbia, Alberta, and Saskatchewan

The **lodgepole needleminer**, *Coleotechnites milleri* (Busck) (Struble 1972, Koerber and Struble 1971), is a notorious forest pest because of its long-sustained and destructive outbreaks in Yosemite National Park, from 1903 to 1921, 1933 to 1941, and 1947 to 1963. Such outbreaks may kill trees extensively through

F–521968

FIGURE 101.—Larval mines of a *Coleotechnites* species in ponderosa pine needles.

F–521083

FIGURE 102.—Sparse, short foliage and dying twigs on a lodgepole pine branch resulting from feeding by five generations of the lodgepole needleminer (*Coleotechnites milleri*).

the cumulative effects of defoliation (fig. 102). Outbreaks are most severe in extensive stands of mature lodgepole pine, the principal host. During epidemics other pines, red fir, and mountain hemlock may also be attacked. The insect occurs west of the crest in the central and southern Sierra Nevada.

The adults are mottled light gray moths that have a wingspread of 8 to 13 mm and strongly fringed hindwings (fig. 103A). The larvae are naked and black-headed (fig. 103B). Their bodies are uniformly colored but vary individually from lemon yellow to orange, pink, and red. This species has a 2-year life cycle, the moths flying from mid-July to mid-August in odd-numbered years.

178

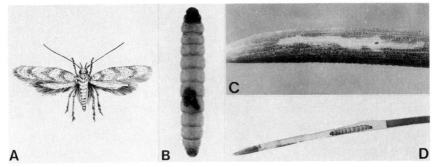

F–521969, F–521085, F–521088, EPQ–2280

FIGURE 103.—Lodgepole needleminer (*Coleotechnites milleri*) : *A*, Adult, wing-spread 10 mm; *B*, mature larva, 8 mm long; *C*, needlemining by first-instar larva; *D*, needlemining by mature larva.

The first-instar larvae mine individually into the needles near the tip and remain there over winter (fig. 103C). The next growing season they develop to the fourth instar, often feeding in several needles, and sometimes webbing the trees in search of food. The fifth and final instar is formed the following spring (fig. 103D). Following a period of heavy feeding, the mature larvae pupate in mined needles. The adults emerge a month later.

An undescribed species (Mason and Tigner 1972) that closely resembles *C. milleri*, but having a 1-year life cycle, periodically defoliates lodgepole pine in central Oregon. Outbreaks have occurred during the years 1925–28, 1945–47, and 1964–70. Damage is greatest in extensive basins of pure lodgepole and consists principally of loss in growth.

Another undescribed species that resembles *C. milleri*, even to having a 2-year life cycle, feeds on lodgepole in California but is not notably destructive.

Coleotechnites moreonella (Heinrich) was described from Colorado. This species or a near twin periodically causes considerable defoliation of ponderosa pine on local areas in Utah and Oregon. Old needles are mined.

Coleotechnites piceaella (Kearfott) (Freeman 1967a, McLeod 1962) mines the needles of various spruces from Eastern Canada and New England to Alberta and Colorado. Several adjacent needles of the previous year's growth are mined and loosely webbed together by each larva. The larvae overwinter in mined needles. As a needleminer, it sometimes is a pest on ornamentals. It also is a scavenger in cones and galls.

The **cypress leafminer,** *Coleotechnites stanfordia* (Keifer), in the caterpillar stage mines the twiglets of Monterey cypress in California.

179

The **northern lodgepole needleminer**, *Coleotechnites starki* (Freeman) (Stark 1954, 1959), looks and acts like *C. milleri* and was long considered to be that species. In the 1940's and early 1950's a sustained outbreak occurred in the Canadian Rocky Mountain Parks, principally in Alberta. At its peak, prior to 1950, the outbreak covered 450 square miles. Reduction of growth was the principal effect. Increment began to slow when defoliation approximated 40 to 50 percent.

The **juniper webworm**, *Dichomeris marginella* (Denis and Schiffermüller) (Andison 1937, Bauman and Sugden 1968), is a European species established in 1934 or earlier as a pest of ornamental juniper in British Columbia. The larvae are light yellowish red with dark reddish-brown lines on the back. They feed together in nests of webbed needles and frass. Half-grown larvae overwinter in the webs. There is one generation annually.

Exoteleia contains four species in North America. One of the two western species is a pest of ornamental pines.

The **Monterey pine shoot moth**, *Exoteleia burkei* Keifer (Brown and Eads 1967, Burdick and Powell 1960, Stevens 1969), occurs in California on *Pinus attenuata, P. coulteri, P. radiata* and *P. sabiniana*. It is a pest on ornamental Monterey pine in central and southern California. In the early instars the larvae mine the needles. Later stage larvae mine in the buds, developing shoots, and staminate cones. The mature larva is 5 to 6 mm long and is brownish yellow with a black head. The adults have a wingspread of 8 to 10 mm. The forewings are grayish brown with three white crossbands edged with black.

FAMILY WALSHIIDAE

The Walshiidae (Hodges 1962b) is a small family similar to the Gelechiidae.

Periploca (Hodges 1962a) contains 12 species of small, dark, shiny moths. Several feed upon juniper in the West.

Periploca atrata Hodges (Powell 1963) develops in juniper berries in California and Arizona.

The **juniper twig girdler**, *Periploca nigra* Hodges (Koehler and Tauber 1964a), is an important pest of ornamental *Juniperus* in California. The larvae tunnel beneath the bark, scoring the wood and girdling the twig (fig. 104). Several to many larvae per branch are usual. The mature larvae are yellowish to pinkish white with a shiny brown head and are 6 to 7 mm long. The adults are shiny brownish black. There is one generation per year.

SUPERFAMILY PYRALOIDEA

This superfamily (Munroe 1972), one of the largest in the Lepidoptera, consists of four families.

COURTESY KOEHLER AND TAUBER (1964a)

FIGURE 104.—Larva of juniper twig girdler (*Periploca nigra*) in feeding tunnel.

FAMILY PYRALIDAE (PHYCITIDAE)—PYRALID MOTHS

The Pyralidae (Heinrich 1956, Munroe 1972) is the largest and most diverse family in this superfamily and is the only one containing species of significance in forestry. The forest inhabitants are moderate-sized, drab-colored moths with mouth parts that are somewhat snout-like.

In the caterpillar stage, the species of *Dioryctria* (Heinrich 1956, Munroe 1959, Mutuura et al. 1969a, 1969b) bore into the cambium of the trunk, branches, and shoots, or into the fresh green cones of *Pinus* and to a lesser extent *Pseudotsuga, Abies,* and *Picea* (table 9). Overlapping habits within species is prevalent. Several species also mine in branch and stem galls caused on *Pinus* by species of fungi in *Cronartium* and *Endocronartium.*

The trunk-infesting species girdle and deform young trees and are particularly damaging to ornamentals and forest plantations. The species that attack cones are among the most damaging insect pests of forest tree seeds (Keen 1958). The shoot-mining species on pines cause little damage but are easily confused with *Rhyacionia* which are generally more destructive. An unidentified shoot-mining species on young Douglas-fir occasionally causes serious damage to leaders and tips (fig. 105).

Dioryctria zimmermani (Groté), long recorded as a western species, now is considered to be eastern only (Munroe 1959).

The **fir coneworm**, *Dioryctria abietivorella* (Groté), often recorded as *D. abietella* (Denis and Schiffermüller), is a transcontinental species that attacks cones of many conifers and is particularly destructive in fir and Douglas-fir cones (Hedlin 1974, Keen 1958). It also mines in buds, shoots, and trunk. In California it has damaged grafts of Douglas-fir and ponderosa pine. In cones, it leaves a round clear hole. In contrast to the work of *Barbara,* its webbed castings on the surface of an infested cone are free of pitch (fig. 106A). In fir cones it has one and a partial second generation annually, and in pine it has only one (Keen 1958). The forewings of the adults (fig. 106B) are bluish gray with zig-

Table 9.—*Hosts and distribution of* Dioryctria *species
that occur in western forests*

Species	Host tree	Tree part affected	Distribution
D. abietivorella (Groté) **fir coneworm**	*Pinus, Pseudotsuga, Abies,* and *Picea*	Cones,[2] shoots, foliage, trunk, and *Cronartium* galls	Transcontinental, British Columbia, and Western States
D. albovittella (Hulst)	*Pinus monophylla*	Cones	Nev., Ariz., N. Mex., and Colo.
D. auranticella (Groté) **pine coneworm** (= *xanthoenobares* Dyar)	*Pinus ponderosa,*[1] *P. attenuata,* and *P.* spp.	Cones[2] and twigs	Western States and British Columbia
D. banksiella Mutuura, Munroe and Ross	*Pinus banksiana*	*Endocronartium harknessii* and *Cronartium* galls	Saskatchewan, Alberta, and Northwest Territories
D. baumhoferi Heinrich	*Pinus ponderosa*	Twigs	Ariz.
D. cambiicola (Dyar)	*Pinus ponderosa, P. contorta,* and *P. coulteri*	Twigs, cones, and *Cronartium* galls	British Columbia, Wash., Oreg., Calif., Ariz., N. Mex., Colo., and Mont.
D. contortella Mutuura, Munroe and Ross	*Pinus contorta*	*Cronartium* galls	British Columbia, Alberta, and Wash.
D. monticolella Mutuura, Munroe and Ross	*Pinus monticola*	Trunk	British Columbia
D. okanaganella Mutuura, Munroe and Ross	*Pinus ponderosa*	*Cronartium* galls	British Columbia
D. pentictonella Mutuura, Munroe and Ross	*Pinus ponderosa* and *P. contorta*	Buds	British Columbia
D. ponderosae Dyar **ponderosa twig moth**	*Pinus ponderosa*	Trunk	Calif., Mont., Colo., and Nebr.
D. pseudotsugella Munroe	*Pseudotsuga menziesii,*[1] *Abies, Picea,* and *Tsuga*	Shoots, foliage, and cones	British Columbia, Wash., Oreg., Idaho, Mont., Utah, Colo., and N. Mex.

Table 9.—*Hosts and distribution of* Dioryctria *species that occur in western forests*—Continued

Species	Host tree	Tree part affected	Distribution
D. reniculelloides Mutuura and Munroe **spruce coneworm**	*Picea, Abies, Pseudotsuga menziesii, Pinus contorta*, and *Tsuga*	Cones, foliage, and flowers	Transcontinental, British Columbia, Idaho, Mont., and Calif.
D. rossi Munroe	*Pinus ponderosa*	Cones	British Columbia, Oreg., Wash., Calif., Colo., Ariz., and N. Mex.
D. tumicolella Mutuura, Munroe and Ross	*Pinus ponderosa*	*Cronartium* galls	British Columbia, Wash., Mont., and Colo.

[1] Principal host.
[2] Principal part affected.

F–521970

FIGURE 105. — Larva of a *Dioryctria* species in a Douglas-fir shoot.

FIGURE 106.—Fir coneworm (*Dioryctria abietivorella*): *A*, Damage by larvae to cones of Douglas-fir; *B*, adult, 25 mm wingspread.

zag darker cross markings. The hindwings are uniformly dusky white with darker borders. The mature larvae are 17 to 20 mm long, naked, and greenish red to amber brown above and flesh colored below.

The **ponderosa twig moth,** *Dioryctria ponderosae* Dyar, has caused considerable injury in the plantations of the Nebraska National Forest, where it attacks ponderosa, Scotch, Austrian, jack, and Norway or red pines. Most of the trees attacked are under 20 cm (8 in) in diameter, and the bole and tops are frequently girdled by the larval tunnels. Damage to Scotch and Austrian pines is particularly serious.

The adults are blackish-gray moths with a wing expanse of 27 to 30 mm. There are two narrow W-shaped bands extending across each forewing; the hindwings are dusky white. The moths appear from late in July to early in September and deposit eggs singly on the under side of bark scales, on trunk, or on branches.

The small larvae hatch in 1 to 4 weeks, depending on the temperature, and spin small hibernacula under bark scales, in which they overwinter. The first evidence of attack appears the following spring in the form of a small quantity of larval castings on the bark surface, followed by an exudation of pitch from the entrance hole. The larvae feed in the cambium region and construct irregularly shaped galleries beneath the bark somewhat as does *Vespamima*, but without heavy pitch exudation. Some of these are rounded cavities with short side galleries, while others extend several centimeters around the tree. The mature larvae are about 25 mm long, usually light brown, occasionally with a greenish tinge, and the bodies are marked with about six rows of small, dark-brown dots, or tubercles. These larvae spin white, papery cocoons in the burrows, or sometimes in the dried-pitch mass near the surface, in which pupation takes place in July. The new adults leave the pupal skins in the cocoons and force their way through exit holes previously prepared by the larvae but concealed by flakes of bark or small webs.

Dioryctria pseudotsugella Munroe (Mutuura and Munroe 1973) feeds commonly on the foliage or cones of Douglas-fir and rarely on *Abies grandis*, *Picea*, and *Tsuga*.

The overwintering first-instar larva of the **spruce coneworm**, *Dioryctria reniculelloides* Mutuura and Munroe (= *reniculella* (Groté)), mines in one or two needles in the spring before entering a developing bud, cone, or staminate flower (Freeman 1967a). It has one generation annually.

Herculia contains several species, two or more of which feed on the foliage of trees.

The **cypress webber**, *Herculia phoezalis* Dyar (Brown and Eads 1967), is a significant pest of ornamental *Cupressus*, *Chamaecyparis*, and *Thuja* in southern California. It also feeds on broadleaved trees and shrubs. Its damage somewhat resembles that of *Epinotia subviridis* but the larvae of *H. phoezalis* live gregariously in loosely-webbed tunnels rather than singly in cocoon-like shelters. The mature larva is about 18 mm long and shiny black. The adult has a wingspread of 17 to 25 mm and is dark brown with two narrow, indefinite, wavy cross bands. The larvae overwinter and pupate in the spring. There is one generation per year.

Herculia thymetusalis Walker (Wong 1960) occurs from the Atlantic coast to Alberta, principally on spruce. In Manitoba and Saskatchewan it is one of a complex of insects that defoliate the tops of black spruce. There it is presumed to have a 2-year life cycle.

Nomophila nearctica Munroe (*noctuella* (Denis and Schiffer-müller)) (Johnson and Duffield 1961, Munroe 1973) is a transcontinental species that feeds on various crops and wild plants. In the West it has been reported to feed on Douglas-fir seedlings in a forest nursery in Washington. The larvae cut off the tree seedlings near the groundline and drag them into burrows to feed upon the foliage. The mature larva is 15 to 20 mm long, gray green, and spotted. The forewing of the adult is gray with black and bronze markings. There are two to four generations per year.

Promylea lunigerella Ragonot (Prentice 1965) is a little-known solitary defoliator of grand fir, Douglas-fir, western hemlock, and other conifers. It is recorded from coastal British Columbia and Washington and from California and Colorado. The forewings are gray or brownish gray and have an expanse of 20 to 24 mm.

SUPERFAMILY BOMBYCOIDEA

This superfamily is represented in North America by four families. Two of the families, Lasiocampidae and Saturniidae, contain species which damage forest trees or browse plants. The adult moths are hairy and of moderate to very large size.

FAMILY LASIOCAMPIDAE—TENT CATERPILLAR MOTHS AND ALLIES

The Lasiocampidae (Franclemont 1973) are a small family of leaffeeders. Some of the most common and destructive ones feed as colonies in silken nests, hence the common name, tent caterpillars. In western North America, species in several genera feed on trees, but only species of *Malacosoma* are rated forest pests. The caterpillars are cylindrical or flattened and very hairy. The adults are medium- to large-sized, hairy moths, generally of subdued brown, buff, or gray colors.

Gloveria (Franclemont 1973) contains five species in the Southwestern States. The larvae are large and hairy and irritate the skin when handled. They feed on foliage of trees and shrubs, but none is recorded to be a pest. The adults generally are dark-brown moths with a wingspread of 60 to 80 mm. Males fly during the day; females at night. *G. arizonensis* Packard occurs from California to western Texas and north into Colorado. Recorded hosts are *Juniperus, Pinus torreyana, P. radiata* and "cypress" (*Cupressus?*).

Tent caterpillars, *Malacosoma* spp. (Stehr and Cook 1968), are a familiar part of the American scene. In spring, their white silken tents often are conspicuous on forest, fruit, and shade trees, and clusters of hairy larvae are found nearby or in the tents. During periods of abundance, larvae may strip the foliage from trees and shrubs over wide areas and then wander in droves across open ground. Their feeding can result in reduced tree growth, damage to browse plants, and impairment of esthetic values.

Six species of *Malacosoma* are native to North America; the five of these that occur in the West are as follows:

Species	Principal hosts	Distribution
M. *californicum* (Packard) western tent caterpillar	*Quercus, Salix, Prunus, Purshia, Ceanothus, Populus, Betula*, and *Alnus*	Western States, Northern States, and Canada
M. *constrictum* (Henry Edwards) Pacific tent caterpillar	*Quercus*	Baja Calif., Calif., Oreg., and Wash.
M. *disstria* Hübner forest tent caterpillar	*Populus, Salix, Alnus, Betula, Prunus, and Quercus*	Southern Canada, and continental United States, except Alaska
M. *incurvum* (Henry Edwards) Southwestern tent caterpillar	*Populus, Salix*, and *Prunus*	Colo., Utah, Nev., Ariz., and central Mexico
M. *tigris* (Dyar) Sonoran tent caterpillar	*Quercus*	Southern Great Plains, southern Rocky Mountains, most of Mexico

All *Malacosoma* have similar life cycles. Adults are stout, yellowish- to reddish-brown moths, having a wingspan of 25 to 35 mm. They appear in midsummer, flying at night, and deposit eggs in clusters of 150 to 250 either in bands encircling twigs or as flattish masses on limbs and boles. Eggs are usually covered with a yellow to dark brown frothy substance produced by the female. Within 2 to 3 weeks, the young caterpillars are fully formed within the eggs where they overwinter. In spring they chew out of the eggs about the time the new leaves appear. The young larvae are gregarious. Larvae of some species form substantial tents where they rest between feeding periods. Other species, which spin no tent or only rudimentary tents, will cluster on twigs, branches, or boles when not feeding. Mature larvae have blue, black, and orange markings, and are about 50 mm long. They tend to wander and feed on a great variety of woody plants. Their dusty, silken cocoons, about 25 mm long, are spun in folded leaves, under loose bark, or in litter. Pupation occurs and moths emerge in about 2 weeks. There is one generation a year.

Outbreaks of tent caterpillars are eventually controlled by a variety of biotic factors. Eggs, larvae, and pupae are killed by various insect parasites; larvae are consumed by predaceous beetles or bugs; and eggs, larvae, and moths are eaten by birds. Larvae are often decimated by a nucleopolyhedrosis virus.

The **western tent caterpillar,** *Malacosoma californicum* (Packard) (Stehr and Cook 1968; Stelzer 1968, 1971) is the most variable tent caterpillar in North America. It consists of a widespread typical form and six subspecies which occupy rather well-defined geographic areas. For instance, the subspecies *pluviale* (Dyar) occurs in areas of moderate rainfall from the Pacific Northwest eastward through Canada and the Northern States to Quebec; *lutescens* (Neumoegen and Dyar) inhabits the Great Plains; and *fragile* (Stretch) is restricted to the Southwestern States and eastern California. Three other subspecies have localized distributions in California. Usual hosts include *Quercus, Salix, Prunus, Rosa, Amelanchier, Purshia, Ceanothus, Cercocarpus, Ribes, Populus, Betula* and *Alnus.* Preferred hosts vary with different forms and availability of food plants within their ranges. Economic damage is generally minor. Exceptions are outbreaks of *fragile* causing tree mortality and severe loss of annual increment on trembling aspen in the southern Rocky Mountains and partial killing of bitterbrush, an important browse plant in the Southwest.

The moths (fig. 107A and B) are similar in size to *M. disstria* but range in color from dark reddish brown to yellow and gray, with many intermediate shades. The forewings are marked with two lines which may be either lighter or darker than the ground color. Eggs are laid as a flat clasping mass (fig. 107C) on twigs, limbs, and small trunks and vary from pale gray to dark brown. Mature larvae vary widely in color. Their heads are blue to black and body color patterns are mixtures of black, orange, and blue. A broken bluish or bluish-white stripe usually occurs on the dorsum (fig. 107D). Cocoons are loosely to compactly spun, and dusted with a yellowish or whitish powder (fig. 107E).

Larvae of this species form large tents (fig. 107F). Their habits are similar to those of other western *Malacosoma.*

The **Pacific tent caterpillar,** *Malacosoma constrictum* (Henry Edwards) (Stehr and Cook 1968), is restricted to areas in the Pacific Coast States where oaks grow. It oviposits only on species of *Quercus,* but late instar larvae will feed on other hosts. It has caused serious defoliation of oaks, particularly *Quercus douglasii,* only in the dry areas west of the Sierra Nevada. A subspecies replaces the principal form in southern California.

The adult male is usually straw yellow and the female reddish brown. Lines on the forewings are darker than the ground color. The egg mass is laid as a spiral ring, encircling small twigs, as in

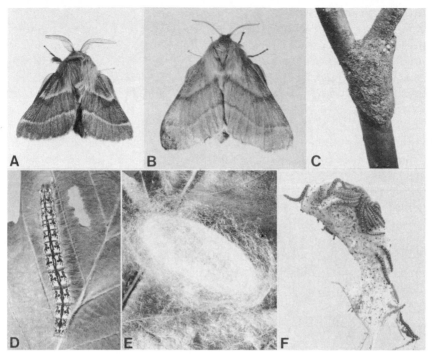

F–521971, F–521972, F–521973, F–521974, F–521975, F–521976

FIGURE 107 —Western tent caterpillar (*Malacosoma californicum pluviale*):
A, Male adult, body 12 mm long; B, female adult, body 15 mm long; C, egg
mass, 20 mm wide; D, mature larva, 50 mm long; E, cocoon, 20 mm long;
F, larval tent.

M. disstria. However, the frothy substance covering the eggs is
bright yellow and contains large bubbles. The mature larva has a
bluish-black head and hourglass-shaped orange blotches, outlined
by black, on the dorsum. Its lateral areas are bluish gray. The
cocoons are rather tightly constructed and dusted with a white
powder.

The tent consists of a few thin layers of silk which follow the
shape of the twigs and leaves, and rarely exceeds 75 to 100 mm
in width. It is used as a retreat when larvae molt, rather than a
resting place between feeding periods.

The **forest tent caterpillar**, *Malacosoma disstria* Hübner (Brown
1966, Hildahl and Reeks 1960, Stehr and Cook 1968), is the
most widely distributed and destructive tent caterpillar in North
America. Its preferred host is trembling aspen but it also feeds on
other *Populus, Salix, Alnus, Betula, Prunus,* and other deciduous
trees. Large larvae will wander to, and feed on, various unnatural
hosts, such as conifers. In the Western States outbreaks normally
last only 2 or 3 years and cover up to 200 square miles. In Western

Canada, some outbreaks have persisted for 6 years and have been extremely widespread. In 1962, at the peak of one such epidemic, moderate to severe defoliation was recorded on 75,000 square miles in Alberta, and 64,000 square miles in Manitoba and Saskatchewan. In such outbreaks, some tree mortality may occur. However, reduced growth and some branch killing are the usual extent of damage.

Adults (fig. 108A) are light yellow to yellow brown, with a wingspread of 25 to 37 mm. The forewings are crossed with two straight lines of slightly darker color, and the space between the lines is often darker so as to form a band. The egg masses (fig. 108B) are deposited as dark-brown, spiral rings completely encircling small twigs. The mature larva (fig. 108C) is dark brown with a bluish head and blue to blue-black sides. Its dorsum is characteristically marked with whitish or yellowish, keyhole-shaped spots and patches of very fine orange- or reddish-brown lines. The silken cocoon is dusted with a lemon-yellow color.

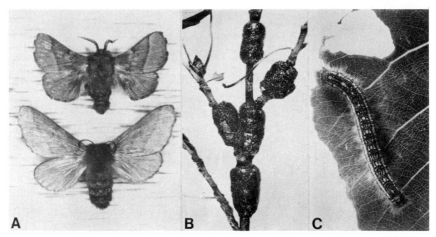

COURTESY CANADIAN FORESTRY SERVICE (A,B), F–521977 (C)

FIGURE 108.—Forest tent caterpillar (*Malacosoma disstria*): *A*, Male and female adults, wingspread 25 and 37 mm; *B*, egg masses, 12 to 15 mm wide; *C*, mature larva, 40 mm long.

Adults frequently are seen flying about lights at night during midsummer. After mating, females deposit egg masses which are noticeable once the leaves fall from the trees. In spring larvae issue from the egg masses and feed without building a tent. When not feeding, small larvae cluster on leaves and twigs, and large larvae on branches and trunks. During periods of abundance, large larvae wander in such numbers as to impede traffic. They usually spin cocoons on trees in one or more webbed-together leaves.

190

Infestations may be spread when adults are transported long distances by weather fronts. Declines in outbreaks are often associated with cold weather at the time larvae are hatching. A parasitic fly, *Sarcophaga aldrichii* Parker, a predaceous ground beetle, *Calosoma frigidum* Kirby, and nucleopolyhedrosis virus also may cause further reductions in tent caterpillar populations.

The **southwestern tent caterpillar**, *Malacosoma incurvum* (Henry Edwards) (Stehr and Cook 1968), ranges from the southern Rocky Mountains into Mexico, feeding mainly on cottonwoods and willows. Its damage is mostly to shade trees and trees along water courses. Three subspecies are recognized.

Moths are darker in color than other *Malacosoma*. Eggs are laid as a flat clasping mass, as in *M. californicum*, but the frothy covering ranges from nearly white to dark brown. Larval tents and mature larvae resemble those of *M. californicum*.

The **Sonoran tent caterpillar**, *Malacosoma tigris* (Dyar) (Stehr and Cook 1968), is the most southerly distributed species, ranging from Colorado through New Mexico and west Texas to Southern Mexico. Its chief hosts are scrubby oaks of little economic value.

In coloration, moths resemble those of *M. disstria* and *M. constrictum*. Eggs are laid in a spiral band around very slender twigs and lack the frothy covering found in egg masses of other *Malacosoma*. Mature larvae are marked above with longitudinal, black and orange stripes, crossed on each body segment by a blue line. Cocoons are dusted with a white powder.

Tents are small, resembling those of *M. constrictum*, and are used for molting rather than resting.

The **lappet moth**, *Phyllodesma* [*Epicnaptera*] *americana* (Harris) (Franclemont 1973), is a transcontinental, nondestructive species that occurs in most Western States and Provinces. It is a solitary feeder on the leaves of many trees and shrubs, including *Quercus*, *Populus*, and *Salix*. The larvae are bluish gray with two orange-red bands on the thorax and are flattened with flaplike folds along the sides. The adults are reddish brown, about the size and shape of *Malacosoma*, but differ in having scalloped outer edges of the wings. There are one or two generations per year depending upon length of the growing season. Winter is spent as pupae in tough, flattened cocoons.

FAMILY SATURNIIDAE—GIANT SILKWORM MOTHS

The **giant silkworm moths** (Michener 1952, Ferguson 1972) are a family of very large, broad-winged moths, often with "eyespots" in the wings. The males have plumelike antennae. The caterpillars are armed with conspicuous spined tubercles. Most species spin dense silken cocoons in which to pupate, hence their common name. Except for a few, they feed principally on broad-leaved trees and shrubs. The pandora moth feeds on pines and is by far the most important forest pest in this group.

The **polyphemus moth**, *Antheraea* [*Telea*] *polyphemus* (Cramer) (Ferguson 1972), ranges throughout the United States and Southern Canada. It feeds on alder, madrone, maple, oak, poplar, willow, and other trees and shrubs, causing no appreciable damage. The adult is a beautiful buff-colored to reddish-brown moth with a wingspread of 100 to 125 mm and a translucent eyespot in each wing. The eyespots of the hindwings are conspicuously encircled with yellow, blue, and black. The mature larva is apple green, large and sluggish, and has six rows of similar-sized, orange, or golden tubercles arising from red spots. The pupae overwinter in broadly oval cocoons that either drop to the ground or remain suspended from a branch.

The genus *Coloradia* consists of three species in the United States. Two are significant forest pests. So far as known, the larvae feed only on pines.

The **Black Hills pandora moth**, *Coloradia doris* Barnes, occurs in Colorado, Wyoming, Montana, and South Dakota. It became epidemic in 1938 and 1939 on ponderosa pine near Osage, Wyo., and on the Harney National Forest, S.D. Little is recorded of its habits. The large caterpillars (fig. 109) have much longer and

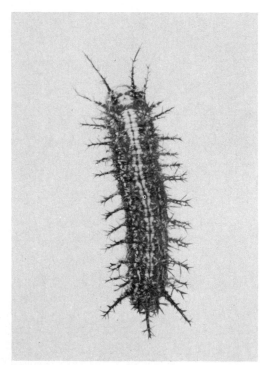

F–521978

FIGURE 109.—Large larva of Black Hills pandora moth (*Coloradia doris*), 50 mm long.

more conspicuously branched spines than those of the pandora moth. The adults resemble the pandora moth except that the hindwings are more translucent and the eyespots on the forewings are not so prominent and are oblong instead of round.

Coloradia luski Barnes and Benjamin (Ferguson 1972), the smallest species of *Coloradia* in the United States, closely resembles *C. doris*. It occurs in Arizona and New Mexico. Its host is not recorded.

The **pandora moth**, *Coloradia pandora* Blake (Carolin and Knopf 1968), is an important defoliator of pines in western forests. It has three recognized subspecies (Ferguson 1972), but in this manual they are treated as one species. *Pinus ponderosa, P. contorta,* and *P. jeffreyi* are the principal hosts. *P. coulteri* and *P. lambertiana* are sometimes attacked. The moth is recorded in the United States from the Rocky Mountains west, except Idaho and Washington. Outbreaks have occurred only on areas with soils loose enough for the larvae to bury themselves prior to pupation—chiefly pumice soils in Pacific Coast States and decomposed granite soils in Rocky Mountain States.

A destructive outbreak occurred on the Klamath Indian Reservation of southern Oregon in 1918–25 (Patterson 1929). Thousands of acres of ponderosa pine forest were heavily defoliated, with an accompanying serious loss of timber. Lodgepole pine in mixture with ponderosa pine was also attacked. Heavily defoliated trees died after 2 to 3 years. Others were greatly reduced in growth and recovered only after several years. The loss in growth throughout the defoliated area mounted to several million board feet. Even more serious was the bark beetle damage that followed the defoliation and increased to alarming proportions in the weakened trees. On the Arapaho National Forest in north-central Colorado, an epidemic during the period 1937–40 defoliated lodgepole stands on an area of approximately 100,000 acres. This defoliation killed more than 4,000 trees and weakened many others (Wygant 1941). During the period 1959–66, outbreaks occurred in Oregon, California, Utah, Wyoming, and Colorado.

In parts of the West, epidemics occur at intervals of about 20 to 30 years and continue 6 to 8 years. During periods of abundance, feeding may be fairly heavy without serious consequences. This is because the terminal buds are not eaten, and, since the insect has a 2-year life cycle and most of the feeding occurs in alternate years, the trees have an opportunity to recover. The more vigorous trees survive the attacks, and only during major outbreaks are losses likely to be heavy. In nonepidemic years, the pandora moth is scarce and seldom seen.

The adults are large, heavy-bodied, grayish-brown moths, with a wing expanse of 70 to 110 mm and a small dark spot near the center of each wing (fig. 110A and B). The base and interior margins of the hindwings are clothed with pinkish hairs, which in the male shade to wine color. The males have large, feathery antennae, while the females have slender antennae. During epidemics thousands of these large moths will be seen fluttering over the tree trunks and flying through the woods. The eggs are globular, about 3 mm long, and are deposited in clusters of 2 to 50, usually on the needles or bark of pine (fig. 110C). The newly hatched caterpillars are about 5 mm long, with shiny black heads and black or brownish bodies covered with short, dark hairs. When mature, the caterpillars are from brown to yellowish green and 60 to 80 mm long, with each segment supporting a few stout branched spines (fig. 110D). The pupae are dark purplish brown, from 25 to 35 mm long, and are not enclosed in a cocoon (fig. 110E).

The pandora moth requires 2 years to complete its life cycle. Adults appear the latter part of June and in July, and the eggs hatch in August. The young larvae crawl up the trees and during

F-517863, F-517864, F-517857, F-521979, F-517861

FIGURE 110.—Pandora moth (*Coloradia pandora*): *A*, Male adult, 75 mm wingspread; *B*, female adult, 80 mm wingspread; *C*, egg cluster, 15 mm long; *D*, mature larva, 65 mm long; *E*, pupa, 30 mm long.

the early molts feed in groups on the new foliage (fig. 111). At the end of the season they are about 25 mm long. These immature larvae spend the first winter hibernating in clusters at the base of the needles. They resume feeding the following spring, and the caterpillars reach full growth by the last of June. When mature, they crawl down the trees and enter the soil to a depth of 25 to 125 mm where they form elliptical cells in which they transform into pupae. Typically the pupal stage lasts 1 year; however some pupae remain in diapause for as many as 5 years before transforming into adults (Carolin 1971).

F-517859

FIGURE 111.—Pandora moth (*Coloradia pandora*) larvae feeding as colony in the fall.

The pandora moth is one of many insects that has been used as human food (Bodenheimer 1951, Patterson 1929). Sporadic abundance limits its use as a staple. The Mono Indians of California dug trenches around the infested trees and built smudge fires which caused the caterpillars to drop to the ground in great numbers. They were caught in the trenches, killed, dried, and eaten cooked with vegetables to make a stew. The Klamath Indians in Oregon preferred the pupae, which were dug from the ground and roasted.

Epidemics of the pandora moth are controlled by a number of natural factors. Perhaps the most important is a wilt disease (probably caused by a polyhedrosis virus) that affects the mature larvae. Once this disease becomes established it runs rampant and few of the insects survive. Ground squirrels and chipmunks dig up and destroy large numbers of pupae. Birds, insect parasites, and high soil temperatures also exert some control. Direct control measures have not been devised specifically for this insect.

Hemileuca [*Pseudohazis*] (Ferguson 1972) is closely related to *Coloradia*. Antennae of male adult *Hemileuca* are bipectinate; those of *Coloradia* are quadripectinate. *Hemileuca* larvae are distinctive in having two dorsal rows of short quill-like spines arranged in rosettes (fig. 112). The lateral spines are branched and barbed and cause a rash on humans. Eight of the 20 or so North American species are common in the West, especially the Southwest (table 10). None is a significant forest pest. The adults of some species fly in daytime; others at night. The larvae feed

Table 10.—*Principal species of* Hemileuca *in Western North America*

Species	Color of wings	Hosts	Distribution
H. eglanterina (Boisduval) **brown day moth**	Both wings deep yellow with black markings; some pink shading	*Salix, Populus, Betula, Acer, Arctostaphylos, Ceanothus, Purshia,* and other shrubs	N. Mex. to Calif., Oreg., British Columbia, and Wyo.
H. hera Harris	Both wings mostly white; inner edge of outer black band strongly serrate	*Artemisia*	Calif. to British Columbia, Wyo., and Colo.
H. juno Packard	Both wings black except for white median band on forewing	*Prosopis*	N. Mex., Calif., and Idaho
H. nevadensis Stretch **Nevada buck moth**	Both wings mostly white; inner edge of outer black band evenly curved	*Salix* and *Populus*	N. Mex. to Calif., Oreg., Manitoba, and S. Dak.
H. nuttalli Strecker	Similar to *eglanterina* but without pink	*Purshia* and *Symphoricarpos*	N. Mex. to Calif., British Columbia, and Wyo.
H. oliviae Cockerell **range caterpillar**	Forewings very light brown with faint whitish bands	Grasses	Ariz., N. Mex., and Tex.
H. tricolor Packard	Forewings gray with three white bands	*Cercidium*	Ariz. and N. Mex.

principally on shrubs and deciduous trees. In some species, eggs overwinter on twigs of the host; in others, the pupa overwinters in the soil. One generation per year is usual.

The **brown day moth**, *Hemileuca eglanterina* (Boisduval), is a showy yellow to orange-brown moth with black markings and pinkish overtones and has a wing expanse of 75 mm (fig. 113). The caterpillars are shiny brown to black and have reddish spots on the back and a narrow red line on each side. The form in British Columbia has a 2-year life cycle (Evans 1958).

The **Nevada buck moth**, *Hemileuca nevadensis* Stretch, has a wingspread of about 75 mm (fig. 114). The spiny, black caterpillars feed gregariously during their early stages, then disperse. Throughout the 1960's *H. nevadensis* occurred abundantly on cottonwood in White Sands National Monument, N.Mex., necessitating repeated chemical control.

F–521980

FIGURE 112.—Mature *Hemileuca* larva, 55 mm long, with characteristic rosettes of spines.

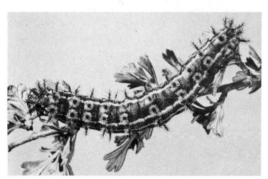

F–521981

FIGURE 113.—Adult of brown day moth (*Hemileuca eglanterina*), wingspread 75 mm, hanging from bitterbrush twig.

COURTESY CALIFORNIA DEPARTMENT OF FOOD AND AGRICULTURE

FIGURE 114.—Adult of Nevada buck moth (*Hemileuca nevadensis*), wingspread 75 mm.

Hyalophora [*Platysamia*] (Ferguson 1972) consists of four closely related species, three of which occur in Western United States and Canada. Western species feed predominantly upon broad-leaved trees and shrubs, but one feeds at least occasionally on Douglas-fir in California and Oregon. The body of the adult is hairy and red with white crossbands. Wing spots are crescent-shaped and opaque, not translucent and eye-like as in *Antheraea*. The mature larva (fig. 115) is pale green, large, and sluggish. The dorsal tubercles are of strongly contrasting colors and those of the thorax and first abdominal segment are conspicuously larger than the others. The cocoon is rounded at one end, pointed at the other, and overwinters firmly attached to a branch.

F–521983

FIGURE 115.—*Hyalophora* larva, 55 mm long, feeding on Douglas-fir.

The **cecropia moth**, *Hyalophora cecropia* (L.), is an eastern species which ranges west into Montana and Alberta. The larva feeds individually on a large number of forest trees, including ash, birch, maple, and willow.

The **ceanothus silk moth**, *Hyalophora euryalus* (Boisduval), occurs in the Pacific Coast States, British Columbia, and east to Wyoming. It feeds principally on ceanothus, alder, willow, birch, manzanita, and bitterbrush. At maturity, the caterpillars are 80 to 90 mm long. The adult has a wingspread of 100 to 125 mm.

Hyalophora gloveri (Strecker) feeds on maple, willow, and many other trees and shrubs. It ranges from Alberta through the Rocky Mountains and the Southwest. The caterpillars are 75 mm long when full grown.

SUPERFAMILY SPHINGOIDEA

This superfamily consists of the Sphingidae only.

FAMILY SPHINGIDAE—SPHINX MOTHS

The **sphinx moths** (Hodges 1971), also known as **hawk moths,** are medium to large, narrow-winged, conical-bodied, fast-flying, often colorful moths that frequent flowers much as do humming-birds. The larvae usually have a conspicuous, curved, anal horn.

Pupae usually are naked in the soil. Some of the 115 North American species are important pests of agricultural crops; some feed on broad-leaved trees and shrubs, but none is rated as a significant forest pest in the West.

The **big poplar sphinx**, *Pachysphinx modesta* (Harris) (Hodges 1971), is a transcontinental species that occurs in the West from Colorado and Alberta to British Columbia and Washington. It feeds on *Populus* and *Salix*. The wings have a spread of about 100 to 120 mm and are fawn colored with purplish-red markings. The mature larva is whitish green with seven oblique white lines on each side. *P. occidentalis* (Henry Edwards) is a similar but larger species that feeds on the same genera of trees in Southwestern States.

Smerinthus cerisyi Kirby (Hodges 1971) is a considerably smaller, highly variable, transcontinental species that occurs in the Western States and British Columbia on *Salix* and *Populus*. The forewings are brown and gray above, rosy below, and are strongly indented along the outer margin. The hindwings have a rosy cast and a large black and blue eyespot. The larva is pale green with a pair of pale yellow lines along the back and six oblique, white lines on each side.

Sphinx sequoiae Boisduval (Hodges 1971) feeds on *Juniperus* in California, Arizona, Nevada, and Oregon. The adults are bluish gray and the larvae juniper green with reddish-brown markings.

SUPERFAMILY GEOMETROIDEA

This superfamily consists of one large family, the Geometridae.

FAMILY GEOMETRIDAE—GEOMETRID MOTHS

Caterpillars of the **geometrid moths** (McGuffin 1967, 1972; Prentice 1963), feed on the leaves of many kinds of trees and other plants. Some species in this large family are among the most destructive defoliators of forest trees. The caterpillars are nearly hairless. At rest, many closely resemble the twigs or foliage of their hosts (fig. 116). Most are elongate and have two pairs of prolegs, one pair on the sixth segment and one on the last. The caterpillars travel in a characteristic way. They move along by grasping with the hind pairs of prolegs while they extend the body forward, then holding with the front legs while they hump their backs to bring up their rear. This produces a looping motion, from which arises the common names of **loopers, spanworms, inchworms,** or **measuring worms.** Adults are medium-sized, slight-bodied, fragile-winged, generally light-colored moths.

Alsophila contains one species, the **fall cankerworm**, *A. pometaria* (Harris) (Jones and Schaffner 1953). It occurs extensively

F-521984

FIGURE 116.—Larva of mountain mahogany looper (*Anacamptodes clivinaria profanata*) resting in twiglike pose.

in the East and in the Prairie States and Provinces westward to Alberta, Montana, and Colorado. It also occurs in Utah, New Mexico, and California. It attacks many deciduous trees and shrubs including maple, elm, oak, birch, aspen, and willow. It is principally a pest of shade trees and of shelterbelt plantings.

The males have a wingspread of about 25 mm. The females are wingless. Both are brownish gray. The males have pale bands across the forewings. The larvae range from pale green to nearly black and have several thin longitudinal stripes on their sides. A rudimentary pair of prolegs on the fifth abdominal segment of the fall cankerworm distinguishes it from the spring cankerworm which has no prolegs on that segment.

The eggs, resembling tiny brownish-gray flowerpots, are laid late in the fall in compact clusters of about 100 on the bark of twigs and branches (fig. 117). The larvae hatch about the time the leaves begin to show in the spring. They first eat holes in the young leaves; later they consume the leaves, except for the larger veins. They mature in 6 to 7 weeks and drop to the ground where they spin a cocoon in the soil and remain until late fall.

Anacamptodes (Rindge 1966) contains 24 species, nine of which are western. The larvae feed on various trees and herbaceous plants.

The **mountain mahogany looper**, *Anacamptodes clivinaria profanata* (Barnes and McDunnough) (Furniss and Barr 1967), occurs in California, Oregon, Washington, British Columbia,

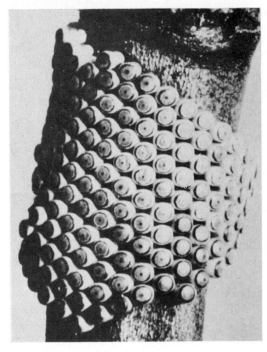

F-519582

FIGURE 117.—Egg cluster of the fall cankerworm (*Alsophila pometaria*).

Idaho, Utah, and Colorado. It feeds upon mountain-mahogany and bitterbrush and is destructive to both. In 1962–64 it killed 50 percent of a 6,000-acre stand of mountain-mahogany in southern Idaho, and in 1957 it killed bitterbrush extensively in eastern Oregon.

The larvae strongly resemble the grayish-brown twigs of their hosts (fig. 116). The adults have a wingspan of 27 to 36 mm and are grayish with subdued black and brown markings (fig. 118).

Eggs are laid in June in bark crevices. In Idaho, the larvae feed during July and August. They pupate in the soil where they spend the winter.

F-521985

FIGURE 118.—Adult of mountain mahogany looper (*Anacamptodes clivinaria profanata*) in resting position.

The **pepper-and-salt moth,** *Biston cognataria* (Guenée) (Sugden 1968), is transcontinental in Northern United States and Canada. More than 50 trees and shrubs are recorded as hosts. Willow, birch, alder, larch, aspen, and maple are most commonly attacked. It is a solitary feeder. Not an economic forest pest, it is notable principally for its large size and common occurrence. The mature larva is about 75 mm long, has a deeply bilobed head, and is variously colored gray, brown, orange, or green.

Caripeta larvae feed on the foliage of conifers but cause no significant damage.

Caripeta aequaliaria Groté (Prentice 1963) occurs in Oregon, British Columbia, and Alberta. It feeds upon Douglas-fir, pine, and hemlock. It resembles *C. divisata* in the larval stage but in British Columbia is much less common.

The **gray pine looper,** *Caripeta angustiorata* Walker (Prentice 1963), also is transcontinental but is less numerous than *C. divisata.* In Alberta it occasionally causes noticeable damage to lodgepole pine, its preferred host (Hopping 1962). It also feeds upon other pines, spruce, fir, and larch. Habits and appearance are similar to *C. divisata.*

The **gray forest looper,** *Caripeta divisata* Walker (Ross and Evans 1959), is transcontinental in Northern United States and Canada. It is a solitary feeder upon western hemlock, Douglas-fir, true firs, spruce, larch, western redcedar, and pine. The mature larva is about 37 mm long. The head is pale brown with dark, herringbone markings; the body is yellowish and gray or brown with off-white or yellowish stripes. In British Columbia there is one generation annually. The eggs are laid in June. Larvae are present until mid-October. The pupae overwinter.

Ectropis contains one species, *E. crepuscularia* (Denis and Schiffermüller) (Morris 1970, Silver 1961), the **saddleback looper.** It is transcontinental. On the Pacific coast it ranges from Oregon into Alaska and commonly occurs with the hemlock looper and blackheaded budworm. It feeds on many kinds of trees and associated vegetation. In the West, western hemlock is preferred. Douglas-fir, western redcedar, true firs, spruce, alder, willow, and poplar are other principal hosts.

Until recent years the saddleback looper has been considered economically inconsequential. Outbreaks from 1951 to 1953 and 1960 to 1961 in British Columbia and in Alaska in 1969 put it in the ranks of significant pests for which foresters should be alert.

In British Columbia, the moths emerge in May and lay eggs. The larvae feed first on the groundcover and understory, later moving upward on the trees. In August the larvae drop to the ground where they pupate and spend the winter.

The full-grown larva is about 35 mm long (fig. 119A). The head is brownish, often mottled. The body is mottled dark gray to brown, sometimes reddish. A pair of blunt tubercles tops the eighth abdominal segment. The young larvae have a V-shaped marking on the dorsal side of the second abdominal segment. This marking becomes indistinct or lacking in the last instar. The mottled, light gray nondescript moth has a wingspan of 30 mm (fig. 119B).

There are four species of *Enypia* (Evans 1960), all of which are confined to the West. The larvae feed singly on coniferous foliage of the current year but cause no significant damage.

E. venata (Groté) is the most widely distributed species, occurring from southern Alaska to southern Arizona and New Mexico and east to Alberta and Colorado. Principal hosts are western hemlock, Douglas-fir, true firs, pine, and spruce. The mature larva is 26 to 31 mm long and pale golden brown with a longitudinal pattern of several broken blackish lines. Wingspan of adults is 37 to 39 mm; wing color pale gray brown with fine darker bands and indistinct markings. The **redheaded looper**, *E. packardata* Taylor, is a coastal form occurring from southern Alaska to southern California. The mature larva is green with two conspicuous, near-white stripes dorsally. Adults are similar to *E. venata* and the hosts are essentially the same.

Epirrita [*Oporinia*] (Prentice 1963) contains two species.

The **green velvet looper**, *Epirrita autumnata omissa* Harrison (Sugden 1966), is a common, potentially damaging defoliator of conifers in British Columbia and Alberta. Two minor outbreaks

F–521986, F–521987

FIGURE 119.—Saddleback looper (*Ectropis crepuscularia*): *A*, Mature larva, 35 mm long; *B*, adult, wingspread 30 mm.

are recorded. Western hemlock, true firs, and spruce are the principal hosts. The larva is velvety green with olive-green, yellowish-green, and whitish stripes.

The **whitelined looper**, *Epirrita pulchraria* (Taylor) (Sugden 1966), is common in coastal British Columbia, rare in the interior. Western hemlock, Sitka spruce, and true firs are the principal hosts. The larvae are apple green with two wide white lines along the back.

Erannis (Prentice 1963) contains two species that defoliate broad-leaved trees in the West. The females are wingless.

The **linden looper**, *Erannis tiliaria* (Harris), is an eastern species that extends westward in Canada to central Alberta. It feeds on leaves of many kinds of hardwoods. At times it heavily defoliates maple in shelterbelts in Alberta. The mature larvae are yellow with wavy black lines along the back.

Erannis vancouverensis Hulst occasionally severely defoliates birch, willow, maple, oak, alder, aspen, and other hardwoods in British Columbia and Oregon. It also occurs on western hemlock and western white pine.

Eupithecia (McGuffin 1958, Ross and Evans 1956) is a large genus of predominantly small moths. In the West, three species feed in cones. Of the others, about half feed on foliage of conifers and half on hardwoods. Some are common, but the only recognized pest is one of the cone feeders. The larvae are small, slender loopers with pebblelike skin. Some resemble the foliage on which they feed.

Eupithecia annulata (Hulst) is a transcontinental species that occurs principally in the West from California to British Columbia. It is common and feeds principally on the foliage *of Pseudotsuga menziesii*, but also on *Abies, Picea,* and *Tsuga. E. luteata* Packard likewise is transcontinental and common. In addition to the above hosts, it also feeds commonly on *Larix.*

The **fir cone looper**, *Eupithecia spermaphaga* (Dyar) (Keen 1958), occurs from California to British Columbia and eastward to Colorado and Arizona. It feeds in cones of *Abies, Pseudotsuga, Pinus,* and *Tsuga,* sometimes causing considerable damage to seeds, principally those of fir. The adult has a reddish-brown body, gray forewings with reddish-brown and black markings, and a wing expanse of 20 to 25 mm. The full-grown larvae are about 20 mm long and vary from pale green to gray or brown. *E. albicapitata* Packard is a transcontinental species that develops in spruce cones in Alberta, British Columbia, and Yukon Territory. *E. columbrata* McDunnough feeds in cones of spruce and fir in Oregon, Washington, and British Columbia.

Galenara (Rindge 1964), which resembles *Melanolophia*, contains nine species, principally in Arizona and New Mexico. One is a significant, possibly a major, forest pest.

The **New Mexico fir looper**, *Galenara consimilis* (Heinrich), is surprisingly little known. It is reputed to be a destructive defoliator of Douglas-fir and white fir. Outbreaks occurred in 1924, 1928, 1951, and 1958 in New Mexico, the only State in which this insect is known to occur. The forewings of the adults are light gray overlain with grayish-brown and brownish-black scales. The immature stages have not been described and the biology is unrecorded.

Iridopsis emasculata (Dyar) (Sugden 1964) resembles *Anacamptodes* in which genus it was described. In British Columbia it occurs as a solitary defoliator principally on alder, willow, and maple, but is not an economic pest. The mature larva is 28 mm long and its body color is yellowish green, yellow, or orange. The dorsum is blotched with orange or reddish brown and marked on abdominal segments two to five with a diamond pattern.

Itame (McGuffin 1972) contains many species, several of which feed on deciduous trees in the West. *I. loricaria* (Eversmann) is common on trembling aspen and willow in Alberta, causing light to moderate defoliation locally (Kusch 1963). The mature larva is about 25 mm long and varies from yellowish green to medium brown. The yellowish-green phase has a green head and its body is unmarked except for a solid yellow lateral line. The brown phase has a reddish-brown head and usually has dark slanted marks on the third, fourth, and fifth abdominal segments. The yellow lateral line is broken. In Alberta the larvae feed from about mid-May to the end of June.

The genus *Lambdina* (Capps 1943) contains several species and subspecies of very similar appearance. Several are western and one of them is a major forest pest.

Lambdina athasaria (Walker) (Capps 1943) is an eastern species, varieties of which occur in Colorado and New Mexico, presumably on oak.

Lambdina fiscellaria (Guenée) ranges from coast to coast. It has several subspecies, three of which occur in the West. The basic species, the **hemlock looper**, *L. fiscellaria fiscellaria* (Guenée), is principally eastern but extends westward into Alberta. Its preferred hosts are species of *Abies*, *Picea*, and *Tsuga*, but during epidemics it feeds on many other forest trees including broadleaved species.

The **western hemlock looper**, *Lambdina fiscellaria lugubrosa* (Hulst) (Jardine 1969), is periodically destructive in coastal forests of Oregon, Washington, and British Columbia. It occurs less destructively in Alaska and in interior forests of Oregon, Washington, British Columbia, Idaho, and Montana. In coastal areas outbreaks develop in forests in which the preferred host, western hemlock, predominates. Associated Sitka spruce, Pacific silver fir, and Douglas-fir also are readily fed upon and even huckleberry, vine maple, salal, and other understory shrubs may be defoliated. Heaviest losses of timber have occurred in extensive old-growth hemlock stands; however, outbreaks also occur in vigorous 80- to 100-year-old stands.

In the earliest outbreak recorded, about 1889 to 1891, a vast amount of timber in Tillamook and Clatsop Counties, Oreg., and Grays Harbor County, Wash., was destroyed. From 1911 to 1914 the hemlock looper killed much hemlock in Stanley Park, Vancouver, B.C. Another major outbreak occurred again in Tillamook County in 1918–21, when several townships were affected and 500 million fbm of hemlock and Douglas-fir were reported to have been killed. A severe outbreak occurred in Pacific and Grays Harbor Counties, Wash., from 1929 to 1932, when over 50,000 acres were involved and about 200 million board feet of hemlock timber was destroyed. Losses in Pacific County were reduced in 1931 through the first airplane dusting experiment attempted against a forest defoliator in the western part of the United States. Again, between 1943 and 1945 there was another outbreak in Clatsop County, Oreg., covering some 17,000 acres, with a loss of timber estimated at 40 million fbm. In the years 1944 to 1946 approximately 500 million fbm were killed on Vancouver Island. From 1961 to 1963 outbreaks occurred in northwestern Oregon and southwestern Washington, but losses were minimized by prompt spraying and intensive salvage. In 1937 an extensive outbreak occurred in true fir in northern Idaho and northwestern Montana. In 1947 another large outbreak occurred in northwestern Montana.

The moths of the hemlock looper are light buff, with a wing expanse of about 35 mm. The forewings are marked with two wavy lines and the hindwings with one wavy line (fig. 120A). They fly, mate, and lay eggs late in September and during October. The eggs are about the size of a pinhead, blue to gray green or brown with a characteristic impression. They are attached to moss and lichens on tree boles and limbs and on moss on understory shrubs and down logs (fig. 120B). The winter is passed in the egg stage, and the eggs hatch the following spring. The first-instar larvae are conspicuously banded light gray and black (fig. 120C). For a time before crawling up the tree trunks, many of them are on understory vegetation. The first feeding on the needles takes place in May, June, and the early part of July and is not particularly noticeable. The first and most of the second instar is spent feeding in buds. From the middle of July to October the feeding of the caterpillars causes a heavily infested forest to turn yellowish red and then brown, as though scorched by fire. Late in summer the caterpillars feed on the foliage, clip off small twigs, crawl over tree trunks, cling to shrubs, and drop by silken webs from the trees to the ground. These silken webs may become so abundant that the whole forest looks and feels like one big cobweb.

F–521988, F–518127, F–521990, F–521991, F–521992

FIGURE 120.—Western hemlock looper (*Lambdina fiscellaria lugubrosa*): *A*, Adult, wingspread 35 mm; *B*, egg, 0.7 mm long, on moss; *C*, first-instar larva, 7 mm long, on huckleberry; *D*, mature larva, 25 mm long; *E*, pupa, 12 mm long.

When full grown, the caterpillars are 25 to 30 mm long, pale yellowish brown to gray brown, and have a complex pattern of markings (fig. 120D). Viewed from above, each abdominal segment is marked by four prominent dark dots. The caterpillars drop to the ground or lower branches in August and September and secret themselves in protected places, such as in moss or crevices of the bark or under debris on the ground and there transform to pupae. The mottled, greenish-brown pupae, about 12 mm long, are unprotected by a cocoon (fig. 120E). The moths appear within 10 to 14 days and during an epidemic are so abundant as to give the impression of a snowstorm in the woods. Creeks, springs, and rivers are covered with the dead bodies, and tree trunks are plastered with them until heavy rains wash them to the ground or carry them away. There is one generation annually.

Outbreaks of the hemlock looper usually last about 3 years, after which they are generally brought under control by the action of parasites, predators, and disease. A nucleopolyhedrosis virus disease is particularly effective in decimating the caterpillars. Heavy rains during the flight period reduce egg-laying, checking an epidemic and hastening its decline.

Although Nature will ultimately bring outbreaks under control, a vast amount of timber may be saved if artificial control measures are applied to protect the trees from heavy defoliation. It has been found that trees can recover from a 50-percent defoliation, and in some cases a 75-percent defoliation is not fatal. At present, aerial spraying offers the only practical means of controlling this defoliator on large forest areas at a reasonable cost. Treatment should be made after all the eggs have hatched, and while the larvae still are in the early instars.

The **western oak looper**, *Lambdina fiscellaria somniaria* (Hulst), is practically identical with the western hemlock looper except for its preferred host, Oregon white oak, on which it feeds in Oregon and northward into British Columbia. Other trees may be attacked, but usually only when intermingled with the preferred host tree. In some seasons the oaks over large areas in the Willamette Valley, Oregon, are completely defoliated by this insect. No permanent damage is done, however, since the oaks are able to leaf out again the following year. Outbreaks are of short duration.

Lambdina punctata (Hulst) (Minnoch and Parker 1971) feeds on oak in Arizona, New Mexico, Colorado, and Utah. In 1968 and 1969 it defoliated Gambel oak extensively in the Wasatch Mountains of Utah, but the trees soon recovered except for some dead twigs. Bigtooth maple was fed on incidentally during the outbreak on oak.

208

The first-instar larva is light gray with dark gray bands. The mature larva is light yellow with wavy black longitudinal lines and is about 38 mm long. Adults are similar in size, color, and markings to those of the hemlock looper.

Eggs are laid from August until October in leaf litter, on bark scales on the bole of oak, and on associated plants. The eggs hatch in May and June. The larvae migrate up the tree and feed on the developing buds and leaves, gradually consuming all except the main veins of the leaves. Larvae are present from May until early September; pupae from mid-July until late September; and adults from early August until mid-October. Pupation is in the litter under infested trees.

Lycia ursaria (Walker) is a generally rare, solitary defoliator of hardwoods such as birch, willow, alder, and poplar in the Western Provinces. In 1952 it defoliated willow extensively in northeastern Alberta. The larvae are brownish with a speckled head.

The **greenstriped forest looper,** *Melanolophia imitata* (Walker) (Dawson 1970, Evans 1962), is distributed along the Pacific coast from Alaska to southern California and eastward to Alberta, showing a preference for the more humid areas. The larvae are solitary feeders, mainly on conifers. The principal hosts are Douglas-fir, western hemlock, western redcedar, true firs, and spruce. Common associated geometrids are *Lambdina fiscellaria lugubrosa, Nepytia phantasmaria,* and *Nyctobia limitaria.*

The greenstriped forest looper normally is quite abundant, but it was not considered to be destructive until 1960 and 1961 when an epidemic killed some 2,400,000 cubic feet of western hemlock on the west coast of Vancouver Island. Extensive outbreaks occurred in 1963–64 on the Queen Charlotte Islands and again in 1968–69 on Vancouver Island. All three outbreaks subsided abruptly from natural causes.

The adults (fig. 121A) are mottled gray brown with a wing-spread of 25 to 39 mm. They fly from mid-March to mid-June and deposit their eggs (fig. 121B) on tree branches and trunks. The larvae feed on foliage of all ages but 1-year-old foliage is preferred. Feeding is heaviest in the upper crown. The mature larva is apple green with whitish and yellowish stripes and is 30 to 37 mm long (fig. 121C). In late summer the larvae drop to the ground and pupate in the duff where they overwinter. There is one generation per year.

The **filament bearer,** *Nematocampa filamentaria* Guenée (Bitz and Ross 1958), is a transcontinental species. It is common on Douglas-fir and western hemlock in interior British Columbia, sometimes causing noticeable defoliation, but it is not reported as a significant pest. It also feeds on other conifers and many hardwoods. The larvae are solitary defoliators. When mature they are generally greenish brown, about 20 mm long, and have two long, slender, flexible projections on the dorsum of both the second and third abdominal segments, and paired knobs on the first and eighth segments (fig. 122).

Neoalcis contains one species, the **brownlined looper**, *N. californiaria* (Packard) (Prentice 1963). It is a common nondestructive solitary feeder on foliage of conifers in Oregon and British Columbia, principally Douglas-fir, western hemlock, western redcedar, and true firs.

Nepytia includes four species that feed on conifers in the West. Two are potentially important, particularly in city forest parks.

The **false hemlock looper**, *Nepytia canosaria* (Walker), which attacks various conifers in the Eastern States and Provinces, extends into Manitoba and Saskatchewan on spruce. Previous

COURTESY CANADIAN FORESTRY SERVICE

FIGURE 121.—Greenstriped forest looper (*Melanolophia imitata*): *A*, Adult, 30 mm wingspread; *B*, eggs, each 1.0 mm long; *C*, mature larva, 32 mm long.

F–521993

FIGURE 122.—Mature larva of filament bearer (*Nematocampa filamentaria*), 20 mm long.

records of this species from the Rocky Mountains westward generally relate to *N. freemani*.

The mature larva is about 25 mm long. Its head is whitish or reddish brown with five or six large black dots; its body is whitish with a yellowish or reddish tinge and marked with black dots and a yellowish lateral stripe, below which are four dark, wavy, hair lines.

Nepytia freemani Munroe (Klein and Minnoch 1971) (fig. 123) occurs in British Columbia, Idaho, and Utah. In British Columbia Douglas-fir is the preferred host; in Utah white fir is preferred. Western larch, western hemlock, and Engelmann spruce also are fed upon. New foliage is eaten first, then the old. Local outbreaks occur in pole- and sapling-sized stands, but so far have not caused damage warranting control.

The adults of *N. freemani* resemble those of *N. phantasmaria* except that the ground color of the wings is gray instead of white

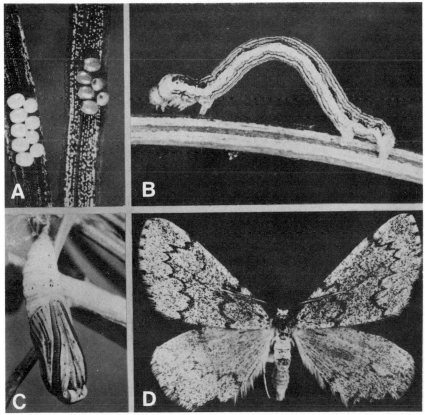

F–521994

FIGURE 123.—*Nepytia freemani*: *A*, Egg clusters; *B*, mature larva, 24 mm long; *C*, pupa, 15 mm long; *D*, adult, wingspread 25 mm.

and the vertex of the head is gray without yellow tints (Munroe 1963). The mature larva is 24 to 32 mm long. Its head is square, tan on the vertex and sides, and pale yellow in front. Its body is slim, alternately striped with tan and yellow outlined in black above and pinkish below. The eggs are laid in late summer and early fall in small clusters on the needles. They hatch in spring. There is one generation annually.

The **phantom hemlock looper,** *Nepytia phantasmaria* (Strecker) (Wickman and Hunt 1969, Sugden 1968), occurs in British Columbia, Oregon, and California. Douglas-fir and western hemlock are its preferred hosts. Western redcedar, Sitka spruce, true firs, and pines also are recorded hosts.

The phantom hemlock looper is common but is not often seen by foresters because outbreaks are local and sporadic. It has been reported abundant in outbreaks of the hemlock looper and black-headed budworm. In British Columbia local outbreaks of the phantom hemlock looper have killed mature Douglas-fir and western hemlock in city parks. In northern California Douglas-fir and understory white fir of pole size and smaller have been killed.

The adults are generally white to very light gray with strong black markings and the vertex of the head is yellowish (fig. 124A). The mature larva is 28 mm long; head green with black dots; body smooth, lime green with dark-edged, yellowish subdorsal and spiracular lines (fig. 124B).

In northern California there is one generation annually. Eggs are laid from late September to late October and overwinter. They

F–521995, F–521996

FIGURE 124.—Phantom hemlock looper (*Nepytia phantasmaria*): *A*, Adult, wingspread 25 mm; *B*, mature larva, 28 mm long.

hatch in late May and early June. The larvae feed first on the new foliage, then on the old. At rest they strongly resemble Douglas-fir needles. Pupation starts in late August. A virus evidently is an effective natural control agent in California.

Nepytia umbrosaria nigrovenaria (Packard) (Sugden 1968) occurs as scattered individuals on Douglas-fir, western hemlock, fir, pine, spruce, and western redcedar in British Columbia. In California the larvae tie the needles of young Monterey pine together at the tips of branches and feed upon them. The mature larva is 35 mm long. Its head is pale brown; its body is cream colored above with broken orange dorsal and subdorsal lines, dark brown red laterally, with black-edged light lines, and pale brownish green below.

The **yellowlined forest looper**, *Nyctobia limitaria* (Walker) (Prentice 1963), is a transcontinental species that is common to abundant in British Columbia. It is a solitary feeder on foliage of many conifers, especially true firs, spruce, hemlock, Douglas-fir, and larch. It is rated a potential forest pest though no destructive outbreaks are recorded. The larva is green with yellowish and whitish stripes.

Operophtera resembles *Alsophila* and *Paleacrita* in that the females are wingless.

The **Bruce spanworm**, *Operophtera bruceata* (Hulst) (Brown 1962, Sugden 1966), occurs from Newfoundland to the interior of British Columbia and presumably extends into the Northwestern States. Preferred hosts in Western Canada are trembling aspen and willow. Birch, maple, alder, apple, and various shrubs also are fed upon. Extensive outbreaks on aspen have occurred in Alberta in 1903, 1913, and 1957–59, the last covering about 50,000 square miles.

The adult males (fig. 125A) have a slender, light brown body and thin semi-transparent wings banded with brown or gray and marked with numerous light brown scalloped lines slightly accented on the veins. Wing expanse is 25 to 30 mm. The adult female (fig. 125B) is wingless and covered with large scales. The color is dull ochreous brown interspersed with irregular patches of white. The mature larva is stout, about 18 mm long, and light green with three yellowish lines on each side (fig. 125C). The newly laid eggs are pale green later turning to bright orange.

The eggs are laid singly in bark crevices (fig. 125D) in the fall and remain dormant until spring. The larvae hatch when the aspen buds begin to burst. Many of the first-instar larvae spin down on silk threads and are dispersed by the wind. Larval development is completed by late June in Alberta. Pupae are formed in cocoons in the soil and remain there until late fall.

FIGURE 125.—Bruce spanworm (*Operophtera bruceata*): *A*, Male adult, wing-spread 28 mm; *B*, wingless female adult, 12 mm long; *C*, mature larva, 18 mm long; *D*, eggs in bark crevice, each 1 mm long.

Operophtera occidentalis (Hulst) (Sugden 1966) feeds on poplar, willow, maple, oak, and alder in coastal Oregon and British Columbia. The larvae resemble those of *O. bruceata*.

The **spring cankerworm,** *Paleacrita vernata* (Peck) (Jones and Schaffner 1953), is distributed over much the same area as the fall cankerworm but is not reported from Alberta. These two insects also are similar in appearance and habits. The spring cankerworm differs from the fall cankerworm in that the larvae do not have prolegs on the fifth abdominal segment; the pupae are not enclosed in cocoons; the eggs are pearly and oval rather than brownish gray and shaped like a flowerpot; and the moth emerges in the spring rather than in the fall. The spring cankerworm is a pest of orchards and shelterbelts and especially likes Siberian elm.

Phaeoura mexicanaria (Groté) (Dewey 1975) occurs in British Columbia, Montana, Wyoming, South Dakota, New Mexico, Arizona, California, and other Western States. It feeds on *Pinus ponderosa.* The only reported outbreak was in 1969 and 1970 when it moderately to heavily defoliated 63,000 acres of pine in southeastern Montana. Collapse of the outbreak was attributed to disease organisms, principally a bacterium. *Ips* killed a high percentage of the trees completely defoliated by the looper.

The adults are mottled brownish gray with zigzag markings on the wings, characteristic of many loopers. The wingspan is about 45 to 60 mm. The larvae markedly resemble a rough twig of the host tree. Mature larvae are 45 mm long, tan to dark brown, and covered with granules and tubercles. The head is strongly notched.

Eggs are laid on the needles in clusters averaging 160 per cluster. The larvae feed indiscriminately on new and old foliage. Pupation is in the litter under infested trees. Pupae overwinter. There is one generation per year. Specific control measures have not been developed.

Rheumaptera [*Eulype*] (McGuffin 1973) contains two species in North America. Both are predominantly day flyers, and occur in northern forests from Newfoundland to Alaska and in most Western States except those of the Great Basin. The adults are black and white moths of widely varied patterns (fig. 126). They occur together and can be distinguished only by differences in genitalia. The larvae of both feed on leaves of northern hardwoods, principally birch, alder, and willow.

The **spearmarked black moth,** *Rheumaptera hastata* (L.) (Hard 1967, Sugden 1966), apparently prefers birch. Outbreaks on birch have occurred in South Dakota, British Columbia, and Alaska. The most extensive covered nearly 6 million acres in 1957 in central Alaska. A rapid decline of that outbreak was attributed to a granulosis virus and parasites. Effects of such outbreaks are not recorded. The larvae, sometimes called the **black looper,** are dark brown to black. Spiracles on front abdominal segments are surrounded by one large or several small light patches. The larvae tie the leaves into tentlike shelters and skeletonize them. They overwinter as pupae in the soil. Adults (fig. 126) fly in spring.

F–521997

FIGURE 126.—Adult of spearmarked black moth (*Rheumaptera hastata*), wingspread 30 mm.

Rheumaptera subhastata (Nolcken) (McGuffin 1973) closely resembles *R. hastata* and has essentially the same distribution, but usually occurs on alder. The body of the mature larva is light brown with darker lines on the back. Spiracles on front abdominal segments are in a light stripe.

Semiothisa (McGuffin 1972, Ferguson 1974) contains about 100 species in North America, many of which occur in the West. Most of them feed on conifers, some on broad-leaved trees and shrubs. Two or more species sometimes are very numerous without causing economic damage (Ross and Evans 1958). The **larch looper,** *S. sexmaculata sexmaculata* (Packard), is transcontinental on *Larix laricina*; a western subspecies, *S. sexmaculata incolorata* (Dyar), occurs in British Columbia, Idaho, Oregon, and Washington on *Larix occidentalis* and *Pseudotsuga menziesii*. At maturity larvae are greenish or brownish, marked with off-white, and about 15 mm long. *S. signaria dispuncta* (Walker), to which the name *S. granitata* has been erroneously applied, occurs from California to Montana and Washington, and northward through the Western Provinces to the Northwest Territories and southeast Alaska. Larvae feed on *Picea, Abies, Tsuga, Larix,* and *Pseudotsuga.* At maturity larvae are bluish green, shaded with white, and 20 to 28 mm long.

SUPERFAMILY NOCTUOIDEA

This superfamily contains a very large number of species. Although the adults of the various families display similarities, larvae in some families are extremely hairy while in others they are smooth skinned.

FAMILY ARCTIIDAE—TIGER MOTHS

The **tiger moths** are a rather small family of stout-bodied moths with broad and attractively colored wings. They are so named because many of the moths are spotted or striped. The caterpillars are robust and very hairy. The ones with uniformly dense hair are called **woolly bears.** Some others having the hair in brushes and tufts are called **tussock moths,** although this name is more commonly applied to some species of the Lymantriidae.

Halisidota consists of about 15 species, most of which feed on deciduous trees and shrubs. Two species feeding on conifers are occasional forest pests. Larvae of some *Halisidota* are gregarious and construct unsightly webs, others are solitary feeders.

The **silverspotted tiger moth**, *Halisidota argentata* Packard (Silver 1958), ranges from California to southwest British Columbia, feeding principally on Douglas-fir but also on western hemlock, lodgepole pine, grand fir, Sitka spruce, western redcedar, and several other conifers. In 1954–55 it occurred in outbreak form on southern Vancouver Island. It is a recurrent pest of conifers, especially in coastal areas. Damage is usually spotty and the insect is controlled by its natural enemies.

The adult is a strikingly colored, yellowish-brown moth having a wingspread of 39 to 53 mm (fig. 127A). The forewings are reddish brown with numerous distinct silvery-white spots, and hindwings are whitish with a few brown marks near the outer margin. Adults fly in July and August and deposit green, hemispherical eggs in loose clusters on twigs and needles of host trees. The eggs hatch in about 3 weeks, and the small brown, hairy caterpillars feed in colonies on needles of lateral branches, forming loose webs containing dead needles and other debris (fig. 127B). Feeding continues into fall and the larvae overwinter in the webs. In spring, larvae continue their gregarious feeding until they are about two-thirds grown, then disperse and feed individually. The mature larva (fig. 127C) is about 37 mm long, generally reddish brown but with forward-projecting tufts of yellow and brown hair and dorsal tufts of black hair flanked with yellow hairs. These tufts contain poisonous hairs that cause a rash on some people. In June, larvae spin brownish cocoons composed of silk and larval body hairs, which are attached to parts of the defoliated trees or to debris on the forest floor.

F–521998, F–518946, F–521999

FIGURE 127.—Silverspotted tiger moth (*Halisidota argentata*): *A*, Adult, wingspread 45 mm; *B*, larval colony on spruce; *C*, mature larva, 35 mm long.

Halisidota argentata sobrina Stretch is a form which feeds on Monterey pine in the coastal area of California. In comparison with *argentata,* the wings of the adult have smaller white spots and a more uniform brown ground color. The larva is usually darker in color with less yellow hair on its body.

Halisidota argentata subalpina French is a form which feeds on juniper and occasionally pinyon in the Rocky Mountain region. In 1964, it caused considerable defoliation of juniper in Utah over an area of 5,000 acres. The moth closely resembles that of *argentata.*

Halisidota ingens Hy. Edwards occurs in Colorado, Utah, New Mexico, and Arizona on young ponderosa pine and pinyon. Its larvae feed gregariously in large webs and damage is usually limited to the upper foliage (fig. 128). The adult has dark brown forewings with large, white splotches and white hindwings; its body is covered with buff-colored hairs.

The **spotted tussock moth,** *Halisidota maculata* (Harris), ranges from coast to coast in the Northern States and Southern Canada, and through the Western States. It feeds on willow, oak, maple, birch, alder, poplar, and many other trees and shrubs. It is a solitary defoliator, periodically causing light damage in Alberta and Saskatchewan. The adult has tan forewings with wavy brown splotches and has a spread of about 44 mm. The hindwings and body are buff colored. The caterpillar is about 30 mm long and is

F–516029

FIGURE 128. — Large tent formed by larvae of *Halisidota ingens.*

densely covered with black hairs with a few white and yellow hairs intermixed and a wide belt of shorter, tufted black hair in the middle.

The **pale tussock moth**, *Halisidota tesselaris* (J. B. Smith), is an eastern North American species that is recorded in the West only from New Mexico. Here it feeds on alder and boxelder and is a nuisance in recreational areas. The adult is pale yellow and has a wingspread of about 50 mm. The forewings are translucent and crossed by five broad, darkish bands. The mature larva is darkish but densely clothed with compact tufts of light yellow or whitish hairs, and bears two pairs of black pencil tufts, one in front and one in the rear.

Hyphantria consists of one very common species, *H. cunea* (Drury). *H. textor* Harris, referred to in the older literature as a separate species or form, is now considered synonymous with *H. cunea*.

The **fall webworm**, *Hyphantria cunea* (Drury) (Warren and Tadic 1970), is a common defoliator of many hardwood trees, and occurs coast to coast from southern Canada through the 48 States to northern Mexico. In the West it is found mostly on alder, ash, chokeberry, cottonwood, madrone, maple, willow, and various fruit trees. Its damage is of minor importance in forestry. However, infestations in ornamental plantings sometimes affect esthetic values enough to warrant control.

Adults have a nearly white body, white wings with occasionally a few black spots, orange markings on body and legs, and a wing expanse of about 30 mm. Eggs are light green or yellow, globular, and are laid in masses consisting of several hundred eggs. In the larval stage, two races are recognizable—a blackheaded race predominant in the northern part of the range, and a redheaded race in the southerly areas. At maturity, larvae are 30 to 35 mm long. Mature larvae of the northern strain have a black head, a pale yellowish or greenish body with a dark stripe on the back, and long whitish hairs on the sides arising from black and orange tubercles. Mature larvae of the southern strain have a deep orange or reddish head, a yellowish-tan body, with orange to reddish tubercles and brownish hair. Pupae are 8 to 14 mm long, stout, and a reddish-brown color.

In the northerly part of the range and also in mountainous areas, the fall webworm has one brood a year. Adults appear from late June to early July, fly at night, and lay eggs in flat masses on the underside of leaves. Larvae feed gregariously, forming large webs on the branches of trees. In the northern form, which appears to predominate in the West, the webs are thin and flimsy. Small larvae feed on the epidermis of both leaf surfaces, leaving the veins untouched (fig. 129A), while large larvae (fig. 129B) consume the whole leaf except for the petiole. Larvae feed until about mid-September, then form thin transparent cocoons in the soil, among litter, on sides of buildings, or on tree trunks. Here they pupate and overwinter.

F–522000, F–522001

FIGURE 129.—Fall webworm (*Hyphantria cunea*): *A*, Small larvae skeletonizing elm leaves; *B*, mature larva, 30 mm long.

The **cinnabar moth**, *Tyria* [*Hypocrita*] *jacobaeae* (L.) (Hawkes 1968), was introduced from Europe to control tansy ragwort, a weed toxic to cattle and horses. It has been colonized locally in the Pacific Coast States and British Columbia. Under favorable conditions, it can drastically reduce density and flowering of tansy ragwort in about 5 years.

The adult is a brightly-colored, black and red moth which flies in May and June. The yellow- and black-banded hairy larvae feed at first on the undersides and edges of leaves, then consume flowers and stems as well as leaves. Pupae are formed in late summer and overwinter. There is one generation a year.

Cinnabar moth populations build up gradually and disperse slowly; hence to effect control by this moth, it usually has to be introduced into new areas of ragwort infestation.

FAMILY DIOPTIDAE

This family consists of a single genus containing a single species in North America.

The **California oakworm**, *Phryganidia californica* Packard (Brown and Eads 1965a, Wickman 1971), feeds on oaks from northern to southern California, mostly in coastal, areas. It is an important pest of ornamental California live oak and to a lesser degree California white oak and other oaks. In Oregon its occurs on golden chinkapin. Chestnut, tanoak, eucalyptus, and azalea are recorded as incidental hosts. Most years it causes little concern, but at irregular intervals it becomes epidemic and defoliates oaks over extensive areas. It slows growth of the attacked trees and makes them unsightly but seldom if ever kills them directly. The young larvae skeletonize the leaves in patches. The older larvae eat all except the main veins.

The adults are weak fliers. They have translucent, thinly-scaled, gray-brown wings, with darker veins (fig. 130A). Wingspread is 25 to 35 mm. The mature larvae (fig. 130B) are 25 mm long and olive green, with conspicuous black and yellow longitudinal stripes on the back and sides, and the head as wide or wider than the body. The pupae (fig. 130C) are 12 mm long, shining, smooth, and whitish or yellowish with black markings. The eggs (fig. 130D) are about 1 mm long, spherical, white turning to gray, and laid in

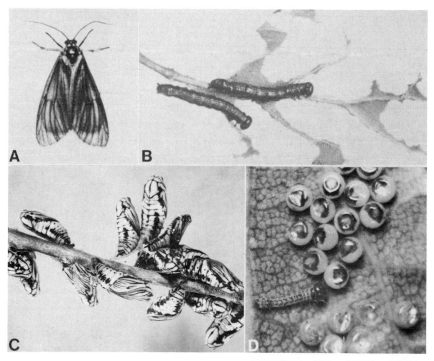

F–501522, EPQ–8511, F–516041, F–501520

FIGURE 130.—California oakworm (*Phryganidia californica*): *A*, Adult, body 9 mm long; *B*, mature larvae, 25 mm long; *C*, pupae, 12 mm long; *D*, eggs, each 1 mm in diameter.

masses on leaves and elsewhere. Eggs laid on live oak leaves are the principal survivors in the overwintering generation.

There are two generations a year in northern California and three in southern California. In the latter area there is much overlapping of broods. In northern California eggs laid in October and November mostly hatch by December but some not until March. The larvae mature in May and June. The adults from this generation lay eggs in June and July. By September the feeding of the summer generation is largely completed.

Outbreaks are of short duration, presumably being controlled by starvation, parasites, predators, and a virus disease. Spraying may be necessary for esthetic reasons during epidemics. It is directed against the small larvae in March and April or in July and early August.

FAMILY LYMANTRIIDAE (LIPARIDAE)— TUSSOCK MOTHS

The **tussock moths,** a small family of very destructive defoliators, feed on coniferous as well as broad-leaved trees. In western forests the family is represented by several native species in two genera and two introduced species, both in different genera.

Adults of the Lymantriidae are either dark brown or white, hairy moths, chiefly nocturnal in habit. The males are active fliers but the females are generally sedentary. In some species, females are flightless because their wings are reduced to small pads. In others, females are restricted in movement by the size of their egg-laden abdomens. Full-grown larvae are strikingly marked with colored glands or tubercles and have prominent tufts of hairs on their bodies. The larval hairs are easily detached and in some species are somewhat poisonous to humans, causing a skin rash or other form of allergy.

Females lay small white eggs, usually in large masses cemented with a frothy secretion and covered by a mat of hairs. The eggs hatch into tiny, very hairy caterpillars which are often picked up and carried by air currents for long distances. The dispersion of airborne larvae is an important means of initiating new infestations. Larger larvae, when disturbed or in search of food, lower themselves to the ground by silken threads and disperse to other food plants. Pupation usually takes place in dense, silken cocoons, often containing larval hairs, attached to parts of trees, underbrush, or man-made objects. Transport of cocoons or egg masses on recreational vehicles is now recognized as an important means of long distance dispersal, particularly for introduced species.

Orgyia [*Hemerocampa*] is represented in the West by at least five species. One of these feeds almost exclusively on conifers; the others prefer hardwoods but occasionally feed on conifers. Female moths have rudimentary wings and deposit egg masses on their cocoons; eggs overwinter. The genus poses taxonomic problems not yet fully resolved.

The **rusty tussock moth**, *Orgyia* [*Notolophus*] *antiqua* (L.), (Hardy 1945, Prebble and Graham 1945), occurs throughout Southern Canada and Northern United States, and also in Europe. In the West it is distributed from California to Alaska and eastward to Montana. Its hosts are many. In the West, common hardwood hosts include alder, blueberry, willow, birch, maple, and apple, and common coniferous hosts are western hemlock, spruces, western larch, Douglas-fir, and true firs. Conspicuous defoliation of western hemlock sometimes occurs in coastal forests of British Columbia. Both new and old foliage of hemlock is fed upon.

The adult male is an erratic-flying rusty-brown moth having a conspicuous white dot and a light brown band on each forewing. The female is a sedentary, humped creature, about 12 mm long, with rudimentary wings (fig. 131A). The body is black and densely covered with light tan hairs, and appears grayish above and light tan on the sides. In contrast with most other species of *Orgyia*, its egg mass (fig. 131B) is free of froth and scales. The dark hairy caterpillar (fig. 131C) is about 28 mm long at maturity. It has two black hair-pencils projecting forward and one projecting to the rear, four golden brushes of hairs on its back, and eight warty protuberances on each segment from which arise yellowish and blackish hairs. There are either one or two generations a year depending on the location. Overwintering is in the egg stage.

The **whitemarked tussock moth**, *Orgyia leucostigma* J. E. Smith (Baker 1972), occurs mainly in Eastern Canada and Eastern

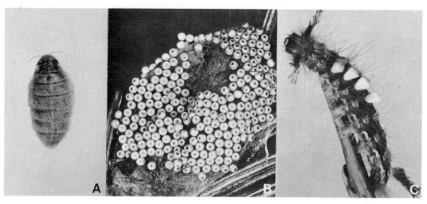

F-522002, F-522003, F-522004

FIGURE 131.—Rusty tussock moth (*Orgyia antiqua*) : *A*, Adult female, 12 mm long; *B*, egg mass, 14 mm long; *C*, mature larva, 28 mm long.

United States and feeds on a wide variety of deciduous and coniferous trees. It is a pest of shade trees, but also occurs in forested areas where it causes only minor damage. In the West it is recorded from Alberta, the Prairie Provinces, Colorado, and Texas. In Texas it has damaged shade trees, particularly oaks. The mature larva may be recognized by its coral-red head and yellow coloration on the sides.

The **Douglas fir tussock moth**, *Orgyia pseudotsugata* (McDunnough), also recorded as *oslari* Barnes (Johnson and Ross 1967, Wickman et al. 1973b), is a defoliator of major importance in the interior Douglas-fir and true fir forests of western North America. It ranges from southern British Columbia through the eastern half of the Pacific coast States and through the Rocky Mountain States south to Arizona and New Mexico. In the central part of its distribution, this tussock moth shows equal preference for Douglas-fir, grand fir, white fir, and subalpine fir. In British Columbia it feeds mainly on Douglas-fir and in California mainly on white fir. It will feed on other conifer species such as ponderosa pine when they are intermixed with firs, and on adjacent shrubs such as bitterbrush.

Outbreaks develop explosively and after about 3 years subside abruptly. Between outbreaks this insect is seldom seen. Since the first reported outbreaks at Chase, British Columbia, in 1916, and at Jarbridge, Nevada, in 1927, numerous infestations have caused economic losses. Among the most severe were those in northeastern Washington in 1927 to 1930, which killed over 300 million board feet of Douglas-fir and grand fir; in eastern Oregon from 1937 to 1939; in northern Idaho and eastern Oregon and Washington from 1946 to 1948; in the Sierra Nevada of central California from 1954 to 1956; and again in northern Idaho from 1961 to 1965. The last three outbreaks were controlled by aerial spraying before much timber was killed. Severe but generally less extensive infestations occurred in British Columbia during the periods 1919–21, 1928–31, 1945–49, and 1961–64. An outbreak in Oregon, Washington, and northern Idaho that began in 1971 covered almost 800,000 acres in 1973. Accumulated timber and growth losses reached 1 billion fbm of timber, thus creating major problems in salvage, forest regeneration, and fire prevention.

When young, the caterpillar of the Douglas fir tussock moth is blackish with very long body hairs. As it grows, it becomes a striking looking creature, with brightly colored tufts of hair. The mature larva (fig. 132A) is 25 to 30 mm long, with a gray or brown body and shiny black head. Two long pencils of black hairs project forward from behind the head and a similar pencil occurs at the rear of the body. Dense light brown or cream colored

FIGURE 132. Douglas fir tussock moth (*Orgyia pseudotsugata*): *A*, Mature larva, 28 mm long; *B*, adult female, 18 mm long; *C*, adult male, 28 mm wingspread; *D*, egg mass, 12 mm in diameter, covered with body hairs.

brushes of hairs and red spots occur on the first four and last abdominal segments. On each side of the body is an orange stripe, while the lower part of the body is nearly naked. The body hairs are irritating to some humans and may cause a severe rash. The larva spins a brownish-gray, spindle-shaped cocoon covered with larval hairs and transforms to a stout yellow-brown pupa.

The adult is a dull brownish-gray moth with a furry body, 12 to 20 mm long. The female (fig. 132B) has tiny rudimentary wings and a fat abdomen, and is camouflaged as it rests on its cocoon. The male (fig. 132C) has full-sized, brownish-gray forewings spreading about 30 mm, and marked with a whitish dot near the wing margin and irregular light and darkish lines. The hindwings are a uniform brown color. The egg mass (fig. 132D), which is formed on the female's cocoon, consists of about 300 white spherical eggs in one to three layers, covered with a frothy gelatinous substance containing intermixed body hairs.

There is one generation a year. Adults appear from late July to early September, depending upon locality and season. Females remain on their cocoons where, after mating, they lay eggs. The egg masses overwinter. Larvae hatch from eggs in late May or early June after the new foliage has appeared. Because of their light bodies and long hairs, they are readily dispersed by winds. At first the larvae feed on the unfolding new needles causing them to die and give the forest a strong reddish cast for a short time. During this period the tips of trees often wear conspicuous white caps of silk laid on by the migrating larvae. As the larvae mature, they feed on both new and old foliage. A heavily infested forest becomes brownish, even purplish, as the bare twigs are exposed. The larvae mature late in summer. In light infestations cocoons are formed mostly on the foliage; whereas in heavy infestations cocoons are mostly on tree trunks and objects on the ground. The pupal stage is completed in 10 to 14 days. The cocoons and egg masses are among the most conspicuous evidence of tussock moth abundance.

The Douglas fir tussock moth has many natural enemies including disease organisms, insect parasites and predators, and birds. A nucleopolyhedrosis virus is capable of wiping out populations, but it usually appears after trees have been seriously defoliated. Infected larvae hang limply from the twigs. A scelionid wasp egg parasite, *Telonomus* species, and two parasites which attack larvae: an ichneumon, *Phobocampe pallipes* (Provancher), and a tachinid fly, *Carcelia yalensis* Sellers, sometimes hasten the decline of an outbreak.

Direct control is often needed to subdue tussock moth infestations before severe economic damage occurs. Formulations of the nucleopolyhedrosis virus show promise for operational use. Chemical insecticides presently registered for tussock moth control are only partially effective.

The typical form of the **western tussock moth**, *Orgyia vetusta* Boisduval, occurs in the Pacific Coast States and especially in California, where it feeds on oak, poplar, willow, deciduous and citrus fruit trees, and walnut. It is of minor importance in the forest.

A subspecies, *O. vetusta gulosa* Hy. Edwards (Furniss and Knopf 1971), is an important defoliator of big game browse plants in Idaho and western Nevada. It feeds on snowbrush, bitterbrush, and to a lesser extent willow, serviceberry, wild rose, desert peach, and bittercherry. Damage is in the form of branch-killing. The mature larva differs from related *Orgyia* species by having yellowish stripes on its upperbody. The brownish female is almost completely covered with wavy, whitish-gray hair, and its egg mass, laid on the cocoon, is covered with the whitish-gray body hairs.

An *Orgyia* (Flake and Lyon 1967) of uncertain specific name occurs in New Mexico, Arizona, and Utah. It is a nuisance pest of boxelder, sometimes requiring control, as in 1966 on the Gila National Forest, N. Mex. It also feeds on black walnut, sycamore, willow, and cherry. The caterpillars are light colored, as with *O. leucostigma.*

Parorgyia [*Dasychira, Olene*] consists of about 20 species in North America, most of which occur in the East. In this group of tussock moths, the females have normal wings but are limited in movement by their heavy bodies. Mature larvae are very hairy and have two long hair pencils in the front, as in *Orgyia,* but in contrast have three hair pencils in the rear. Two essentially eastern species range through Southern Canada to the West. *P. plagiata* Walker, which feeds mostly on conifers, ranges as far as Alberta. *P. vagans* Barnes and McDunnough, mostly a hardwood feeder, ranges to central British Columbia.

A **pine tussock moth,** *Parorgyia grisefacta* (Dyar) (Ross and Evans 1954, Tunnock 1966), occurs in interior British Columbia, southern Alberta, and eastern Montana. In British Columbia common hosts are Douglas-fir, western hemlock, and white spruce, but several other conifers are fed upon. In eastern Montana, ponderosa pine is the principal host. In 1965 a major epidemic was discovered in the Custer National Forest of Montana. Defoliation of young ponderosa pines on 42,000 acres was visible from the air, and the tussock moth was found on another 250,000 acres. The infestation gradually declined during the following 3 years, largely due to a nucleopolyhedrosis virus.

The adult is a grayish-brown moth with light and dark bands across the forewings, and it has a wingspread of 30 to 40 mm. Eggs are spherical and whitish and occur in loose clusters. The mature larva has a dark-brown head, a mostly rusty-brown body with the sides blackish, and is about 44 mm long. It has four dirty-white brushes of hairs above, and numerous tufts of white plumed hair scattered over the body. Its fore and aft black hair pencils are typical of the genus. The pupa is enclosed in a whitish silken cocoon.

Adults appear from late July to mid-August, and the females deposit their eggs in small clusters on the pine needles. After a limited amount of feeding, small larvae hibernate under the bark scales on pine trees. In spring they resume feeding and in midsummer pupate in cocoons fastened to twigs.

This tussock moth may become a pest of increasing importance as extensive pine areas are converted to young stands. Little is known of its population dynamics, except that a nucleopolyhedrosis virus appears to be of some importance in natural control.

The **gypsy moth**, *Porthetria dispar* (L.) (Godwin 1972), was introduced from Europe into Massachusetts in 1869. Over the past 100 years, it has gradually spread through the hardwood forest of the Eastern States from Maine to North Carolina and Alabama, with infestations also found in Quebec and the Lake States. In 1970 it was found at one location in California; in 1973 spot infestations were found in Santa Clara, Ventura, Butte, and San Mateo Counties. In the East, the gypsy moth feeds on most hardwoods and some intermixed conifers; hosts acceptable to all larval stages include oaks, willows, poplars, most birches, larch, linden, and apple.

Damaging outbreaks have occurred often in the Northeast, resulting in tree mortality, growth reduction, and impairment of esthetic values. In 1953 severe defoliation occurred on an estimated 1,500,000 acres. Dry sites and open stands are most susceptible to gypsy moth build-up and damage. Thus some parts of the West probably will provide conditions conducive to damage by this insect.

The male moth is light to dark brown and has a wingspread of 37 to 50 mm (fig. 133A). The forewings have a band of dark brown or black along the edge and irregular bands or lines of the same color across the center of the wings. The female has a light brown, or buff-colored body, which is very large for the size of the wings (fig. 133B). The forewings are white, with a pattern of light brown zigzag bands and a row of dark dots along the outer edge. The roundish, cream-colored eggs are laid in masses of 100 to 1,000, covered with buff-colored hairs from the female's abdomen (fig. 133C). The small larva is grayish, with both long and short hairs. The full-grown larva (fig. 133D) varies in size according to its sex, with the males about 37 mm and the females about 50 mm long. It has a mottled yellow head and a grayish body, and each body segment has six or eight wartlike lumps bearing tufts of black or brown hairs. Its dorsum is marked with five pairs of blue spots, followed by six pairs of red spots. The pupa (fig. 133E) is reddish brown and sparsely covered with reddish hairs.

Adults appear in late July and August. The females crawl a short distance from their pupal cases and are mated by the strong-flying, searching males. Females lay their egg masses on tree parts, stumps, stones, buildings, or other objects, and the eggs overwinter. In spring, eggs hatch about the time the oak leaves unfold and the tiny larvae crawl about in search of foliage, often spinning down on silk threads. At this time they may be blown considerable distances. Newly hatched larvae feed first on leaf bases, and then on leaf surfaces. Older larvae feed usually

FIGURE 133.—Gypsy moth (*Porthetria dispar*): *A*, Adult male, wingspread 42 mm; *B*, adult female, wingspread 52 mm; *C*, egg mass, 14 mm long; *D*, mature larva, 48 mm long; *E*, pupa, 22 mm long.

from the edges of leaves, and mostly at night. When trees are stripped, larvae migrate considerable distances in search of food. Mature larvae seek sheltered places for pupation, and pupae are attached by silken threads to tree limbs and trunks, or other objects. The pupal stage lasts 10 to 14 days.

In the Northeast a program of introducing parasites, predators, and pathogens was initiated in 1905 and carried on for 25 years. Two egg parasites, seven larval parasites, and two beetle predators were established. The effectiveness of these insect agents has been limited. A nucleopolyhedrosis virus, apparently introduced by accident, has been effective in wiping out gypsy moth populations after populations have become epidemic. Low winter temperatures may kill gypsy moth eggs and late spring frosts often kill newly-hatched larvae. Despite natural control and intensive chemical control and eradication programs, the gypsy moth continues to be a serious problem in Eastern States and now directly threatens western forests.

The **satin moth**, *Leucoma* [*Stilpnotia*]*salicis* (L.) (Lejeune and Silver 1961), a native of Europe, was found in North America in

1920, both in New England and southwestern British Columbia. In the West it has spread southward to northern California, and into the interior of Oregon, Washington, and southern British Columbia. It now is an occasional pest of poplars planted as shade trees or in windbreaks and will feed on native poplars and willows.

The adult is a white moth with a satiny luster, a wingspread of 37 to 50 mm, black eyes and legs, and a body clothed with long white satiny hairs. The full-grown caterpillar is about 50 mm long, blackish with a row of nearly square white marks along the back and white markings on the sides. On the upper part of its body are prominent reddish-brown tubercles bearing clumps of brownish hair.

There is one generation a year. Moths fly in July and deposit eggs in oval masses, covered with a white satiny secretion, on trees or various objects. The young larvae feed for a short time, then spin hibernacula in bark crevices where they pass the winter. They resume feeding in the spring and larvae reach maturity in June. They pupate in loosely woven cocoons attached to leaves, twigs, or other objects.

Following its introduction into British Columbia, the satin moth was considered a pest of economic importance. However, the introduction of European parasites of the moth during 1929 to 1934 resulted in successful biological control (Turnbull and Chant 1961). Three parasites have become generally distributed, and of these the braconid, *Apanteles solitarius* (Ratzeburg), is particularly effective. A combination of introduced and native parasites now generally restricts the amount of damage, except in new, outlying infestations.

FAMILY NOCTUIDAE (PHALAENIDAE)—OWLET MOTHS AND UNDERWINGS

The Noctuidae (Crumb 1956) is the largest family of the Lepidoptera. The larvae (fig. 134A) are generally drab, hairless, sluggish, and nocturnal. Some are known as **cutworms** because they often cut off the stems of young succulent plants. Many are destructive to agricultural crops. Many feed on trees and shrubs but few are forest pests. The adults are dull-colored, heavy-bodied, night-flying moths (fig. 134B) that hold their wings folded tent-fashion at rest. The pupae generally are naked and overwinter in the soil (fig. 134C).

Achytonix, in contrast with most genera of the Noctuidae, contains only one species in North America.

Achytonix epipaschia (Groté) (= *praeacuta* Smith) (Crumb 1956) occurs in British Columbia, the Pacific Coast States, Idaho, Colorado, and Arizona, feeding principally on Douglas-fir and

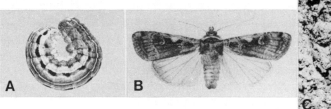

F–522007, COURTESY WASHINGTON STATE UNIVERSITY, F–522008

FIGURE 134.—Examples of Noctuidae: *A*, Mature larva, 40 mm long; *B*, adult, 40 mm wingspread; *C*, pupa, 16 mm long.

occasionally on associated conifers. It rarely causes damage by itself but in conjunction with other Noctuidae has caused noticeable defoliation on Douglas-fir.

The small larva feeds in spring on opening buds and then on the expanding new foliage. At first it is brownish with a black head, but soon becomes green with three longitudinal white stripes above and a pale head. The mature larva is 20 to 28 mm long, tapering from front to rear. It pupates in a silken cocoon amongst the fir needles, and the grayish adult emerges in midsummer. There is one generation a year.

Acronicta has over 100 species, many of which feed on the foliage of forest and shade trees. At least 25 species occur in the West. They are solitary feeders and mostly rare. Some are known as **dagger moths** because of a daggerlike mark near the anal angle of the forewing.

The **American dagger moth**, *Acronicta americana* (Harris) (Crumb 1956), is an eastern species ranging westward to Alberta, Idaho, Utah, Colorado, Nevada, and Arizona. It feeds on the leaves of several deciduous trees and shrubs and particularly on maples and birches. In the West it is an occasional pest of shade trees, such as boxelder and silver maple, but is of little importance in the forest.

The mature larva is about 50 mm long and has a black head and greenish-white body, marked with single dark stripes above and on the sides. The body is clothed with fine yellowish hairs and bears two divergent black hair pencils forward and one similar hair pencil at the rear. Larvae feed through most of the summer and in early fall spin dense silken cocoons in which they pupate.

The **cottonwood dagger moth**, *Acronicta lepusculina* Guenée (Crumb 1956), occurs from coast to coast in Southern Canada and the Northern States, and in the West ranges southward to California and Arizona. It feeds on leaves of *Alnus*, *Betula*, *Populus*, and *Salix*, with trembling aspen its favorite host.

231

The mature larva is about 40 mm long and differs from the American dagger moth in having a yellowish body and black hair pencils on the middle of most abdominal segments. Larvae feed through most of the summer, then pupate in dense silken cocoons. Pupae are the overwintering stage.

The **black army cutworm**, *Actebia fennica* (Tauscher) (Wood and Neilson 1956), occurs from Maine to British Columbia and north to Alaska. It is a climbing species that feeds on the foliage of many herbs and shrubs. Occasionally it damages coniferous plantings on new burns devoid of vegetation. Lodgepole pine and white spruce seedlings were damaged in this manner in 1973 at several places in British Columbia. The mature larvae are velvety black above, grayish below, and have two narrow white stripes on each side. They feed in the spring. First-instar larvae hibernate. There is one generation per year.

Euxoa has about 200 species in North America, many of which are of economic importance in agriculture. The larvae are typical cutworms. One species known usually as a pest of vegetable gardens occurs in fields and forests as a pest of conifer seedlings.

Euxoa excellens Groté (Fowells 1940, Gibson 1917) occurs in British Columbia, Oregon, California, Colorado, and probably elsewhere in the West. Although usually an agricultural pest, in the late 1930's it killed large numbers of natural and nursery-grown tree seedlings in the California pine region. In nurseries the seedling kill was about 50 percent for incense-cedar and progressively less for white fir, ponderosa pine, and sugar pine. In artificially seeded spots, the highest kill of ponderosa and Jeffrey pine seedlings was in cutover areas.

Larvae feed in spring on the young seedlings, damaging the cotyledons and cutting off the stems. Full-grown larvae are about 40 mm long and have a pale brown head and grayish-white body dotted with brown tubercles. They pupate in the soil after forming earthen cells. Moths emerge in August and are in flight into September. They lay eggs which presumably overwinter.

Homoncocnemis (Crumb 1956) contains two closely related species. *H. fortis* (Groté) occurs in Oregon, California, Arizona, Utah, and Colorado. The larvae feed on *Fraxinus*. They are black with four white lines along the back. The moths fly in late summer.

Orthosia and at least one closely related genus contain some species known as **green fruitworms**. Although these species occur in the forest they are best known as feeders on the green fruit of apple, pear, and cherry.

Orthosia hibisci (Guenée) (Prentice 1962) is a transcontinental species that feeds on the foliage of many deciduous trees and shrubs and on some conifers. It is common in the Pacific Northwest, Manitoba, Saskatchewan, and Alberta, particularly on trembling aspen, and in Alaska has been recorded as defoliating birch, willow, and alder. Mature larvae are about 40 mm long, green with yellow flecks, and have a middorsal white line and two narrower lines on each side. Pupae overwinter in the soil and adults fly in spring.

Peridroma consists of one cosmopolitan species, *P. saucia* (Hübner) (= *margaritosa* Haworth) (Crumb 1956), known as the **variegated cutworm**. *P. saucia* is widely distributed in the Americas from Alaska to Patagonia and is common on the Pacific Slope. It is an important pest of field and garden crops and an occasional pest of seedling conifers. It has damaged ponderosa, Jeffrey, and sugar pine seedlings in seed spots in California, and Douglas-fir seedlings in nursery beds in southwest British Columbia.

The adults are difficult to distinguish from those of many other cutworm moths. The large larvae usually hide in the soil during the day and feed at night; small larvae often stay on the plants. The mature larva (fig. 135) is smooth skinned, pale gray to dark brown, and about 40 mm long. The body is marked above with a single line of four or more yellow to orange dots and two rows of linear black marks bordered with a broken yellow or orange line.

Three or more generations may occur in a single year depending on the locality. The spring-feeding generation causes the most damage. Overwintering takes place in the pupal stage.

Scoliopteryx libatrix (L.) occurs in Northern United States and Southern Canada and throughout the West from Alaska to the Southwestern States and California. It is common in Alberta, British Columbia, Washington, and Oregon, and has caused conspicuous defoliation of willow, its principal host, in southwest British Columbia.

FIGURE 135.—Mature larva of the variegated cutworm (*Peridroma saucia*), 40 mm long.

Adults appear in spring and larvae feed on leaves from late May to mid-September. The mature larva has a grayish-green head and a green body marked with a yellowish line on each side. It is about 40 mm long and the body tapers toward the rear. Pupation occurs from late June to late September. Adults emerge the same summer and overwinter in sheltered places, such as caves.

Xylomyges consists of slightly over a dozen species, mostly restricted to the West. Some feed on conifers, others on hardwoods, and some on both. A few species are sufficiently common in some areas to warrant attention.

Xylomyges simplex (Walker) (Hardy 1962, Godfrey 1972) is recorded from British Columbia, the Pacific Coast States, Colorado, Arizona, and New Mexico. Its hosts include *Pseudotsuga menziesii*, *Alnus rubra*, *Populus*, *Prunus*, *Ribes*, *Salix*, and *Quercus arizonensis*. In 1964 this species defoliated Douglas-fir and associated conifers on an area of 8,000 acres in western Oregon.

The adult is a light ash-gray moth having a 40 mm wingspread and forewings marked with black bars, lines, and dots. It flies in spring and deposits eggs in groups on foliage. On Douglas-fir the larva feeds in the opening buds and then on the new foliage. In the intermediate instars it has a shiny black head and an olive-green body marked above with longitudinal white lines and black tubercles (fig. 136). At maturity the larva is 30 mm long, with a large reddish-brown head and a translucent green body tinged with yellow or lavender. The lines and tubercles are now inconspicuous. In mid- or late July, the larvae drop to the ground and pupate in the soil. The pupa overwinters.

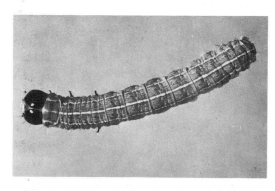

F–522009

FIGURE 136.—Partly grown larva of *Xylomyges simplex*, 18 mm long.

FAMILY NOTODONTIDAE—NOTODONTID MOTHS

More than 100 species of **notodontid moths** occur in the United States and Canada, and their larvae feed on the foliage of deciduous trees and shrubs. The moths of some species have a prominence or backward-projecting lobe on the front wings, which suggested the early common name of "prominents" for this group. Many of the larvae have striking protuberances while others are humpbacked. Some are gregarious feeders, others are solitary. Although many species occur in the forest, the ones feeding on fruit trees and shade trees are best known.

Datana consists of some 15 species, known collectively as the **handmaid moths**. The larvae feed in colonies and are common on various forest, fruit, and shade trees. When a colony is disturbed, larvae exhibit a defensive behavior in which each larva elevates both ends of its body. All species have a single generation a year. Moths appear in midsummer, eggs are laid in a cluster on a leaf, larvae are conspicuous in late summer, and pupae overwinter in the soil.

The **yellownecked caterpillar**, *Datana ministra* (Drury), occurs from coast to coast in Southern Canada and over most of the United States. In the West it is recorded from the Prairie Provinces, Alberta, interior British Columbia, the Pacific Coast States, Idaho, and the northern Great Plains. Hosts include species of *Betula*, *Crataegus*, *Amelanchier*, *Prunus*, *Salix*, *Quercus*, and other trees and shrubs. Conspicuous defoliation of birch and serviceberry sometimes occurs in the interior of British Columbia. In California damage is chiefly to orchard trees.

The adult is a medium-sized moth having a dark prothorax and cinnamon-brown forewings marked with a network of black lines. Wingspread is about 50 mm. The mature larva is 44 mm long, and has a black head, a yellowish-brown thoracic shield, and a black body marked with several yellow lines and bearing a few long gray hairs.

Small larvae skeletonize the lower surface of leaves, but the larger larvae consume entire leaves except for the petioles. Clusters of striped larvae feeding on the foliage or resting on tree trunks are the best evidence of infestation.

The **walnut caterpillar**, *Datana integerrima* Groté and Robinson, occurs principally in the East where it is frequently a serious pest of black walnut, butternut, and hickories. It has been recorded in outbreak numbers in southeastern New Mexico, feeding on Texas black walnut. Larvae resemble those of *D. ministra* but are hairier and lack a yellowish thoracic shield. They feed in colonies (fig. 137A) until almost full grown, and often congregate on the trunk and lower limbs at molting time. Eggs are laid in flat masses on the upper surface of leaflets (fig. 137B).

The **variable oakleaf caterpillar**, *Heterocampa manteo* (Doubleday) (Wilson 1971b), is the most important of several eastern

FIGURE 137.—Walnut caterpillar (*Datana integerrima*) : *A*, Larval colony on walnut; *B*, egg masses on tree leaflets.

species of *Heterocampa* that impinge on the western region. In the East it often causes widespread defoliation of oaks, particularly white oaks, and many other hardwoods. In the West it has been recorded as damaging oaks in Texas; basswood, paper birch, elm, and oak in North Dakota; and plum in South Dakota.

The ash-gray adults, having a wingspread of 37 to 42 mm, appear in midsummer and deposit eggs singly on the leaves. Young larvae skeletonize the lower leaf surfaces and larger larvae eat the entire leaves, except for the veins. Mature larvae are yellowish green, usually with a dark band down the back, and about 37 mm long. In northerly areas they complete feeding around mid-September, spin cocoons in the ground litter or soil, and overwinter as prepupae.

The **mirrorback caterpillar**, *Pheosia rimosa* Packard (Prentice 1962), occurs from coast to coast in Southern Canada and Northern United States. It is a solitary defoliator on *Populus*, *Salix*, and *Betula*, and occasionally common in Alberta and British Columbia. The larva is about 50 mm long and glossy green or yellowish brown, with a horn on the eighth abdominal segment. Like many other notodontids, the larvae feed late in summer and the pupae overwinter.

Schizura is represented by about 10 species in North America, all of which feed on deciduous trees and shrubs. Some of these range westward, but only one is an economic pest in the West.

The **redhumped caterpillar**, *Schizura concinna* (J. E. Smith) (Ross and Evans 1961), occurs westward in Canada to southeastern British Columbia, and throughout the United States as an occasional pest of forest, fruit, and shade trees. In Western Canada it feeds on *Populus, Salix, Betula, Prunus, Alnus, Acer,* and other hardwoods, and farther south is commonly found on fruit and shade trees. It has severely defoliated trembling aspen locally in British Columbia and Saskatchewan and periodically damages various shade and forest trees in California.

The grayish-brown adults, having a wingspread of about 35 mm, appear in midsummer. Females deposit small roundish white eggs in groups of 50 to 100 on the underside of leaves. Upon hatching, the caterpillars feed on the lower surface of the leaves, but later eat the entire leaves except for the veins. They feed in groups most of the time. The mature larva is about 35 mm long and bears a double row of spines which are particularly prominent at the head end. Its head and a hump on the first abdominal segment are red, and its body is dull yellow and streaked with black or reddish brown. In late summer, the caterpillars spin loose silken cocoons in the ground litter and pupate. The pupa overwinters.

SUPERFAMILY HESPERIOIDEA

This superfamily is known as the **skippers** (Lindsey et al. 1931), because of the erratic flight of the adults. The skippers resemble butterflies in wing patterns and in holding the wings vertically when at rest. However, their bodies are stout like those of many moths and the tips of their antennae are usually recurved. The larvae feed in concealment, either webbing leaves or boring into succulent stems. They have large heads and a constricted neck.

The Hesperiidae, with over 200 species in North America, is much the larger of the two common families. Most of the species feed on herbaceous vegetation. Three species have been recorded occasionally on forest trees in British Columbia. The larva of one of them, *Erynnis icelus* Scudder and Burgess, is a leafroller on *Salix* and *Populus*.

SUPERFAMILY PAPILIONOIDEA

All the North American butterflies are in this superfamily. Adults have frail bodies, large and showy wings, and slender antennae enlarged at the tips. They have a typical, gay flight and at rest hold their wings directly overhead. The larvae often have striking markings or protuberances, but some are plain. They are mostly plant-feeders, but some species in the Lycaenidae are carnivorous on aphids.

Five families, consisting of more than 500 species, occur in North America. Two of these contain species of importance in Western forests.

FAMILY NYMPHALIDAE—BRUSHFOOTED BUTTERFLIES

The **brushfooted butterflies** are the largest butterfly family in North America. Adults are generally medium or large in size, with striking wing patterns involving contrasting colors. Males of most species show a territorial behavior, patrolling well-defined parts of fields or forest openings on a regular basis. Some attract attention by their fall migrations. Many species feed on herbaceous plants. Some feed on hardwood trees or shrubs. None is a serious forest pest.

Nymphalis has two species of occasional significance in forestry. The adults of both are large with a wingspread of 50 to 70 mm. Mature larvae are blackish, conspicuously spiny, and about 30 mm long. The bare pupae, 25 to 30 mm long, are attached to twigs by a few strands of silk; they hang head downward.

The **mourningcloak butterfly**, *Nymphalis antiopa* (L.), occurs in Southern Canada and throughout the United States. It feeds on willow, elm, poplars, and other hardwoods, occasionally defoliating individual trees (Sugden 1970). Larvae are occasionally abundant in shelterbelt plantings; and an infestation in a shelterbelt nursery in 1958 required chemical control (Wilson 1962). The blackish larvae, marked above with a row of red dots, feed in groups from the margin of the leaves inward, silking as they move from one leaf to another (fig. 138). In northerly areas, pupae are formed in midsummer and the brownish-black butterflies with wing tips marked by a yellow stripe and a row of blue dots, appear late in summer. The butterflies eventually hibernate and in spring deposit masses of orange-brown eggs on limbs and twigs. Two broods may occur in southerly areas.

The **California tortoiseshell**, *Nymphalis californica* (Boisduval) (Essig 1926, Furniss and Barr 1975), occurs throughout Western

FIGURE 138.—Larval colony of the mourningcloak butterfly (*Nymphalis antiopa*) on willow.

United States and on Vancouver Island, British Columbia. Its principal hosts are snowbrush (*Ceanothus velutinus*) and mountain whitethorn (*C. cordulatus*), but it also feeds on serviceberry, willow, manzanita, wild lilac, and other plants. Many outbreaks have occurred on *Ceanothus* in northern California, notably in 1911, 1932, 1951, and 1971. The caterpillars severely defoliated snowbrush in the Cascade Mountains of Oregon in 1959 and in southwestern Idaho in 1959 and 1961. Outbreaks last only a year or two.

The black larva is marked above with a row of bright yellow spines mounted on blue tubercles between which are numerous yellow dots (fig. 139A). The pupa is shiny brown with stout points above and on the sides. The forewing of the butterfly is brown and deep orange, with black spots and a black border, and the hindwing has a large black dot and purple spots (fig. 139B). Larvae are present from late June until mid-July, at which time they pupate. Adults appear in late July, swarm in large numbers, and migrate to other areas, often attracting considerable attention. They overwinter and lay eggs in spring, presumably on twigs of host plants. There is normally one generation a year.

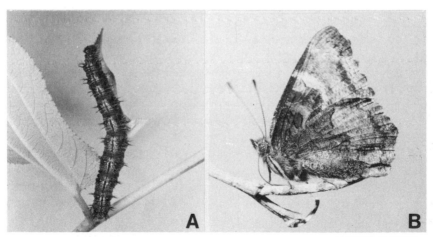

F–522013, F–522014

FIGURE 139.—California tortoiseshell (*Nymphalis californica*): *A*, Mature larva, 30 mm long; *B*, adult, 60 mm wingspread.

FAMILY PAPILIONIDAE—SWALLOWTAIL BUTTERFLIES

Swallowtails are a group of large black and yellow butterflies having tail-like prolongations on the hindwings. Their larvae feed on leaves, some on forest trees, others on herbaceous plants.

Papilio (Sugden and Ross 1963) has at least four species in the West which feed on forest trees. None is a forest pest. Mature larvae are velvet green, 37 to 50 mm long, and widest on the metathorax. The metathorax bears two "eyespots" and the first abdominal segment has a transverse yellow band bordered by a black band.

Papilio rutulus Lucas is a common western species feeding on *Populus, Salix, Betula,* and *Alnus.*

FAMILY PIERIDAE—WHITES AND SULFUR BUTTERFLIES

The **pine butterfly**, *Neophasia menapia* (Felder and Felder) (Cole 1971), is one of the most destructive insect enemies of ponderosa pine in the Northwestern States. One of the earliest recorded outbreaks occurred in 1882 near Spokane, Washington. Since then several outbreaks have developed in Oregon, Washington, Idaho, and British Columbia. The worst was in 1893 to 1895 on the Yakima Indian Reservation, Washington. On some 150,000 acres the pine butterfly, augmented by bark beetles, killed nearly a billion board feet of ponderosa pine. The affected area is still evident from the extensive even-aged forest that developed after the outbreak (Weaver 1961). In 1922 and 1923 the butterfly killed up to 25 percent of the ponderosa pine on some areas in the New Meadows-McCall region of Idaho. In 1953 some 169,000 acres of ponderosa pine on the Boise National Forest, Idaho, were heavily infested. Aerial spraying the following year prevented serious losses. The old needles are eaten first, but new needles also are eaten by older larvae. Old trees are more susceptible to injury than younger thriftier trees. During outbreaks in ponderosa pine, intermixed western white pine, lodgepole pine, Douglas-fir, and larch also are fed upon.

The adult is a white butterfly with black markings and a wing expanse of about 30 mm. It resembles the common cabbage butterfly (fig. 140A). The wings of the male are white except for some black markings on the tips. The forewings of the female have similar black markings, but have a distinct yellowish cast; the hindwings have the same yellowish cast but have a much heavier black marking than in the male. Many, but not all, females have bright orange spots along the apical margin of the hindwings. These butterflies may be seen nearly every year flying about in pine and fir forests and hovering about the tops of trees.

A smaller variety of the pine butterfly occurs in the Southwestern States, but it is not reported to be damaging. Sometimes clouds of the butterflies are seen hovering around the tops of Douglas-firs along the coast of Oregon, Washington, and British

FIGURE 140.—Pine butterfly (*Neophasia menapia*): *A*, Female adult, wing-spread 30 mm; *B*, eggs on pine needles; *C*, colony of small larvae, each 7 mm long; *D*, mature larva, 25 mm long, and pupae, 12-14 mm long.

Columbia, but effects of larval feeding are seldom evident. An exception occurred in 1961 when it became necessary to spray 1,500 acres on Vancouver Island to protect mature Douglas-fir (Silver and Ross 1962).

Adults fly in August, September, and October, and lay emerald-green eggs, about 1 mm wide and 1.25 mm long, attached to needles near the tops of trees. Eggs are laid in rows at an angle of 45° with 5 to 20 eggs in each row, firmly cemented together (fig. 140B). They overwinter and hatch the following June, or about the time the new needles begin to appear on ponderosa pine. Hatching larvae are very small, pale green caterpillars with shiny black heads. They feed in clusters, encircling the needle with their heads pointed toward the tip, forming a little ring of tiny black heads somewhat like sawfly larvae (fig. 140C). Later they feed singly and mature by late July. At maturity they are about 25 mm long, dark green except for a pale green head, and covered with fine, closely set hairs. Each has two white lateral stripes on its side (fig. 140D), and the anal shield has two blunt, well-separated

241

projections. Larvae attach themselves to needles, twigs, bark, or other objects before changing into pupae, which are marked with white lines as in the larvae (fig. 140D). After 15 to 20 days the adults emerge and fly. There is one generation a year. Rate of development varies widely by individuals.

Recorded outbreaks have lasted only a few years. Decline of the 1922–23 outbreak was attributed to natural enemies, principally a native ichneumon parasite, *Theronia atalantae*. Aerial spraying has proven effective when necessary to protect extensively threatened mature forests. Population trends sometimes are forecast from aerial counts of butterflies fluttering about tree tops.

ORDER COLEOPTERA—BEETLES

Beetles comprise the largest order of insects. In western forests their role ranges from innocuous to highly destructive. Some kill trees outright. Others damage or weaken living trees, reducing their value and slowing their growth. Some damage forest products. Some are beneficial as predators or scavengers. Many live in the forest, neither benefitting nor damaging it appreciably.

Beetles have four life stages—egg, larva, pupa, and adult. The adult has hardened forewings (elytra) which cover the membranous hindwings used in flying, though the latter may be lacking. The larva is grublike. The adult and larva both may cause damage, but the larva generally is more destructive. The pupa is a transformation stage that does not feed.

Species in North America are listed in Leng's catalog (Leng 1920) and its supplements (Leng and Mutschler 1927, 1933; Blackwelder 1939, Blackwelder and Blackwelder 1948).

Keys to the adults of beetle families and genera of the United States and extensive references are given by Arnett (1960). Hatch (1953, 1957, 1962, 1965, 1971) covers the beetles of the Pacific Northwest, providing keys to species. Böving and Craighead (1931) key and illustrate representative larvae.

This manual follows Arnett (1960) in listing beetle families under four suborders and designating superfamilies only for the largest suborder, Polyphaga. Superfamilies are in natural sequence; families are arranged alphabetically within a superfamily.

SUBORDER ARCHOSTEMATA

FAMILY CUPEDIDAE

The Cupedidae (Atkins 1963) is a small family of elongate, somewhat flattened, medium-sized tuberculate, scale-covered, cerambycidlike beetles of no economic importance. They inhabit forested areas. Little is known concerning their habits. The larvae of some feed in moist rotting wood.

Priacma serrata (LeConte) (Atkins 1957) occurs in California, Oregon, Washington, and British Columbia. Its biology is not recorded.

SUBORDER ADEPHAGA

FAMILY CARABIDAE—GROUND BEETLES

The **ground beetles**, Carabidae (Arnett 1960, Hatch 1953), are a large family of small to large, generally black and shiny, occasionally metallic, strong-jawed, ground-inhabiting, mostly nocturnal beetles. In daytime the adults hide under stones and logs, in litter, and in other out-of-way places. When disturbed, many give off a strong odor. Most feed upon insects, especially caterpillars, hence are largely beneficial. Some feed on plant materials, including tree seeds. The larvae move about freely. They are flattened, hairless, tough skinned, and tapered at both ends.

Calosoma (Burgess and Collins 1917, Gidaspow 1959) is a large genus of large, generally black beetles that feed upon caterpillars and other insects. Many species of *Calosoma* are native in the West but none of them is reported effective in control of forest pests. *Calosoma frigidum* Kirby is recorded as a predator of the forest tent caterpillar. Efforts have been made without success to colonize *C. sycophanta* (L.) in British Columbia, Washington, California, New Mexico, and Colorado against various insects, including the Douglas fir tussock moth, western hemlock looper, California oakworm, satin moth, and western tent caterpillar. This European ground beetle is an important predator of the gypsy moth. The adults and larvae both climb trees in search for prey. The adults have black bodies and brilliant green elytra.

Pterostichus (Arnett 1960) is a large genus of medium-sized, rather flattened, black beetles. They are predaceous, but some are among the species of ground beetles that also feed on plant materials.

Soil-inhabiting insects, principally ground beetles, cause significant loss of Douglas-fir seeds. Studies in Washington and California implicated *Pterostichus algidus* LeConte (Johnson et al. 1966) (fig. 141) as the principal ground beetle that feeds upon Douglas-fir seeds.

Scaphinotus (Arnett 1960) contains numerous species in the West. They are large, long-legged, generally black, sometimes metallic beetles, strongly constricted between the thorax and elytra. They are fast-moving beetles, some of which live in forests where they feed upon snails, slugs, and caterpillars.

Scaphinotus angusticollis (Mannerheim) (fig. 142) occurs in coastal forests from northern California to Alaska. It has been

FIGURE 141.—Adult ground beetle, *Pterostichus algidus,* carrying off a Douglas-fir seed.

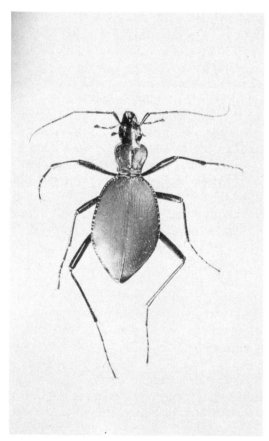

F–522016

FIGURE 142.—Adult of *Scaphinotus angusticollis,* 22 mm long, predaceous in coastal forests.

reported to prey upon the larvae and pupae of the western hemlock looper. Adults are 20 to 24 mm long.

SUBORDER POLYPHAGA

SUPERFAMILY STAPHYLINOIDEA

FAMILY STAPHYLINIDAE—ROVE BEETLES

The **rove beetles**, Staphylinidae (Arnett 1960, Hatch 1957), are a very large family of diverse habits. Mostly they are predators or scavengers. The adults are elongate and usually have short wing covers that leave three or more segments of the abdomen exposed. The ones of principal interest to foresters are small species that live in galleries of bark beetles; for example, *Nudobius cephalicus* (Say) (= *pugetanus* Casey) (Struble 1930). It is 8 to 9 mm long, shiny brownish black, and very active (fig. 143). It preys upon insects that inhabit galleries of *Dendroctonus brevicomis* but does not feed upon the primary bark beetle.

F–522017

FIGURE 143.—Adult rove beetle, *Nudobius cephalicus*, 8 mm long, found in bark beetle galleries.

SUPERFAMILY HISTERIOIDEA

FAMILY HISTERIDAE—HISTER BEETLES

The **hister beetles** are hard-shelled, predaceous beetles with clubbed antennae and short elytra. Several of the small or flattened species live in the galleries of bark beetles and wood borers.

Platysoma punctigerum LeConte (Struble 1930) is a squarish, flattened, shiny black beetle 4 to 5 mm long that occurs in the galleries of *Dendroctonus brevicomis* and of other *Dendroctonus* and of *Ips*. It preys in both the larval and the adult stage upon various insects encountered in the bark beetle galleries, including adults of *D. brevicomis*. The bark beetles are fed upon after they have laid most of their eggs, hence there is little effective control.

Plegaderus nitidus Horn (Struble 1930) is an oval, shiny black beetle about 2 mm long. The thorax is grooved along both sides and across the middle. This species enters the galleries of *Dendroctonus brevicomis* during the early stages of attack. Adults feed upon the bark beetle eggs and may be significant in natural control.

SUPERFAMILY SCARABAEOIDEA

FAMILY LUCANIDAE—STAG BEETLES

Stag beetles (Ritcher 1966) breed in decaying stumps and logs, contributing to their natural decomposition. The larvae are whitish or bluish and C-shaped and resemble their relatives, the scarabs. The adults are elongate, broadly convex dorsally, and usually chestnut brown to black. The mandibles of the males are elongate and sometimes prominently toothed, giving the family its common name. There about 40 species, many of them in the West.

The **blue-black stag beetle**, *Platycerus oregonensis* Westwood, is one of three species in this genus in the West (Benesh 1946, Ritcher 1966). It occurs in California and north into British Columbia. The adults are black except for the bluish-black elytra and are 10 to 15 mm long. The larvae feed in rotting ash, alder, maple, madrone, and live oak. The life cycle is 1 year.

Ceruchus (Doane et al. 1936) resembles *Platycerus* except that the head and mandibles of the male are more massive and the elytra more conspicuously punctured. The adult *C. striatus* LeConte is jet black, has strongly striate elytra, and is 15 to 20 mm long. It occurs in California and north into British Columbia and feeds in rotting Douglas-fir and redwood. *C. punctatus* LeConte is smaller and less striate. It occurs from California north into British Columbia and in Colorado and feeds in rotting Douglas-fir.

The **rugose stag beetle**, *Sinodendron rugosum* Mannerheim, occurs from California into British Columbia and Idaho (Ritcher 1966). The adult is black, cylindrical, roughly punctured and 10 to 17 mm long. The male has a prominent rhinoceroslike horn on the head and the front half of the prothorax is scooplike. The larvae feed in moist rotten oak, alder, willow, cherry, poplar, birch, ash, and maple.

246

FAMILY SCARABAEIDAE—SCARABS

Scarabs were held sacred in ancient Egypt. The scarabs of principal concern to foresters today are pests that feed as adults on foliage and as larvae on roots of trees (Ritcher 1958, 1966). There are many species ranging from small to large. They are robust, dull- to brightly-colored beetles with antennae ending in a club composed of three to seven blades. The legs are long and spiny. The front tibiae are toothed on the outer edge. The larvae, known as **white grubs,** are whitish, hairy, generally curled, enlarged at the rear, and have well-developed legs.

Dichelonyx contains 20 species, mostly western (Cornell 1972). There are two main groups—one with a longitudinal groove in the thorax (sulcate) ; the other without such a groove (nonsulcate). Specific identification requires examination of the male genitalia. The adults are 6 to 13 mm long, with a light brown to black body, and usually with metallic-colored wing covers. In repose the outer edges of the wing covers are parallel. Adults feed in spring upon the leaves of trees, frequently conifers, sometimes causing conspicuous defoliation. Larvae feed upon roots of grasses and other plants, presumably including trees. The life cycle is 2 to 3 years.

Dichelonyx backi Kirby (= *crotchi* (Horn) = *testaceipennis* (Fall)), the most widely distributed species in the genus, is abundant in the Rocky Mountain and Pacific Coast States and Provinces. The thorax is not grooved. Color of the wing covers varies from metallic green to shiny brown. The body may be brown or black. The adults feed upon the needles of *Pinus ponderosa, Pseudotsuga menziesii, Abies,* and *Picea,* often leaving only the midrib. In California it feeds upon immature cones of ponderosa pine and materially reduces seed production (fig. 144) (Koerber 1967). Some forms of this species seem to prefer deciduous trees and shrubs, as in Alberta and Saskatchewan.

Dichelonyx truncata (LeConte) belongs to the nonsulcate group. It feeds on pine and various shrubs in many Western States and in Saskatchewan. It is a small species of varied color, often bronze with outer edges of the elytra lighter.

Dichelonyx valida (LeConte) belongs to the sulcate group. It occurs extensively in the West and has four named varieties. The most widely distributed variety, *D. v. vicina* (Fall), usually has light green elytra. It occurs from California to British Columbia and eastward to Wyoming and Nevada. Recorded hosts are species of *Abies, Pinus, Pseudotsuga,* and *Juniperus.*

Diplotaxis is a large genus of hard-shelled, oval-shaped, brown to black beetles from 6 to 14 mm long (Vaurie 1958, 1960). They resemble small *Phyllophaga* and have habits similar to *Serica.* The

FIGURE 144.—Adult of a scarab, *Dichelonyx backi*, 10 mm long.

adults are chiefly nocturnal. In the Western United States they occur northward into Canada but most of them inhabit dry lands from California to Texas where they feed on such plants as mesquite, catclaw, creosote bush, and juniper. Their biology is little known.

About 200 species of *Phyllophaga* occur in the United States and Canada, preponderantly in Eastern States and Provinces (Luginbill and Painter 1953). In the West, they are most numerous in Arizona (Butler and Werner 1961). The adults are brown to nearly black, shiny, stout beetles, mostly 10 to 20 mm long. Often called **May beetles,** the adults feed at night upon the foliage of many plants including broad-leaved trees and shrubs and some conifers. The larvae feed upon roots of plants, particularly grasses. In the West, *Phyllophaga* occasionally damages coniferous seedlings in plantations and in nurseries on newly broken sandy land (Molnar et al. 1967). In the Black Hills, the larvae were reported to reduce the grazing capacity of range land. The life cycle is from 2 to 4 years.

Phyllophaga anxia (LeConte) and *P. fusca* (Froelich) are among the few species that occur both commonly and extensively in the West (Luginbill and Painter 1953). The adults feed upon the leaves of numerous broad-leaved trees. Larvae of *P. falsa* (LeConte) are recorded as damaging seedlings of *Pinus ponderosa* in Arizona by feeding on the roots. Adults of *Phyllophaga langeri* Chapin feed on the foliage of *Pinus ponderosa* in Utah and Colorado. Adults of several species of *Phyllophaga* feed on foliage of *Juniperus* in Arizona.

There are 30 species of *Pleocoma,* known as **rain beetles** because the males fly and seek mates during fall rains (Linsley 1946, Ritcher 1966). They occur from Mexico through California and Oregon into southern Washington. Two species occur in Utah and one in Alaska. Males are about 20 to 30 mm long, winged, and are hairier and less inflated than females (fig. 145A, B). Females are from about 25 to 40 mm long and have small useless wings. Color is tan to nearly black, with the females generally lighter. Females seldom leave their burrows, hence distribution is spotty (Fellin and Ritcher 1967, Linsley 1957). The adults do not feed. The larvae (fig. 145C) feed on roots of forest and orchard trees and of grasses, often 0.3 to 1 m (1 to 3 ft) in the ground, and sometimes to a depth of 2.6 m (8 ft). The life cycle is 8 to 12 years.

Pleocoma carinata Linsley, *P. dubitalis* Davis, and *P. simi* Davis are associated with Douglas-fir forests in Oregon (Fellin and

COURTESY FRANK MCWHORTER (A,B),
COURTESY D. G. FELLIN (C)

FIGURE 145.—Rain beetles: *A*, Male adult of *Pleocoma crinita*, 30 mm long; *B*, female of *P. crinita*, 40 mm long; *C*, larva of *P. dubitalis*, 20 mm long, feeding on root of Douglas-fir.

Ritcher 1967). Coniferous roots, including Douglas-fir, are a major part of the larval diet of the larvae of these species (Fellin 1966). On cutover land in Oregon, the roots of young ponderosa pine, sugar pine, Douglas-fir, and grand fir are fed upon by *P. simi* (Stein 1963) (fig. 146). *P. crinita* Linsley, *P. minor* Linsley, and *P. oregonensis* Leach occur in woodland areas in Oregon and feed upon the roots of orchard trees (Ellertson and Ritcher 1959). *P. linsleyi* Hovore and others feed on oak roots in California (Hovore 1971).

F-522019, F-522020

FIGURE 146.—Root damage caused to forest seedlings by larval feeding of *Pleocoma simi*: *A*, On Douglas-fir; *B*, on sugar pine.

There are 20-some species of **whitelined June beetles**, *Polyphylla*, in the United States, mostly in the West (Cazier 1940). The adults are large, robust, brown beetles with conspicuous longitudinal white stripes (fig. 147). During early rains in fall they sometimes are seen in considerable numbers in sandy areas. The larvae feed on the roots of trees, shrubs, and other plants.

The **tenlined June beetle**, *Polyphylla decemlineata* (Say) (= *perversa* Casey), occurs extensively in the West. The adults are 25 to 35 mm long and the mature larvae range up to 50 mm. The life cycle requires 3 to 4 years. On sandy grassy land in western Washington the larvae killed 30 percent of the trees in a Christmas tree plantation. Douglas-fir, grand fir, and Scotch pine were killed (Buckhorn and Orr 1961). On Vancouver Island and elsewhere the larvae are reported as damaging in forest nurseries (fig. 148A). The adults feed on the foliage of conifers (fig. 148B) including Douglas-fir, hemlock, spruce, and pine (Downes and Andison 1941, Johnson 1954). *P. crinita* LeConte is a smaller species reported to feed both on the foliage and the roots of pine (Burke 1937).

The **Japanese beetle**, *Popillia japonica* Newman (Fleming 1962), long a garden, orchard, and ornamental pest in Eastern States, was found in Sacramento, California, in 1961 and sub-

FIGURE 147.—Adult of a whitelined June beetle, *Polyphylla decemlineata*, about 30 mm long.

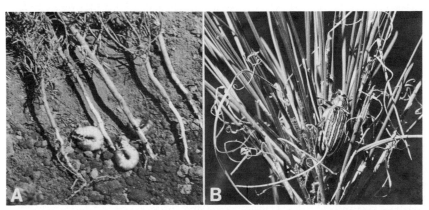

F–522021, F–522022

FIGURE 148.—Damage by the tenlined June beetle caused by: *A*, Grubs (larvae) feeding on roots of seedlings in a forest nursery; *B*, adult feeding on foliage of ponderosa pine.

251

sequently eradicated there. In 1973 it appeared in San Diego, California. Efforts to eradicate it there are in progress. Extensive surveys indicate that it has not become established elsewhere in the West though it is a continuing threat to ornamentals. The adult is broadly oval, 10 to 12 mm long, and metallic green with reddish-bronze wing covers. There are two patches of white hairs just behind the wing covers and five patches along each side. Adults feed on foliage and flowers of many plants, including non-coniferous trees and shrubs; larvae feed on roots. The life cycle usually is completed in 1 year but may require 2 years in the North. In the extreme South there may be two generations a year.

Serica are brownish or blackish robust beetles that resemble *Phyllophaga* but are much smaller. There are about 75 species in the United States. The adults of most species feed at night on foliage. The larvae feed on roots of many kinds of plants (Ritcher 1966). *S. anthracina* LeConte ranges from British Columbia to California, occuring on manzanita, ceanothus, and oak and at times defoliating orchard trees. The adults are about 7.5 mm long.

SUPERFAMILY BYRRHOIDEA

FAMILY BYRRHIDAE—PILL BEETLES

The **pill beetles**, Byrrhidae (Arnett 1960), are oval, convex, dull-colored or lustrous beetles, 5 to 10 mm long. When disturbed, the adults retract their legs and antennae and remain motionless for a considerable time, hence the common name. Adults and larvae feed on plants. Species of *Byrrhus* and *Cytilus* (Lindquist and Ingram 1968) have damaged forest tree seedlings including *Pinus* in eastern North America. These and other genera of Byrrhidae occur in the West but are not recorded as western forest pests.

SUPERFAMILY BUPRESTOIDEA

FAMILY BUPRESTIDAE—FLATHEADED OR METALLIC WOOD BORERS

The Buprestidae (Arnett 1960) is a large and important family of beetles that attack trees and woody plants. There are about 700 species in North America, many of them in the West. The larvae are keyed to the genus by Burke (1917a).

A few species attack and kill apparently healthy trees; most attack weakened, dead, and recently felled trees. Typically, the larvae bore first in the cambium region of the trunk, branches, and roots, then often penetrate the wood, sometimes mining it extensively. The flattened oval wormholes usually are tightly packed with boring dust arranged in ridges in patterns similar to the tip of a fingerprint (fig. 149). A few species bore in cones and seasoned wood; some are leafminers. In general, the family is among the more destructive ones in the forest. Their good side is that they aid in the natural process of returning deadwood to the soil.

FIGURE 149.—Example of flat-headed borer larval galleries, packed with boring dust.

The adults are flattened, compact, often brightly-colored beetles with a metallic luster (fig. 150). The antennae are 11-segmented and serrate. The beetles emerge in spring and summer through elliptical exit holes. Some species feed on tree foliage and twigs before laying eggs. Some visit flowers and feed on pollen. They lay their eggs in crevices of the bark or wood or on outer surfaces. They move rapidly, are disturbed easily, and prefer sunshine to shade.

The larvae are the stage usually found in trees. Most of them are long, legless, and shaped like a horseshoe nail (fig. 151). The head is small, and the first segment back of the head is much broader than the following body segments and has horny plates on the top and bottom. Growth of the larvae continues until fall, when activity ceases with the advent of cold weather. The winter usually is passed in the larval stage, although some larvae may pupate in the fall and pass the winter as adults. Development from egg to adult requires from 1 to many years.

For the control of **flatheaded borers** that mine in the inner bark, the same methods are used as for bark beetles. Infested trees usually are felled, peeled, and burned, and this work is frequently carried on in connection with the control of bark beetles. The prevention of fire scars and other injuries to standing trees and the prompt utilization of dead or felled trees will reduce potential

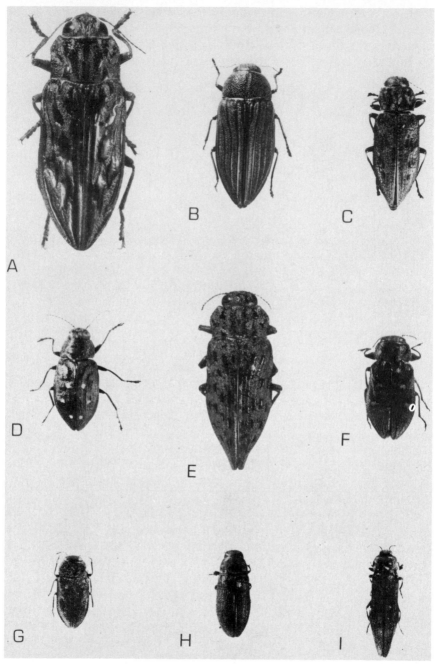

F-522024

FIGURE 150.—Adults of nine genera of Buprestidae: *A, Chalcophora anguli-collis; B, Buprestis aurulenta; C, Trachykele blondeli; D, Melanophila drummondi; E, Dicerca tenebrosa; F, Chrysobothris mali; G, Anthaxia expansa; H, Chrysophana placida; I, Agrilus anxius.*

damage to wood products. In wood that has become infested after being put into place, the grubs usually can be reached and killed by liberal application of penetrating chemicals.

There are more than 100 species of *Acmaeodera*, mostly in the Southwest. The larvae bore in dead and injured branches, stems, and roots of broad-leaved trees and shrubs; none in the West is a forest pest. The adults are subcylindrical, strongly tapered to the rear, and generally spotted and hairy. *A. connexa* LeConte is an abundant, widely distributed, western species that breeds in oaks. The adults, 7.5 to 12 mm long and yellow-spotted, frequent yellow flowers.

Agrilus (Fisher 1928) contains well over 100 species in North America. They develop in broad-leaved trees and shrubs. Of the western species, one is a forest tree killer; a few damage ornamentals; most are of little consequence in the forest. Some common western species are as follows:

Species	Hosts	Western distribution
A. angelicus Horn **Pacific oak twig girdler**	*Quercus*	Calif.
A. anxius Gory **bronze birch borer**	*Betula*	Alberta, British Columbia, Wash., Oreg., Idaho, Utah, S. Dak., and Colo.
A. arbuti Fisher	*Arbutus menziesii,* and *Arctostaphylos*	Calif. and Oreg.
A. burkei Fisher	*Alnus*	British Columbia, Wash., Oreg., Calif., Nev., Idaho, and Wyo.
A. fulminans Fisher	*Salix* and *Quercus*	Calif. and Oreg.
A. granulatus (Say)	*Populus*	Alberta, Mont., and Colo.
A. liragus Barter and Brown **bronze poplar borer**	*Populus*	Saskatchewan, Alberta, British Columbia, N. Dak., Colo., Utah, and Oreg.
A. politus (Say)	*Salix* and *Acer*	Presumably wherever willow grows.
A. populi Fisher	*Populus*	British Columbia, Wash., Oreg., Calif., Idaho, and Mont.
A. quercicola Fisher	*Quercus*	Ariz., N. Mex., Colo., and Utah

Agrilus larvae bore long, winding, shallow galleries between the bark and wood of the bole, branches, and occasionally roots (fig. 152A). Often the larvae kill branches by spiraling their galleries around and around them. The larva (fig. 152B) has two spinelike projections at the rear and is only slightly widened at the head end. The adult is a slender, cylindrical, metallic beetle (fig. 150I).

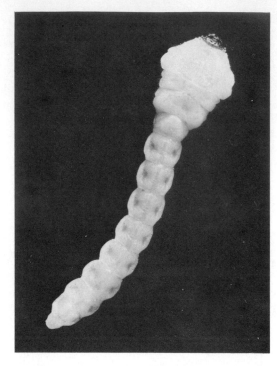

F–522025

FIGURE 151.—Example of a flatheaded borer larva, *Buprestis aurulenta*, 30 mm long.

The **Pacific oak twig girdler,** *Agrilus angelicus* Horn (Brown and Eads 1965a), is rated the number one pest of ornamental oaks, especially live oaks, in southern California. Trees weakened by drought are most affected. The small branches are girdled and killed by the larval mines. Adults are 5 to 7 mm long and a dark brownish-copper color. They feed on oak leaves but cause no significant damage. The life cycle requires 2 years.

The **bronze birch borer,** *Agrilus anxius* Gory (MacAloney 1968), attacks and kills weakened and injured birch extensively in forests of the Eastern States and Provinces. In the West it is principally a pest of ornamental birch but occurs on water birch. Attacks usually begin in the smaller branches and progress downward over a period of years. A generation is completed in 1 or 2 years, depending upon temperature.

In Alberta, *Agrilus granulatus* Say (Brown and Stevenson 1964, 1965) damages drought-weakened and winter-injured planted and native poplars.

Anthaxia (Barr 1971) contains about two dozen species in North America, many of them in the West. The larvae bore in branches of injured, dying, and dead *Abies, Pinus, Pseudotsuga, Sequoia,* and various broad-leaved trees and shrubs. The adults resemble *Melanophila* but are considerably smaller, ranging from 4 to 8 mm long. They are unspotted, dark brown to black, some-

F-522026, F-522027

FIGURE 152.—Examples of *Agrilus*: *A*, Long winding galleries of *A. politus* on willow; *B*, larva of *A. anxius*, 24 mm long.

times green, often metallic, and are clothed with short stiff hairs. They frequent flowers, especially yellow ones. *A. aeneogaster* Laporte and Gory attacks branches of conifers, especially *Pinus*, from California to British Columbia and Idaho. *A. expansa* LeConte (fig. 150G) is the most common species in the Northwest. It is presumed to feed in branches of conifers.

Buprestis (Barr 1971, Helfer 1941) contains 26 species in North America, 14 of which occur in the West (table 11). The larvae are wood borers in the trunk of injured, dying, and dead trees. Some species attack only conifers; others only deciduous trees. Several species cause a small amount of cull in trees cut for lumber. Two bore extensively in lumber in buildings. The adults range from about 10 to 23 mm long and most are brightly colored with metallic reflections.

The **golden buprestid**, *Buprestis aurulenta* L. (Every and Rudinsky 1962), is the most damaging western species in this genus. The larvae mine in and around fire scars and mechanical

257

Table 11.—*Western species of* Buprestis

Species	Hosts	Distribution
B. adjecta (LeConte)	Pinus ponderosa, P. jeffreyi, P. contorta, Pseudotsuga menziesii, Abies, and Picea	Western States and British Columbia
B. aurulenta L.	Pinus, Pseudotsuga, Picea, and Abies	Western States and British Columbia
B. confluenta Say	Populus	Western States, Alberta and British Columbia
B. connexa Horn	Pinus ponderosa and P. jeffreyi	Calif., Oreg., Wash., and Idaho
B. fremontiae Burke	Fremontia californica	Calif.
B. gibbsi (LeConte)	Quercus	Calif., Oreg., and Wash.
B. intricata Casey	Pinus contorta	Calif. to British Columbia, Wyo., and N. Mex.
B. laeviventris (LeConte)	Pinus ponderosa, P. contorta, P. lambertiana, other Pinus, and Pseudotsuga menziesii	Calif. to British Columbia, Mont., and Ariz.
B. langi Mannerheim	Pseudotsuga menziesii	Western States incl. Alaska and British Columbia
B. lecontei Saunders (= rusticorum Kirby)	Pinus, Pseudotsuga, and Abies	Western States and British Columbia
B. nuttalli Kirby	Pinus ponderosa and Pseudotsuga menziesii	Western States incl. Alaska and British Columbia
B. prospera Casey	Pinus	Ariz. and N. Mex.
B. subornata (LeConte)	Pinus ponderosa, P. contorta, Pseudotsuga menziesii	Western States and British Columbia
B. viridisuturalis Nicolay and Weiss	Populus and Alnus	Calif., Oreg., and Wash.

injuries causing additional defect, especially in ponderosa pine and Douglas-fir. They are of principal concern in buildings, especially in the Pacific Northwest. The damage consists of mined timbers and boards (fig. 153) and of exit holes through finished surfaces. The mining may require replacement of some boards and timbers but major structural damage occurs only in special situations, such as in wooden storage tanks. Infestations may originate in the forest, in lumberyards, and sometimes in exposed portions of wooden structures.

The eggs are laid in flat masses wedged in cracks in the wood. The newly hatched larvae have numerous long hairs and the body ends in two sharp projections similar to those of *Agrilus*. Older

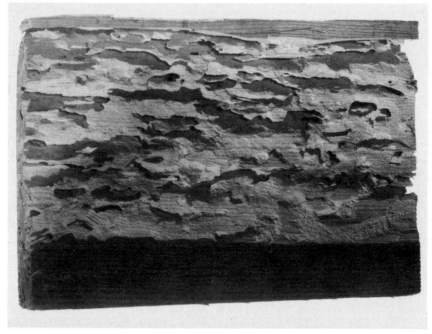

FIGURE 153.—Damage by the golden buprestid (*Buprestis aurulenta*) to a Douglas-fir timber.

larvae lack the hairs and spinelike projections (fig. 151). The adults are iridescent green or blue green with the margins of the elytra bordered with copper and range from 12 to 20 mm long (fig. 150B). They feed on needles of Douglas-fir and perhaps other conifers before egg laying. In the forest, the life cycle requires several years. In buildings the egg to adult development may be prolonged to 30, 40, even 50 years (Smith 1962).

Buprestis langi Mannerheim resembles *B. aurulenta* in habits, including prolonged development in seasoned wood, but it is less abundant in buildings and is recorded only in Douglas-fir. The adult is green, sometimes with yellow markings. Compared with *B. aurulenta*, it is more flattened and the elytra are not copper-margined. The adults feed on leaves of *Salix* and *Alnus*.

B. lecontei Saunders (= *rusticorum* Kirby) is a greenish-black to black species with orange spots on the sides of the abdomen. It lays its eggs under bark flakes, not in wood. Although abundant in the forest, it is not recorded as developing in seasoned wood.

The **sculptured pine borer**, *Chalcophora angulicollis* (LeConte), (fig. 150A) is the largest of the western species of flatheaded borers and the only western representative of this genus. The adults are 22 to 31 mm long and dark brown to black, with an iridescent bronze luster, especially on the underside. The upper surface is marked with irregularly sculptured areas. Many a woodsman has been startled on a warm summer day to have one of these large beetles suddenly take flight with the noise of a small airplane from its quiet resting place on a nearby tree trunk. The larvae feed in the wood of injured and dead pines, firs, and Douglas-fir extensively in the Western States and Provinces, causing little damage.

Chrysobothris (Fisher 1942) contains well over 100 species in North America. Many of them are western. Most bore in the bark and outer wood of limbs, trunks, and roots of weakened, dying, and dead conifers and broad-leaved trees and shrubs. Generally they are of little importance in the forest. The **Pacific flatheaded borer**, *C. mali* Horn (Burke 1929), (fig. 150F), is a pest of fruit trees and many ornamental trees and shrubs. It resembles *C. femorata* (Olivier) in appearance and habits (Fenton 1942). The **flatheaded cedar borer**, *C. nixa* Horn, sometimes damages ornamental junipers and arborvitae in nurseries. Adult *Chrysobothris* are medium-sized, generaly dull-colored, rather flattened beetles with sculptured wing covers that often are serrate along the outer edge at the rear. The following are some representative species that western foresters are likely to encounter:

Species	Hosts	Distribution
C. caurina Horn	*Pinus ponderosa, P. jeffreyi, P. lambertiana,* and other conifers	Western States and British Columbia
C. dentipes (Germar)	*Pinus,* many species	North America
C. femorata (Olivier) **flatheaded appletree borer**	*Acer, Alnus, Populus, Quercus, Salix,* and many other broad-leaved trees	North America
C. mali Horn **Pacific flatheaded borer**	*Acer, Alnus, Betula, Populus, Quercus, Salix,* and many other broad-leaved trees and shrubs	Western States and Provinces
C. nixa Horn **flatheaded cedar borer**	*Libocedrus decurrens, Cupressus macrocarpa,* and *Juniperus*	Calif., Oreg., and Nev.
C. octocola LeConte	*Acacia, Cercidium,* and *Prosopis*	Southwestern States and Calif.
C. texana LeConte	*Juniperus scopulorum, J. osteosperma,* and *Cupressus arizonicus*	Southwestern States, Calif., Idaho, and Colo.
C. trinervia (Kirby)	*Pinus ponderosa, P. flexilis, P. edulis,* and *Pseudotsuga menziesii*	Western States, including Alaska, and Western Provinces

Chrysophana (Barr 1971) contains two closely related species, both western.

Chrysophana placida (LeConte) (fig. 150H) occurs from California to British Columbia, Colorado, and New Mexico. It is a rather common but unimportant and seldom observed borer in the trunk and branches of dead and injured pines, true firs, Douglas-fir, and hemlock. The adult is 6 to 10 mm long, bright green, usually has a reddish-bronze stripe on each wing cover, and overall is a smaller more slender version of some green species of *Buprestis*. The larval mines contain powdery borings. In dry wood the life cycle requires many years.

The **flatheaded cone borer**, *Chrysophana conicola* Van Dyke (Keen 1958), until recently was considered to be a variety of *C. placida*. The latter is shining green below and the former copper colored. *C. conicola* is native in California and Oregon. The larvae mine in the axis of cones of *Pinus attenuata* and *P. coulteri* (fig. 154) causing very little damage to the seeds.

The species of *Dicerca* (Barr 1971) (fig. 150E) are medium-sized, robust, sculptured, metallic, wood-boring beetles of a dull

EPQ–7713

FIGURE 154.—Larvae and damage of the flatheaded cone borer (*Chrysophana conicola*) in knobcone pine cone.

bronze color, with the tips of the wing covers prolonged into narrow points. The larvae work under the bark and into the wood of various species of trees that are sickly, dying, or dead. Some develop only in conifers; others only in broad-leaved trees and shrubs. About 10 species occur in the West; none is a forest pest. *D. tenebrosa* (Kirby), a transcontinental species that occurs extensively in the Western States and Provinces, feeds in *Pinus, Abies, Picea,* and *Pseudotsuga menziesii. D. tenebrica* (Kirby) (= *prolongata* LeConte) has a similar distribution. Its hosts are *Populus* and *Salix. D. horni* Crotch occurs from California to British Columbia and Colorado. *Alnus, Ceanothus, Cercocarpus,* and *Prunus* are among its many hosts.

Melanophila (Sloop 1937) (fig. 150D) contains 15 North American species, 13 of which occur in the West. Practically all attack conifers. Two western species are significant pests that kill trees weakened by drought, smog, fire, or injury and often are associated with *Dendroctonus* and other bark beetles. Most species of *Melanophila* attack only dead and dying trees. The larvae bore in the inner bark barely scoring the wood. The adults are black or metallic, sometimes with light-colored spots. Some species are attracted to smoke and acrid fumes (Linsley 1943a). Known as "firebugs" in the pine region, these beetles flock to forest fires, often bite the firefighters, and lay their eggs on the scorched, sometimes still smoldering trees. *M. acuminata* (De Geer) and the **charcoal beetle**, *M. consputa* LeConte are examples of species that chase smoke in coniferous forests of the West. Both species commonly attack ponderosa and lodgepole pines, and *consputa* attacks knobcone pine as well.

The **California flatheaded borer**, *Melanophila californica* Van Dyke (Lyon 1970, West 1947) (fig. 155), principally attacks Jeffrey and ponderosa pines but also attacks sugar, Coulter,

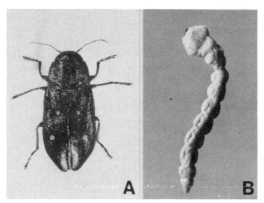

F–522029, F–483145

FIGURE 155.—California flatheaded borer (*Melanophila californica*): *A,* Adult, 10 mm long; *B,* larva, 25 mm long.

Monterey, digger, and knobcone pines. Most abundant and most destructive in California, it also occurs in Oregon, Washington, Idaho, and Nevada. It attacks pines growing on rocky slopes, in fringe-type stands, or in other situations where soil moisture is insufficient for normal tree growth, most frequently attacking old, decadent, or unhealthy trees, but thrifty, vigorous trees are not immune.

The adults of *M. californica* are 7 to 11 mm long, greenish bronze above, and brassy green below. Many of them have one to three small yellow spots on each wing cover; the others have no spots. The adults feed on pine foliage. Females must feed before they can lay viable eggs. The eggs are laid in clusters in bark crevices of the host trees during the summer. On hatching, the larvae bore into the cambium, where they may feed from a few months to 4 years without apparent injury to the tree, except a scarring of the sapwood and a general weakening due to blocking of sap-conducting tissues. This is called the incipient stage. If they do not succeed in killing the tree, they finally die in this stage; but if the tree is overcome, the larvae pass into a fast-growing stage, begin to kill the cambium, and rapidly develop. Prepupal larvae appear in the outer bark in July and August, but new adults do not appear until April and May of the following year. This species is of primary importance in weakening trees and causing them to become increasingly susceptible to pine beetle attack. Direct control is generally impractical because of the prevalence of the beetle in trees that survive attacks for many years. Some control may be achieved by harvesting "flathead" trees, trees that have dead or dying tops or have larval mines under the bark of the bole. Such trees are often classified as "high risk" trees and are promptly harvested in sanitation-salvage cuts. Maintaining trees in good vigor is the best way to prevent attack by *M. californica*.

The **flatheaded fir borer,** *Melanophila drummondi* (Kirby), occurs extensively in the Western Provinces and Western States, including Alaska. It is the species of *Melanophila* most frequently found attacking Douglas-fir, true firs, spruce, western hemlock, and western larch. Mostly, it attacks injured, mistletoe-infected, dying, fire-killed, and recently felled trees, but sometimes it attacks and kills apparently healthy trees, especially on dry sites. The adults (fig. 150D) are bronzy black and usually have three small yellow spots on each wing cover. The wing covers each may have three ridges somewhat like *Chrysobothris*. The larvae bore in the inner bark forming galleries packed with frass in a characteristic pattern (fig. 156).

263

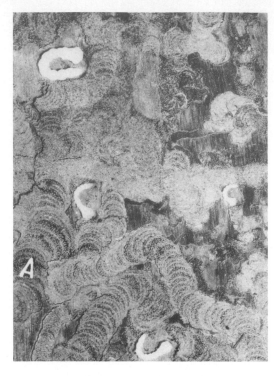

EPQ-8817

FIGURE 156.—Flatheaded fir
borer (*Melanophila drum-
mondi*) larval galleries.

The **flatheaded pine borer**, *Melanophila gentilis* LeConte, occurs
extensively in the Western States, working beneath the bark of
Pinus ponderosa, *P. jeffreyi*, and *P. lambertiana*. It often is associated with *M. californica* and has sometimes been confused with
it. *M. gentilis* is the species usually found infesting felled trees
and logs, windfalls, and injured trees or occurring as a secondary
species in the bole of standing trees. The adults are bright bluish
green and have no yellow spots. The larvae are primarily bark-
boring in habit and rarely enter the wood. On reaching maturity
the larvae work out into the outer bark and pupate in oval cells
close to the surface. There appears to be one generation annually.

Melanophila occidentalis Obenberger (Barr and Linsley 1947)
occurs from California to British Columbia, Idaho, Utah, and
Arizona. It attacks oaks and other broad-leaved trees and shrubs.
The adult is black and 6 to 12 mm long.

The **flatheaded piñon borer**, *Melanophila pini-edulis* Burke,
works in injured, dying, and dead pinyon in Colorado, Utah,
Nevada, Arizona, and New Mexico. The yellow spots on the elytra
of the adult are large, covering more than half the surface.

Poecilonota (Evans 1957) contains eight North American species, all of which occur in the West and five of them in California.
The adults closely resemble *Dicerca*. The larvae bore under the

bark and in the wood of injured *Populus* and *Salix*. None is reported to be a pest.

Poecilonota cyanipes (Say), the most widely distributed species, occurs from Yukon Territory east of the Pacific coast mountains to Arizona and eastward to the Atlantic Coast. It bores in various native and ornamental species of *Populus*, usually in decayed wood, and is sometimes associated with *Saperda*.

Poecilonota montana Chamberlin occurs in *Populus trichocarpa* from British Columbia to California, Nevada, Idaho, and Montana.

Poecilonota salicis Chamberlin bores in *Salix* in southern California.

Polycesta (Barr 1949) contains 11 species in the United States, eight of them in the West. The adults are black or dark bronze and of the general size and shape of *Buprestis*. The elytra are coarsely punctured and strongly ridged. The larvae bore in the wood of injured and dead broad-leaved trees and shrubs. None is a pest. *P. californica* LeConte occurs in California and Oregon. *Arbutus menziesii*, *Quercus*, *Populus*, *Alnus*, *Acer*, *Cercocarpus*, and *Salix* are among the recorded hosts. *P. arizonica* Schaeffer is common on oaks in Arizona and New Mexico.

Trachykele contains six species in North America. Four of them, including one serious pest, are western. The larvae bore principally in the heartwood of living trees. The adults are green or bronze, roughly sculptured beetles about the size of *Buprestis*. They are seldom seen because they live in tree tops during their flight period.

The **western cedar borer**, *Trachykele blondeli* Marseul (Burke 1928, Hopping 1928), including two named varieties, occurs from British Columbia to California and New Mexico. *Thuja plicata* is the principal host. Other hosts are species of *Juniperus* and *Cupressus* and perhaps *Libocedrus decurrens*. The larval mines cause degrade and cull in trees cut for poles, shingles, boats, and other products requiring sound wood (fig. 157). For undetermined reasons, some forest areas are especially subject to damage by this insect; others are not. The adult is 11 to 17 mm long, bright emerald green with a golden sheen, and has several darker spots on the wing covers (fig. 150C). On *T. plicata* the adults feed on the foliage and the eggs are laid under bark scales on branches of living trees. The larvae bore from the branches into the bole where they mine principally in the heartwood. The life cycle is presumed to take 2, 3, or more years. Adults form in the fall and emerge the following spring. No practical method of prevention or control has been developed.

Trachykele hartmani Burke is bronze colored. It develops only in *Cupressus goveniana* in central California.

F–522030

FIGURE 157.—*Trachykele blondeli* larval galleries in western redcedar lumber.

Trachykele nimbosa Fall occurs from California to British Columbia and Idaho. The larvae bore in *Tsuga mertensiana* and species of *Abies,* causing little damage. The adult is bronze colored.

Trachykele opulenta Fall (De Leon 1952) is similar to *T. blondeli* and has been confused with it in the literature. *T. opulenta* develops in *Sequoia gigantea* and *Libocedrus decurrens* in California. In *Sequoia* the larvae mine in the wood around fire scars and apparently can also develop wholly in the bark.

SUPERFAMILY ELATEROIDEA

FAMILY ELATERIDAE—CLICK BEETLES OR WIREWORMS

Elateridae (Arnett 1960) is a large family of trim, elongate, beetles that snap to their feet when placed on their back. The larvae are long, cylindrical, and tough-surfaced and often have horny hooks at the rear end. In the forest a few species are predaceous on other insects, including wood borers (Kirk 1922) and tip moth pupae in the soil; some mine under the bark and in rotten wood of dead trees; and many live in the soil where their role is largely unknown. Some of the soil-inhabiting forms have been considered to be potential pests in forest nurseries and out-plantings, but no such damage is recorded.

Adults of the **eyed click beetles** of the genus *Alaus* are upward of 25 mm long and have twin, oval, black, eyelike spots on the thorax (fig. 158). The larvae are reported to prey on other wood borers and to feed on rotting wood. *A. melanops* LeConte in Pacific Coast States develops in dead trees, including ponderosa pine and Douglas-fir.

F–522037

FIGURE 158.—Adult of an eyed click beetle, *Alaus melanops*, about 28 mm long.

Ampedus (formerly *Elater*) contains numerous western species. The wiry, tannish larvae feed under the bark and in the decaying wood of dead trees. The adults are 8 to 12 mm long and black or brown, often marked with red, orange, or yellow.

Lacon (formerly *Adelocera*) are somber black or reddish-brown, scale-covered beetles, 12 mm or more in length, and with a broadly grooved pronotum. There are several western species. The larvae feed under the bark and in the wood of dead trees, especially ponderosa pine and Douglas-fir.

FAMILY EUCNEMIDAE (MELASIDAE)

Adults of Eucnemidae closely resemble elaterids but generally are more cylindrical and they do not snap to their feet when placed on their back. Eucnemid larvae are soft, elongate, flattened, and buprestidlike in that the first and second thoracic segments are broader than the abdominal segments which are of uniform width. The mandibles are toothed externally. The larvae mine in dead wood, often that which is soft and rotten. The mines cut horizontally across the grain giving the mined wood a honeycombed appearance.

Anelastes druryi Kirby is a reddish-brown species, 10 to 12 mm long, that often is seen in flight in western coniferous forests. The larvae are presumed to feed in decomposing wood.

Two species of *Melasis* occur in the West (Hopping 1926). The thorax of the adult is widest in front and the antennae of the male are strongly pectinate. *M. rufipennis* Horn (Chamberlin 1920) is about 12 mm long and has dark reddish-brown elytra. It ranges from British Columbia to California and breeds in true firs and Douglas-fir. The adult bores into the wood to lay eggs. *M. tsugae*

Hopping is smaller and pitch black. It occurs in British Columbia, Washington, and Oregon, and breeds in western hemlock and Douglas-fir.

Dromaeolus basalis LeConte resembles *Melasis tsugae* in color and size but is more shiny, does not have pectinate antennae, and the thorax is widest behind. It occurs in Oregon, Washington, and British Columbia. The larvae breed in conifers including incense-cedar.

SUPERFAMILY DERMESTOIDEA

FAMILY DERMESTIDAE—DERMESTID BEETLES

Dermestid beetles are a small family of inconspicuous but common insects (Arnett 1960). Adults are small, usually roundish beetles covered with fine dense brownish hairs and sometimes marked with colorful scales. Larvae are small, cylindrical, and covered with long brownish or blackish hairs, brushed to the rear.

Larvae of most species feed on dried animal and plant materials of high protein content, including cereal products and wool. They are well-known pests of insect collections. Some occur in the forest as predators or scavengers on associated insects. A few are recorded as damaging the surface of lumber stored in ships' holds, or in warehouses.

FAMILY DERODONTIDAE—TOOTHNECK FUNGUS BEETLES

This is a small family of small elongate, oval beetles most often encountered under bark of trees and in shelf-fungi. *Laricobius erichsonii* Rosenhauer from Europe has been colonized in Oregon, Washington, and British Columbia where it is established as one of the two most effective predators of the balsam woolly aphid (Mitchell 1965).

SUPERFAMILY BOSTRICHOIDEA

FAMILY ANOBIIDAE—DEATHWATCH AND DRUGSTORE BEETLES

There are 53 genera of Anobiidae in North America and about 280 species in the United States (White 1971). Many bore in wood. None is a major pest in the forest. Some are significant pests of wood products which may be reduced to powder by successive generations of the beetles. Similar damage is caused by many species of Bostrichidae and Lyctidae; as a result all three families are often referred to as "powderpost beetles." The tunnels of anobiid larvae are 2 mm or less in diameter. They contain minute pellets, notably smaller than those of the drywood termites and less powdery than the leavings of lyctids and bostrichids (Simeone 1965). The adults are elongate-cylindrical, generally grayish or brownish beetles, usually less than 6 mm long, and with the thorax hoodlike over the retractile head. The eggs are laid in cracks and crevices. The larvae are curved and hairy (Böving 1927). Yeasts of the *Endomycetales* live symbiotically in the digestive tract of anobiids and are presumed to aid digestion (Graham 1967). Control is as for *Lyctus*.

The **furniture beetle**, *Anobium punctatum* (De Geer), is an introduced species causing occasional damage to furniture and structural wood in houses in coastal British Columbia and Washington (Hatch 1962). It attacks both coniferous and nonconiferous wood. The adults are cylindrical, brown beetles 2.7 to 4.5 mm long and have sparse short pubescence.

There are 29 species of *Ernobius* in the United States (White 1971), 16 of them in California (Ruckes 1957). The adults (fig. 159) are small, reddish-brown to black, elongate, parallel-sided beetles with prominent eyes and a sharply margined thorax. They are clothed with fine short hairs. The larvae live in dry twigs, in dead cones, under bark, and in fungus-caused galls of conifers generally causing little damage (Keen 1958). They resemble *Conophthorus* larvae but are distinguished by having legs.

Ernobius melanoventris Ruckes, recorded in California, Oregon, Washington, and Idaho, attacks and aborts cones of *Pinus ponderosa* and *P. jeffreyi* at the beginning of the second year of cone development. In northern California there is one generation annually and pupae overwinter (Ruckes 1958). *E. pinicola* Ruckes causes similar damage to the same hosts in California and Oregon.

Hosts and distribution of other representative species are:

Species	Hosts	Distribution
E. conicola Fisher	*Cupressus macrocarpa* cones	Calif. and Oreg.
E. montanus Fall	*Pinus coulteri, P. jeffreyi, P. monophylla,* and *P. ponderosa* cones and twigs	S. Calif.
E. nigrans Fall	*Picea mariana* cones	British Columbia
E. pallitarsis Fall	*Pinus ponderosa* and *P. lambertiana* cones and twigs	Calif., Oreg., Wash., Idaho, Mont., and British Columbia
E. punctulatus (LeConte)	*Pinus attenuata, P. ponderosa, P. radiata,* and *Pseudotsuga menziesii* cones	Calif., Oreg., and Wash.

The **dry-rot beetle**, *Hadrobregmus* [*Coelostethus*] *quadrulus* (LeConte), commonly attacks dry-rotted Douglas-fir in buildings in Oregon, Washington, and British Columbia, also snags in the

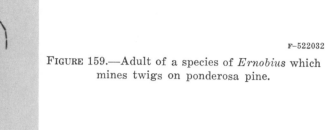

FIGURE 159.—Adult of a species of *Ernobius* which mines twigs on ponderosa pine.

forest. It does not seriously affect sound wood. The adults are dark brown and somewhat more robust than *Hemicoelus gibbicollis*. The thorax of *H. quadrulus* is as wide as the base of the elytra, and viewed laterally, is evenly rounded at the summit.

The **Pacific powderpost beetle,** *Hemicoelus gibbicollis* (LeConte), formerly *Hadrobregmus*, is the most damaging of the native powderpost beetles in buildings along the Pacific coast from California to Alaska (Linsley 1943b). *H. destructor* (Fisher) is a synonym. The under portions of older buildings without basements are most frequently infested. Structural timbers, subflooring, and other wooden parts may be repeatedly attacked and ultimately pulverized (fig. 160A). Well-seasoned, unrotted sapwood is preferred. Structures and dead trees of Douglas-fir, true fir, western hemlock, spruce, redwood, maple, alder, cherry, willow, oak, and other woods are attacked. The adults (fig. 160B) range from 2.5 to 5.5 mm long, have striate elytra, and are covered with short, recumbent, yellowish hairs. The thorax is notably narrower than the elytra and, viewed laterally, is strongly humped at the summit. The biology is not recorded.

Hemicoelus [*Cacotemnus*] *umbrosus* (Fall) is similar to *H. gibbicollis*. The range is the same on the Pacific coast, but *H. umbrosus* extends eastward to New Brunswick. *Abies* and *Betula* are recorded hosts.

Microbregma emarginatum (Duftschmid), which closely resembles *Hemicoelus gibbicollis*, ranges from California to British Columbia and Idaho (Hatch 1962). Spruce and hemlock are recorded hosts.

Priobium [*Trypopitys*] *punctatum* (LeConte) occurs from California to New Mexico and Colorado and northward in Oregon, Washington, and Idaho (Hatch 1962). It attacks products

F-522033, F-522034

FIGURE 160.—Pacific powderpost beetle (*Hemicoelus gibbicollis*) : *A*, Shot-holes and pulverizing of structural wood; *B*, adult, 4 mm long.

made of Douglas-fir, pine, Monterey cypress, oak, and maple. The adults resemble *Hadrobregmus quadrulus* in color and size.

Ptilinus basalis LeConte occurs from California to British Columbia (Hatch 1962). It attacks dead and cured wood of *Umbellularia californica, Acer macrophyllum, Populus tremuloides, Prunus*, and *Salix*. It causes considerable damage to myrtlewood used in turning and will multiply through successive generations in stored wood. It has also been collected from redwood siding (De Leon 1952). The adults are 3.0 to 5.5 mm long, chestnut brown, cylindrical, and covered with very short yellowish hairs. The pronotum is very convex and is toothed in front somewhat like that of the Bostrichidae. The males are smaller than females and have comb-like rather than serrate antennae.

The **drugstore beetle**, *Stegobium paniceum* (L.) is a cosmopolitan pest of stored food products. Occasionally it damages wood, usually in conjunction with food storage (Linsley 1942). The adults are elongate, robust, reddish-brown, pubescent beetles 2.2 to 3.7 mm long with abundant yellowish hairs that do not hide the surface.

Trichodesma cristata (Casey) occurs in California, Oregon, and British Columbia. It is reported to attack Douglas-fir (Hatch 1962). It is a stocky beetle, 5 to 7 mm long, and clothed with white, brown, and black hairs. Several tufts of black hairs on the wing covers are characteristic.

Tricorynus, formerly *Catorama*, are small, hairy, oval, reddish-brown to black beetles from 1.4 to 5.6 mm long. There are 82 species in North America, mostly in the Southwest (White 1965). They are recorded from seeds, stems, wood, galls, fungi, and under bark. None is a forest pest. *T. conophilus* (Fall) is a little known species that occurs in New Mexico and Texas and is recorded from cones of *Pinus edulis*.

There are three species of *Utobium* (White 1966), all in the West. They are 5 to 7.4 mm long and mottled with grayish and few to numerous orange hairs. *U. marmoratum* Fall occurs in Oregon, Washington, and Idaho and has been reared from dead dry lodgepole pine.

There are 12 species of *Vrilletta* in North America (White 1971), predominantly along the Pacific Coast. None is an economic pest. They are cylindrical, brownish to black beetles, 3.5 to 8 mm long. *V. decorata* Van Dyke is black variegated with yellowish spots and stripes on the elytra. It occurs from California to British Columbia and has been reared from dead *Quercus*, *Umbellularia*, *Alnus*, *Cornus*, and *Malus*. *V. convexa* LeConte is black and the male has very strongly serrate antennae. This species has been reared from *Quercus* and *Alnus*.

There are four species of *Xestobium*, three native and one introduced (White 1971). They are similar to *Utobium* in size and appearance. *X. abietis* Fisher has been reared from *Abies grandis* and *Acer macrophyllum* in British Columbia. The **deathwatch beetle**, *X. rufovillosum* (De Geer), a native of Europe, occurs occasionally in the West (Linsley 1943b). It infests structural timbers and heavy furniture in old buildings. Oak is preferred. The ticking sound associated with this beetle is said to be a mating call of the adults.

There are 12 species of *Xyletinus* in North America, mostly in the West (White 1962). They are elongate-oval, brownish to blackish, finely pubescent beetles 3 to 7 mm long. In Eastern States, *X. peltatus* (Harris) damages wood in houses and barns, but none of the western species is recorded to be of economic importance. *X. fucatus* LeConte occurs from California to British Columbia and Idaho. It is reported on *Prunus* and *Pseudotsuga* in British Columbia.

FAMILY BOSTRICHIDAE—FALSE POWDERPOST BEETLES

The **bostrichids** (Fisher 1950) are most abundant in the tropics where they seriously damage felled timber, buildings, and furniture. In temperate America they are often encountered as pests of stored vegetable products and imported furniture and novelties made of bamboo. About 70 species are native or have become established in America north of Mexico. They are especially abundant in broad-leaved trees and shrubs in the East and the Southwest.

The adults are elongate and cylindrical. Many species differ from other powderpost beetles by having a tuberculate and rasplike pronotum. The smaller bostrichids resemble scolytids, but have straight rather than elbowed antennae. Most are less than 10 mm long, but they average larger than the anobiids and range up to 50 mm for the giant *Dinapate wrightii*. The larvae are curved as with the anobiids. Eggs are laid in open tunnels made by the adults. The larval tunnels are frass-filled.

Melalgus [Polycaon] confertus (LeConte) is prevalent in California and is recorded northward into British Columbia. The larvae bore in various hardwoods including madrone, bigleaf maple, canyon live oak, tanoak, manzanita, and fruit trees. The adults prune twigs by boring at the fork of small branches. These beetles are cylindrical, black with reddish-brown elytra, and 7 to 13 mm long. The prothorax is not asperate and does not hide the head from above.

Polycaon stoulii (LeConte) (fig. 161) is a jet-black beetle, 11

FIGURE 161.—Adult of a false powderpost beetle, *Polycaon stoutii*, 16 mm long.

to 22 mm long, with prominent mandibles. It occurs naturally in California, Arizona, and Oregon. The larvae bore in various hardwoods including oak, California-laurel, madrone, alder, maple, sycamore, and eucalyptus. The larvae cause damage by mining in inner layers of plywood and adults by emerging through veneer surfaces. They require 1 to several years to complete development and are not known to reinfest manufactured wood.

Numerous bostrichids feed in desert trees and shrubs of the Southwest reducing the dead branches and stems to powder (Fisher 1950). Some examples are:

Insect	Hosts	Distribution
Amphicerus cornutus (Pallas)	*Prosopis*	Calif. to Tex. north into Colo. and Utah
A. simplex (Horn)	*Parkinsonia microphyllum,* and *Cercidium torreyanum*	Ariz., N. Mex., and Tex.
Apatides fortis (LeConte)	*Prosopis* and *Cercidium*	Calif. to Tex. and north into Utah
Dendrobiella aspera (LeConte)	*Cercidium torreyanum, Prosopis juliflora,* and *Tamarix gallica*	Calif. and Ariz.

The **giant palm borer**, *Dinapate wrightii* Horn, develops in and riddles the dead trunks of California fan palm, *Washingtonia filifera*, on the edges of the Colorado desert in California (Michelbacher and Ross 1939). On ornamental trees, the adults are reported to bore into the growing tip sometimes causing the tree to die (Wymore 1928). The adults range from 33 to 51 mm long and are dark brown, shiny above, and hairy below. They fly from mid-June until late August. The life cycle requires at least 2 years.

The **bamboo powderpost beetle**, *Dinoderus minutus* (F.), is a cosmopolitan pest of bamboo in tropical regions and is frequently carried into temperate zones (Fisher 1950). It pulverizes bamboo products. The adult is a reddish-brown to black, cylindrical beetle, 2.5 to 3.5 mm long and with the forepart of the thorax armed with concentric rows of rasplike teeth. *D. minutus* strongly resembles *Xyleborus*. Control is as for *Lyctus*.

The **leadcable borer**, *Scobicia declivis* (LeConte) (Burke et al. 1922) (fig. 162), is a shiny dark brown to black, cylindrical beetle averaging about 6 mm long and superficially resembling *Xyleborus*. The leadcable borer occurs in California and Oregon. It feeds in many kinds of seasoned hardwood including oak, maple, California-laurel, acacia, and eucalyptus. It has a 1-year life cycle and will reattack. The common name refers to its earlier-day habit of boring into lead-covered telephone cables. It also has damaged wine casks.

F-522036, F-522037

FIGURE 162.—Adult of the leadcable borer (*Scobicia declivis*), 6 mm long: *A*, Top view; *B*, lateral view.

Stephanopachys substriatus (Paykull) (Fisher 1950) is a brownish-black beetle, 3.5 to 6.5 mm long, with granulate elytra, and with numerous teeth on the front half of the pronotum. It occurs extensively in northern Europe, Asia, and North America, including most Western States and Provinces. Ponderosa pine, Jeffrey pine, and other pines are common hosts. Douglas-fir and various true firs also are attacked. It bores in the bark and outer sapwood, sometimes in air-dried lumber with bark on it. *S. sobrinus* (Casey) is a similar species that ranges from British Columbia to South Dakota and Arizona. It infects *Pinus edulis*.

FAMILY LYCTIDAE—POWDERPOST BEETLES

The Lyctidae (Gerberg 1957) probably are the most destructive of the **powderpost beetles** attacking wood products. Their natural range is in tropical and warm temperate areas. Through commerce, they have been widely distributed and established in lumber, furniture, flooring, decorative trim, tool handles, and other hardwood products. Bamboo also is a preferred host.

Adults are flattened, slender, dark brown to nearby black beetles generally 3 to 6 mm long (fig. 163). Mature larvae are yellowish white, somewhat curved, and about 5 mm long. Seasonal history is generally similar for all species. Eggs are laid only in pores of wood which open to the surface. The larvae bore in the sapwood often reducing it to a flourlike powder, except for a thin surface veneer. The damage is very similar to that by *Hemicoelus gibbicollis* (fig. 160). When wood is first attacked, there is little external evidence. Near maturity, the larvae cut circular holes through the surface of the wood. These holes and the boring dust expelled through them are the usual first signs of attack.

F–522038

FIGURE 163.—Adult powderpost beetle, *Lyctus* species,
4.5 mm long.

Powderpost beetles breed in seasoned and seasoning wood containing starch and having a moisture content of about 6 to 20 percent. One generation annually is typical in northern areas where larvae overwinter, pupae form in the spring, and adults appear early in the summer. Under favorable food, moisture, and temperature conditions, the beetles develop continuously without regard to season.

Measures should be taken systematically to prevent buildup of infestations in storage facilities (Snyder 1936). Stock should be inspected at least annually and infested material should be treated or destroyed. Scrap material and old stock should not accumulate. If structural damage is not serious, infested material can be saved by heat treatment or application of penetrating sprays (USDA Forest Service 1954). Painting, varnishing, or coating with linseed oil or wax will prevent damage to uninfested wood products (Snyder 1944).

In wood products in the West, the **old world lyctus beetle,** *Lyctus brunneus* (Stephens), **the southern lyctus beetle,** *L. planicollis* LeConte, and the **western lyctus beetle,** *L. cavicollis* LeConte apparently are most prevalent; some common hosts are *Fraxinus, Quercus,* and *Umbellularia.* The **European lyctus beetle,** *L. linearis* (Goeze), and *Trogoxylon aequale* (Wollaston) also occur. *L. cavicollis* and *T. aequale* develop under natural conditions in California.

FAMILY PTINIDAE—SPIDER BEETLES

The Ptinidae are small, long-legged beetles with long threadlike antennae, small thorax, and generally globular body, giving them a spiderlike appearance. Some are pests in stored products. A few occur in the forest, but none is reported to be damaging.

The **whitemarked spider beetle,** *Ptinus fur* (L.), is a cosmopolitan, reddish-brown beetle, 2 to 4 mm long and with white markings on the elytra. It feeds on dried animal and plant material and has been reared from ponderosa pine and western redcedar cones being processed for seed (Keen 1958). It also has been reported as boring in woodwork, but that habit likely is incidental.

SUPERFAMILY CLEROIDEA

FAMILY CLERIDAE—CHECKERED BEETLES

The Cleridae (Barr 1962) comprise some 300 species in 35 genera in North America. They are predominantly predaceous both as adults and larvae. Many feed upon insects that attack trees and shrubs. They are particularly abundant in the Southwest. Well known to foresters as "clerids," the genera *Enoclerus* and *Thanasimus* contain some of the most important predators of western bark beetles and wood borers. The adults are medium-sized, strong-legged, bug-eyed, generally hairy, fast-moving beetles (fig. 164A). The larvae (Böving and Champlain 1920) generally are hairy and may be white, pink, bluish, or red depending on species and stage of development. All have a pair of hooks on the last abdominal segment (fig. 164B).

F–522039, F–522040

FIGURE 164.—A checkered beetle, *Enoclerus sphegeus*: *A*, Adult, 10 mm long; *B*, larva, 18 mm long.

The genus *Enoclerus* contains 40 species, many of which are western. Two species are very effective predators of destructive bark beetles.

The **blackbellied clerid**, *Enoclerus lecontei* (Wolcott) (Person 1940, Berryman 1966), is the most important insect predator of *Dendroctonus brevicomis*. It occurs widely in the West, preying upon various species of *Dendroctonus*, *Ips*, *Scolytus*, *Pseudohylesinus*, and *Pityophthorus*. In central California the life cycle of *E. lecontei* is closely synchronized with that of the western pine beetle, its preferred host. First generation broods are most heavily preyed upon. The clerid adults prey upon bark beetle adults and clerid larvae feed upon bark beetle larvae and pupae. Many of the clerid larvae migrate to the base of the tree where they pupate in ovoid cells lined with a silvery secretion. They overwinter as larvae, pupae, and adults. On direct control operations it has been the practice to leave stumps untreated so as to protect the clerids and increase their abundance relative to the host. The effectiveness of this operation has not been evaluated quantitatively.

The adults are 6 to 8 mm long, black with gray markings on the elytra, the most prominent being a broad band at the rear. The larvae are pink, turning purplish near maturity, at which time they are 9 to 14 mm long.

The **redbellied clerid**, *Enoclerus sphegeus* (F.), (Kline and Rudinsky 1964, Reid 1957, Struble 1942a), is abundant in the coniferous forests of the West. It is rated as an important predator of *Dendroctonus pseudotsugae* (Kline and Rudinsky 1964) and *D. ponderosae* (Struble 1942a), and it preys on other bark beetles including species of *Scolytus* and *Ips.*

The adult is hairy, blackish with a metallic luster except for the red abdomen, 8.5 to 12 mm long, and it has a distinctive wide gray band across the middle of the elytra. The larvae (fig. 164B) are white when small, then pink, and finally purplish. The prepupal larva overwinters. There is one generation annually in Oregon. The adult feeds upon adult bark beetles (fig. 164A) and the larvae feed upon the immature stages. Efforts to propagate this clerid in quantity in the laboratory for biological control have been unsuccessful (Struble 1942b).

Enoclerus barri Knull (Rice 1969) occurs extensively in the Western States and British Columbia. It is much less abundant than *E. sphegeus* which it resembles, and it is smaller and has an angulate gray band behind the middle. It feeds on *Dendroctonus, Ips,* and *Scolytus* in the laboratory and is presumed to be a general feeder on bark beetles, principally on ponderosa pine. *E. moestus* (Klug), practically a twin of *E. barri* in appearance and habits, is a southwestern species.

Enoclerus eximius (Mannerheim) is a redbellied species with black head and thorax and orange-red elytra with three purplish-black spots in front and a broad black band in back. The length is 6 to 8 mm. It occurs commonly from California to British Columbia and less abundantly in the Intermountain Region, preying upon various borers including *Paratimia conicola* and *Chrysophana placida* in knobcone pine cones and *Hemicoelus gibbicollis, Ptilinus basalis,* and other powderpost beetles, principally in willow, alder, and California-laurel.

Enoclerus schaefferi Barr is widely distributed in the West. The adult is black, except for red shoulders of the elytra, and is about 5 mm long. The larvae feed on insects infesting cones of *Abies,*

Pseudotsuga, Pinus, Picea, and *Cupressus* (Keen 1958). The cone moths, *Barbara colfaxiana* and *Laspeyresia* spp., are recorded hosts.

Thanasimus contains four species, two of them western. They closely resemble *Enoclerus* and have similar habits, but the adults differ by having coarse deep punctures on the basal third of the elytra.

Thanasimus undatulus (Say), variously recorded as *T. monticola* Wolcott, *T. rubriventris* LeConte, and *T. dubius* (F.), is a transcontinental species that occurs in the West from New Mexico to Alaska. It preys upon bark beetles, including *Dendroctonus, Scolytus,* and *Pseudohylesinus.* The adults are about 7 to 10 mm long and rather slender. They are red-legged; the shoulders of the elytra often are reddish; and the thorax and abdomen range from partially to wholly black. The larvae and pupa are described by Kline and Rudinsky (1964).

Thanasimus repandus Horn is somewhat larger and stouter than *T. undatulus* and its thorax and abdomen are entirely red. *T. repandus* occurs in California, Oregon, and Washington. It reportedly preys upon the bark beetle, *Phloeosinus sequoiae.*

Chariessa elegans Horn preys upon *Neoclytus conjunctus* and other cerambycids in oaks and madrone (Doane et al. 1936). It occurs in Texas, Arizona, California, Oregon, and British Columbia. The adults are 11 mm long, orange red with blue elytra, and black feet.

The genus *Cymatodera* contains some 60 species primarily in the Southwestern United States. They are generally yellowish brown with indistinct markings and are widest toward the rear. *C. ovipennis* LeConte is a common but economically unimportant species, 7 to 11 mm long, and wingless that occurs in California, New Mexico, Oregon, British Columbia, and other western areas. It preys upon *Paratimia* and *Laspeyresia* (Keen 1958) in cones and apparently on a variety of other wood-inhabiting insects in a wide variety of host trees, both conifers and broad-leaved species (MacSwain 1945).

Monophylla californica Fall occurs in California, Arizona, Utah, and Oregon. In California it preys upon the beetles, *Scobicia declivis* and *Lyctus,* principally in oaks (Burke et al. 1922). The adults are 4 to 7 mm long and dark brown to black, with a medium transverse whitish stripe. The terminal segment of the antennae is longer than the other segments combined.

FAMILY TROGOSITIDAE (OSTOMIDAE)

In North America this family, also known as Ostomidae, contains 57 small- to medium-sized species. The more elongate subcylindrical ones generally prey upon insects that live under the bark and in the wood of trees and shrubs. The elliptical, much-flattened ones feed principally on fungi. Barron (1971) published keys to the genera and species.

Seven of the 10 North American species of *Temnochila* (Barron 1971) are western. *T. chlorodia* (Mannerheim) is best known to foresters. It is a subcylindrical, metallic blue-green beetle, 9 to 20 mm long and with powerful mandibles for holding and crushing prey (fig. 165). The larva resembles a clerid larva in appearance, including two forked hooks at the end of the abdomen. This species is prevalent from South Dakota and Texas to the Pacific and from the Northwest Territories into Mexico. It preys upon many kinds of bark- and wood-boring insects and is rated an important predator of the western pine beetle (Stark and Dahlsten 1970), the mountain pine beetle (Struble 1942a), and of other bark beetles. When associated with the mountain pine beetle in California, *T. chlorodia* requires a full year to complete its life cycle. Efforts to develop a method to mass rear this predator for biological control have been unsuccessful (Struble 1942b).

F–522041

FIGURE 165.—A predaceous beetle, *Temnochila chlorodia*, 14 mm long.

Several species of *Tenebroides* (Barron 1971) occur in the West, frequently under the bark of conifers killed by bark beetles. The native species prey upon various insects which feed after bark beetles have completed their life cycles. The adults are shiny black and resemble *Temnochila*, but are flatter, broader, and generally shorter. *Tenebroides corticalis* (Melsheimer) is a transcontinental species occurring throughout the West, including Alaska and the Yukon. The **cadelle,** *T. mauritanicus* (L.), is an introduced pest of stored grain, the larva of which is reported to damage the wood of storage bins (Hatch 1962).

SUPERFAMILY TENEBRIONOIDEA

FAMILY MELANDRYIDAE

Various melandryids live under the bark and in the wood of dead trees. Only one, the **blazed-tree borer**, *Serropalpus substriatus* Haldeman, is recorded as of any economic importance in western forests. In British Columbia it infests felled white spruce and Engelmann spruce on logging operations (Ross 1968). It lays its eggs in dying or dead trees or living trees from which the bark has been peeled. The long, slim, white larvae mine the sapwood, making oval tunnels filled with very fine dustlike frass. After two seasons in the larval stage, the slender reddish-brown beetles, 12 to 18 mm long (fig. 166), emerge in June and July through perfectly round holes cut in the bark. Both the exit holes and the larval mines resemble those of siricids. This woodborer is widely distributed in North America, breeding in various coniferous trees. In the West it has been bred from red fir, incense-cedar, lodgepole pine, ponderosa pine, redwood, Port-Orford-cedar, Engelmann spruce, and Douglas-fir, and probably will be found in many other conifers.

F–522042

FIGURE 166.—Adult of the blazed tree borer (*Serropalpus substriatus*), 16 mm long.

FAMILY OEDEMERIDAE

Adults of the Oedemeridae (Arnett 1951) generally are slender, elongate, soft-bodied beetles of light brown to black color, and some closely resemble Cerambycidae. The larvae resemble melandryids. Many breed in moist, rotting wood. As a group, the oedemerids are of little economic importance.

Calopus angustus LeConte is an elongate brown beetle, 12 mm or more in length, that breeds in the wood of dead pine, fir, cedar, willow, and cherry. It is a transcontinental species that occurs extensively in the West.

Ditylus quadricollis LeConte is a cerambycidlike, black or dark brown beetle upward of 25 mm long. It occurs in coastal forests from California to Alaska and is recorded as breeding in wet, rotten logs of *Thuja plicata*.

The **wharf borer**, *Nacerdes melanura* (L.) (Arnett 1951, Balch 1937), is an introduced species now present along the coast from California to British Columbia. It develops in moist, rotting wood such as wharfs, piling, posts, and the under portions of buildings, and is not considered economically important. The adult (fig. 167) is narrow, about 10 mm long, brownish to yellowish above with the tips of the elytra blackish. The full-grown larva is about 30 mm long and strongly constricted between segments. Properly creosoted timbers are immune to attack.

F–522043

FIGURE 167.—Adult of the wharf borer (*Nacerdes melanura*), 10 mm long.

FAMILY TENEBRIONIDAE—DARKLING BEETLES

The Tenebrionidae (Arnett 1960) are a large family of brown to black beetles, many of which live in the forest. Principally, they feed as scavengers on plant materials. A few are pests of stored products. None is destructive in the forest.

There are several western species of *Corticeus*. They are cylindrical, shiny, brown to black beetles, 2 to 4 mm long, that live in the galleries of various bark beetles, often in large numbers. *C. substriatus* (LeConte), one of the larger species, is commonly associated with *Dendroctonus brevicomis* and *D. ponderosae*. Struble (1930) reported that the adults and larvae both feed upon fungi under the bark. Parker and Davis (1971) found that they also will feed on eggs, larvae, and pupae of *D. ponderosae* and associated insects.

Iphthimus serratus (Mannerheim) is one of the more common and abundant western tenebrionids that feed in very rotten wood of conifers, such as Douglas-fir, aiding in its return to the soil.

282

The adults (fig. 168) are dull black, somewhat flattened, long-legged beetles, 20 to 25 mm long. The yellowish-brown larvae, resembling somewhat inflated wireworms, have a pair of horny hooks at the rear end.

F–521982

FIGURE 168.—Adult of *Iphthimus serratus*, 25 mm long, a common scavenger in rotten wood.

Phellopsis porcata (LeConte) is one of the more conspicuous of the several tenebrionids that feed on the woody fruiting bodies of *Fomes* and other fungi. The adults are dark brown to black, rough-surfaced, flattened beetles about 15 mm long.

SUPERFAMILY CUCUJOIDEA

FAMILY COCCINELLIDAE—LADY BEETLES

The common reddish or orange colored variously spotted species of Coccinellidae (Hagen 1962) (fig. 169A) need no description. In addition to these well-known forms there are some tiny nondescript gray to black or brown species that are among the more important ones in foresty (fig. 169B). Most **lady beetles** feed both as adults and larvae upon aphids, scales, mites, and other insects (fig. 169C). Some aggregate in large numbers to spend the winter. As a group they are important in natural and biological control of pest insects, particularly in agriculture.

There are three species of *Anatis* (Hatch 1962) in North America, all occurring in the West. They are notable chiefly because of their size, being the largest of the North American coccinellids, ranging from about 7 to 10 mm long. *A. rathvoni* LeConte is common in true fir forests from California to British Columbia and eastward into Idaho. The larvae are black with

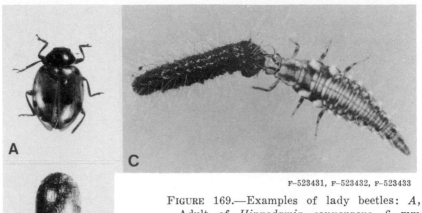

F-523431, F-523432, F-523433

FIGURE 169.—Examples of lady beetles: *A*, Adult of *Hippodamia convergens*, 6 mm long; *B*, adult of *Scymnus impexus*, 2.5 mm long; *C*, larva of a large lady beetle feeding on a small tent caterpillar larva.

yellow markings and prey upon aphids. The adults are yellowish to reddish brown above with black spots.

The **twicestabbed lady beetle,** *Chilocorus stigma* (Say) is a transcontinental species occurring commonly in Arizona, New Mexico, California, Nevada, Oregon, Washington, Idaho, British Columbia, and Alberta. It feeds on many kinds of scales including the pine needle and the oystershell scales. The adults are 4 to 5 mm long, nearly hemispherical, shining black, with two red spots, one on each elytron. The larvae are spiny, and black with a yellow band across the middle.

There are 18 species of *Hippodamia* (Chapin 1946) in North America and nearly all occur in the West. They are elongate-oval, moderately convex, black-bodied beetles with reddish or yellowish pronotum and elytra, usually marked with black (fig. 169A). Their length ranges from about 4 to 8 mm. They feed upon aphids of many kinds, but do not exert much control against forest insect pests. Several species of *Hippodamia* congregate in great numbers in the mountains to hibernate (Rockwood 1952). The **convergent lady beetle,** *H. convergens* Guérin-Méneville is one of the commonest of all lady beetles. It occurs throughout the West and is one of the species that aggregate in forested areas to hibernate. Efforts have been made to collect the assembled beetles and colonize them in agricultural areas but without much success because they soon disperse widely. The adults have orange-red elytra usually marked with 12 black spots. The larvae are velvety black with orange spots.

The **pine ladybird beetle,** *Mulsantina* [*Cleis*] *picta* (Randall), occurs extensively in the West from Arizona to British Columbia.

It feeds on pine- and fir-infesting aphids, including *Adelges* (Mitchell 1962). The adults are 3.5 to 5 mm long, moderately convex, with yellowish elytra variegated with black in the female and immaculate in the male. The mature larvae are about 7 mm long and mostly black with white markings on the sides and down the middle.

Scymnus impexus Mulsant, also known as *Pullus*, was imported from Europe and colonized in Oregon, Washington, and British Columbia to control *Adelges piceae* (Mitchell and Wright 1967). It has become established but does not exert sufficient control to prevent tree-killing. The adult is a somewhat shiny brown beetle about the size of a pinhead (fig. 169B). In Oregon it has one generation per year. The adults and larvae both feed upon the aphid but the larvae do most of the feeding.

FAMILY COLYDIIDAE

The Colydiidae are small, generally elongate beetles many of which live in the galleries of bark beetles and other wood borers. Some are predaceous. The role of most has not been determined.

There are four North American species of *Aulonium* (King-solver and White 1967), one of which is western. *A. longum* LeConte is a flat, elongate beetle about 5.5 mm long. It is widely distributed in the West often occurring abundantly in the galleries of *Dendroctonus brevicomis*, *D. ponderosae*, and other bark beetles. It is suspected of being predaceous, but at best is of little importance.

Deretaphrus oregonensis Horn (Burke 1919), the largest of the colydiids, is uncommon. It occurs in Oregon, Washington, Idaho, and British Columbia. The adult is black, elongate, cylindrical, and about 10 mm long. The larvae prey upon larvae and pupae of *Buprestis*, *Trachykele*, and *Asemum* and are occasionally associated with *Dendroctonus*.

There are about 20 species of *Lasconotus* (Kraus 1912) in North America, predominantly in the West. They are elongate, flattened, strongly-sculptured, brownish beetles, about 3 mm long. They live in the galleries of bark beetles, often abundantly. They are considered to be predaceous. *L. subcostulatus* Kraus occurs extensively in the West associated with various bark beetles including *Dendroctonus brevicomis* but is not considered to be a factor in their control.

FAMILY CUCUJIDAE—FLAT BARK BEETLES

Adults are small- to medium-size, usually greatly flattened beetles, some of which are yellowish or reddish, and others brownish or black. Larvae are 3 to 30 mm long, also flattened, and yellow to reddish brown (Arnett 1960); some have a pair of anal protuberances. Some species occur under the loosened bark of trees or logs infested by bark beetles and borers, as predators or scavengers. Others are pests of stored products such as cereals.

Cucujus flavipes F. is a common associate of wood borers and has a northerly distribution from coast to coast. The adult is a brillant scarlet, flattened beetle, 10 to 14 mm long.

FAMILY NITIDULIDAE—SAP BEETLES

The **sap beetles** (Parsons 1943, Hatch 1962) are generally small, flattened, shiny beetles, some of which resemble Staphylinidae in that the abdomen extends beyond the wing covers. Many species feed on decaying and fermenting fruit and on fungi. Some occur in the galleries of bark beetles and ambrosia beetles, most abundantly in "sour sap" situations. *Glischrochilus vittatus* (Say) and *Epurea linearis* Mäklin are recorded as possibly predaceous on *Dendroctonus ponderosae* (De Leon 1934). Potentially significant to western foresters, some species of Nitidulidae are vectors of oak wilt (Dorsey and Leach 1956, Jones and Phelps 1972).

FAMILY RHIZOPHAGIDAE

This small family contains several genera, of which only *Rhizophagus* (Hatch 1962) is likely to be encountered by western foresters. Adults of this genus are elongate, somewhat flattened, shiny, reddish-brown beetles, 2 to 4 mm long. They often are abundant in galleries of *Dendroctonus, Ips, Scolytus,* and other bark beetles. Adults and larvae of *R. procerus* Casey have been observed to feed upon eggs and larvae of *Dendroctonus ponderosae* and other associated insects (De Leon 1934). Their role in natural control of bark beetles probably is minor.

SUPERFAMILY CHRYSOMELOIDEA

FAMILY CERAMBYCIDAE—LONGHORNED BEETLES OR ROUNDHEADED WOOD BORERS

The **longhorned beetles** or **roundheaded wood borers**, Cerambycidae, are grouped in seven subfamilies (Linsley 1961), all of which are included in this manual. The species are many and their roles diverse (Linsley 1958, 1959). Most of the western species are cambium-wood feeders, in that the larvae first mine in the cambium region of trees and shrubs and then extend their tunnels into the sapwood and in some cases into the heartwood. Some that mine extensively under the bark are tree killers, but none of these is rated as a major pest. Others that bore deeply in the wood frequently damage logs and wood products. A few are beneficial in that they feed so voraciously that they destroy some associated bark beetle larvae either directly or by depriving them of food. As a group, the Cerambycidae are important in the process of cycling wood back to the soil, in part, presumably by their galleries providing avenues for invasion by wood-rotting fungi (Basham and Belyea 1960).

The adults are medium- to large-sized, oblong to cylindrical beetles, with antennae often longer than the entire body. These long antennae, or feelers, are their most characteristic feature and give them the name "longhorned beetles." Eggs are laid in bark crevices and in slits cut by the females. The larvae bore through the bark and wood, constructing long irregular mines. These increase in size with the growth of the larvae and are usually packed with coarse borings.

The larvae (Craighead 1915, 1923) are the destructive stage and the one most often seen by foresters. The larvae generally are fleshy, cylindrical, elongate grubs, having a thin body texture sparsely clothed with fine hairs. Often they are plump at the head end (thorax), hence are called "roundheaded borers;" however, some that mine the cambium region are very much flattened. A horny plate on the top surface of the first segment behind the head and no plate on the underside of this segment distinguish roundheaded borer larvae from flatheaded borer larvae. Most of the latter have a plate both above and below.

No measures have been developed to control tree-killing roundheaded borers in the West and none seems warranted. Likewise, there seems little likelihood that practical measures will be developed to prevent attacks on dead and down trees. As with other insects that attack unseasoned wood, about the only thing that can be done is to remove the logs from the woods as quickly as possible and place them in water or run them through the mill and kiln-drying process. A few of these insects are of economic importance even after the lumber is placed in storage or put into use.

Parandrinae—The subfamily Parandrinae (Linsley 1962a) is the oldest living group of Cerambycidae. In North America this subfamily contains one genus and three species.

The **pole borer**, *Parandra brunnea* (F.), is by far the most abundant species. It occurs extensively in the Eastern States and westward into Colorado (Linsley 1962a). West of the Great Plains it is recorded only from Boise, Idaho. The larvae bore gregariously in moist heartwood of many hardwoods and some conifers. *P. brunnea* is rated as a destructive borer in crossties, poles, and structural wood in contact with the ground (Baker 1972). The larval mines in the base of shade trees are an important cause of breakage. The adult is a shiny, brown, elongate, somewhat flattened beetle with prominent mandibles and ranges from about 10 to 20 mm long. Attacks on wood products can be prevented by using chemically treated wood. Shade trees should be kept vigorous and exposed wood should be treated so as to prevent egg-laying. *P. marginicollis punctillata* Schaeffer (fig. 170) is a similar but little-known species that occurs in Arizona and southern California and bores in *Platanus* and *Alnus*.

FIGURE 170.—Male adult of *Parandra marginicollis punctillata*, 18 mm long, on New Mexican alder.

Prioninae—The subfamily Prioninae (Linsley 1962a) contains some of the largest North American beetles. The adults generally are brownish, somewhat flattened, nocturnal beetles often with sharp projections on the side of the prothorax. The larvae bore principally in dead moist wood; sometimes in the roots of living trees. They are large, leathery, and practically hairless. Their head is broader than long and their mandibles acute.

Derobrachus (Linsley 1962a) contains two species in the Southern United States. One is western. *D. geminatus* LeConte, a little-known species, occurs from California to Texas. The larvae bore in roots of *Populus*, *Quercus*, *Prosopis*, and other broad-leaved trees. The adults are brown, hairless, about 40 to 70 mm long, and have four sharp projections on each side of the prothorax.

Ergates (Linsley 1962a) contains two species in North America, both western. Only one is significant in forestry.

The **ponderous borer**, *Ergates spiculatus* (LeConte), occurs in the forested States of the West and in British Columbia. *Pseudotsuga menziesii* and *Pinus ponderosa* are principal hosts. Other pines, some true firs, and redwood also are recorded hosts. The larval mines in the heartwood of fire-killed Douglas-fir speed deterioration and limit the amount of salvage from large burns such as the Tillamook Burn of 1933 in Oregon (Kimmey and Furniss 1943). Ponderosa pine trees killed by the western pine beetle often are mined at the base by *E. spiculatus* and other borers. Borer-weakened snags fall more quickly than sound snags, hence the borers contribute somewhat to fire hazard reduction.

The adults (fig. 171A) are 42 to 65 mm long. The elytra of the subspecies along the Pacific coast and in the Northern Rocky Mountains are uniformly reddish brown; those of the subspecies in the Central and Southern Rocky Mountains are reddish brown with irregular pale blotches. The sides of the thorax have many spines or are unarmed. The adults lay eggs in crevices of the bark of dead trees and stumps. The larvae, known to loggers as "timber worms," excavate very large, meandering galleries, first in the sapwood then deep into the heartwood. When full grown the larvae (fig. 171B) are thick-bodied, 60 to 70 mm long, creamy white with a reddish-brown head bearing four toothlike processes just above the mandibles. The life cycle is presumed to require several to many years. No practical control measures are known. The mandibles and boring action of this beetle gave a logger the idea for the modern saw chain.

Prionus (Linsley 1962a) is a large genus of root borers, but only one is significant in western forests.

The **California prionus**, *Prionus californicus* Motschulsky (Linsley 1962a), also known as the **giant root borer**, is distributed from Alaska through California and eastward into the Rocky

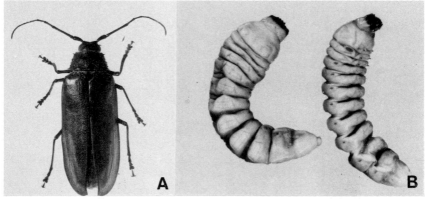

F–523434, EPQ–6882

FIGURE 171.—The ponderous borer (*Ergates spiculatus*): *A*, Adult, 55 mm long; *B*, larvae, 60 to 70 mm long.

Mountain Region and the Southwest. It is principally a root borer in living deciduous trees and is reported injurious to oak, madrone, cottonwood, and various fruit trees. It also bores in moist dead wood of pine, Douglas-fir, true fir, and especially wood in contact with the soil. The adult resembles *Ergates spiculatus* but is stouter and has three prominent teeth on each side of the thorax. The life cycle requires 3 to 5 years.

Tragosoma (Linsley 1962a) contains three species in North America. All occur in the West. None is a forest pest.

The **hairy pine borer,** *Tragosoma depsarius* (L.) (= *harrisii* LeConte), occurs extensively in the coniferous forests of the Western States and British Columbia. Recorded hosts in the West are *Pinus ponderosa, P. contorta,* and *Pseudotsuga menziesii.* The larvae resemble those of *Ergates* in appearance and habits but are smaller. They are most often found in the sapwood and outer heartwood of long-dead and down trees. The adults are brown, densely hairy on the thorax, 18 to 36 mm long, and have one spine on each side of the thorax.

Spondylinae—The subfamily Spondylinae (Linsley 1962a) contains two genera in North America. One is western.

Spondylis upiformis Mannerheim occurs from Alaska through California and eastward to South Dakota, Colorado, and New Mexico. It has been reported to bore in the roots of pines, specifically lodgepole in Alberta. Little is known of its habits except that the adults fly abundantly in pine forests in late spring and early summer. The adults are black, robust, 8 to 20 mm long, and have prominent mandibles (fig. 172). Each elytron has two longitudinal ridges.

Aseminae—The subfamily Aseminae (Linsley 1962a) contains several genera of mostly somber-colored beetles, several species of

FIGURE 172.—Adult of *Spondylis upiformis,* a longhorned beetle, 14 mm long.

which damage forest trees and forest products. The larvae of most species have a pair of spines at the end of the last abdominal segment.

Arhopalus [*Criocephalus*] (Linsley 1962a) contains four species, all of which occur in the West. The adults are black to brownish and are the largest in the subfamily. The larvae bore in the wood of conifers (fig. 173A). The pair of spines on the last abdominal segment are sharp and incurved (fig. 173B). The life cycle is presumed to be 2 or more years.

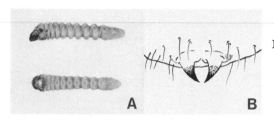

FIGURE 173.—Wood borers in genus *Arhopalus*: *A*, Views of typical larva, 30 mm long; *B*, closeup of anal spines of the larva.

Arhopalus asperatus (LeConte) occurs in British Columbia and the forested States of the West. The larvae are reported to bore in the wood of dead *Abies magnifica, A. concolor, Pseudotsuga menziesii, Picea*, and *Pinus*. The adults are robust, black beetles 17 to 31 mm long, largest of the genus. They are sometimes attracted in numbers to scorched pines (Wickman 1964a), and perhaps pines are a principal host. *A. foveicollis* (Haldeman), a very similar eastern species, ranges westward into the Northern Rocky Mountains.

The **newhouse borer**, *Arhopalus productus* (LeConte) (Eaton and Lyon 1955), occurs in Alberta, British Columbia, and the forested States of the West. Hosts are *Pseudotsuga menziesii, Pinus*, and *Abies*. The adults are slender, black beetles 12 to 25 mm long (fig. 174A). The larvae mine under the bark and into the sapwood and heartwood of fire-killed Douglas-fir, causing much damage to the wood (fig. 174B and C) and sometimes limiting salvage (Kimmey and Furniss 1943). Lumber cut from salvaged trees sometimes contains living brood of *A. productus* which mature and emerge, causing damage to new houses, hence the common name.

Arhopalus rusticus (L.) occurs in Europe and North America. The subspecies *A. r. montanus* (LeConte) bores principally in the roots of dead pines. It occurs in Colorado, Utah, Arizona, and New Mexico.

Asemum (Linsley 1962a) contains four species in North America. Three occur in the West. The adults are uniformly black or brown. The larvae bore in conifers. One species causes economic damage.

291

F-523436, F-523437, F-523438

FIGURE 174.—Newhouse borer (*Arhopalus productus*): *A*, Adult, 23 mm long; *B*, larval tunnel with packed frass; *C*, cross section of tunnels in board.

The **black spruce borer,** *Asemum striatum* (L.) (= *atrum* Esch-scholtz), is a transcontinental species that occurs in British Columbia and all Western States. *Pseudotsuga menziesii, Abies, Larix, Picea,* and *Pinus* are recorded hosts. *A. striatum* is the most abundant borer in Douglas-fir killed by fire and causes damage in the woods similar to that of *Arhopalus productus* (Kimmey and Furniss 1943). The adult is black or brownish and 10 to 17 mm long. The mature larvae first mine under the bark, then extensively in the sapwood. As deterioration progresses, they mine into the heartwood. Presumably standing dead trees are repeatedly attacked.

Asemum nitidum LeConte (= *mokelumne* (Casey)) and *A. caseyi* Linsley are similar species that occur in the Pacific States.

Atimia (Linsley 1962a) contains seven species six of which occur in the West and are borers in cedars, cypresses, and related trees. None is a forest pest. The larvae bore beneath the bark and score the sapwood of branches and the thin-barked portions of the bole of seriously weakened and recently dead trees. The adults are 6 to 14 mm long, resemble Lepturinae and are clothed with matted hairs except for scattered bare spots. A 1-year life cycle is usual.

Atimia confusa (Say) is transcontinental. Two named subspecies, *dorsalis* LeConte and *maritima* Linsley, occur from British Columbia to southern California. *Libocedrus decurrens, Thuja plicata, Sequoia sempervirens, Cupressus,* and *Juniperus* are recorded hosts. Other species of *Atimia* are:

292

Species	Hosts	Distribution
A. gannoni Hovore and Giesbert	*Libocedrus decurrens*	Calif.
A. helenae Linsley	*Cupressus goveniana*	Calif.
A. hoppingi Linsley	*Chamaecyparis nootkatensis*	Oreg. and Wash.
A. huachucae Champlain and Knull	*Cupressus arizonica* and *Juniperus*	Ariz.
A. vandykei Linsley	*Juniperus*	N. Mex.

Megasemum (Linsley 1962a) contains one species in North America.

Megasemum asperum (LeConte) occurs from British Columbia to California, Montana, Colorado, and New Mexico. The larvae bore in the heartwood of *Pseudotsuga menziesii* and *Abies*. The adult is reddish brown, cylindrical, 15 to 23 mm long, and resembles *Arhopalus*. It is not recorded as damaging.

Paratimia (Linsley 1962a) contains one species.

The **roundheaded cone borer**, *Paratimia conicola* Fisher (Keen 1958), occurs in California and southern Oregon. The larvae bore through the woody axis and scales of knobcone pine cones, much as does *Chysophana conicola* but cause more damage to the seeds. The larvae also work in the dry limbs of this pine and in the cones of lodgepole along the California coast. The adults are slender, cylindrical, rusty-brown beetles, 8 to 13 mm long. Emergence is in March and April. The life cycle sometimes takes several years.

Tetropium (Linsley 1962a) contains five species in North America, and all of them occur in conifers in the West. Four are economically significant. The larvae bore principally between the bark and wood, sometimes killing trees. They often bore into the wood to pupate, thus causing timber degrade. The spines on the last abdominal segment are small. The adults are 8 to 20 mm long, brown to black, often bi-colored, and have divided eyes.

The **roundheaded fir borer**, *Tetropium abietis* Fall (Struble 1957b), occurs from Washington to California. *Abies concolor, A. magnifica,* and other true firs are attacked. Often in combination with *Scolytus ventralis*, it will kill weakened trees but it is not reported as becoming epidemic. The adult is uniformly brown. The life cycle is 1 year.

Tetropium cinnamopterum Kirby (Raske 1973a) is a transcontinental species that occurs in the Western Provinces and Territories and probably in Alaska and Colorado. *Picea glauca* is the preferred host in the West. *Pinus* and *Abies* are reported eastern hosts. Reports of *Larix* as a host are now considered erroneous. The thorax of the adult is dark brown or black and the elytra reddish brown.

The **northern spruce borer,** *Tetropium parvulum* Casey (Raske 1973a, 1973b) (fig. 175A), has been considered to be a subspecies of *T. cinnamopterum* which it closely resembles. These species can best be identified in the larval stage (fig. 175C). The caudal spines of *T. parvulum* are peglike and distinctly separated (fig. 175B). Those of *T. cinnamopterum* are fused into a conelike structure notched at the tip. *T. parvulum* occurs in Alaska, the Western Provinces and Territories, and probably some Northern States in the West. *Picea glauca* and *P. engelmannii* are hosts. It has a 1-year cycle in Alberta. Apparently this is the species causing most of the damage to spruce logs and degrade of lumber (fig. 175D) in British Columbia (Ross and Vanderwal 1969).

The **western larch borer,** *Tetropium velutinum* LeConte (Ross 1967), occurs from British Columbia to central California, Montana, and Utah. *Larix occidentalis, Pseudotsuga menziesii,* and *Tsuga heterophylla* are principal hosts. *Abies, Picea,* and *Pinus* also are recorded hosts. Drought-weakened, insect-defoliated, and fire-scorched trees are attacked and sometimes killed. During the drought of the 1930's this species caused extensive deterioration of larch stands in northern Washington. In British Columbia it normally has one annual generation.

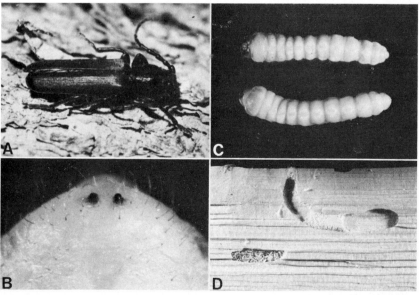

COURTESY CANADIAN FORESTRY SERVICE

FIGURE 175.—The northern spruce borer (*Tetropium parvulum*): *A*, Adult, 12 mm long; *B*, caudal spines of larva, greatly enlarged; *C*, larvae, 12 mm long; *D*, typical L-shaped larval mine and pupal cell in wood of white spruce.

Lepturinae—The subfamily Lepturinae (Hopping 1937, Linsley and Chemsak 1972, Swaine and Hopping 1928) contains numerous species, most of which bore in dead rotting wood, hence are of little economic importance. The adults of many species are colorful and feed on pollen. Typically they are widest through the shoulders, taper to the rear, and have a bell-shaped thorax, often toothed or swollen at the sides. The larvae commonly have numerous padlike structures (ampullae) on the upper surface of the abdominal segments and their legs are more developed than those of other roundheaded wood borers.

Acmaeops (Linsley and Chemsak 1972) contains two species, one western.

Acmaeops proteus (Kirby) (Gardiner 1970) is transcontinental. In the West it occurs from Mexico to Alaska. The larvae feed in recently dead *Pinus, Picea, Tsuga,* and *Abies.* The adults are 7 to 11 mm long and have shiny elytra that are yellowish to black or striped. Pupation is in the soil. The life cycle is 2 or 3 years.

Anoplodera is a large, diverse, predominantly western genus according to Swaine and Hopping (1928). Linsley and Chemsak (1972) break it into many genera. The larvae feed in deadwood—some in conifers, some in hardwoods, and some in both.

Anoplodera canadensis (Olivier) (Swaine and Hopping 1928) occurs from Mexico to Alaska and from coast to coast. The larvae feed in dead, rather solid wood, principally *Pinus, Picea,* and *Tsuga* but also *Populus* and other hardwoods. Adults are 10 to 20 mm long. The elytra are black, red, or red and black.

Anoplodera chrysocoma (Kirby) (Swaine and Hopping 1928) is a transcontinental species that occurs in most Western States and Provinces. The larvae feed in *Pinus, Picea,* and *Populus.* Adults are 10 to 18 mm long, rather chunky, and clothed with bright golden hairs. They are abundant on yellow flowers.

Centrodera (Linsley and Chemsak 1972, Leech 1963) contains 11 species, mostly western. They are elongate, parallel-sided, brownish beetles with coarsely granular eyes and generally with prominent tubercles on the sides of the thorax. The larvae feed on dead wood of conifers and hardwoods.

Centrodera spurca (LeConte) (Leech 1963) ranges from British Columbia to California and Utah. *Quercus, Arbutus,* and woody shrubs are hosts. The adults are 20 to 30 mm long, shiny and yellowish, except for a black spot at the side near the middle of each elytron. The larvae move freely in the soil, feed upon dead roots and stumps, and require 2 or more years to mature.

Desmocerus (Burke 1921, Linsley and Chemsak 1972) contains three species, two of which are western. The larvae of all bore in the pith, stems, and roots of living elderberry, *Sambucus.*

Desmocerus auripennis Chevrolat ranges from central California to British Columbia and Montana. There are four named subspecies. The adults are 12 to 30 mm long and variously marked in yellow and metallic green. Males are smaller and more slender than the females. The larvae bore in the stems of various species of elderberry without killing them. The life cycle is 2 years.

Leptura (Swaine and Hopping 1928) contains a dozen species, half of them western. Most develop in the wood of dead conifers.

Leptura obliterata Haldeman is the most abundant of the western species. It occurs from California to British Columbia and Montana and bores in the wood of dead *Abies, Picea, Pinus, Pseudotsuga,* and *Tsuga.* It is one of several roundheaded borers that are abundant in fire-killed Douglas-fir. The larvae frequently extend their galleries an inch or so into soundwood but mostly they mine wood that already is far deteriorated (Kimmey and Furniss 1943). Successive generations may develop in a tree for several decades after its death. The adults are 12 to 20 mm long, dark brown to black with yellowish markings (fig. 176).

F–523439

FIGURE 176.—Adult of *Leptura obliterata,* a common borer in fire-killed timber, 16 mm long.

Necydalis (Linsley and Chemsak 1972) is one of two genera in the Lepturinae with abbreviated elytra. It contains seven species, six of them western. Most, perhaps all, bore only in dead wood of broad-leaved trees and shrubs.

Necydalis cavipennis LeConte is the most abundant species. It occurs from British Columbia to California and Arizona. Oaks are the principal hosts. *Lithocarpus, Alnus,* and *Eucalyptus* also are attacked. The larvae bore in stumps and dead standing trees. Adults are reddish brown to black and 13 to 24 mm long. The life cycle is presumed to be 2 years.

Necydalis laevicollis LeConte is a smaller more slender species that occurs from British Columbia to central California. It has been recorded from *Picea, Alnus, Salix, Arbutus, Quercus,* and *Lithocarpus.* The coniferous host record needs to be verified.

Pachyta (Linsley and Chemsak 1972) contains two species in North America. The adults are chunky, broad through the shoulders, and strongly tapered to the rear. The larvae bore in dead conifers.

P. lamed (L.) occurs from Labrador to Alaska and extensively in mountains of the West. *Abies, Picea, Pinus,* and *Pseudotsuga* are hosts. The adults are black with reddish-brown elytra. *P. armata* LeConte occurs from California into British Columbia and Idaho. Its elytra are yellow, tipped with black. *Tsuga* and *Pinus* are hosts.

Rhagium (Linsley and Chemsak 1972) contains one species in North America.

The **ribbed pine borer,** *Rhagium inquisitor* (L.) (= *Stenocorus lineatum* Olivier), is a noneconomic, transcontinental species present extensively in the Western States and Provinces. Pines are most frequently attacked. Other hosts are species of *Abies, Larix, Picea, Pseudotsuga,* and *Tsuga.* The larvae (fig. 177A) are much flattened and have broad brownish heads. They bore between the bark and wood of recently dead trees and form typical oval pupal cells ringed with coarse fibers. The adults (fig. 177B) are 10 to 18 mm long, and have black bodies and mottled, grayish, strongly-ribbed elytra.

Ulochaetes (Linsley and Chemsak 1972) contains one species.

The **lion beetle,** *Ulochaetes leoninus* LeConte (Linsley and

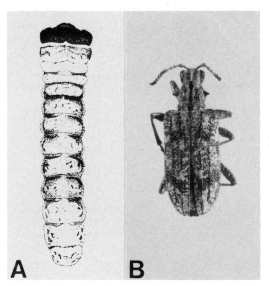

FIGURE 177.—Ribbed pine borer (*Rhagium inquisitor*): *A*, Larva, 22 mm long; *B*, adult, 14 mm long.

297

Chemsak 1972), ranges from California into British Columbia and Idaho. The larvae bore in the roots and lower bole of dead pines, Douglas-fir, true fir, hemlock, and spruce. The adults are 20 to 30 mm long, black-bodied, very hairy, and have short, yellow-tipped wings that leave the underwings exposed (fig. 178). In flight, the adults strongly resemble bumblebees.

F–523441

FIGURE 178.—Female adult of *Ulochaetes leoninus*, 28 mm long; note abbreviated wing covers.

Cerambycinae—The Cerambycinae (Linsley 1962b, 1963, 1964) are a large subfamily containing a considerable number of species that damage forest trees and forest products. Many are somber colored and fly at night; many others are bright colored and fly in daytime. The larvae are quite hairy. They have short mandibles with a rounded, gougelike cutting edge, and usually have legs.

Aneflomorpha (Linsley 1963) contains about 20 species, mostly natives of the Southwestern States. The adults are slender and elongate and have a spine on at least the third antennal segment. The larvae are twig-borers and twig-girdlers. *A. lineare* (LeConte) occurs in Arizona, California, and Oregon. The larvae girdle small branches of *Quercus agrifolia* and other oaks, and also of *Purshia tridentata* (Tyson 1970). The adults are slender, cylindrical, brownish-yellow beetles, 11 to 19 mm long and lightly clothed with whitish hairs.

Brothylus (Linsley 1962b) consists of two noneconomic species that bore in dry dead limbs and trunks of oaks. The adults are cylindrical, 12 to 22 mm long, and have granulate, pitted elytra. *B. gemmulatus* LeConte ranges from Washington to Colorado and southward. *B. conspersus* LeConte occurs in Oregon and California.

Callidium (Linsley 1964) contains 17 species in North America, 12 in the West. They attack the trunk and branches of dead or

298

seriously weakened conifers. Their galleries are meandering, intertwined, and packed with dry granular frass except for the open pupal cell. The larvae first mine extensively in the inner bark and outer wood, often loosening the bark. Later they may riddle the entire sapwood, especially in branches and small stems. The adults of most species are broad and flattened, bluish, and have leathery rather than hardshelled wings.

The **blackhorned pine borer**, *Callidium antennatum hesperum* Casey (Miller 1943), is a common species in western forests, attacking boles and limbs of dead or dying *Pinus ponderosa*, *P. jeffreyi*, *P. flexilis*, *P. aristata*, *Pseudotsuga menziesii*, and *Tsuga mertensiana*. It ranges from California into British Columbia and the Rocky Mountains. It attracts attention occasionally by boring in air-dried lumber with bark on the edges, and also injures seasoned rustic work by mining out the cambium area, causing the bark to loosen. The adult is 9 to 13 mm long and has a black body and antennae and blue or violet elytra. The life cycle is 1 year.

Some other species of *Callidium* likely to be encountered in western forests are:

Species	Hosts	Distribution
C. cicatricosum Mannerheim	*Pseudotsuga menziesii* and *Abies*	Alaska to Oreg. and Northern Rocky Mountains
C. hoppingi Linsley	*Juniperus*	British Columbia to Utah and Ariz.
C. juniperi Fisher	*Juniperus*	N. Mex. and Utah
C. pseudotsugae Fisher	*Pseudotsuga menziesii* and *Abies*	Oreg. and Calif.
C. sempervirens Linsley	*Sequoia sempervirens*	Calif.
C. sequoiarum Fisher	*Sequoia gigantea*	Calif.
C. texanum Schaeffer	*Juniperus*	N. Mex., Ariz., Utah, and Nev.

Crossidius (Linsley 1962b) contains 14 species and many named subspecies; almost all are exclusively western. The larvae bore in the roots of shrubs such as *Chrysothamnus*, a genus of significance on dryland ranges and one which has attracted the attention of foresters and others as a potential source of natural rubber. Adult *Crossidius* are contrastingly marked beetles, generally about 10 to 20 mm long. They feed upon pollen of their host plants. Most species have a 2-year life cycle.

Crossidius hirtipes LeConte (Linsley 1962b), consisting of 16 named subspecies, occurs from Arizona and California to Washington and Colorado. Species of *Chrysothamnus* are the principal hosts. The larvae mine the underground stem, weakening and sometimes killing attacked plants.

Dicentrus bluthneri LeConte (Linsley 1962b) ranges from California into British Columbia. The larvae bore in small, dead branches of *Pseudotsuga menziesii, Abies concolor, Tsuga mertensiana,* and other conifers. The adults are 3 to 7 mm long, black with two pale spots on each elytron, and have two teeth on each side of the thorax.

Eucrossus contains one species. *E. villicornis* LeConte (Wickman and Seminoff 1968) occurs from California to New Mexico. The larvae bore between the bark and wood of the bole and branches of recently dead pines. Late stage larvae penetrate the wood 12 to 76 mm to pupate. The adults are brownish, parallel-sided beetles, 16 to 26 mm long. The thorax usually bears a tooth on each side and the antennae are hairy and spiny. A 1-year life cycle is usual.

Haplidus (Linsley 1962b) contains two species, one of which is western. *H. testaceus* LeConte ranges from Washington to California and New Mexico. *Pinus ponderosa, P. contorta, P. monophylla,* and *P. jeffreyi* are recorded hosts. The larvae bore in the cambium region and then in the wood of dry, dead limbs and sometimes the main trunk. In northeastern Washington they have been recorded as damaging rustic building timbers. The adults are slender brown beetles, 8 to 16 mm long.

Holopleura (Linsley 1962b) contains one species. *H. marginata* LeConte ranges from British Columbia into California. The larvae bore in small dead branches of *Pseudotsuga menziesii* and *Umbellularia californica.* The adult is flattened, 5 to 11 mm long, and has red elytra with black markings.

Hylotrupes contains one species, the **oldhouse borer,** *H. bajulus* (L.) (Hickin 1963, McIntyre and St. George 1961). From Europe, it has become extensively established in the Eastern United States and is likely to spread to the West. It bores in the sapwood of *Pinus, Picea, Abies,* and *Larix* in buildings, sometimes causing serious damage. The adults are 10 to 20 mm long and brownish black with gray hairs (fig. 179). They have black, owl-like eyespots on the thorax. Midway on each elytron there are two gray patches that tend to form a crossband. Larval development usually is from 3 to 6 years. Extremes of 1 to 32 years have been reported.

Megacyllene (Linsley 1964) contains nine species north of Mexico, two of which are significant pests of shade and woodland trees in the West. Most species are moderately large, full-bodied beetles contrastingly banded. Early-stage larvae bore beneath the bark, deeply scoring the wood. Late-stage larvae mine the wood extensively. Much frass is exuded through holes in the bark.

The **mesquite borer,** *Megacyllene antennata* (White) (Craighead and Hofer 1921) ranges from Texas into southern California and is the most destructive borer in mesquite. The adult is 12 to

F-494430

FIGURE 179.—Female adult of the oldhouse borer (*Hylotrupes bajulus*), 20 mm long.

25 mm long and reddish brown with gray bands. Felling and drying of mesquite in winter is recommended to prevent attacks.

The **locust borer**, *Megacyllene robiniae* (Forster) (Wollerman 1970), is an eastern insect that has been introduced extensively in Western States on its native host, *Robinia pseudoacacia*. The larvae mine principally in the wood (fig. 180A), often causing breakage of shade and woodland trees. The adults are 12 to 28 mm long and black with several bright yellow bands (fig. 180B). They fly in fall, feed on pollen of goldenrod, and lay their eggs in bark crevices and around wounds. In spring the larval mining is marked by sap flow. Later, frass is pushed out through holes in the bark. The life cycle is 1 year. Attacks on ornamentals can be minimized by spraying in late summer and early fall or at bud-opening time in spring to control small larvae. In forest plantings, the most practical approach is to maintain the trees in good vigor.

Meriellum (Linsley 1964) contains one species. *M. proteus* (Kirby) is a transcontinental species in northern forests. In the West it ranges from Alaska to British Columbia and Colorado. Hosts are *Picea, Abies*, and *Pinus ponderosa*. The adult is black or bluish and generally similar to *Callidium*. It attacks dead trees. The larvae bore beneath the bark and enter the wood to pupate. The life cycle is 1 year. *M. proteus* damages rustic woodwork and occasionally emerges through finished wood in buildings.

Neoclytus (Hopping 1932, Linsley 1964) contains 26 species and several named subspecies in North America. Mostly they are wood borers in eastern broad-leaved trees. A few damage untreated, roundwood products. The adults have white or yellow bands on the elytra and resemble *Xylotrechus* but are distinguishable by having transverse ridges on the pronotum.

301

F-8363, F-523442

FIGURE 180.—Locust borer (*Megacyllene robiniae*) : *A*, damage by larvae to wood of black locust; *B*, adult, 20 mm long.

A   B

The **redheaded ash borer,** *Neoclytus acuminatus* (F.) (Baker 1972), is principally an eastern species that attacks a wide variety of dead and dying hardwoods. It also occurs naturally in Colorado and New Mexico and has been introduced into southern Idaho where it is a pest of woodlot and windbreak plantings of black locust. The adult is reddish brown with four narrow yellow bands on the elytra.

The **western ash borer,** *Neoclytus conjunctus* (LeConte) (Linsley 1964), ranges from British Columbia to southern California. Principal hosts are *Fraxinus*, *Quercus*, and *Arbutus menziesii*. The adult is 7 to 18 mm long, black, and has bold white or yellow "O"-like markings at the base of the elytra. The larvae riddle the sapwood of freshly cut, bark-covered, unseasoned wood. Frequently the adults emerge in houses from stored fuelwood, sometimes in 2 or more successive years, indicating prolonged development in dry wood.

The **banded ash borer,** *Neoclytus caprea* (Say) (Baker 1972), is an eastern species that ranges westward into Utah, Nevada, and Arizona. *Fraxinus*, *Quercus*, and *Prosopis* are common hosts. It closely resembles *N. conjunctus* in appearance and habits.

Neoclytus muricatulus Kirby (Linsley 1964) is one of two species in this genus that attack conifers. It is transcontinental in northern forests and occurs extensively in the Western Provinces and States, including Alaska. *Picea, Larix, Abies, Pinus,* and *Pseudotsuga menziesii* are recorded hosts. The adult is 7 to 11 mm long, dark brown, and has four broken white lines on the elytra. The larvae bore in dead dry branches and larger material.

Oeme (Linsley 1962b) contains two species in the United States. The adults are slender, brown to black beetles. The larvae bore beneath the bark and into the wood of dead or dying branches. *O. costata* LeConte occurs from Oregon and Idaho to California and Texas. Hosts are *Pinus ponderosa, P. edulis,* and *P. contorta. O. rigida* (Say) is principally eastern, but extends into Colorado, Utah, and Arizona, attacking *Juniperus* and *Cupressus.*

Opsimus (Linsley 1962b) contains one species. The **spruce limb borer,** *Opsimus quadrilineatus* Mannerheim, occurs along the Pacific coast from central California into Alaska. Principal hosts are *Picea sitchensis, Pseudotsuga menziesii, Pinus contorta, Tsuga heterophylla,* and *Abies.* The larvae bore in the wood of suppressed branches and also have been reported as damaging the seasoned wood of rustic homes in Oregon. The adults are grayish brown, about 10 mm long, and have a spine on each side of the thorax and four ridges on each wing cover.

Phymatodes (Linsley 1964) contains 24 species and several subspecies in North America. Most of them are western. They attack dead or dying branches and thin-barked portions of the bole. The adults are small, slender, and spotted or banded beetles. *P. dimidiatus* (Kirby) (fig. 181) has been recorded as damaging rustic wood in buildings; *P. lecontei* Linsley as frequently emerging from fuelwood in houses, and *P. nitidus* LeConte as occurring in cones of redwood. Some species likely to be encountered by western foresters are:

Species	Hosts	Distribution
P. aeneus LeConte	Pseudotsuga, Tsuga, Quercus, and Castanopsis	British Columbia to Calif.
P. blandus (LeConte)	Salix and Populus	Wash. to Calif. and Nev.
P. decussatus (LeConte)	Quercus	British Columbia to Calif.
P. dimidiatus (Kirby)	Pseudotsuga, Picea, Tsuga, and Larix	Alaska to Calif. and Rocky Mountain States
P. hirtellus (LeConte)	Pinus	British Columbia to Calif., Mont., and N. Mex.
P. lecontei Linsley	Quercus	British Columbia to Calif.
P. maculicollis LeConte	Abies, Picea, and Pseudotsuga	British Columbia to Calif. and Eastern States
P. nitidus LeConte	Cupressus, Libocedrus, Sequoia, and Thuja	British Columbia to Calif.
P. vulneratus (LeConte)	Acer and Fraxinus	British Columbia to Calif.

FIGURE 181.—Adult of *Phymatodes dimidiatus*, 9 mm long.

The **banded alder borer**, *Rosalia funebris* Motschulsky, is the only species of this genus in North America. It occurs from Alaska to southern California and in the Rocky Mountains from Idaho to New Mexico. The larvae bore in the trunks of dead *Acer, Alnus, Fraxinus, Platanus, Quercus, Salix*, and *Umbellularia californica*, but are not recorded as economically damaging. The adults (fig. 182) are elongate, flattened, parallel-sided beetles about 25 to 35 mm long. The body and long antennae are conspicuously black-and-white banded. The adults usually are encountered singly in summer, but occasionally they are attracted in numbers to fresh paint (Chemsak and Linsley 1971).

Semanotus (Linsley 1964) contains four species in North America. They attack the bole and large limbs of dead, dying, injured, and down conifers. The larvae mine principally in the inner bark and score the outer sapwood (fig. 183). At maturity they bore into the wood to pupate.

The **amethyst cedar borer**, *Semanotus amethystinus* (LeConte), attacks the bole and large branches of *Libocedrus decurrens, Thuja plicata*, and *Chamaecyparis lawsoniana*. It ranges from British Columbia into California. The adult is 20 to 28 mm long and black except for the brilliant blue elytra.

Semanotus juniperi (Fisher) is similar to *S. amethystinus* except that the elytra are black. It attacks *Juniperus* in California, Nevada, Idaho, and Arizona.

The **cedartree borer**, *Semanotus ligneus* (F.), is a complex of five named subspecies which together range from coast to coast

F–523444

FIGURE 182.—Adult of the banded alder borer (*Rosalia funebris*), 30 mm long.

and from Alaska to southern California, attacking species of *Chamaecyparis, Cupressus, Juniperus, Libocedrus, Thuja,* and *Sequoia.* The adults are 9 to 16 mm long, moderately hairy, and black with red-, yellow-, or orange-marked elytra. The larvae sometimes damage rustic woodwork.

F–523445

FIGURE 183.—Larval mine of *Semanotus amethystinus* engraving the sapwood of Port-Orford-cedar.

The **firtree borer**, *Semanotus litigiosus* (Casey) (Wickman 1968), is a transcontinental species that ranges from Alaska to California and New Mexico in the West. Species of *Abies* are most commonly attacked. Other hosts are *Pseudotsuga, Picea, Tsuga,* and *Larix.* The adult (fig. 184A) resembles *S. ligneus* but is more hairy, more generally black, and somewhat smaller. The larvae (fig. 184B) sometimes degrade lumber cut from windthrown and fire-scorched trees and also cause damage by emerging through finished surfaces in new buildings. The life cycle normally is 1 year. Logging and milling salvaged timber by mid-June will minimize damage by this beetle.

305

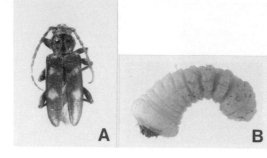

F-523446, F-518151

FIGURE 184.—*Semanotus litigiosus*: *A*, Adult, 15 mm long; *B*, larva, 18 mm long.

Styloxus (Linsley 1962b) contains two species in North America. The larvae girdle and bore in small branches of living trees. Though common, they cause little damage. The adults are slender, delicate beetles with narrow, tapered elytra that do not cover the entire abdomen.

The **juniper twig pruner**, *Styloxus bicolor* (Champlain and Knull), ranges from California to New Mexico. Hosts are *Juniperus* and *Cupressus*. The adults are 7 to 11 mm long, brownish to black, and have orange-red heads. Larvae, by boring, cause conspicuous twig-killing (fig. 185).

F-523447

FIGURE 185.—Twig-killing on juniper caused by larvae of *Styloxus bicolor*.

Styloxus fulleri (Horn) (Brown and Eads 1965a) consists of two subspecies, one of which occurs in California and Oregon. The larvae girdle 6 to 12 mm branches on *Quercus agrifolia*. The adults are somewhat larger than *S. bicolor* and the head is entirely or mostly brownish. The life cycle is presumed to be 2 years.

Xylotrechus (Linsley 1964) contains 22 species and several subspecies in North America, a majority of them in the West. The larvae of most bore principally in the wood of the main stem of dead, injured, and down trees. They riddle the wood and pack their galleries with granular frass (fig. 186A). The adults are stout and cylindrical, with antennae only slightly longer than the head and thorax, and with wavy, zigzag, or crescent-shaped markings across the wing covers (fig. 186B).

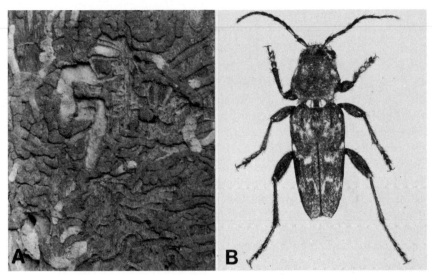

F–523448, F–523449

FIGURE 186.—*Xylotrechus nauticus*: *A*, Larval galleries in oak; *B*, adult, 15 mm long.

The **poplar butt borer**, *X. obliteratus* LeConte, is a serious pest of aspen and poplar in the Rocky Mountain Region. The larvae work under the bark and into the wood, especially at the base of trees, and attacks are repeated until the heartwood is completely honeycombed and the trees break off during wind or snowstorms. Extensive areas of aspen above 2,130 m (7,000 ft) in Colorado and Utah have been killed by this species. The adults are about 15 mm long, and are dark with three yellow bands across the wing covers. The **oak cordwood borer**, *X. nauticus* (Mannerheim) (fig. 186B), is a dark brown beetle with grayish markings. The larvae commonly bore in dead oak and madrone, especially in firewood, from British Columbia to California. *X. undulatus* (Say) is a transcontinental species that bores in *Picea* and *Pinus* and occurs only in Alaska and northern Canada in the West. *X. longitarsus* Casey is a similar but larger species that bores in *Pseudotsuga menziesii* from British Columbia to California and Colorado. Other western species likely to be encountered are:

Species	Hosts	Distribution
X. *albonotatus* Casey (=*abietis* Van Dyke)	*Abies*	Calif.
X. *annosus* (Say)	*Salix* and *Populus*	British Columbia to Calif., Colo., and Eastern States
X. *insignis* LeConte	*Salix*	Oreg., and Calif.
X. *sagittatus* (Germar)	*Pinus*	Ariz., N. Mex., and Eastern States

Lamiinae—The Lamiinae are the largest and most varied subfamily of the Cerambycidae. In the West it contains several destructive species, particularly ones that bore in logs and in weakened and recently dead trees. No comprehensive modern classification of this subfamily in North America exists. Craighead (1923) described the larvae of numerous species and gave information on their biology. The adults usually are somber colored and nocturnal. The larvae are legless and differ from all other cerambycids by having an elongate head with sides that are parallel or converge to the rear.

The genus *Acanthocinus*, consisting of several subgenera (Dillon 1956), contains about eight species in North America, six of them in the West. The larvae feed in the inner bark of injured and recently-killed conifers, predominantly pines. They commonly attack trees killed by bark beetles and have been recorded as robbing the beetle larvae of food. Effectiveness in natural control is limited because these bark borers do most of their feeding after the bark beetles leave a tree. Adult *Acanthocinus* are mottled in colors and patterns that resemble bark. They have very long antennae with tufts of hairs at the lower joints, especially in the males. Females have a long, hornlike ovipositor extending from the end of the abdomen.

The **ponderosa pine bark borer**, *Acanthocinus princeps* (Walker), is the large white larva (fig. 187A) frequently found in ponderosa pines killed by the western pine beetle. It also occurs in other pines and ranges from British Columbia into California. The larvae pupate in nestlike cells between the bark and the wood. The adults (fig. 187B) are 14 to 24 mm long. The life cycle is 1 year.

Acanthocinus spectabilis (LeConte) closely resembles *A. princeps* and has been confused with it. *A. spectabilis* ranges from Montana and South Dakota to Arizona and New Mexico on *Pinus ponderosa* and other pines.

Acanthocinus obliquus (LeConte) is smaller, more slender, and less boldly marked than *A. princeps*. The larvae feed under the bark of the bole and larger branches of pines and spruces. In pon-

EPQ–6808, F–523450

FIGURE 187.—Ponderosa pine bark borer (*Acanthocinus princeps*): *A*, Larva,
32 mm long, in its tunnel; *B*, female adult, 23 mm long.

derosa pine it attacks principally in the top in contrast with *A.
princeps* in the lower and mid bole. In lodgepole pine *A. obliquus*
mingles with *Dendroctonus ponderosae* and may exert some control on it. The range is from British Columbia to South Dakota,
California, and New Mexico.

Acanthocinus pusillus (Kirby) is a somewhat smaller image of
A. obliquus. It ranges from Alaska to the east coast, attacking
injured and recently-dead pine, spruce, and fir.

Lophopogonius (Linsley 1935) contains one species. *L. crinitus*
(LeConte) occurs from California to British Columbia. The larvae
bore in dead branches of *Quercus agrifolia* and *Q. garryana*. The
adults are 6 to 10 mm long, ashy gray, and have long hairs on the
antennae, legs, and body. The elytra are spined at the rear end.

Moneilema (Raske 1966) contains 20 species, all of which bore
in living pricklypear cactus in the Southwest. The adults are large,
shiny black beetles without hindwings. *M. annulata* Say sometimes
kills large areas of pricklypear, *Opuntia*, a pest on rangeland in
Colorado (Turner and Costello 1942).

Monochamus (Dillon and Dillon 1941) contains about 10 species
in North America. Biological research is needed to determine
their exact number and status. The larvae, known as **sawyers,**

are responsible for extensive damage to the wood of dying, recently dead, and felled conifers, especially *Pinus, Picea, Abies,* and *Pseudotsuga.* The larval mines also provide entrance for wood-rotting fungi. Adults feed upon needles and upon the bark of young twigs but cause negligible damage.

The eggs are laid in slitlike niches in the bark. The larvae are legless, and in the later instars their heads slant strongly downward. They feed for several weeks between the bark and wood, loosening the bark and filling the space between with long fibrous borings. Later the larvae enter the wood, forming oval holes that progressively become nearly round. The tunnels extend through the sapwood and often deep into the heartwood. The excelsiorlike borings are dropped from the galleries and often accumulate in conspicuous piles along infested logs. As the larvae near maturity they pack the gallery solid with frass, except for an open cell at the end where pupation occurs. The adults are large, brown or black beetles with a toothlike projection on each side of the thorax and with antennae longer than the body, especially those of the male. When mature, the adults emerge by gnawing a round hole through the thin layer of wood and bark separating the pupal cell from the surface. The life cycle normally is 1 year in southern areas and may be either 1 or 2 years in northern ones such as Alberta.

Prevention is the best approach to control of *Monochamus* in logging areas. Logs should not be exposed to attack during the July–September egg-laying period. If exposed, they should be promptly utilized.

The **whitespotted sawyer,** *Monochamus scutellatus* (Say) (Raske 1973c, Wilson 1975), is a transcontinental species that occurs extensively in Western Canada and the Western States, including Alaska. The larvae bore in and seriously degrade firescorched, injured, dying, and recently-felled spruce, pines, Douglas-fir, and true firs (fig. 188A). The adults are 18 to 27 mm long, shiny black with a white spot between the elytra at the base (fig. 188B). Females usually and males occasionally have scattered patches of white hairs on the elytra. The subspecies *M. s. oregonensis* LeConte, known as the **Oregon fir sawyer,** is a generally larger form, sometimes considered to be a separate species, that occurs from California to Alaska, Alberta, and Montana.

The **spotted pine sawyer,** *Monochamus maculosus* Haldeman (= *clamator* LeConte), occurs extensively in the Western States and Provinces. It attacks dying and recently dead and down pines and Douglas-fir. The adult is 15 to 27 mm long and shiny black with scattered tufts of white hairs in irregular bands across the elytra.

COURTESY CANADIAN FORESTRY SERVICE, F-523451

FIGURE 188.—Whitespotted sawyer (*Monochamus scutellatus*) : *A*, Excelsiorlike borings by larvae in wood; *B*, female adult, 25 mm long.

Monochamus notatus morgani Hopping (Morgan 1948), a subspecies of the **northeastern sawyer**, bores in *Pinus monticola* in British Columbia, Washington, Idaho, and Montana. The adults are 16 to 35 mm long and dark brown with rows of alternating patches of gray and velvety-black hairs on the elytra. The life cycle is 2 years in British Columbia.

The **obtuse sawyer**, *Monochamus obtusus* Casey, is a reddish brown, somewhat smaller copy of *M. maculosus*. It ranges from California to British Columbia and Idaho, attacking pines, Douglas-fir, and true firs.

Oberea (Hicks 1962) contains about 20 species, mostly eastern, in North America. The larvae mine in the branches, stems, and roots—most commonly the branches—of living broad-leaved trees and other woody plants. The adults are very slender, cylindrical beetles, often with black spots on the thorax.

The **poplar branch borer**, *Oberea schaumii* LeConte (= *quadricallosa* LeConte, = *ferruginea* Casey) (Nord 1968), occurs from coast to coast. In the West it is recorded from British Columbia to California, Montana, and Colorado. The larvae mine in and sometimes kill branches of *Populus* and *Salix* (fig. 189), but are not of pest significance. The adults are 11 to 15 mm long. Their thorax is orange, usually with four black spots and the elytra are black. They feed on the leaves and tender bark of the hosts. In the East the life cycle is 3 years.

Oncideres (Linsley 1940) contains numerous species, mostly in South America. Three occur in Southwestern States. They girdle the branches of broad-leaved trees and shrubs and sometimes are pests in orchards and ornamental plantings. The adults are cylindrical and their elytra are granulate on the base. They girdle

311

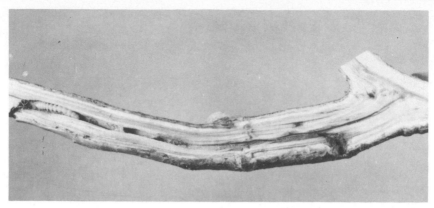

FIGURE 189.—Larva of *Oberea schaumii* in its burrow in a poplar branch.

branches (fig. 190) causing them to break and fall. The larvae bore in the severed branches. The life cycle is 1 year.

The **huisache girdler,** *Oncideres pustulata* LeConte (High 1915), ranges from Arizona to Texas. *Acacia, Prosopis,* and related trees are hosts. The adults are 18 to 24 mm long and brownish gray. They girdle limbs up to about 40 mm in diameter.

The **oak twig girdler,** *Oncideres quercus* Skinner, is a small, slender, gray, brown-spotted Arizona species that girdles oak branches up to about 10 mm in diameter.

The **mesquite girdler,** *Oncideres rhodosticta* Bates, occurs from southern California to Texas. It girdles small branches of *Prosopis.* The adult is 12 to 16 mm long, brown and gray with tawny spots, and has three callouslike areas in a row across the thorax.

Plectrodera contains one species. The **cottonwood borer,** *P. scalator* (F.) (Baker 1972), is principally a southeastern species but extends westward into Montana and New Mexico. The larvae bore in the base of living poplar and willow trees, often subjecting them to breakage by wind. The adults are 25 to 35 mm long, checkered black and white, and resemble *Monochamus* in outline. The life cycle is 2 years.

Plectrura contains one species. *P. spinicauda* Mannerheim occurs in coastal forests from California to Alaska. The larvae mine under the bark and in the sapwood of dead *Acer, Alnus,* and *Salix.* The adults are flightless, warty, gray-brown beetles, 8 to 14 mm long and with spinelike projections at the end of the wing covers. They emerge in the fall, overwinter, and resume activity in spring.

Poliaenus (Linsley 1935) is a western genus with several species, most of which bore in dead and dying branches of conifers. At least two bore in hardwoods. The adults resemble *Lophopogon-*

FIGURE 190.—*Acacia* branches girdled by *Oncideres pustulata.*

ius but the elytra are rounded rather than spined in back. *P. oregonus* (LeConte) is the most common and widely distributed species, being recorded from California to British Columbia, Colorado, and Utah. The larvae bore in dead branches and the tops of *Abies* and *Pseudotsuga.* The adults are 6 to 9 mm long and have gray elytra with a wide black band behind the middle. The life cycle is 1 year.

Pseudastylopsis [*Leptostylus*] (Dillon 1956) contains two species that bore in the inner bark of western conifers. *P. nebulosus* (Horn) is the more abundant. It occurs from California and Nevada to Washington under bark in the tops of recently dead *Abies,* often in trees killed by *Scolytus ventralis.* The adult is 10 to 13 mm long and covered with ashy gray hairs. The life cycle is 1 year.

Saperda (Baker 1972) contains about a dozen species, predominantly eastern. All attack broad-leaved trees. Most of them bore in the stems and branches of living trees, some causing galls. Others bore in dying and recently dead trees. The adults feed upon leaves and tender bark of the hosts. Some species are significant pests.

The **poplar borer,** *Saperda calcarata* Say (Baker 1972, Hofer 1920), attacks *Populus* throughout its natural range in North America and also attacks *Salix.* In the West it is most damaging in aspen stands of the Rocky Mountains. *S. calcarata* causes damage similar to that of *Xylotrechus obliteratus* and *Acossus populi.*

313

The bole and large branches of living trees are repeatedly attacked. The extensive mines increase wind breakage, provide access for wood rots, and cause log degrade. In Saskatchewan, the larvae bore in the root crown of small aspen on poor sites.

The adults are elongate, robust, grayish beetles, about 20 to 30 mm long, and have yellow stripes on the thorax and yellow spots on the elytra. They emerge late in July and in August. The female chews a slit in the bark, in which she deposits one or two eggs. The young larvae mine into the bark and remain there during winter. The following spring they enter the sapwood and heartwood, where they feed for 2 years. During this time they maintain an opening through the bark where the eggs were laid, and through this, boring dust is expelled. When mature the larvae construct pupal cells near the lower end of the larval mines, and in these they remain inactive until the following spring. In July of the third year the adults emerge through the holes used by the larvae for expelling frass.

The **poplar gall borer,** *Saperda inornata* Say (= *concolor* LeConte) (Nord 1968), is an eastern species that extends into Colorado, New Mexico, and Arizona. It mines in branches of *Populus* causing galls. The adult is covered with dense gray hairs.

Saperda populnea L. is a European species that now occurs in the West from British Columbia to California, Arizona, and New Mexico, causing twig galls (fig. 191) on *Populus*. The adult is

FIGURE 191.—*Saperda populnea* twig galls in which larvae feed.

314

darker than *S. calcarata* and about half the length. The life cycle is 1 or 2 years.

Synaphaeta contains one species. *S. guexi* LeConte ranges from California to British Columbia. The larvae bore in the wood of dead and dying oak, poplar, maple, willow, and other hardwoods. Their burrows are large and loosely filled with fibrous frass. The adults are 12 to 20 mm long, broad, "square-shouldered," and have two zigzag black stripes across the mottled white and orange-brown elytra.

FAMILY CHRYSOMELIDAE—LEAF BEETLES

The Chrysomelidae (Arnett 1960) is a large family containing hundreds of species and numerous genera in North America. Many species seriously damage agricultural crops; a few are economically important on forest trees. All feed on plants. The larvae and adults of most species feed upon leaves; the larvae of some feed upon roots. The adults are small to medium-sized, compact, generally oval, often brightly colored, and variously marked beetles. Some of the smaller ones known as **flea beetles** are powerful jumpers.

The numerous species of *Altica* (Blake 1936) are relatively large, shiny flea beetles, some of which skeletonize leaves of western alders, willows, and poplars.

The **alder flea beetle**, *Altica ambiens* LeConte, is a transcontinental species occurring in the West from California and New Mexico northward into Alaska. Alder is the principal host. The larvae skeletonize the leaves (fig. 192A) and the adults chew holes in them.

The adults (fig. 192B) are dark shiny blue, and about 5 to 6 mm long. The mature larvae are a trifle longer but narrower, brown to black above and yellowish below, with shining black head and thorax, and with short legs. The adults hibernate during the winter in debris beneath the trees and in other sheltered places, appearing early in the spring to resume feeding. Clusters of yellow eggs are deposited sometime after the spring appearance of the adults. The larvae, which appear a few days later, reach maturity in August, and pupate on the ground in the duff. New adults appear in a week to 10 days and feed voraciously on the foliage until the close of the season, when they hibernate for the winter, to appear the following spring, thus completing the cycle of one generation a year.

Altica bimarginata Say (Barstow and Gittins 1971), a metallic blue species that resembles *A. ambiens* but is less shiny, feeds

F-523452, F-523453

FIGURE 192.—Alder flea beetle (*Altica ambiens*): *A*, Larvae on skeletonized leaf; *B*, adult, 5 mm long.

abundantly on willows from New Mexico and California to Manitoba and Alaska. In Idaho it has one complete and a partial second generation annually. *A. prasina* LeConte, a metallic green species, also is abundant on willow and ranges from California to British Columbia, Idaho, and Utah. *A. populi* Brown feeds on poplars in Alberta.

Sixteen species of *Chrysolina* (Brown 1962, Wilcox 1972) are recorded in North America, most of them in the West. This genus is of interest to foresters because two species were imported to control Klamath weed, *Hypericum perforatum*, a noxious weed that depletes western ranges. This was the first effort in North America to control a weed by introducing plant-feeding insects.

The **Klamathweed beetle**, *Chrysolina quadrigemina* (Suffrian), recorded also as *C. gemellata* Rossi, was colonized in 1946 in California from Australia to control Klamath weed. The beetle quickly became established and exerted effective control (Huffaker and Kennett 1959). *C. quadrigemina* now occurs from California to southern British Columbia to Montana and Colorado. It has a 1-year life cycle well synchronized for weakening and killing its host plant. The adults are strongly convex, 6 to 7 mm long, and usually blue above but sometimes greenish or bronzy.

Chrysolina hyperici (Forster) was colonized in 1945 in California to control Klamath weed. It became established more slowly and has been much less effective than *C. quadrigemina* (Holloway 1958), except in British Columbia where it is somewhat more effective (Harris 1962). The adults strongly resemble *C. quadrigemina*, except that they are 5 to 6 mm long and always green or bronzy.

Several species of *Chrysomela* (Brown 1956) feed on leaves of willows, poplars, and alders in the West, rarely causing economic damage. The adults are moderately to strongly convex, elongate-

316

oval, 5 to 10 mm long, and usually with black markings. Structurally the species are very similar. Color and markings vary widely, even within species. Information on locality and host plants is essential for specific determination. Wilcox (1972) keys 17 species, of which 14 occur in the West.

C. aeneicollis (Schaeffer) is a small, heavily marked species that ranges from California to Colorado, Alberta, and Alaska. It is one of several that feed only on *Salix*. The **aspen leaf beetle,** *C. crotchi* Brown, is a transcontinental species that feeds on *Populus*, especially *P. tremuloides*. In the West it occurs from New Mexico to Alaska. Adults are light brown to dull orange and without markings. The **cottonwood leaf beetle,** *C. scripta* F., another transcontinental species, occurs widely in the West. It is representative of the species that feed both on *Salix* and *Populus*. It does not feed on *P. tremuloides*. The adults (fig. 193) appear early in the spring and feed on the tender shoots. The eggs are yellowish or reddish and are deposited in clusters on the under surface of the leaves, and it is here that the black grubs feed as soon as hatched. In hot weather the period of growth to the mature larval stage is about 15 days. Five generations a year are reported in the West. Varieties of *C. mainensis* Bechyne feed on *Alnus* from Oregon to Alaska. Their host sets them apart.

F–523454

FIGURE 193.—Cottonwood leaf beetle (*Chrysomela scripta*) adult, 6 mm long.

Several species of *Colaspis* occur in the West but none is reported to be a forest pest such as *C. pini* Barber (Barber 1936), a defoliator of pines in the Gulf States westward to Texas.

There are approximately 20 species of *Glyptoscelis* (Blake 1967) in the United States, predominantly in the West and many of them in California. They are stout beetles, 5 to 14 mm long, and range in color from reddish brown to shining black, some with coppery, bronzy, or greenish reflections, and all conspicuously pubescent with white, yellowish, or brown hairs. The adults of several species feed on the foliage of conifers but cause no appreciable damage.

317

The larvae feed underground on roots. The biology of *G. pubescens* (F.), an eastern species, has been studied (Klein and Coppel 1969). Not much is known of the biology of the western species (Doane et al. 1936).

Several species feed on broad-leaved trees and shrubs. The species of *Glyptoscelis* recorded or suspected of feeding as adults on conifers in the West are:

Species	Hosts	Distribution
G. albida LeConte	*Libocedrus decurrens*	Calif.
G. aridis Van Dyke	*Pinus monophylla*	Calif.
G. illustris Crotch	*Pinus ponderosa* and *Juniperus occidentalis*	Calif. and Oreg.
G. juniperi Blake	*Juniperus occidentalis*	Calif.
G. juniperi zanthocoma Blake	*Libocedrus decurrens*	Calif.
G. septentrionalis Blake	"Fir," *Pinus ponderosa,* and *P. contorta*	Calif., Oreg., Wash., Idaho, Mont., and British Columbia
G. sequoiae Blaisdell	*Sequoia sempervirens*	Calif.
G. vandykei Krauss	*Juniperus*	Oreg.

There are four species of *Gonioctena,* also known as *Phytodecta* (Brown 1942), in North America, all occurring in the West. They feed on willows and aspen in the Northern United States and Canada.

The **American aspen beetle,** *Gonioctena americana* (Schaeffer), is a transcontinental species that periodically defoliates *Populus tremuloides* in the Western Provinces and Yukon Territory in Canada, particularly in Alberta and Saskatchewan. The adults are 5 to 6 mm long and variable in color, ranging from red to brown or blackish. *G. notmani* (Schaeffer) is a similar but somewhat smaller species that feeds on willows in Alberta, British Columbia, and Northwest Territories. *G. arctica* Mannerheim is an arctic and alpine brownish species that feeds on willows from Colorado and Manitoba westward and northward to Alaska.

Melasomida closely resembles *Chrysomela.* The **California willow beetle,** *Melasomida californica* Rogers, is 4 to 5 mm long and has a black body and bluish-green elytra. It feeds on willows in California.

Phratora is a small, northern, transcontinental genus of no recorded economic importance. Brown (1951) and Wilcox (1972) key the species. Lindquist and Davis (1971) illustrate the life stages. The adults are unspotted, metallic, bluish to greenish beetles 3.5 to 5 mm long. There is one generation annually. The adults overwinter under bark and in litter. The larvae and adults feed gregariously on the under surface of the leaf skeletonizing it. The principal western forms, and their hosts and distribution are:

Species	Hosts	Distribution
P. frosti remisa Brown	*Salix* and *Populus*	Manitoba to Alaska, Wyo., and Colo.
P. hudsonia Brown	*Betula*	Manitoba to Alaska
P. interstitialis Mannerheim	*Salix*	Northwest Territories to Alaska, and British Columbia
P. kenaiensis Brown	*Populus*	Alaska
P. purpurea purpurea Brown	*Populus* and *Salix*	Manitoba to Yukon Territory and British Columbia

Until recently, *Pyrrhalta* (Wilcox 1965) has generally been recorded as *Galerucella*. In the West, one species is a serious pest of ornamental elms and two subspecies frequently are epidemic on willows, poplars, and alders.

Pyrrhalta decora (Say) is a transcontinental species that feeds principally on willows but also upon poplars and alders. The **Pacific willow leaf beetle**, *P. decora carbo* (LeConte), is the black form generally encountered in Oregon, Washington, and British Columbia. The adults are dull black and 4.3 to 5.7 mm long. The **gray willow leaf beetle**, *P. decora decora* (Say), is the grayish to yellowish-brown form that is typical in Alberta and Saskatchewan where it periodically becomes epidemic on willows. Spraying of farm shelterbelts sometimes is necessary. Intermediate color forms occur in Montana.

Pyrrhalta punctipennis (Mannerheim) is larger and less abundant than *P. decora*. It feeds on willow, poplar, and alder and occurs in Oregon, Washington, Montana, British Columbia, and Northwest Territories.

The **elm leaf beetle**, *Pyrrhalta luteola* (Müller) (USDA 1960), is an introduced species now established practically everywhere in North America that elms grow. It is a serious pest of ornamentals but is of little significance in the forest. The adults are 5.5 to 6.8 mm long and yellowish to olive green with black stripes along the outer side of the elytra (fig. 194A). The full-grown larva is dull yellow with a pair of black stripes down the back. The yellowish-orange eggs are laid in clumps or irregular rows. The larvae skeletonize the leaves by feeding on the under surface causing them to dry and turn brown (fig. 194B). The adults overwinter in sheltered places, often invading houses in great numbers. There are two or more generations annually but the spring generation usually is most abundant because the young larvae require tender leaves (Wene 1968).

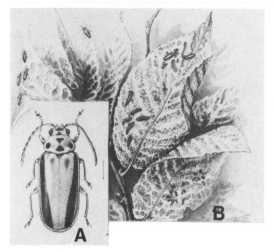

USDA–FI–6417

FIGURE 194.—Elm leaf beetle (*Pyrrhalta luteola*): *A*, Adult, 6 mm long; *B*, larvae feeding on underside of leaf.

The species of *Syneta* (Edwards 1953) are straw-colored, brown or nearly black, cerambycidlike, beetles ranging from about 4 to 7 mm long. None is economically important in the forest. The adults of *S. carinata* (Mannerheim), which feed on the foliage of true firs and mountain hemlock, occur throughout the West, including Alaska. The elytra are yellowish brown with black sutural margins. The head and prothorax are shiny black. The adults of *S. albida* LeConte feed on various hardwoods including alders and willows from California to British Columbia. The larvae are root feeders. *S. simplex* LeConte adults feed on leaves of oaks from California to British Columbia.

There are 25 species of *Trirhabda* (Blake 1931, Wilcox 1965), mostly on herbs and shrubs of the Compositae in the West. Two species are of potential use in biological control of range plants. Three spots, two lateral and one median, on the prothorax of the adult are characteristic.

Trirhabda nitidicollis LeConte feeds on *Chrysothamnus*, *Artemisia*, and *Gutierrezia*. It ranges from New Mexico to California, Idaho, and Montana. Massey and Pierce (1960) have suggested its possible use in biological control of *Chrysothamnus nauseosus*. The adults are 7 to 9 mm long. The elytra are black, blue, green, or purple with yellowish stripes and the pronotum is yellow with three blue-green spots. The larvae are metallic blue green.

Trirhabda pilosa Blake feeds on *Artemisia tridentata* in California, Nevada, Wyoming, Alberta, and British Columbia. In British Columbia it sometimes kills sagebrush and has been considered for use in biological control of its host (Arnott 1957, Banham 1961). The adults are 4.5 to 6.5 mm long with green elytra and black abdomen. There is one generation a year. The eggs overwinter.

FAMILY BRUCHIDAE—SEED BEETLES

The **seed beetles**, Bruchidae (Bridwell 1946), develop in plant seeds, especially those of the Leguminosae. The **bean weevil**, *Acanthoscelides obtectus* (Say), and the **pea weevil**, *Bruchus pisorum* (L.), are examples known to most gardeners. In the Southwest, seeds of *Acacia*, *Prosopis*, *Parkinsonia*, *Cercidium*, and *Robinia* often are infested and destroyed by the small, white, curled, legless larvae of various genera of seed beetles. The adults are small, compact, oval, densely hairy beetles with the head deflexed in a short broad snout.

SUPERFAMILY CURCULIONOIDEA

FAMILY CURCULIONIDAE—SNOUT BEETLES OR WEEVILS

This large family of beetles contains numerous species that are forest pests. The most destructive ones attack young trees, hence will be increasingly important as forestry becomes more intensive. Many feed on foliage of trees and shrubs; some feed in wood and under the bark; still others feed in tree seeds. The adults can be recognized by the snoutlike, downward-curved extension of the head and the elbowed antennae attached to the snout. The larvae are curved and legless. Keys to the adults of the approximately 400 genera in North America north of Mexico are given by Kissinger (1964). Identification of larvae is for specialists only.

Agronus (Buchanan 1929) contains three species. Adults of *A. cinerarius* Horn defoliated *Abies concolor* locally in northern California in 1961 (Hall 1962). This dark brown weevil covered with gray scales is 4 mm long and its abdomen is much broader than its thorax. Larval habits are not recorded.

About half of the 30 species of *Cossonus* are western. They often occur abundantly under the bark and in the decaying sapwood of bark beetle-killed trees, causing no economic damage. The adults are black, shiny, elongate, hairless, somewhat flattened weevils 4 to 7 mm long. Among the western species, *C. crenatus* Horn and *C. ponderosae* Van Dyke occur in various pines and *C. quadricollis* Van Dyke in poplar. Van Dyke (1915) keys the species.

The **poplar-and-willow borer**, *Cryptorhynchus* [*Sternochetus*] *lapathi* (L.) (Furniss 1972b), is a European insect now extensively established in southern British Columbia and Alberta south to California, Nevada, Utah, and Colorado. It is a pest of ornamental trees and of trees in windbreaks. *Salix* is its preferred host. *Populus* is less commonly attacked and *Alnus* and *Betula* rarely. The larvae first mine beneath the bark, then into the wood, making irregular generally cylindrical tunnels (fig. 195A) that often riddle the wood and cause the stem to break. Fibrous wood borings expelled by larvae through holes in the stem commonly indicate attack, as do broken stems. The adult is a chunky, rough-surfaced weevil with a long, curved, shiny snout (fig. 195B). It is about 8 mm long and predominantly black except for the hind third of the elytra which is gray or sometimes pinkish. In British Columbia development from egg to adult requires 1 year (Harris 1968, Harris and Coppel 1967). The adults are long-lived, hence the entire life cycle may last up to 3 years.

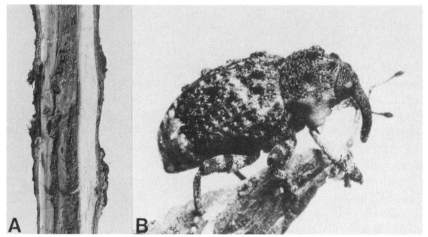

FIGURE 195.—Poplar-and-willow borer (*Cryptorhynchus lapathi*): *A*, Larval tunnels in willow; *B*, adult, 8 mm long.

The genus *Curculio* contains 27 species in North America; about half of them occur in the West. Gibson (1969) keys the species and provides information on biology, hosts, and distribution. Most species attack oak acorns. Some attack the nuts of *Corylus, Carya, Castanea,* and *Lithocarpus.*

The **filbert weevil,** *Curculio occidentis* (Casey), formerly *C. uniformis* (LeConte), breeds natively in the acorns of various *Quercus* and in the nuts of *Lithocarpus densiflorus* and *Corylus californica* var. *cornuta*. In the Pacific Northwest it has become a pest of filberts. It occurs from British Columbia to Mexico and in Arizona, New Mexico, and Utah. According to Keen (1958), the larvae may destroy 20 to 60 percent of the acorn crop. Fermented sap dripping from infested acorns sometimes is a problem under ornamental oaks in dry areas (Brown and Eads 1965a).

The adults are 5.5 to 7.5 mm long. They have robust brownish bodies covered with tan to yellowish scales, long slender legs, and a slender beak that is about half the length of the body. Eggs are laid in late summer in small holes bored into the acorn or nut. The short, fat, curved larvae feed on the nutmeat destroying the seed (fig. 196). They develop to maturity about the time the nuts fall. Late in November they burrow several centimeters into the soil where they hibernate 2 or 3 years before pupating (Dohanian 1944).

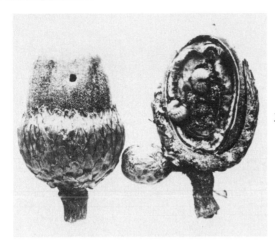

EPQ–1966

FIGURE 196.—Damage by the filbert weevil (*Curculio occidentis*) to California black oak acorns.

Several species of *Cylindrocopturus* attack the twigs and bole of young conifers, including pine, true fir, Douglas-fir, larch, and hemlock in the West (Buchanan 1940, Sleeper 1963). One or more species feed in fungus-caused galls on pine. The adults are about 3 mm long and densely covered with nearly circular scales; bronze ones predominate above and white ones below. The adults are so similar in appearance that host, habits, and locality are the only practical means of field identification. The larvae are cream-colored, legless, curled grubs, about 4 mm long when mature. Generally these weevils are unimportant, but sometimes they cause severe damage in plantations and on Christmas tree areas where the trees are growing under stress.

The **pine reproduction weevil**, *Cylindrocopturus eatoni* Buchanan, is the most destructive species of this genus on conifers (Eaton 1942, Stevens 1965). Its recorded range is central and northern California. Presumably it extends into Oregon. Under natural forest conditions, it attacks ponderosa and Jeffrey pines principally, sugar and digger pines occasionally. It also attacks various planted hybrid pines. Its presence in natural stands is seldom noted. Damage has been greatest in plantations suffering competition by brush and at times it has decimated such plantations. It attacks mostly trees from 0.5 to 1.0 m (1.5 to 3 ft) high but sometimes trees up to 3.2 m (10 ft) high.

Successful weevil attack is first indicated by fading of infested trees, usually in the fall. The foliage turns straw-colored and progressively darkens to deep reddish brown. Feeding punctures on the twigs and needles are evident on close examination (fig. 197A). The larval galleries meander between the wood and outer bark and do not originate from a central gallery or chamber. The adult emergence holes in the bark resemble birdshot punctures.

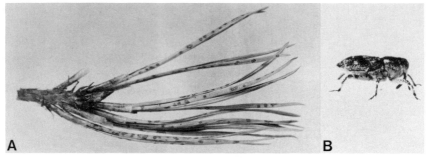

F–481407, F–510322

FIGURE 197.—Pine reproduction weevil (*Cylindrocopturus eatoni*) : A, Feeding punctures on pine needles; B, adult, 2.6 mm long.

Emergence occurs from late May until mid-July. The adults (fig. 197B) are very active. They feed for 2 or 3 weeks by making punctures with their beaks in the needles, twigs, and stems. The eggs are laid individually in punctures in the cortex below the current year's growth. The young larvae chew through the inner bark to the phloem-cambium region where they feed until mature. When mature, the larvae bore into the wood, and in small trees enter the pith, where they rest in their burrows from September until the following spring. Pupation occurs late in April and in May. There is one generation per year.

Cylindrocopturus eatoni can be controlled by chemical spraying or by burning infested trees. Brush clearing to reduce competition for soil moisture is a helpful preventative measure. Jeffrey pine-Coulter pine hybrids are resistant to the weevil, but site preparation still is the prevention measure in practical use.

The **Douglas fir twig weevil**, *Cylindrocopturus furnissi* Buchanan, attacks and kills small branches on open-grown, Douglas-fir reproduction in British Columbia, Washington, Oregon, and

California (Furniss 1942). It or a closely related species also attacks white fir and Pacific silver fir in Oregon. *C. furnissi* causes little damage in natural stands, but on Christmas tree areas and in plantations it sometimes is important. Damage is greatest in drought years and on dry sites. Heavy attacks deform trees and retard their growth. Some trees less than 1.5 m (5 ft) high are killed outright. By the time Douglas-firs attain a height of 4.5 to 6 m (15 to 20 ft) they are no longer subject to appreciable damage.

On Douglas-fir, adults emerge from the middle of June to the first week in August. After feeding on the tender twigs for about 1 month, they deposit eggs in small punctures on stems and branches. The small larvae bore down to the surface of the wood, where they extend their feeding galleries. On approaching maturity, the larvae frequently bore through the wood into the pith. Larvae of all sizes overwinter, and pupation takes place the following spring, chiefly during May and June. Some adults overwinter by clinging to the branches and resume egg laying in the spring. There is one main generation and possibly a partial second each year. Chemical control may be needed at times in seed orchards and Christmas tree plantings, especially when trees are growing under stress.

Cylindrocopturus deleoni Buchanan attacks the roots and root crown of small lodgepole pine and also has been reared from a fungus-caused gall on ponderosa pine and from *Cronartium comandrae* on lodgepole pine (Powell 1971). Distribution includes Idaho, Montana, Wyoming, and Alberta. It is not recorded as an economic pest. *C. dehiscens* (Fall) attacks Monterey and Bishop's pines in California. Unidentified *Cylindrocopturus* are recorded on various other pines, true firs, western larch, and mountain hemlock.

The genus *Dorytomus* (O'Brien 1970) contains 22 species in North America, most of which occur in the West. They develop in catkins of *Populus* and *Salix* and have been reared from gall midge and sawfly galls on *Salix*. None is a forest pest. The adults range from about 2.5 to 8 mm long and have grayish, hairlike scales, usually in spotted patterns on the wing covers. They occasionally attract attention by migrating into homes. The larvae are less curved than those of weevils generally.

Thirty-some species of *Dyslobus* are native to Western North America. Many occur in coniferous forests where the adults frequently are collected from the foliage during surveys by beating. Several species are agricultural pests, principally on strawberries. The role of the larvae in the forest has not been determined. The adults are scale-covered, gray, or tan, smooth-surfaced beetles ranging from 7 to 14 mm long. Adults overwinter in the soils. Some species are parthenogenetic. *D. granicollis* (LeConte) is a common species ranging from British Columbia to central California. Van Dyke (1933) keys most of the species.

Three of the seven North American *Hylobius* [*Hypomolyx*] occur in the West (Warner 1966). The larvae feed in the root crown of various conifers. The adults are look-alike, black weevils with scattered patches of gray scales. They resemble the black vine weevil but are larger.

Warren's collar weevil, *Hylobius warreni* Wood, attacks pines and spruces throughout Canada. It also occurs in southeastern Alaska and presumably other Western States bordering Canada. It is the most prevalent and most damaging of the western species (Cerezke 1970). In addition to causing growth loss by girdling, it provides an important avenue of infection for root-rotting and staining fungi (fig. 198A). In Alberta, *Pinus contorta* is the primary host. It also attacks *Pinus monticola*, other species of *Pinus*, *Abies*, *Picea*, and *Larix*. Trees from 6 to 8 years old to maturity are attacked. Trees growing on moist sites with heavy duff are preferred. The larval stage lasts about 2 years. The adults are flightless and feed upon the bark of small roots and twigs and on the needles of the host. They resemble *Otiorhynchus sulcatus* but are dull black and clothed with fine gray scales between the patches of white (fig. 198B), rather than being shiny black and bare of scales except the white patches. They live and lay eggs up to 4 years. *H. pinicola* (Couper) and *H. congener* Dalla-Torre, Schenkling and Marshall, have similar distributions and habits but are much less common and tend to be more northern in the West.

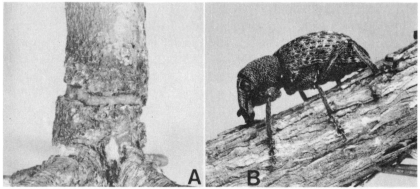

FIGURE 198.—Warren's collar weevil (*Hylobius warreni*): *A*, Damage to root crown of lodgepole pine; *B*, adult, 4.5 mm long.

Lechriops californica (LeConte), formerly *Gelus*, bores under the bark of the bole and large branches of Jeffrey, ponderosa, and many other pines from British Columbia to California, Arizona, and Mexico. The adults often are abundant on pine twigs and foliage. *L. californica* resembles *Cylindrocopturus eatoni* and *furnissi* but is slightly larger and more robust and has toothed femora. It is noneconomic. Sleeper (1963) keys the species.

The larvae of several species of *Magdalis* (Fall 1913) bore and develop in twigs and branches of western conifers and broad-leaved trees, often in combination with other borers. Boring by *Magdalis* is of little economic consequence because the attacked branches usually are dying or dead from other causes. The adults of some species feed on foliage, sometimes causing conspicuous defoliation.

The larvae are white, legless, curled, and practically indistinguishable from those of *Pissodes*, though generally smaller. *Magdalis* larvae work into the wood more than do *Pissodes*, the larval borings are fine-grained and powdery instead of shredded, and the pupal cells are without the lining of shredded wood fiber (fig. 199A). The adults are 3 to 8 mm long, bright metallic blue or green to dull black, with prominent curved beaks, and without scales; viewed from above, they are wedge-shaped, widest behind (fig. 199B).

M. gentilis Le Conte is a black species occurring from California to British Columbia to Montana. The larvae are recorded as min-

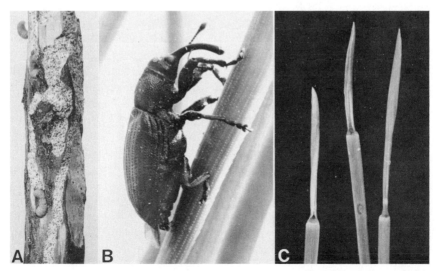

EPQ–6566, F–523457, F–523458

FIGURE 199.—Examples of *Magdalis*: *A*, Larval gallery of *M. lecontei*; *B*, adult of *M. gentilis*; *C*, needle feeding of *M. gentilis* adult.

ing branches of ponderosa pine and Jeffrey pine. The adults have caused conspicuous dying of lodgepole pine needles in thinned young stands in Montana by feeding upon the needles (fig. 199C) (Fellin 1973). *M. lecontei* Horn and its varieties are metallic green and blue to black and infest branches of ponderosa, Jeffrey, sugar, lodgepole, and other pines in the Western States and Provinces. On the foliage of ponderosa pine reproduction in southern Oregon it causes damage similar to that by *M. gentilis* on lodgepole. The **bronze appletree weevil**, *M. aenescens* LeConte, attacks alder, hawthorn, and various fruit trees. It occurs from Alaska to California and eastward to Montana. Hosts and distribution of some other western species are:

Species	Hosts	Distribution
M. alutacea LeConte	*Picea*	Oreg., British Columbia, Mont., and Colo.
M. cuneiformis Horn	*Pinus ponderosa* and *P. jeffreyi*	Western States and British Columbia
M. gracilis LeConte	*Alnus, Salix*, and other broad-leaved trees	Calif., Nev., and N. Mex.
M. hispoides LeConte	*Pinus contorta* and other *Pinus*	Maine to British Columbia, N. Mex., and Calif.
M. proxima Fall	*Pinus radiata* and other *Pinus*	Calif. to Wash.

Nemocestes (Van Dyke 1936) contains 10 species, predominantly in the Pacific States. The **woods weevil**, *Nemocestes incomptus* (Horn), is 6 to 9 mm long and is similar to the **obscure root weevil** but is more robust and generally darker and with rows of erect scalelike hairs. It occurs in and near wooded areas from California to British Columbia. It is a serious pest of strawberries but also attacks Monterey pine and rhododendrons (Eide 1966) and has been observed to feed on roots of Douglas-fir (Cram in correspondence).

Species of *Otiorhynchus* [*Brachyrhinus*] (Wilcox et al. 1934) are among the few insects that cause significant damage in western forest nurseries. All consist of females only, and all are without hindwings. They occur extensively in North America, Europe, and Asia. Adults sometimes are a nuisance by crawling into houses in the fall and larvae are serious pests of strawberries, caneberries, and ornamental shrubs. Three species are recorded as feeding upon the roots of young conifers in the West, causing damage especially to spruce and Douglas-fir in forest nurseries in Oregon, Montana, British Columbia, and Alberta, and in a forest tree seed orchard in Oregon. Damage in forest nurseries is most likely to occur on land recently in sod. Infestations may be prevented through clean cultivation and rotation of seed and transplant beds, allowing infested plots to remain fallow and be cleanly cultivated in alternate years. Chemical treatment of the soil sometimes is necessary.

The **strawberry root weevil**, *O. ovatus* L. is the smallest species. The adult is a jet black, hard-shelled, rough-surfaced, flightless snout beetle about 4 to 6 mm long. In western Oregon the curled white larvae overwinter half- to full-grown in the soil. They resume feeding in the spring and pupate and emerge in April and May. After about 2 weeks of feeding at night on the foliage of various broad-leaved plants, commonly including rhododendrons (Breakey 1967), they begin to lay eggs in surface layers of the soil. Egg laying continues until September. The eggs hatch in about 3 weeks and the small larvae work their way several centimeters into the soil where they feed first on the fine roots and later in the larger roots.

The **black vine weevil**, *O. sulcatus* (F.) is 8 to 11 mm long and has scattered patches of gray scales (fig. 200). The **rough strawberry root weevil**, *O. rugosostriatus* (Goeze), is intermediate in size and without scales. The habits and damage of these two are similar to those of *O. ovatus*.

F–523459

FIGURE 200.—Black vine weevil (*Otiorhynchus sulcatus*) adult, 10 mm long.

The genus *Panscopus* contains 27 species many of which occur in the West (Buchanan 1936).

Panscopus gemmatus (LeConte) occurs generally on conifers in coastal forests from British Columbia to California; its role there is not known. Green scales on the thorax and elytra give *P. gem-*

matus a decidedly greenish cast. About the size and shape of *Steremnius tuberosus*, it is strongly tuberculate, and the elytra are prominently ribbed.

Panscopus torpidus (LeConte), a brownish weevil, 6.5 to 8 mm long, that resembles *Nemocestes incomptus*, occurs in Washington and Oregon. In Washington the adults have damaged small noble firs by girdling them (Mitchell in correspondence).

Pissodes ranks high among forest insect pests because of the **white pine weevil**, *P. strobi* (Peck), which attacks terminals of young pines and spruce from coast to coast, causing heavy loss of growth and quality. Most other *Pissodes* attack the bole and root collar of dying trees, hence are of little economic importance. Hopkins (1911) described, keyed, and illustrated 29 species. Based upon rearings and cytogenetic studies, Smith and Sugden (1969) reduced the number of valid species to 20 or less. Seventeen species now are listed for the West (table 12). Several of them are rarely encountered, and some likely are synonyms.

The adults are rough-surfaced, brown to black beetles, usually with spots and patches of white, yellow, or brown scales on the elytra (fig. 201A). The head is prolonged into a slender beak or snout, which is used to puncture buds or tender bark for feeding, and by the female to make a hole for the reception of eggs. The larvae (fig. 201B) mine principally in the inner bark. Each mine ends in a pupal cell constructed partly in the bark but mostly in the sapwood. This cell is oval in outline and is lined with excelsior-like shreds of wood fiber. These oval "chip cocoons" remain imbedded in the wood long after the beetles emerge and are characteristic features of *Pissodes'* work (fig. 201C).

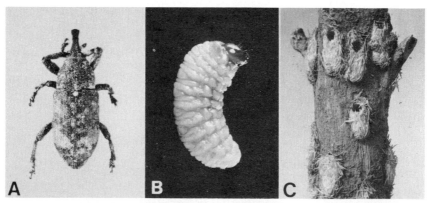

F–523460, F–493005, F–493002

FIGURE 201.—White pine weevil (*Pissodes strobi*): *A*, Adult, 4.5 mm long; *B*, larva, 4.5 mm long; *C*, pupal cells ("chip cocoons").

Table 12.—*Species of* Pissodes *in Western North America*

Species	Basic color and length (mm)	Hosts	Distribution
P. affinis Randall (= *curriei* Hopkins)	Dark brown to black 5.5–8.0	*Pinus contorta* and *P. monticola*	Northern Rocky Mt. States, British Columbia, and Alberta
P. barberi Hopkins	Dark reddish brown 5.0–5.5	*Pinus* ?	Calif., Oreg., and Wash.
P. burkei Hopkins	Gray 6.0–8.0	*Abies concolor* and *A. lasiocarpa*	Wyo., Utah, Colo., and British Columbia
P. californicus Hopkins	Reddish brown 8.0	*Pinus ponderosa*	Calif.
P. coloradensis Hopkins	Dark brown to black 7.5–9.5	*Picea* and *Pinus monticola*	Rocky Mountain States
P. costatus Mannerheim	Dark brown to black 5.5–7.0	*Picea sitchensis* and *Pinus*	Calif. to Alaska
P. dubius Randall (= *piperi* Hopkins)	Dark brown to black 7.5–10.0	*Abies*	Calif., Oreg., Wash., Idaho, and British Columbia
P. fasciatus LeConte	Dark reddish brown 5.0–8.0	*Pseudotsuga menziesii*	Calif., Oreg., Wash., Idaho, and British Columbia
P. fiskei Hopkins	Dark brown 4.0–5.5	*Picea*	Saskatchewan, Alberta, Yukon, and British Columbia
P. murrayanae Hopkins	Dark brown 4.0	*Pinus contorta*	Oreg.
P. radiatae Hopkins **Monterey pine weevil**	Reddish brown 5.0–7.5	*Pinus attenuata, P. contorta, P. muricata,* and *P. radiata*	Pacific Coast
P. rotundatus LeConte (= *alascensis* Hopkins)	Dark brown 6.0–7.5	*Picea engelmannii, P. mariana, Pinus contorta, P. monticola,* and *Tsuga heterophylla*	Alaska, Yukon, and British Columbia
P. schwarzi Hopkins (= *yosemite* Hopkins)	Reddish brown to dark brown 5.0–7.0	*Picea engelmannii, P. pungens, Larix occidentalis, Pinus contorta, P. ponderosa,* and other pines	Calif., Oreg., Wash., Rocky Mountain States, Alberta, British Columbia, and Yukon
P. similis Hopkins (= *utahensis* Hopkins)	Light to dark brown 4.0–5.0	*Abies lasiocarpa*	Utah and British Columbia

Table 12.—*Species of* Pissodes *in Western North America*—Continued

Species	Basic color and length (mm)	Hosts	Distribution
P. strobi (Peck) (= engelmanni Hopkins) (= sitchensis Hopkins) white pine weevil	Reddish brown 4.0–5.0	Picea engelmannii, P. sitchensis, P. pungens, and Pinus contorta	Western Provinces, Western States south to Calif. and Colo.
P. terminalis Hopping lodgepole terminal weevil	Reddish brown 5.5–6.5	Pinus contorta and P. banksiana	Saskatchewan, Alberta, Oreg., Calif., Idaho, Wyo., and S. Dak.
P. webbi Hopkins	Brown 5.0–7.0	Pinus ponderosa and P. contorta	Ariz. and N. Mex.

The **white pine weevil**, *Pissodes strobi* (Peck) (Smith and Sugden 1969), is a transcontinental species now considered to include the forms known as the **Engelmann spruce weevil**, *P. engelmanni* Hopkins (Stevenson 1967) and the **Sitka spruce weevil**, *P. sitchensis* Hopkins (Silver 1968, Wright 1970). This is the most injurious insect attacking Sitka spruce reproduction in coastal British Columbia, Washington, and Oregon. It attacks and kills or seriously injures the terminal shoots of trees from about 8 to 30 years old and up to 15 m (50 ft) tall. Crooked or bushy, low-value trees result. Attacked trees often are overtopped and suppressed by other tree species. Weeviling is most severe on widely spaced trees growing in extensive even-aged stands. Damage to Sitka spruce has been so great that planting is much reduced. Close spacing and planting of this tree in small blocks offer the most practical means of minimizing damage in plantations. Chemical control has not been attempted as a practical measure in the West.

In April and May the adults make feeding punctures on terminal growth of the preceding year. In May and June they lay eggs in these terminals. The developing larvae girdle and kill the terminals but not until the new growth of the current year has elongated considerably. In late summer the new growth wilts and the needles on 2 years' growth turn reddish and fall (fig. 202). From August on into fall many new adults emerge, feed, and then overwinter in forest litter. Other portions of the brood overwinter as larvae and pupae in the infested terminals. There is one generation per year but with considerable overlapping of broods.

Pissodes dubious Randall (= *piperi* Hopkins) is the largest species in the genus. In Oregon it has been observed to breed in storm-damaged 90-year-old noble fir and to attack nearby inter-

F-493003

FIGURE 202.—Sitka spruce terminal killed by the white pine weevil (*Pissodes strobi*).

F-523461

FIGURE 203.—Larval galleries of a weevil, *Pissodes fasciatus*, lightly engraving the sapwood, and its chip cocoons.

mediate and suppressed trees. Attacks are made in the root crown area, sometimes in conjunction with the **fir root bark beetle,** *Pseudohylesinus granulatus*.

Pissodes fasciatus LeConte constructs long meandering galleries (fig. 203) in the inner bark on the bole of Douglas fir saplings and poles suffering severely from drought, freezing, competition, or injury. The host identifies this species.

The **Monterey pine weevil,** *P. radiatae* Hopkins, sometimes attacks pine leaders but characteristically develops in the bole and root collar. *P. schwarzi* is a widely distributed species that attacks the bole of many conifers. It also has been reared from cankers of *Cronartium comandrae*. *P. similis* Hopkins is unique in having been reared from witches broom.

The **lodgepole terminal weevil,** *Pissodes terminalis* Hopping (Stark and Wood 1964), presumably is a hybrid of *P. strobi* and *P. schwarzi* (Drouin et al. 1963). It prefers open-grown young pines. The developing terminals are attacked and killed down to the uppermost whorl of branches. In contrast, *P. strobi* kills 2 years' growth. Small larvae of *P. terminalis* mine in the cambium region. Mature larvae mine and pupate in the pith. Some of the brood overwinter as larvae and pupae in the terminals, some as adults, presumably in the soil. There is one generation per year.

Species of *Rhyncolus* resemble those of *Cossonus* in size and appearance, but are more cylindrical and usually are brownish rather than black. They generally mine deeper than *Cossonus* but seldom penetrate sound wood extensively enough to cause appreciable damage. The detailed biology is not recorded. Buchanan (1946) keys six of the 17 species. *R. brunneus* Mannerheim breeds in the wood of dead *Abies, Picea, Pinus, Pseudotsuga, Thuja,* and *Tsuga* and ranges from Alaska to California, Idaho, Arizona, and New Mexico. *R. oregonensis* Horn and *R. macrops* Buchanan are closely related species that breed in dead *Pinus* and *Abies* from British Columbia to Colorado.

Hexarthrum is related to and resembles *Rhyncolus.* There are two species (Brown 1966a). *H. thujae* Brown (fig. 204) is 2.4 to 2.8 mm long. It attacks overmature *Thuja plicata* in British Columbia, making the wood unsatisfactory for shingles (Silver and Ross 1961). *H. ulkei* Horn, which is somewhat larger and predominantly eastern, infests coniferous wood in old buildings. It has been reported as damaging in Colorado and North Dakota.

COURTESY CANADIAN FORESTRY SERVICE

FIGURE 204.—Adult of a weevil, *Hexarthrum thujae,* 2.5 mm long.

The **obscure root weevil,** *Sciopithes obscurus* Horn, is a grayish-tan, scale-covered weevil 5.0 to 6.5 mm long and with a wavy brown line across the back near the rear end. The elytra are conspicuously wider than the thorax. Woodlands of the Pacific Northwest are its natural habitat. It is a pest of berry crops and ornamentals such as rhododendrons but is not recorded as attacking forest trees (Every 1968).

There are eight species of *Scythropus,* mostly western. The adults are broad-nosed, scale-covered, somewhat elongate weevils ranging from 4.5 to 7.5 mm long (fig. 205A). They feed on old foliage of pines and Douglas-fir in spring and early summer and are most often seen on young trees but also occur on older trees. They bite out chunks and leave a saw-toothed edge (fig. 205B), often causing the needles to die and drop prematurely. The larvae of at least one species feed on pine roots. Some are minor pests on ornamentals but none is reported economically damaging in the forest.

Scythropus californicus Horn is a bronze species about 5 mm long, somewhat speckled with gray (fig. 205A). It occurs from British Columbia to California and Arizona. The adults feed on ponderosa, Jeffrey, Monterey, digger, and other pines and on Douglas-fir. In California on Monterey pine, Jensen and Koehler (1969) reported egg laying from mid-February until May. The eggs are laid in rows in a tube consisting of three needles glued together. The larvae drop to the ground and feed on pine rootlets. Adults overwinter in the soil. The life cycle is believed to be 2 years.

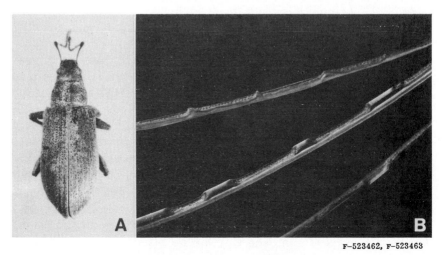

F-523462, F-523463

FIGURE 205.—A weevil, *Scythropus californicus*: *A,* Adult, 5 mm long; *B,* feeding on ponderosa pine needles.

Scythropus albidus Fall is a small ashy-white weevil with a faint metallic lustre which occurs in California, Oregon, and Idaho. Hosts are ponderosa and Jeffrey pines.

Scythropus elegans (Couper) is a metallic blue-green, gold, brass, or bronze species sometimes with lighter stripes along the margins of the wing covers. It occurs in British Columbia, Montana, and California. The adults feed on foliage of lodgepole, western white, and other pines, and Douglas-fir.

The **rusty pine needle weevil**, *Scythropus ferrugineus* Casey, is a metallic, reddish-bronze or copper-colored species occurring from California to British Columbia. Hosts are ponderosa, Jeffrey, Monterey, and knobcone pines.

Two of the three species of *Steremnius* are western (Brown 1966b). The adults are flightless. They resemble *Pissodes* in outline but are rougher and more drab. The immature forms are described and distinguished from related insects of similar habits by Condrashoff (1966a).

Steremnius carinatus (Mannerheim) (Condrashoff 1968) occurs in coastal forests from Alaska to Oregon. The adults feed on many kinds of plant material, mostly dead. The larvae develop in the phloem of slash and in the roots of dead conifers. On Vancouver Island and on the Queen Charlotte Islands, British Columbia, the adults have caused economic damage by girdling 1- and 2-year-old seedlings at the ground line (fig. 206A). Douglas-fir and Sitka spruce are preferred but hemlock and true fir also are attacked. The rough-surfaced, dirt-colored adults (fig. 206B) have scattered patches of rusty scales and are 7 to 10 mm long. Development to maturity requires 1 to 2 years. Adults can live 3 or more years and continue to lay eggs each spring.

Steremnius tuberosus Gyllenhal is a somewhat larger, rougher, weevil with similar distribution and habits.

Thricolepis inornata Horn, 3 mm long, is brown with gray scales (fig. 207) and resembles *Agronus cinerarius*. Normally it feeds on oak, but sometimes nearly defoliates fruit trees close to oaks by feeding on the new leaves of opening buds. Adult weevils have been found seriously injuring tender new foliage on tips of white fir, Douglas-fir, and blue spruce, temporarily ruining such trees for use as Christmas trees. Larval habits are not recorded. This weevil occurs in Oregon, California, Utah, Arizona, and New Mexico.

Thysanocnemis sp. (Keen 1958) is a small yellow weevil, 2.5 to 4 mm long, which lays its eggs in a puncture on the young developing seeds of ash. The tiny larvae penetrate the seed without leaving a visible sign, and the small, white, legless larvae develop within the seed coat, completely consuming the cotyledons.

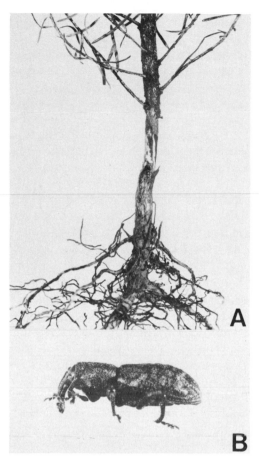

A

B

COURTESY CANADIAN FORESTRY SERVICE

FIGURE 206.—A root-collar weevil, *Steremnius carinatus*: *A*, Girdling of Douglas-fir nursery stock by the adult; *B*, adult, 8 mm long.

F-523464

FIGURE 207.—Adult of a weevil, *Thricolepis inornata*, 3 mm long.

The full-grown larvae leave the seed late in the fall or winter to pupate in the ground, from which they emerge as adults late in June and throughout July. Sometimes over 60 percent of the seed crop is thus destroyed. This weevil has been reared from Oregon ash in California, Oregon, and Washington.

FAMILY PLATYPODIDAE

The Platypodidae are elongate, cylindrical, broad-headed beetles, closely related to the Scolytidae. They are abundant in the tropics. Seven species occur in America north of Mexico; all of them are in the genus *Platypus* and all are ambrosia beetles (Baker 1963). Three of them infest western conifers. Their mines penetrate into the heartwood in contrast with most ambrosia beetles in the Scolytidae which mine only the sapwood. The larvae and adults of native *Platypus* feed upon ambrosia fungi which are stored and disseminated by the adult female.

Platypus wilsoni Swaine (Prebble and Graham 1957) ranges from British Columbia to California and eastward into Idaho. It attacks weakened, injured, recently dead, and felled true firs, western hemlock, Douglas-fir, and occasionally other conifers. The gallery winds through the sapwood and often penetrates deeply into the heartwood (fig. 208A). At intervals along the main tunnel secondary tunnels branch horizontally. This species is not very abundant, hence it is not of much economic importance. It is a reddish-brown, shiny beetle about 5.5 mm long and with long yellowish hairs on the body. The female is smooth and rounded behind and the male is forked and spiny (fig. 208B).

In coastal British Columbia attacks are made from mid-July to mid-September. The male initiates the boring. The eggs are laid loosely in the tunnel in clusters of about 20 to 40. The larvae travel and feed freely in the mines. Larvae and adults overwinter in the logs. Larval development requires a year or more. When full grown, the larvae excavate cells at right angles to the main gallery and parallel to the grain of the wood in which to transform to pupae and adults. Within its range this beetle can be identified by its splinterlike borings (Johnson 1958) (fig. 209A). *Raffaelea canadensis* Batra (Batra 1967), the symbiotic fungus upon which this species feeds, is stored and disseminated by the female.

Platypus abietis Wood (Wood 1958b), a smaller species that resembles *P. wilsoni*, attacks *Abies concolor* in Utah, Arizona, and New Mexico.

FIGURE 208. — *Platypus wilsoni*: *A*, Tunnels in true fir; *B*, male adult, 5.5 mm long.

Platypus pini Hopkins (Wood 1958b) occurs in Arizona and New Mexico principally on *Pinus ponderosa*. It also is recorded on *P. leiophylla*.

FAMILY SCOLYTIDAE—BARK BEETLES

The Scolytidae (Bright and Stark 1973, Chamberlin 1939, Hopkins 1915b, Rudinsky 1962, Swaine 1918, Wood 1961) are related to the Curculionidae and some of the genera are quite similar in appearance, for example, *Hylastes* of the Scolytidae and *Rhyncolus* of the Curculionidae. In this manual the Scolytidae are grouped in two subfamilies, Hylesininae and Scolytinae, as proposed by Wood (1973).

Bark beetles are the most destructive insects in western coniferous forests. These beetles kill billions of board feet of sawtimber annually in the Western United States (USDA Forest Service 1958). Four species of *Dendroctonus*—western pine beetle, mountain pine beetle, Douglas fir beetle, and spruce beetle—cause most of this destruction. West-wide, most of the time, the greater portion of the killing is the result of normal or endemic infestations that are continuously present in mature forests. This normal mortality is widely scattered and usually is greatest in undeveloped areas; hence salvage of the dead timber is costly. Under conditions favorable for the beetles, epidemics occasionally develop and spread over large areas, killing vast amounts of timber (table 1)

339

and setting the stage for devastating fires. This is one of Nature's wholesale ways of renewing the forest, but it is highly disruptive to orderly management for man's use.

Bark beetles are so named because most of them live and mine between the bark and wood of trees and shrubs. The most destructive ones attack the main stem of living trees. Many live in the branches and twigs. Some live in cones and some in roots. The ambrosia beetles and a few others mine in wood. One species breeds in mistletoe; one species, in the roots of clover; and one genus, in wild gourds.

Species that attack and kill trees of normal vigor are said to be primary. Fortunately they are few. Even the primary killers usually prefer trees of reduced growth rate. Outbreaks develop when conditions are adverse for the host tree, as in drought periods, or when an abundance of favorable breeding material is available to the beetles, as in large burns and extensive blowdowns. Secondary bark beetles are those that attack dead or dying trees and very often trees previously attacked by primary species. Bark beetles that breed in twigs and branches without appreciable harm to living trees are also termed secondaries.

If bark beetle attacks are to be successful, the attacking insects must be present in sufficient numbers to overcome the resistance of the tree. Some trees are more resistant than others, or perhaps it would be better to say that some trees are more susceptible and readily overcome than others. There is some difference of opinion as to how the beetles select a tree for attack. The consensus seems to be that pioneer beetles attack at random and, when successful, create an attraction for others that flock in and make the main attack. In some genera, such as *Dendroctonus* and *Ips*, the attraction is created by potent chemicals, pheromones (Borden 1974), given off by attacking beetles and enhanced by volatile emissions from the host tree. These pheromones also attract insects that prey upon the bark beetles. Once fully established, some bark beetles give off pheromones that repel further attack. Some bark beetles carry spores of fungi which help their brood overcome a tree and which begin the process of deterioration and ultimate reconversion to the soil (Graham 1967).

In starting an attack, the beetle bores a tunnel through the bark. In pines, this often starts a flow of pitch which may form into a tube around the entrance. As the gallery system is extended beneath the bark, the beetle often pushes boring dust out through the entrance. When the tree is overcome, the pitch flow ceases but the borings usually continue for a while. Pitch tubes and boring dust are among the earliest signs of attack by bark beetles and serve to distinguish them from most other borers. The foliage

340

of fatally attacked trees changes color and dies, but this may not occur before the brood has developed and flown.

Bark beetle adults are small, compact, cylindrical insects ranging in size from 1 mm long for *Crypturgus* to about 8 mm for the largest *Dendroctonus*. Their antennae are elbowed and the outer segments are enlarged and clublike. Most species are brown or black, and dull or shining. Some have variegated markings comprised of grayish or brownish scales. The head, which is partially to completely hidden from above by the thorax, has strong gouge-like jaws (mandibles) for boring.

Adults of species that rear their brood in the cambium region bore through the bark and make a tunnel between the bark and the wood in which they lay their eggs. Some tunnels have an enlarged area (nuptial chamber) near the entrance. The larvae mine out from the egg tunnel. The egg tunnels and larval mines together often form a characteristic pattern that will identify the genus and sometimes the species, even after the beetles have flown (Swaine 1918).

The eggs are very small, smooth, oval, and whitish. They are deposited singly in niches or in groups along the egg tunnels.

The larvae are grublike, thick-bodied, legless, generally broadly C-shaped, and white or cream colored, and have a distinct head and prominent mandibles. At first the larvae and their mines are very small, but both increase in size as feeding progresses. The larval mines tend to radiate out from the egg gallery. They are always packed with frass.

Transformation to the pupal and adult stages takes place at the end of the larval mine in a specially constructed cell. The pupae are soft, white, and naked. The newly formed immature adults are soft and yellowish. Gradually they harden and darken to full maturity before taking flight.

The adults, after spending a variable time under the bark of the host tree, bore out through the bark, leaving the surface as though riddled by buckshot. Once emerged, the adults may drop to the ground and hibernate there, may feed for a time upon twigs and buds, or may fly directly to the new host tree and begin the life cycle again.

In the West, millions of dollars have been spent on measures to control the western pine beetle (Miller and Keen 1960), mountain pine beetle, spruce beetle (Wygant 1958), and other bark beetles. Much of this effort was during severe outbreaks on extensive unroaded areas at a time when little of the dead and threatened timber could be utilized. Mostly the objective was to protect mature timber on the stump until it could be harvested. On many areas, the extent of outbreaks and the resilience of bark beetle

341

populations made lasting control unattainable. With general opening of commercial forests, development of modern logging equipment, and greatly increased demand for timber, the emphasis has shifted to prevention through stand improvement measures and to salvage when outbreaks occur. Conversion of overmature forests to young vigorous forests has greatly reduced hazards on many areas. For more than two decades, precipitation has been generally adequate for healthy tree growth on areas where lengthy drought previously had been a powerful stimulant for killing by bark beetles. Research on new methods of control, such as the use of pheromones, continues.

Bark beetles still create serious problems. Recurrent drought and attendant bark beetle outbreaks are an ever-present threat. Even young forests, especially overstocked ones, may at times be heavily damaged. Extensive timber-producing forests still are uncut and highly susceptible to bark beetles. Large areas reserved from timber harvesting are subject to outbreaks and are a source for spread to commercial stands. Trees on intensive use areas, as in campgrounds and around homes, often become attractive to bark beetles, and because of their high value, require costly measures for protection (USDA 1972).

Ambrosia beetles (Hubbard 1897) are important enemies of forest products because of their ability to riddle unseasoned wood with small round pinholes or shotholes. These holes often become surrounded with a dark brown or black stain, which causes additional degrade. The beetles of this destructive group derive their name from the symbiotic fungi that they feed upon (Baker 1963). They belong to the Scolytidae and Platypodidae. In the Scolytidae of the West, they consist of *Trypodendron*, *Gnathotrichus*, *Monarthrum*, and *Xyleborus*.

Adult ambrosia beetles are small, reddish-brown to nearly black, cylindrical beetles that select for their attack weakened, recently dead, and freshly felled trees, sawlogs, green lumber, or other unseasoned or moist wood such as stave bolts and wine casks. Small round tunnels are bored directly into the sapwood and sometimes into the heartwood. Since the beetles do not feed on the wood, the borings are cast out of the tunnels and collect on the surface of the bark or wood as a fine, light-colored powder. The character of the tunnels varies with different species. Some construct an open cavity; others a long, winding, branched or unbranched cylindrical gallery in which the larvae move about freely; while others construct what is called a compound tunnel, with small pockets or larval cradles gnawed along the main channel. The borings and the character of the tunnels aid in identify-

342

ing the principal species in a local area or particular forest type (Johnson 1958) (fig. 209).

Ambrosia fungi are of several genera, including *Ambrosiella* and *Raffaelea*. The fungi are stored in specialized structures (mycangia), usually in the female, and are introduced into the galleries during the burrowing process. Each fungus is associated with one or relatively few species of beetle (Batra 1967). As the fungi grow, they are fed upon by the adult beetles and the developing larvae. The requirements of these insects are very exacting. If moisture conditions are not suitable the fungi fail and the beetles starve; or, if the fungi grow too abundantly, the beetles are unable to cope with them and are smothered in their own food. For this reason only moist, unseasoned wood is suitable for attack, and dried seasoned lumber is immune.

Pinholes and staining caused by ambrosia beetles may seriously degrade high quality logs, thus causing heavy financial losses. Damage is greatest in coastal forests, having temperature and moisture conditions that are favorable for ambrosia beetle development. In British Columbia, species of *Trypodendron* and *Gnathotrichus* cause essentially all the damage (Prebble and Graham 1957). Ambrosia beetles are common in coniferous forests

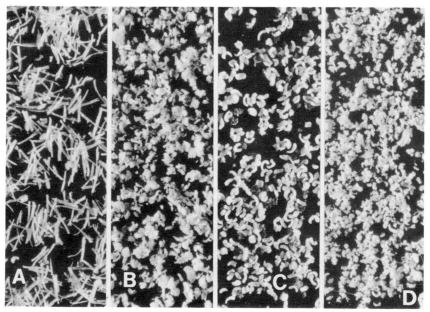

FIGURE 209.—Borings of different genera of ambrosia beetles: *A, Platypus*; *B, Trypodendron*; *C, Gnathotrichus*; *D, Xyleborus* (greatly enlarged).

throughout the West, but in the drier areas they are not reported to cause significant damage.

The control of ambrosia beetles is largely a matter of prevention of damage through woods-practices and proper handling of milled wood (Fisher et al. 1954). There are three principal ways of preventing attacks on logs: (1) Mill or at least debark susceptible logs prior to the attack period, (2) store logs in an area safe from attack, or (3) spray with a suitable chemical. Great care in the application of chemicals is necessary to prevent contamination of water. Logs in the woods generally are safe from attack from October until March (Mathers 1935). Freshly-sawed lumber will be safe from attack if it is dried quickly. Damage may occur in storage if the lumber is piled so as to remain or become moist. Logs or wood either heavily soaked with water or quite dry are not suitable for attack, but the exposed parts of logs left floating in ponds are likely to become infested. In general, the control of these beetles is very difficult, and prompt utilization or kiln drying of the lumber is about the only satisfactory solution. Parasitism has been noted in studies of these beetles in seasoned products, but it is not sufficient to reduce appreciably the number of beetles and the injury they cause.

Hylesininae—The body form of adults is typified by *Dendroctonus* and *Pseudohylesinus*. The front margin of the elytra is raised and notched; the pronotum usually is unarmed; and the head usually is visible from above.

The genus *Alniphagus* contains two species in western North America. Neither is a pest requiring control. They are the principal and largest scolytids that bore between the bark and wood of alder. The adults (fig. 210) are medium-sized bark beetles that somewhat resemble *Phloeosinus*. Their thorax and wing covers are strongly and sharply granulate.

The **alder bark beetle**, *Alniphagus aspericollis* (LeConte) (Borden 1969), attacks *Alnus rubra* and other alders from California to Idaho, British Columbia, and presumably Alaska. The adults and larvae mine in the inner bark. Egg galleries usually are a single channel, roughly parallel to the grain of the wood, and

COURTESY J. H. BORDEN (1969),
PHOTO BY H. SEVERSON,
AGRIC. CANADA

FIGURE 210.—Alder bark beetle (*Alniphagus aspericollis*), adult, 4.5 mm long.

about 8 cm long; some are V-shaped. The larval mines meander without pattern. Injured, decadent, dying, and down trees are attacked. There are two generations per year.

Alniphagus hirsutus Schedl is a somewhat smaller species. It is recorded on *Alnus tenuifolia* and *A. sinuata* and is distributed from California to British Columbia.

Carphoborus (Wood 1954b) contains 19 species in North America; all except two are western. They breed in the inner bark of dead and dying branches of *Pinus, Picea,* and *Pseudotsuga*. None is a pest. All are polygamous. The egg galleries etch the sapwood and several radiate from each nuptial chamber, an enlarged opening off the entrance tunnel. The adults are brownish to black, 1.5 to 3 mm long, and abundantly clothed with small scales. The eyes are deeply emarginate in front. Alternate interspaces on the declivity of the elytra usually are elevated.

Carphoborus carri Swaine is one of seven species that attack *Picea*. It occurs in Yukon and Northwest Territories to Alberta, Wyoming, and South Dakota.

Carphoborus pinicolens Wood is the most widely distributed and abundant species. It occurs from Oregon and California to Wyoming, Colorado, and New Mexico. Recorded hosts are *Pinus edulis, P. flexilis, P. lambertiana, P. leiophylla, P. monophylla,* and *P. ponderosa*.

Carphoborus vandykei Bruck occurs on *Pseudotsuga menziesii* from central California to British Columbia.

Chaetophloeus [*Renocis*] (Blackman 1940) contains nine species in North America. They occur principally in arid and semi-arid regions of the Southwest, attacking the branches and stems of dead and injured shrubs and small trees. None is a forest pest. The adults are stout, scale-covered beetles about 2 mm long and have minute teeth (asperites) on the sides of the pronotum. The larvae bore beneath the bark, deeply scoring the sapwood. Two or more successive generations may develop in the same host material.

The **mountain mahogany bark beetle**, *Chaetophloeus heterodoxus* (Casey), is the species most likely to be seen by foresters. It ranges from California to British Columbia and eastward to Manitoba and west Texas. Most commonly it attacks injured, weakened, and recently dead branches and stems of *Cercocarpus. Amelanchier, Prunus,* and various desert shrubs also are attacked, but less commonly. The larval mines strongly etch the sapwood (fig. 211).

Some other species that foresters may encounter are *Chaetophloeus fasciatus* Blackman in *Prosopis* in Arizona, *C. parkinsoniae* Blackman in *Cercidium* in Arizona, and *C. penicillatus* in *Rhus* in California, Arizona, Utah, and Colorado.

FIGURE 211.—Larval mines of the mountain mahogany bark beetle
(*Chaetophloeus heterodoxus*).

Chramesus (Blackman 1938) contains eight species in North
America, four of them in Southwestern States. They breed
between the bark and wood of dead and dying branches of deciduous trees, including species of *Quercus, Robinia, Rhamnus,* and
Celtis. The adults are about 2 mm long and humpbacked. The
antennal club is large, flat, and unsegmented. *C. asperatus*
Schaeffer is representative of this little-known genus. It occurs in
Arizona attacking *Robinia neomexicana* and also is recorded from
southern California.

Members of the genus *Dendroctonus* (meaning tree killers)
(Hopkins 1909, Wood 1963) are by far the most destructive group
of bark beetles in North America. Twelve species occur in the
West. Most of them are significant in forest management, hence
practicing foresters should recognize and take into account the
ones in their area and forest type. All species breed under the bark
of the trunk of living or dying trees or in fresh stumps or logs of
various conifers. Some species attack only felled, weak, or dying
trees, whereas others attack and kill apparently healthy trees,
especially during epidemics.

The adults are stout, cylindrical, dark, reddish-brown to black
bark beetles ranging from about 3 to 8 mm in length. The eggs,

346

larvae, and pupae are similar to those of other bark beetles (Thomas 1965). *Dendroctonus* adults work in pairs, boring through the bark and then extending an egg gallery between the bark and wood. Egg galleries differ by species of beetle. Some wind in a tortuous manner, crossing and recrossing the galleries made by other pairs of beetles, while others are straight and parallel to the grain of the wood. *Dendroctonus* egg galleries are always packed with boring dust, except for the portion where the parent beetles are working. This will distinguish the work of the *Dendroctonus* beetles from that of most other groups of bark beetles.

Trees attacked by *Dendroctonus* beetles can at first be detected by reddish boring dust caught in bark flakes or crevices and around the base of the tree, or by pitch tubes that form on the bark at the mouth of the entrance tunnels, but in heavily attacked or decadent trees pitch tubes are often either missing or so small that they can be seen only from a short distance. Later, discoloration of the foliage furnishes a more noticeable evidence of attack. It is difficult, however, to correlate accurately the discoloration with the status of brood development, as this varies with different tree species, regions, and seasons. Sometimes trees don't discolor until after the brood have matured and flown away. The most conclusive evidence of attack is the egg and larval galleries on the inner surface of the bark. These form a pattern so characteristic for the work of each species that, when considered with locality and host tree, the identification of the species responsible for the attack is relatively certain.

The **roundheaded pine beetle**, *Dendroctonus adjunctus* Blandford (= *convexifrons* Hopkins) (Chansler 1967, Stevens and Flake 1974, Wood 1963), occurs in Colorado, Utah, Nevada, Arizona, New Mexico, and southward in Mexico. In the Southwest, especially in New Mexico, it is destructive in stands of overstocked, pole-sized ponderosa pine. In southern Nevada, mature and overmature ponderosa pines have been extensively killed by this beetle on high-use areas. Limber pine, Chihuahua pine, and several Mexican pines also are recorded hosts. Outbreaks are sporadic and short-lived. Attacks are made in the basal portion of the bole, often in trees previously attacked by other species of *Dendroctonus* or by species of *Ips*. In dense young stands, trees usually are killed in groups of 3 to 15; sometimes up to 100. Recently felled trees also are attacked.

In southern New Mexico, there is one generation annually; attacks are made principally in October and November; eggs and parents overwinter. The foliage of attacked trees fades the following May or June. From the entrance hole, the egg gallery extends horizontally in the cambium region, either left or right, for 25 to 50 mm and then winds longitudinally with the grain an average distance of 300 mm. Galleries of neighboring pairs often cross, but retain an overall longitudinal pattern. Eggs are laid individually in niches on alternate sides of the egg gallery. The larvae mine across the grain in the cambium region until the third instar, then they bore into the outer bark to complete development. The adult is dark brown, averages about 5 mm long, and is similar to *D. ponderosae* but is more slender.

Penetrating oil spray has been used for direct control on high-use areas. Thinning and control of dwarf mistletoe in dense young stands of commercial forest likely will minimize potential killing by this beetle.

The **larger Mexican pine beetle**, *Dendroctonus approximatus* Dietz (= *parallelocollis* not Chapuis) (Wood 1963), occurs in Colorado, Utah, Arizona, New Mexico, and southward in Mexico. Hosts are *Pinus ponderosa, P. engelmannii, P. leiophylla,* and several Mexican pines. It is a secondary species, attacking near the base of trees infested by *D. ponderosae, D. adjunctus, D. brevicomis,* and species of *Ips*. It also attacks injured trees and the lower side of recently-down trees.

D. approximatus resembles *D. adjunctus*, but generally is larger and the gallery pattern is different. The adult Mexican pine beetle is dark brown to black and averages about 6 mm long. The individual egg gallery is elongate, winding, and much branched. Overall, the galleries form a crisscross network. Unlike other species of *Dendroctonus*, the eggs of *D. approximatus* are laid in niches on the bark side of the gallery rather than in contact with the cambium. The larval mines and pupal cells are entirely in the bark. Flight occurs from June to October, causing the attacks to be correspondingly strung out rather than concentrated. Adults and larvae overwinter. There is one generation annually. Direct control is unnecessary.

The **western pine beetle**, *Dendroctonus brevicomis* LeConte (= *barberi* Hopkins) (Keen 1955, Wood 1963), is periodically destructive to ponderosa pine and Coulter pine. It occurs in California, Oregon, Washington, British Columbia, Idaho, Montana, Nevada, Utah, Colorado, Arizona, and New Mexico. Normally this beetle breeds in overmature trees, in windfalls, in root-rotted trees (Cobb et al. 1974), or in trees weakened by drought, stand stagnation, or fires. Under epidemic conditions it becomes aggressive and kills apparently vigorous trees of all ages having bark sufficiently thick to protect the insect in its development. Trees

348

under 15 cm (6 in) in diameter are seldom attacked, nor does this beetle breed in limbs. During the severe drought of the 1920's and 1930's, losses up to 60 to 90 percent of the ponderosa pine forest on extensive areas were recorded. Many stands of prime timber were ruined for commercial harvest. The heaviest losses of mature ponderosa pine have resulted from outbreaks of this insect in California, Oregon, and Washington. It is less important in the northern and southwestern portions of its range.

The western pine beetle is similar to *D. frontalis* but differs in having uniformly short hairs on the elytral declivity and in part by its distribution. The adult *D. brevicomis* is dark brown and about 3.0 to 5.0 mm long; other life stages are typical of bark beetles in general (fig. 212).

Flight and attacks start late in spring or early in summer and continue until stopped by cold weather. Parent females produce from one to three broods, causing much overlapping of generations. On the average there are three main periods of attack, hence survey and control crews recognize "spring," "summer," and "winter" broods. In the biological sense, there are one to two generations annually in the northern part of the range and from two and one-half to four generations in the southern portion, where activity continues almost without interruption throughout the year.

Initial attacks on a standing tree are made about mid-bole and subsequent attacks fill in above and below. Inconspicuous pitch tubes and red boring dust are indications of success in overcoming a tree. The galleries of individual pairs wind both laterally and longitudinally and are much branched. These galleries cross and recross each other in a mazelike pattern (fig. 213), much like *D. frontalis*. The larvae feed in the inner bark, working away from the egg gallery for about 12 mm and then turn into the outer bark, where they complete their development. Following success-

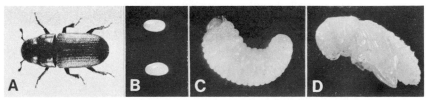

F-523466, F-523467, F-523468, F-523469

FIGURE 212.—Life stages of western pine beetle (*Dendroctonus brevicomis*): A, Adult, 4 mm long; B, eggs, 0.9 mm long; C, larva, 5 mm long; D, pupa, 5 mm long.

EPQ–6800

FIGURE 213.—Western pine beetle egg galleries on surface of sapwood of infested ponderosa pine.

ful beetle attacks, blue-stain fungi invade the sapwood. Of these, *Ceratocystis minor* (Hedg.) Hunt may play a pathogenic role. For detailed information on the biology and control of the western pine beetle, one should consult the comprehensive summary by Miller and Keen (1960).

The western pine beetle frequently attacks a tree jointly with other insects, notably *Ips pini*, *I. paraconfusus*, and *Melanophila californica* in the top; *Dendroctonus ponderosae* and *Ips emarginatus* in the midbole; and *Dendroctonus adjunctus* and *D. valens* at the base. Sometimes the top-killing associates attack first, thus providing favorable breeding material for epidemic buildup of the western pine beetle.

Woodpeckers, *Enoclerus lecontei*, and *Temnochila chlorodia* are natural enemies of the western pine beetle. Many other insects and other small organisms are associated with this beetle in various ways (Stark et al. 1970). Abundance of the western pine beetle is most often determined by climatic influences and the resistance of the host tree. Winter temperatures of −29° C (−20° F) and lower have been found to cause heavy brood mortality. Rapid, vigorous tree growth increases host resistance and discourages epidemics.

During an extended drought in the 1920's and 1930's, this beetle was widely epidemic in the Pacific Coast States. Direct control, largely by felling infested trees and burning the bark, was applied to protect commercial stands for later harvest (Miller and Keen 1960). Control measures were repeatedly applied because the beetle bred prolifically in the drought-stricken trees. Epidemic conditions continued prevalent until the 1940's when rainfall increased and tree vigor improved. Since then, lesser outbreaks have occurred or threatened from time to time. Sanitation-salvage logging is the measure now generally applied to minimize losses caused by the western pine beetle. High-risk trees are removed from the stand and utilized, thus depriving the beetles of favorable breeding material (Keen 1943). The use of pheromones in control is under intensive study but has not been developed to the stage of practical use. In parks and in other areas of intensive use, direct control still appears to be the measure of last resort in curbing this beetle.

The **southern pine beetle**, *Dendroctonus frontalis* Zimmerman (= *arizonicus* Hopkins) (Bennett and Ciesla 1971, Dixon and Osgood 1961), is a very destructive enemy of pines in the Southeastern and Gulf States. In Arizona and New Mexico it attacks ponderosa pine, Chihuahua pine, and Apache pine, but is not recorded as a serious pest in those States. The adults are dark brown, average about 3 mm long, and resemble *D. brevicomis*. They differ in that the hairs on the elytral declivity are sparse and much longer than the width of an interspace; whereas those of *D. brevicomis* are abundant and much shorter than the width of an interspace. The long winding egg galleries of *D. frontalis* cross and recross each other, giving a labyrinthlike effect very similar to the gallery pattern of *D. brevicomis*. A notable difference is that the pupal cells of *D. frontalis* frequently show on the inner bark surface; those of *D. brevicomis* do not.

The southern pine beetle has four to seven generations each year in the Southeastern and Gulf States. Outbreaks characteristically develop and subside rapidly. A blue-stain fungus, *Ceratocystis minor* Hedgc.) Hunt, occurs symbiotically with *D. frontalis*, each of these organisms apparently helping the other overcome a tree. In the Southwest, the biology of the southern pine beetle is presumed similar to that in the Southeast and South, but the generations likely are fewer.

The **Jeffrey pine beetle,** *Dendroctonus jeffreyi* Hopkins (Smith 1971), is the most destructive bark beetle enemy of Jeffrey pine which is its only host. In the period 1930-1970, it killed about 55 million fbm annually in California. Normally it breeds in scattered individual mature and overmature trees that are retarded in growth rate. It also attacks lightning-struck trees and recently windthrown trees but does not breed in slash. During epidemics it kills groups of up to 20 to 30 trees regardless of age or vigor.

The adult Jeffrey pine beetle is very similar to that of *D. ponderosae,* but generally is somewhat larger (Lanier and Wood 1968). The gallery pattern also is similar. There is a slight turn at the bottom of the egg gallery, which then proceeds up the tree in nearly a straight line following the grain of the wood. These galleries are usually 60 to 180 cm long and are packed with boring dust. The eggs are placed in individual niches in alternating groups along the sides of the galleries, and the larvae work out from the egg gallery across the grain of the wood. The pupal cells are formed in the inner bark and are exposed to view when the bark is removed.

As a rule, this beetle attacks the middle and lower bole of trees 30 cm (1 ft) or more in diameter but sometimes attacks trees considerably smaller. The entrance holes usually are in bark crevices. Initial attacks are marked by pitch tubes, later ones by reddish borings. A high percentage of trees killed by *D. jeffreyi* are previously attacked in the top by *Melanophila californica* and some by *Ips pini*. Attacks occur principally in June and July but continue into October. Larvae and adults overwinter. One generation per year is normal in the northern part of its range; two may occur in the southern part.

Logging of high-risk trees is a practical measure for minimizing kill by the Jeffrey pine beetle and thus extending the life of old-growth stands. High-risk trees can be recognized by their poor vigor, declining growth rate, dying tops and branches, and short sparse foliage. Lightning-struck, recently windthrown, and currently infested trees should be promptly salvaged and converted to lumber before the attacking beetles emerge. When an outbreak exceeds salvage capacity, it sometimes is necessary to destroy the brood by felling and burning the infested trees, peeling the bark, or spraying with chemicals. Such direct control measures are applied during the fall, winter, and early spring.

The **lodgepole pine beetle**, *Dendroctonus murrayanae* Hopkins (Wood 1963), breeds in *Pinus contorta* and *P. banksiana*. The western distribution includes Alberta, British Columbia, Idaho, Montana, Wyoming, Colorado, and Utah. It mines in the lower bole and root crown of overmature, injured, and weakened trees and in fresh stumps and windfalls. Characteristically nonagressive, it occasionally kills overmature lodgepole pines left standing after timber harvesting. Normally only a few pairs attack a tree and two or more generations may be required to girdle and kill it. Some trees survive attacks.

The lodgepole pine beetle is very similar to *D. punctatus* and *D. rufipennis*, both of which attack spruces. The adult of *D. murrayanae* is black with reddish-brown elytra and averages about 6 mm long. On living trees, the attacks are marked by large pitch tubes. Upon reaching the cambium, the attacking female constructs an irregularly vertical gallery averaging about 12 cm long. Eggs are laid in groups of 20 to 50 along both sides of the gallery. The larvae feed away from the egg gallery, keeping together in a common excavation or brood chamber between the bark and the wood. Transformation to pupae and adults takes place in the uneaten part of the inner bark or in cocoonlike structures composed of frass in the brood chamber. In Utah one complete generation and a partial second annually appear to be the rule. Farther north, the life cycle presumably takes longer. No direct control of this beetle is recorded and none seems needed.

The **mountain pine beetle**, *Dendroctonus ponderosae* Hopkins (= *monticolae* Hopkins) (Blackman 1931c, Evenden et al. 1943, McCambridge and Trostle 1972, Wood 1963), ranks first in destructiveness among the bark beetles of the West. It ranges throughout the pine forest of British Columbia, Alberta, and the Western States into northern Mexico. *Pinus contorta, P. lambertiana, P. monticola, P. ponderosa,* and *P. albicaulis* are its principal hosts. *P. aristata, P. balfouriana, P. coulteri, P. edulis, P. flexilis, P. monophylla,* and several other pines are recorded hosts. In lodgepole pine, the mountain pine beetle infests mature forests, often decimating them over extensive areas. In ponderosa, western white, and sugar pines, group killing (fig. 214), often on a

FIGURE 214.—Group killing of ponderosa pine by mountain pine beetle (*Dendroctonus ponderosae*) in the Black Hills National Forest, S. Dak.

large scale, occurs both in mature forests and in young over-stocked stands. Mostly, this beetle is a primary killer, but at times it occurs as a secondary, for example in association with *D. brevi-comis.*

An outbreak of the mountain pine beetle from 1894 to 1908 in ponderosa pine in the Black Hills of South Dakota first called public attention to the extensive killing by bark beetles in the West. Between 1 and 2 billion fbm of pine were killed in that early outbreak. Since then many other outbreaks of the mountain pine beetle have occurred. Among the most noteworthy were the Kaibab, Ariz., outbreak of 1917 to 1926 that killed 300 million fbm of ponderosa pine and the series of outbreaks from 1925 to 1935 in Idaho and Montana that killed more than 7 billion fbm of lodge-pole pine and vast numbers of whitebark pine. Western white pine in Idaho and sugar pine in California have repeatedly suffered heavy losses caused by this beetle. Somewhere in the West it is epidemic almost continually in one or more of its principal hosts.

Trees from 10 to 12.5 cm (4 to 5 in) in diameter up to those of the largest size may be attacked by the mountain pine beetle.

Attacks are usually heaviest along the main trunk of a tree from within a meter or so of the ground up to the middle branches but may extend from the root collar very nearly to the top and into the larger limbs. During endemic infestations there is a tendency for the beetles to select the weaker, less vigorous trees for attack, but no such selection is evident during epidemic conditions. Infested trees are recognized first by pitch tubes on their trunk and red boring dust in bark crevices and on the ground at the roots; later, by discoloration of the foliage, as it changes from normal green to light greenish yellow, and then to reddish brown. The wood of successfully attacked trees soon becomes heavily blue-stained by *Ceratocystis montia* (Rumb.) Hunt.

The adults of *Dendroctonus ponderosae* are rather stout, black, cylindrical beetles 4 to 7.5 mm long and practically identical to those of *D. jeffreyi*. They excavate very long, perpendicular egg galleries (fig. 215) through the inner living bark, engraving both bark and wood. The galleries may be nearly straight or slightly sinuous, and, sometimes, particularly in sugar pine, decidedly winding, and at the bottom of these galleries there is a short crook, or bend, 25 or 50 mm (1 or 2 in) in length. The perpendicular portion of the gallery ranges in length from 30 to 90 cm (12 to 36 in) and nearly always follows the grain of the wood.

Eggs are deposited singly in niches in groups on alternate sides during the construction of the egg gallery. These hatch in a few days, and the small white larvae excavate short feeding tunnels at right angles to the egg gallery. These feeding tunnels vary in length and are exposed on the inner bark surface. When fully grown, the larvae construct small pupal cells at the ends of the larval mines and in these transform to pupae and then to new adults. These pupal cells are usually exposed when the bark is removed, but in thick-bark trees they may be concealed in the inner bark. The new adults may bore away the intervening bark between pupal cells and congregate beneath the bark, prior to emergence from a common exit, or individual emergence holes may be constructed directly from the pupal cells. Emerging beetles also take advantage of cracks in the bark or holes made by woodpeckers.

The life cycle of the mountain pine beetle varies considerably over its wide and diverse range. One generation per year is the general rule. In portions of California, two and a partial third generation may develop, and in the coldest portions of its range, one generation may require 2 years. Larvae and adults are the overwintering stages.

Several natural factors affect the abundance of the mountain pine beetle, including sub-zero winter temperatures; nematodes;

FIGURE 215.—Long vertical egg galleries of mountain pine beetle (*Dendroctonus ponderosae*).

woodpeckers; predaceous insects such as *Enoclerus sphegeus, Temnochila chlorodia,* and *Medetera aldrichii*; and the insect parasite *Coeloides dendroctoni*. As stand susceptibility to the beetle increases, the effectiveness of natural control decreases and outbreaks develop. This points to the desirability of harvesting susceptible stands prior to outbreaks or relieving stand stress as in the thinning of dense young ponderosa pine. Control of outbreaks by logging infested timber is good in theory but has proven of limited usefulness because of the large areas to be intensively covered in a brief time and because of the high cost. Direct control measures, such as felling and burning or peeling, and treating with oil or chemical sprays, were used for decades in many parts of the West. These measures now are considered generally uneconomical. This has led to a search for new methods. One such method being tested operationally is to concentrate the beetles during flight by the use of pheromone-baited traps (Pitman 1971).

The **Douglas fir beetle,** *Dendroctonus pseudotsugae* Hopkins (Furniss and Orr 1970, Walters 1956, Wood 1963), is the most important bark beetle enemy of Douglas-fir throughout the range of this tree in western North America. It also attacks western larch but produces brood only in down trees. Normally it breeds in felled, injured, or diseased trees. The resulting endemic mortality is large in amount but widely scattered. At times, *D. pseudotsugae* becomes epidemic and kills apparently healthy trees on extensive areas. In the coastal Douglas fir region from British Columbia to northern California, outbreaks are sporadic and of short duration but are likely to kill large amounts of timber. Usually they develop following extensive windthrow or large fires. In Rocky Mountain forests, outbreaks usually are of longer duration and commonly develop in trees felled by wind, broken by snow, or affected by drought.

Reddish or yellowish boring dust caught in bark crevices or around the base of trees is the usual evidence of attack by the Douglas fir beetle. No pitch tube is formed but resin may exude from the upper attacks. The foliage of attacked trees turns yellow, then sorrel, and finally reddish brown in late summer, in fall, or in early spring, depending upon the region, time of attack, and weather. Viewed from the air these "redtops" provide a means for assessing an outbreak (Greeley et al. 1953).

Adult Douglas fir beetles are dark brown to black with reddish elytra, rather hairy, 4.4 to 7.0 mm long, and similar to the smaller *D. simplex* and the more robust *D. rufipennis,* but distinguished from both by host. Douglas fir beetles work in pairs and construct egg galleries which are mostly in the inner bark, though they also slightly etch the sapwood. Typical galleries are perpendicular, usually straight or slightly sinuous, and average about 30 cm long, though they range about 12 cm to more than 90 cm. The first 2.5 to 5.0 cm of gallery angles to the side as with *D. ponderosae.* The eggs are pearl-white, about 1.2 mm long, and without surface markings. They are laid in masses of 10 to 36 in grooves at intervals along alternate sides of the gallery (fig. 216A). The larval mines diverge from the egg groups and are extended through the inner bark close to the wood. They expand as the larvae grow, so the completed work from each group of eggs is somewhat fan-shaped (fig. 216B). The pupal cells, which are constructed at the ends of the larval mines, may be exposed when the bark is removed from the tree, or they may be concealed in it, depending on the thickness of the bark. In these cells the transformation from larvae to pupae and then to new adults takes place. The new adults bore away the intervening bark between pupal cells and congregate, sometimes for rather long periods, beneath the bark. Finally they bore through the bark to the surface, emerge, and fly to make their attack on other trees.

The Douglas fir beetle has one generation annually. Adults and large larvae overwinter, with the adults predominating. Depending upon area and weather, the overwintering adults emerge and attack from April to June. Some of these adults reemerge and attack additional trees, establishing a second brood. Adults from overwintering larvae emerge and attack in July and August.

In the coastal Douglas-fir region, resistance of the host tree evidently keeps the Douglas fir beetle under control most of the time. Even when outbreaks occur, following stand disturbance

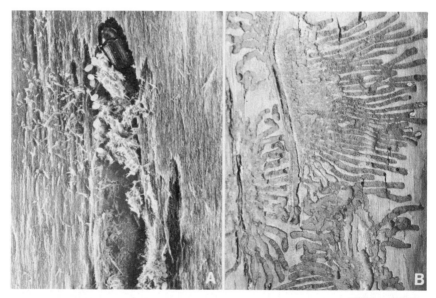

F–520206, F–520206

FIGURE 216.—Douglas fir beetle (*Dendroctonus pseudotsugae*): *A*, Adult females preparing egg galleries; *B*, larval mines fanning outward from egg galleries.

caused by fire or wind, they abruptly subside because the beetles do not thrive in normal green timber. In interior forests tree resistance is a key factor in control, but trees are subject to greater stress and the effectiveness of natural control varies more than in coastal forests. Among the insects rated as important in natural control of the Douglas fir beetle are *Enoclerus sphegeus*, *Thanasimus undatulus*, *Temnochila chlorodia*, *Coeloides brunneri*, and *Medetera aldrichii*.

Direct control of the Douglas fir beetle is of dubious merit and has seldom been attempted. In the coastal Douglas-fir region, where outbreaks are brief but intense, prompt salvage of beetle-killed, wind-thrown, and fire-killed trees before the beetles emerge is the only practical course of action. In this coastal region, slash on clearcut areas does not create a beetle problem, but sometimes does on selectively cut areas. In inland forests, preventive control is obtained by thinning and harvesting. Slash has not caused tree-killing outbreaks of the Douglas fir beetle, but large amounts of cull stems probably should not be left after logging, especially if shaded. Stumps are reported to be significant sources of beetles in British Columbia but have not been involved with tree killing in the Rocky Mountain States. Aggregating pheromones are being developed for use in concentrating attacks in trees to be logged. An antiaggregative pheromone has been shown to prevent infestation of down trees (Furniss et al. 1974).

The **Allegheny spruce beetle**, *Dendroctonus punctatus* LeConte (= *johanseni* Swaine) (Wood 1963), is a transcontinental, little-known species found principally in the Far North. In the West, it attacks *Picea glauca* and *P. sitchensis* and is recorded in Alberta, Northwest and Yukon Territories, and Alaska. It attacks the lower bole and kills scattered trees principally in noncommercial stands. The adult is uniformly brown and averages about 6 mm long. It resembles *D. murrayanae* and *D. rufipennis*, but differs in that the front of the head of the adult *D. punctatus* is not granulate. The female cuts a "C-shaped" gallery and lays clusters of eggs along the outer edge. The larvae feed out en masse, forming a cavity that becomes filled with resinous frass. The life cycle is presumed to be 2 or more years.

The **spruce beetle**, *Dendroctonus rufipennis* (Kirby) (= *borealis* Hopkins, = *engelmanni* Hopkins, = *obesus* (Mannerheim) (Massey and Wygant 1954, Schmid and Beckwith 1975, Wood 1963), occurs throughout the range of *Picea* in North America. In the West, *P. engelmannii*, *P. glauca*, and *P. sitchensis* are principal hosts. Normally this beetle is present in small numbers in weakened or windthrown trees, large pieces of slash, and fresh stumps. Sporadic outbreaks have killed extensive stands of spruce

359

in Alaska, western Canada, Colorado, Montana, and Utah (fig. 217). For example, the spruce beetle killed an estimated 3.8 billion fbm of spruce in Colorado from 1942 to 1948 (Wygant and Nelson 1949). Such outbreaks commonly develop in windthrown timber. During epidemics, trees of all ages and diameters, except reproduction, are attacked, preference being shown for trees of larger diameter. Like fire and wind, the spruce beetle is a natural though destructive means for liquidating overmature forests and making way for the new.

The spruce beetle adult is dark brown to black with reddish wing covers, rather hairy, approximately 4 to 7 mm long, and closely resembles *D. murrayanae* and to some extent *D. pseudotsugae*. The egg gallery is vertical, 6 to 22 mm long, slightly wider than the beetle, and the basal portion usually is filled with pitchy frass. Eggs are laid in elongate grooves on alternate sides of the gallery. At first the larvae bore out en masse transversely. Later they mine individually and their mines frequently cross each other. The pupal cells are usually constructed in the inner bark, being exposed when the bark is removed, but are sometimes deeper in the bark and quite concealed in thick-bark trees.

The life cycle and habits of the spruce beetle differ widely in various portions of its vast range. Two years are required to complete a generation, from attack to attack, in the main body

F-523471

FIGURE 217.—Extensive tree killing by the spruce beetle (*Dendroctonus rufipennis*) on White River National Forest, Colo.

of Engelmann spruce stands. At high elevations 3 years may be required, and in coastal forests a 1-year life cycle is normal. In Sitka spruce in Alaska this beetle sometimes attacks and raises broods in a tree 2 or more years before killing it. In the Rocky Mountains, the principal flight, attack, and egg laying takes place when hibernated adults emerge after the snow disappears late in June and in July. Some of the parent beetles reemerge and establish another brood. Eggs hatch and larvae develop during the summer. The progeny pass the winter as half- to nearly full-grown larvae and complete development to adults by the following August. The new adults emerge and migrate to the basal trunk and root collar of the host tree from August to October; there they bore beneath the bark and hibernate until the ensuing June and July. Overwintering stages consist primarily of hibernating adults of the previous seasonal attacks and half- to three-fourths-grown larvae of the current seasonal attacks.

Spruce beetle populations are kept at low levels most of the time by a combination of natural control factors. During outbreaks the beetle outruns its natural controls, often for years, until much of the mature forest is killed. Woodpeckers are important predators in the Rocky Mountains. Among the insects, *Coeloides dendroctoni,* a parasite, and *Medetera aldrichii,* a predator, are most important. The nematodes, *Sphaerularia dendroctoni* Massey and *Contortylenchus reversus* Thorne significantly reduce the egg laying capacity of the infested female spruce beetles.

The harvesting of stands of overmature spruce by clearcutting is effective as a preventive measure when comprehensively done. Salvage of windthrown trees and infested standing trees before the beetles emerge from them is important both in prevention and control. Green trees systematically felled as "traps" absorb large numbers of beetles which then can be destroyed by treating or salvaging the infested logs. Infested trees and logs can be sprayed with chemicals or burned to kill the contained brood. While effective on individual trees, direct control measures are costly and the benefits are short-lived during extensive epidemics, hence management practices should be focused upon prevention. The start of an outbreak is difficult to detect, because the foliage does not fade until a year after attack, and it turns pale green only before dropping. There are no pitch tubes. First-year attacks can be detected only by the presence of brown boring dust around the base of trees. Woodpecker work also helps to identify the trees after about October 1, when the larvae are large.

The **eastern larch beetle,** *Dendroctonus simplex* LeConte (Hopkins 1909, Furniss 1976), infests *Larix laricina* throughout the range of that tree which includes Alaska and the Western Provinces and Territories. As a rule, *D. simplex* attacks injured and recently down trees, and those weakened by fire, flooding, and the larch sawfly. However, an extensive infestation of normal-appearing trees in the Kantishna River drainage, Alaska, developed in 1973 and is continuing (1975). Successfully infested trees fade during late summer. The bark of the lower bole often is removed during the winter, presumably by birds feeding on the beetle broods.

The dark reddish-brown adult resembles *D. pseudotsugae* but is smaller (4.3 mm long) and differs in gallery characteristics, tree host, and geographic distribution. The broods overwinter as callow adults which mature in the spring. They fly and attack in May and June. Egg galleries are rather winding, commonly 30 cm long, and they lightly etch the wood surface. Turn-around niches are constructed at intervals along the gallery, thus distinguishing *D. simplex* from *D. pseudotsugae*. Eggs are deposited in niches in small groups (usually one to four per group) alternately on opposite sides of the egg tunnel. Larvae mine laterally in the phloem. By the time they mature, the inner bark usually is completely mined and the original gallery pattern practically obliterated. There is no record of direct control of this beetle in the West.

The **red turpentine beetle**, *Dendroctonus valens* LeConte (Eaton and Lara 1967, Smith 1961), occurs in practically all pine forests of the United States and Canada except in the Southeastern and Gulf States. It attacks all species of pine within its range and occasionally spruce and larch. In the West, *Pinus ponderosa, P. contorta, P. jeffreyi, P. lambertiana, P. monticola,* and *P. radiata* are preferred hosts.

D. valens normally attacks injured, weakened, or dying trees, and freshly cut logs and stumps. It often attacks leave trees following logging. Fire-scorched trees and trees in campgrounds and around homes in woodlands also are frequently attacked. Ordinarily this beetle is not aggressive and does not become epidemic. Through repeated attacks, it sometimes kills trees but more often weakens them, thus subjecting them to fatal attack by other bark beetles.

The adult red turpentine beetle, averaging about 8 mm long, is the largest in the genus. Its color is distinctly reddish brown. Woodsmen know it as the "barber beetle" because of its ability to clip hairs with its powerful mandibles. Attacks on a tree are characterized by large reddish pitch tubes at the point of entry (fig. 218). On burrowing beneath the bark, the beetles excavate short, irregular, longitudinal to cavelike galleries between the bark and the wood of the lowermost portion of the bole and of the root

FIGURE 218.—Pitch tubes of the red turpentine beetle (*Dendroctonus valens*) at the base of a pine.

crown. The eggs are laid in elongate groups packed in frass along the sides of the gallery. The larvae feed through the inner bark in mass formation, producing a cavity ranging from about 1 to 9 dm² (0.1 to 1 sq ft) or more in area. Transformation to pupae and adults takes place in cells of frass in the brood chamber or in short mines along its margin. Attacks occur throughout warm weather but peak by midsummer. Winter is passed as adults and larvae. The number of generations varies from one in 2 years in the coldest portions of its range to two or three per year in the warmest.

In commercial forests, care should be taken to minimize injury to standing trees during logging, improvement operations, and road construction. High-value trees on intensive-use areas also should be protected from injury and soil compaction. Chemical sprays can be used to prevent attacks and to kill beetles that have attacked. Screening the lower bole during the flight period may be practical in protecting especially valuable trees.

All species of *Hylastes* (Blackman 1941) breed in conifers. Several are western. The adults are reddish brown to black, elongate, streamlined beetles, 3 to 6 mm long. They closely resemble *Hylurgops* but their third tarsal segment is narrow and emarginate rather than broad and bilobed. During afternoon and evening in spring and early summer the adults fly in great numbers and often are encountered around lumberyards and on tents and even mountain snowfields where they are carried by updrafts (Furniss and Furniss 1972). *Hylastes* are not considered to be primary tree killers, but occasionally the adults feed on the tender bark of young trees and sometimes kill them by girdling at or below the root collar. Suppressed, injured, and drought-weakened saplings are susceptible to this type of attack. The broods develop under the bark of the root crown and the roots of dying and dead trees, and in stumps and the underside of logs and slash in contact with the ground. Direct control is unnecessary.

Hylastes nigrinus (Mannerheim) (Zethner-Moller and Rudinsky 1967) is the species most often encountered in forests of the Pacific slope. It ranges from California to Alaska and Montana. Hosts include *Abies, Picea, Pinus, Pseudotsuga,* and *Tsuga.* The adult (fig. 219) is black and medium-sized for the genus. In western Oregon, where Douglas-fir is the principal host, peak flight occurs in May. Adults feed on small roots of large dead trees and on the roots of small weakened trees. Eggs are laid predominantly in the roots. A 1-year life cycle is usual.

F–523472

FIGURE 219.—Adult of *Hylastes nigrinus,*
5 mm long.

Hylastes gracilis LeConte and *H. longicollis* Swaine are dark reddish-brown species, about 4 mm long, that breed principally in pine and occur from California to British Columbia and eastward to South Dakota and New Mexico. *H. macer* LeConte, 5 to 6 mm long and pitch black, is the largest species. It occurs from California to British Columbia, South Dakota, and New Mexico. Hosts are ponderosa, sugar, Jeffrey, and lodgepole pines and Engelmann spruce. *H. ruber* Swaine is a reddish-brown species about 4.5 to 5.5 mm long. It breeds in Douglas-fir from Oregon to British Columbia, Montana, and Arizona.

Hylurgopinus contains one species in North America. The **native elm bark beetle,** *H. rufipes* (Eichhoff) (Baker 1972), is primarily an eastern species but occurs westward to Saskatchewan, North Dakota, and Nebraska. Elms are its principal hosts. It is a vector of *Ceratocystis ulmi* (Buisman) C. Moreau, the fungus that causes Dutch elm disease (Schreiber and Peacock 1974). The egg gallery is horizontal in contrast with the vertical egg gallery of *Scolytus multistriatus*, the primary vector of Dutch elm disease. Adults of *H. rufipes* are 2 to 3.5 mm long, clothed with short, stiff, yellowish bristles, and resemble *Hylurgops* in body outline.

Species of the genus *Hylurgops* are commonly found in the inner bark at the base of trunks or in the main roots of dying or dead trees, or in freshly cut stumps. The adults are about 4 to 5 mm long. They resemble *Hylastes* but are more robust, and the third tarsal segment is broad and bilobed rather than narrow and emarginate. The species of *Hylurgops* breed in the root crown and lower bole of conifers. Several species occur in the West; none is a pest.

Hylurgops incomptus (Blandford) occurs in Arizona, New Mexico, and southward in Mexico on pines.

Hylurgops porosus (LeConte) is a black species with evenly rounded elytra that are not wider behind the middle. It ranges widely in the West, attacking various pines and white fir.

Hylurgops reticulatus Wood (Wood 1971a, 1971b) occurs abundantly from British Columbia and Montana to California and New Mexico in pines and Douglas-fir.

Hylurgops rugipennis (Mannerheim) is a reddish-brown species with evenly rounded elytra that are somewhat wider behind the middle. It works in pines, spruce, Douglas-fir, and western hemlock and occurs extensively in the West, including Alaska. In Alberta a life cycle requires from $1\frac{1}{2}$ to $2\frac{1}{2}$ years (Reid 1955).

Hylurgops subcostulatus (Mannerheim) is a russet-brown, scaly beetle, frequently encrusted with resin and frass. It differs from most other *Hylurgops* by having strongly ridged elytra. It attacks ponderosa, Jeffrey, sugar, lodgepole, and western white pines and occurs throughout the West. In the days of extensive direct control of the western pine beetle, *H. subcostulatus* was known to treating crews as the "sour sap beetle" because of its habit of breeding in the wet fermenting inner bark at the base of dead ponderosa pines. The egg gallery is short, slightly curved, and longitudinal. Two generations per year are usual in the warmer portions of its range.

Four species of **ash bark beetles**, *Leperisinus*, occur in the West. They breed in felled, injured, or weakened ash trees, causing essentially no economic damage. Often they are abundant in cordwood. They construct uniform, transverse egg galleries (fig. 220A) that score both the wood and inner bark of the bole and branches.

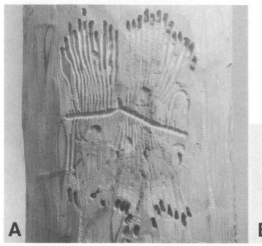

F-523473, F-523474

FIGURE 220.—Oregon ash bark beetle (*Leperisinus oregonus*): *A*, Transverse egg galleries on Oregon ash, with radiating larval galleries; *B*, adult, 3 mm long.

The striking gallery pattern sometimes is featured in rustic furniture. The adults (fig. 220B) are robust beetles, 2 to 4 mm long, evenly rounded behind, and covered with scales that often give them a mottled appearance as in some *Pseudohylesinus*.

The **western ash bark beetle**, *Leperisinus californicus* Swaine, occurs from Washington south to California and east to North Dakota, Colorado, and Oklahoma. In California it is known as the **olive bark beetle** because it attacks weakened olive trees and pruned branches. It has one generation annually (Chamberlin 1958). The **Oregon ash bark beetle**, *L. oregonus* Blackman, is a similar but generally darker species that attacks Oregon ash from Washington to California. The **eastern ash bark beetle**, *L. aculeatus* (Say), ranges westward into North Dakota and Colorado. *L. criddlei* Swaine, a small eastern species, occurs westward into Manitoba, Wyoming, and Colorado.

Liparthrum contains two species, one of them western. *L. arizonicum* Wood (Wood 1959) is an obscure noneconomic species that breeds in branches and twigs of *Arbutus arizonicus* in Arizona and Mexico. The adult is about 1 mm long and the body is brown with rows of lighter colored scales on the elytra.

Phloeosinus (Blackman 1942) contains 25 species north of Mexico. Most of them are western. All except one (in *Pinus* and *Picea*) develop in trees of the genera *Chamaecyparis*, *Cryptomeria*, *Cupressus*, *Juniperus*, *Libocedrus*, *Taxodium*, *Thuja*, and *Sequoia*

366

(table 13). They are known as **cedar bark beetles** although none attacks true cedar, *Cedrus*. Their hosts are infested by almost no other bark beetles; consequently any species found working in the inner bark of cedarlike trees is almost certain to be a species of *Phloeosinus*. As a general rule these beetles are not aggressive in their attack and are found working under the bark of trunks, tops, and limbs of weakened, dying, or felled trees, or of broken branches. Occasionally, however, they become sufficiently numerous and aggressive to attack and kill apparently healthy trees. During the 1920's and 1930's *Juniperus occidentalis* in central Oregon was extensively killed by a combination of severe drought and attacks by *Phloeosinus*. With increased rainfall since then,

Table 13.—*Hosts and distribution of western species*
of Phloeosinus

Species	Hosts	Distribution
P. antennatus Swaine	*Libocedrus decurrens*	Calif. and Oreg.
P. arizonicus Blackman	*Cupressus arizonicus*	Ariz.
P. baumanni Hopkins	*Cupressus arizonicus*	Ariz.
P. cristatus (LeConte)	*Cupressus macrocarpa* and *Cupressus* spp.	Calif., Ariz., and N. Mex.
P. cupressi Hopkins (= *nitidus* Swaine)	*Cupressus macrocarpa*, *Cupressus* spp., and *Chamaecyparis nootkatensis*	Calif. to Alaska
P. frontalis Bruck (= *granulatus* Bruck)	*Cupressus*	Southern Calif.
P. fulgens Swaine	*Libocedrus decurrens*	Calif. and Oreg.
P. furnissi Blackman	*Juniperus monosperma*, *J. pachyphloea*, and *J. osteosperma*	British Columbia, Wyo., N. Dak., Colo., Utah, Ariz., and N. Mex.
P. hoferi Blackman	*Juniperus scopulorum*, *J. pachyphloea*, and *J. osteosperma*	Wyo., Colo., Utah, Ariz., and N. Mex.
P. hoppingi Swaine	*Libocedrus decurrens*, *Juniperus occidentalis*, and *Cupressus macrocarpa*	Calif. and Oreg.
P. keeni Blackman	*Chamaecyparis nootkatensis*	Wash., Idaho, British Columbia, and Alaska
P. pini Swaine (= *alaskanus* Blackman)	*Picea glauca* and *Pinus banksiana*	Alaska, Northwest Territories, and Manitoba
P. punctatus LeConte **western cedar bark beetle** (= *buckhorni* Blackman, = *kaniksu* Blackman, = *rubicundulus* Swaine, = *rusti* Blackman)	*Thuja plicata, Libocedrus decurrens, Juniperus occidentalis*, and *Sequoia gigantea*	Calif. to British Columbia and Idaho

Species	Hosts	Distribution
P. scopulorum Swaine	*Juniperus scopulorum,* and *Juniperus* spp.	British Columbia, Wash., Utah, Colo., Ariz., and N. Mex.
P. sequoiae Hopkins **redwood bark beetle** (= *squamosus* Blackman, = *blackmani* Schedl)	*Sequoia sempervirens, Thuja plicata, Chamaecyparis lawsoniana,* and *C. nootkatensis*	Calif., Oreg., Wash., British Columbia, and Alaska
P. serratus (LeConte) (= *aciculatus* Bruck, = *chamberlini* Blackman, = *juniperi* Swaine, = *rugosus* Swaine, = *utahensis* Swaine)	*Juniperus occidentalis, J. pachyphloea,* and *J. osteosperma*	Calif., Oreg., Wash., Idaho, Utah, Ariz., and N. Mex.
P. setosus Bruck	*Cupressus goveniana* and *Libocedrus decurrens*	Calif.
P. spinosus Blackman	*Cupressus arizonica*	Ariz. and N. Mex.
P. swainei Bruck	*Cupressus goveniana*	Calif.
P. vandykei Swaine	*Libocedrus decurrens* and *Thuja plicata*	Calif. and Oreg.
P. variolatus Bruck	*Cupressus goveniana*	Calif.

the outbreak has ended and for many years *Phloeosinus* attacks in that area have been confined to injured and felled trees.

The adults are reddish brown to black, often shiny beetles, ranging from about 2 to 4 mm long. Rows of teeth on the declivity of the elytra are useful in identification (fig. 221A). Prior to constructing egg galleries, the newly emerged adults feed on twigs of healthy trees of the host species, often hollowing them out and killing them. This twig-killing sometimes is conspicuous on ornamentals. In constructing their blood burrows the beetles work in pairs. While there is some variation in the work pattern, the typical egg gallery consist of one short, longitudinal gallery arising from an enlarged entrance chamber, with the eggs uniformly spaced along the sides and the larval mines extending laterally in a regular pattern. As the feeding progresses, the pattern becomes confused, especially in heavy attacks (fig. 221B). Trees are attacked in the spring and summer, and there may be one or one and one-half generations a year. Keeping trees healthy will minimize attacks for egg laying. Direct control in the forest is impractical.

Phloeosinus cristatus (LeConte) and *P. cupressi* Hopkins are known as **cypress bark beetles** because their principal hosts are species of *Cupressus*. They attack the bole and larger branches,

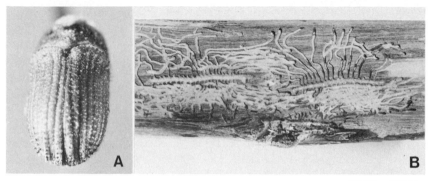

FIGURE 221.—Examples of cedar bark beetles, *Phloeosinus*: *A*, Elytral declivity of *P. cupressi*; *B*, egg and larval galleries of *P. punctatus*.

sometimes killing injured and weakened trees. They also hasten
the death of trees infected by *Coryneum cardinale* and may be a
vector of this tree-killing fungus (Wagener 1939). The newly
emerged adults also mine and kill twigs, presumably a feeding
habit, sometimes making ornamental trees unsightly to the point
of requiring control measures.

The **western cedar bark beetle**, *Phloeosinus punctatus* LeConte,
is a common and variable species as indicated by the number of
synonyms. Generally it is of little importance, but sometimes is
reported to kill trees, for example, western redcedar on Vancouver
Island in 1959. It is common in fallen branches of giant sequoia.
The egg gallery consists of one longitudinal tunnel about 25 mm
long or two shorter ones in the form of a "V" (fig. 221B). The
adults are black and shiny with reddish-brown elytra; length is
2 to 3 mm.

The **redwood bark beetle**, *Phloeosinus sequoiae* Hopkins, ranges
from 3.2 to 4.2 mm long, a shade larger than any other North
American species. It attacks weakened, felled, or fire-scorched
redwood in California and Oregon. It also attacks *Chamaecyparis
lawsoniana*, *C. nootkatensis*, and *Thuja plicata*. Under the name,
P. squamosus Blackman, now considered to be a synonym, it
ranges northward in coastal Oregon, Washington, and British
Columbia into southeastern Alaska. In Alaska it frequently attacks and kills western redcedar and Alaska-cedar on poor sites,
thus being somewhat more aggressive than most other species of
Phloeosinus.

Phloeotribus [*Phthorophloeus*] contains eight species in North
America, four of which occur in the West.

Phloeotribus lecontei Schedl (= *puberulus* LeConte) occurs in
British Columbia and Alberta and southward into Arizona and

New Mexico. It breeds in branches of *Pseudotsuga menziesii*, *Picea engelmannii*, and *Abies*, causing no economic damage. The adults are 2 to 2.5 mm long, dark brown to black, and densely clothed with gray hairs. Viewed under a microscope, the segments of the antennal club are loosely joined and are extended off-center on the inside.

Phloeotribus piceae Swaine is an eastern species that ranges westward into Alaska in branches of *Picea glauca*. *Phloeotribus pruni* Wood occurs in *Prunus* from Colorado into Mexico, and *Phloeotribus dentifrons* (Blackman) occurs in *Celtis* in New Mexico.

Polygraphus contains three species in North America, all western. They resemble *Hylurgops* in body outline, but are smaller and differ from this and other genera of *Hylesininae* by having completely divided eyes. They breed principally in spruce.

Polygraphus convexifrons Wood (Wood 1971) closely resembles *P. rufipennis* in appearance and presumably in habits but differs in that the front of the head of the female is strongly convex rather than flat. *P. convexifrons* occurs in spruce in Alaska, Yukon Territory, Utah, Colorado, and New Mexico.

Polygraphus hoppingi Swaine is a little-known species recorded from *Picea engelmannii* in Arizona. It is somewhat larger and more elongate than *P. rufipennis*.

The **foureyed spruce beetle**, *Polygraphus rufipennis* (Kirby) is a transcontinental species that occurs extensively in the Western Provinces and States, including Alaska. It is a common secondary species that breeds under the bark of the smaller and drier portions of the bole of dead and dying spruce. It also breeds in lodgepole pine, limber pine, and larch. The adults are 2 to 3 mm long, stout, black, and moderately clothed with scalelike hairs. They construct a nuptial chamber in the inner bark from which radiate one to five short, curved egg galleries. There appears to be only one generation annually, but females may reattack and establish two or more broods.

Pseudohylesinus (Bright 1969) contains nine species in North America. As a group, they range from Alaska into Mexico and are most abundant in the fir forests of Oregon, Washington, and British Columbia. Usually they attack dying, dead, and down trees, but at least two species are recorded as destructive tree killers. Two or more species often occur in one tree. Some species hibernate in special niches cut in the bark of the basal portion of a tree or in twigs. Their egg galleries resemble those of *Scolytus* but score the wood less and the nuptial chamber generally is less evident. The adults of these two genera are markedly different in that the wing covers of *Pseudohylesinus* are densely covered with scales, and therefore are dull in appearance instead of bare and shiny as is *Scolytus*. Moreover, *Pseudohylesinus* adults are nearly oval in outline and do not have the "sawed-off" rear end that is such a distinctive feature of *Scolytus*.

Pseudohylesinus dispar Blackman consists of two named subspecies. The typical and more abundant one ranges from central California to Washington, Idaho, and Montana. It attacks *Abies concolor, A. grandis,* and *A. magnifica.* The adult is 2.9 to 4.7 mm long and clothed with light brown and ash-gray scales in variegated pattern. The less common form attacks *Abies procera* and ranges from central Oregon to central Washington. The adult is clothed with dark brown to black scales interspersed with patches of white. Both subspecies attack the bole and larger branches of decadent trees, ranging from saplings to mature trees. Both construct transverse egg galleries ranging from about 4 to 12 cm long.

The **fir root bark beetle,** *Pseudohylesinus granulatus* (LeConte) (Thomas and Wright 1961) (fig. 222), occurs from British Columbia to California. Various species of *Abies* are its principal host. Douglas-fir and western hemlock also are recorded hosts. Normally it is a secondary species but in combination with *P. sericeus* can be highly destructive. The adult is 4.1 to 5.5 mm long. Attacks are made in the basal portion of a tree and often extend below ground as with *Hylastes* and *Hylurgops.* Egg galleries are short and irregularly transverse. The life cycle is 2 years in northern Washington.

F–494373

FIGURE 222.—Adult of fir root bark beetle (*Pseudohylesinus granulatus*), 5 mm long.

Pseudohylesinus maculosus Blackman occurs in Utah, Arizona, and New Mexico. Hosts are *Abies concolor* and *A. lasiocarpa.* The adult is 3.0 to 5.4 mm long and heavily clothed with dark brown, black, and white scales arranged in irregular spots.

The **Douglas fir pole beetle,** *Pseudohylesinus nebulosus* (LeConte) (Walters and McMullen 1956), is the most widespread species of the genus, apparently occurring throughout the range of its principal host, Douglas-fir. The adult is 2.4 to 3.1 mm long. It commonly attacks thin-barked portions of logging slash, windthrown trees, and the tops and branches of trees killed by *Dendroctonus pseudotsugae.* It also attacks saplings and poles infected with root rots. Newly emerged adults bore into twigs of live trees to feed before attacking to lay eggs. In interior British Columbia there is one generation per year. There, attacks begin early in May and emergence is complete by late September. The adults overwinter in niches cut in the bark. Usually a short, longitudinal egg gallery is constructed in the cambium layer, often with two branches, originating from a central entrance tunnel, one up and one down the trunk, parallel with the grain of the wood (fig. 223). The work is similar to, and easily confused with, that of *Scolytus unispinosus,* but is distinctive in that no well-defined nuptial chamber is visible on the inner surface of the bark. The larval mines diverge from the egg gallery and end in pupal cells in the inner bark.

The subspecies, *P. nebulosus serratus* Bruck, is somewhat larger and attacks only *Pseudotsuga macrocarpa* in California.

The **noble fir bark beetle,** *Pseudohylesinus nobilis* Swaine, occurs in Washington and Oregon in *Abies amabilis, A. grandis, A. procera,* and *Tsuga heterophylla.* It attacks the bole and larger limbs of dying trees. The adult is 2.5 to 3.5 mm long and closely resembles *P. sericeus* and *P. tsugae.* The egg gallery is irregularly transverse.

Pseudohylesinus pini Wood is the species long known as *P. sericeus.* It occurs along the coast from Alaska to California and attacks the branches and upper bole of weakened and dying *Pinus contorta* and *P. radiata.* The adult closely resembles that of *Pseudohylesinus sitchensis* but is slightly smaller. The egg galleries of these two species also are similar.

The **silver fir beetle,** *Pseudohylesinus sericeus* (Mannerheim) (= *P. grandis* Swaine) (McGhehey and Nagel 1969, Thomas and Wright 1961), together with *P. granulatus,* killed some 528 million fbm of commercial grade Pacific silver fir from 1947 to 1955, principally in Washington. Usually both these species attack windthrown, felled, injured, and severely suppressed trees. *P. sericeus* ranges from Alaska to California and eastward to Montana. Vari-

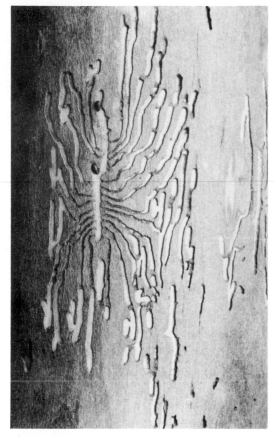

EPQ–6881

FIGURE 223.—Egg and larval galleries of the Douglas fir pole beetle (*Pseudohylesinus nebulosus*).

ous *Abies, Tsuga heterophylla* and *Pseudotsuga menziesii* are principal hosts. The adult is 2.7 to 3.9 mm long and mottled with brown and white scales (fig. 224). In Oregon the duration of a life cycle is reported to be 1 year and in northern Washington 2 years. The egg gallery is transverse and resembles that of *Scolytus ventralis,* but is narrower, less uniformly straight, and etches the wood less deeply. In large trees, attacks are made in the upper bole and in the limbs. Brown-stain fungi and root-rotting fungi such as *Armillaria mellea, Fomes annosus,* and *Phellinus weirii* commonly are associated with this beetle and aid it in killing a tree.

Pseudohylesinus sitchensis Swaine occurs on Sitka spruce from central California to Afognak Island, Alaska. It attacks the upper bole and limbs of dying and down trees. The adult is 2.5 to 3.5 mm long and densely covered with brown and ashy-gray scales. It makes a short, slightly curved, longitudinal gallery. The larvae work laterally and pupation occurs in the bark or slightly submerged in the sapwood.

FIGURE 224.—Silver fir beetle
(*Pseudohylesinus sericeus*)
adult, 3.5 mm long.

Pseudohylesinus tsugae Swaine (McGhehey and Nagel 1969) ranges from Alaska to California. *Tsuga heterophylla* is the principal host. *T. mertensiana, Abies amabilis,* and *A. lasiocarpa* also are attacked. It breeds in the lower bole of dying trees and in recent slash and down trees. The adult is 3.2 to 4.5 mm long. In western Oregon, *P. tsugae* has one generation per year. Some adults reemerge and establish a second brood. Attacks occur from May into August. Winter is spent principally as mature larvae. From June to November adults emerge and construct feeding niches in the bark of living trees. Some adults overwinter in the niches.

Scierus contains two species in North America. The adults are 3 to 4.5 mm long. They resemble *Hylurgops* but are reddish brown and dull rather than dark brown or black and shining. Their elytra are rough and have rows of short yellow setae.

Scierus annectens LeConte (Stewart 1965) is a transcontinental species. In the West it is recorded in Alaska, the Western Provinces, and southward to California, Arizona, and New Mexico. *Picea engelmannii, P. glauca,* and other spruces are the principal hosts. *Pinus contorta* also is attacked. In Colorado *S. annectens* is associated with *Dendroctonus rufipennis* in Engelmann spruce and commonly gains access to a tree through entrance holes of that beetle. The egg galleries average about 35 mm long and run longitudinally. In Colorado, the life cycle is recorded to be 1 to 2 years.

Scierus pubescens Swaine occurs from Alaska and Alberta to Colorado. It infests *Abies lasiocarpa* and *Picea*. The adult resembles *S. annectens* but is hairier and somewhat shiny.

Xylechinus contains two North American species, one of which is western.

Xylechinus montanus Blackman (Chamberlin 1958) occurs from California to Alaska, Montana, and Colorado. Hosts are *Picea engelmannii, P. glauca,* and *Larix occidentalis.* The boles of small weakened, dying, or recently dead trees are attacked. The adult is about 2.5 mm long, shiny brown, and clothed with gray scales and hairs. Two to four egg tunnels radiate from a central chamber.

Scolytinae—Recently (Wood 1973), the Scolytinae and Ipinae were combined as one subfamily. The adults of the western genera in this subfamily are of two types. In most genera, the front margin of the elytra usually is smooth; the pronotum usually is armed by granules or small teeth; and the head usually is concealed. *Scolytus* differs from the Hylesininae and other genera in the Scolytinae in that the abdomen is vertical or nearly so behind, the elytra and pronotum are unarmed, and the outer margin of the front tibia bears no teeth, except for a curved process at the outer end.

Cactopinus (Bright 1967) contains 14 species, five of which occur in the Southwestern United States. They attack pines, desert trees and shrubs, and cactus. None is economically important. They are 1.3 to 2.5 mm long. A V-shaped area on the pronotum is elevated and strongly toothed. The males have a prominent horn extending forward from the head.

Cactopinus koebelei Blackman is recorded from *Pinus lambertiana* and *P. monophylla,* and *C. pini* Blackman from *Pinus jeffreyi* in southern California. *C. koebelei* also occurs in southern Utah. *C. desertus* Bright attacks the limbs and bole of the elephant tree, *Bursera microphylla,* in southern California. The galleries are constructed both in and under the bark. *C. hubbardi* Schwarz is recorded from saguaro, *Cereus giganteus,* in Arizona.

Sixteen species of **cone beetles,** *Conophthorus* (Hopkins 1915a), are recorded from North America, 11 of them from the West. As now defined, the species can be identified most readily by host tree. Several are nearly identical in appearance and habits, hence it is likely that some are distinct in name only. All develop in pine cones. Cones that wither and die before they are half grown, and either drop to the ground or remain attached to the tree, usually have been killed by *Conophthorus* (fig. 225A). The riddled powdery interior of the mined cones (fig. 225B) and the small round exit holes through the cone scales are further evidence of attack by these beetles, even after the brood has emerged.

Periodically, cone crops of sugar, ponderosa, western white, pinyon, and other pines are severely damaged by *Conophthorus.*

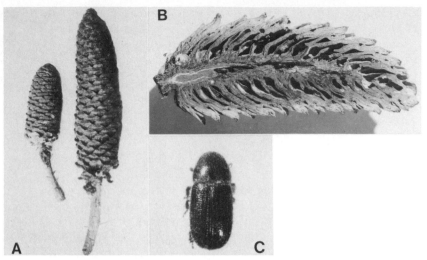

EPQ–9207, F–523477, F–523478

FIGURE 225.—Sugar pine cone beetle (*Conophthorus lambertianae*) : *A*, Damage and dwarfing of sugar pine cones; *B*, overwintering adults in riddled interior of cone; *C*, adult, 3 mm long.

In some years from 25 to 75 percent of the sugar pine cones have been killed by *C. lambertianae* over large areas, thus increasing the difficulty and cost of collecting seeds for reforestation. In the Southwest a 3-year survey showed that *C. ponderosae* was the most damaging insect attacking ponderosa pine cones. Because of the economic importance of *Conophthorus*, the biology of four western species is known in detail—*C. lambertianae* Hopkins (Bedard 1968, Miller 1915), *C. monticolae* Hopkins (Williamson et al. 1966), *C. ponderosae* Hopkins (Kinzer et al. 1970, Miller 1915), and *C. radiatae* Hopkins (Schaefer 1962).

The adults (fig. 225C) are reddish-brown to black, shiny beetles, 2 to 4 mm long, and resemble over-sized *Pityophthorus*. Typically, they bore into the base or supporting stem of the immature pine cones in the spring soon after the beginning of the second year's growth. A small tunnel is projected along the axis of the cone and in this the female beetle deposits her eggs. From these hatch small, white, curled, legless grubs which feed on the scales, seeds, and tissues of the withering cone. Development to the adult stage is completed during the summer within the dead cone, where the beetles usually remain over the winter. In the case of *C. lambertianae*, some adults emerge in the fall and mine and kill the tips of twigs on living trees and overwinter there.

There is an increasing need to protect seed orchards and seed collecting areas from damage by *Conophthorus*, but practical measures have not yet been developed.

The hosts and distribution of the western species of *Conophthorus* are:

Species	Hosts	Distribution
C. apachecae Hopkins **Apache pine cone beetle**	*Pinus engelmannii*	Ariz.
C. cembroides Wood	*Pinus cembroides*	Ariz.
C. contortae Hopkins **lodgepole cone beetle**	*Pinus contorta*	Wash., Oreg., and Calif.
C. edulis Hopkins **piñon cone beetle**	*Pinus edulis*	Colo., Ariz., and N. Mex.
C. flexilis Hopkins **limber pine cone beetle**	*Pinus flexilis*	Colo., Mont., Calif., and Southern Rocky Mountains
C. lambertianae Hopkins **sugar pine cone beetle**	*Pinus lambertiana* and *P. monticola*	Oreg. and Calif.
C. monophyllae Hopkins **singleleaf piñon cone beetle**	*Pinus monophylla*	Calif., Nev., Ariz., Utah, and Idaho
C. monticolae Hopkins **mountain pine cone beetle**	*Pinus monticola*	British Columbia to Idaho and Calif.
C. ponderosae Hopkins **ponderosa pine cone beetle**	*Pinus ponderosa* and *P. jeffreyi*	Wash. to Calif., Ariz., and N. Mex.
C. radiatae Hopkins **Monterey pine cone beetle**	*Pinus radiata*	Calif.
C. scopulorum Hopkins	*Pinus ponderosa*	Ariz., N. Mex., and Colo.

Cryphalus [*Taenioglyptes*], *Procryphalus*, and *Trypophloeus* are closely related, small bark beetles of similar appearance and habits (Wood 1954a). None of the western species is of economic importance. *Trypophloeus* and *Procryphalus* mine in the outer bark of the bole and larger branches of living broadleaved trees. The species of *Cryphalus* attack only conifers. They mine in the bole of weakened young trees and in small branches of older trees. The adults of all three genera are brown to black beetles about 1.5 to 2.0 mm long and have scaly elytra, especially toward the rear. Hosts and distribution of some common western species in these genera are:

Species	Hosts	Distribution
Cryphalus pubescens Hopkins	*Abies grandis, Pseudotsuga menziesii*, and *Picea sitchensis*	British Columbia to Calif.
C. ruficollis (Hopkins)	*Abies amabilis, A. grandis, A. lasiocarpa, Pseudotsuga menziesii,* and *Picea engelmannii*	British Columbia to Calif., Utah, Idaho, Colo., and Ariz.
Procryphalus mucronatus (LeConte)	*Populus tremuloides*	Nev., Idaho, Utah, Colo., and N. Mex.

Species	Hosts	Distribtuion
P. utahensis Hopkins (= aceris Hopkins)	Salix, and Acer macro- phyllum	Western U.S. and Canada
Trypophloeus striatulus (Mannerheim) (= nitidulus Swaine)	Alnus and Salix	Alaska, Idaho, and Utah to East Coast
T. populi (Hopkins)	Populus tremuloides and other Populus	Ariz., Nev., Utah, Colo., and Saskatchewan to East Coast
T. salicis (Hopkins)	Alnus and Salix	Calif. and Wash.
T. thatcheri Wood	Populus tremuloides	Calif. and British Columbia

Crypturgus contains one species in the West. *C. borealis* Swaine ranges from coast to coast and is abundant in dying spruce in the Rocky Mountain Region and along the Pacific slope. It is the smallest bark beetle, about 1 mm long, commonly encountered and is of no economic importance. The adult is brown, cylindrical, and has a two-segmented antennal club. Attacks are made through the entrance holes of *Dendroctonus*, *Ips*, and probably other bark beetles.

Dolurgus contains one species, *D. pumilus* (Mannerheim). Not a pest, it ranges from Alaska to California. *Picea sitchensis* is the principal host. *P. engelmannii*, *Pinus monticola*, *P. radiata*, *P. muricata*, and species of *Abies* also are recorded hosts. The adult resembles *Crypturgus borealis* but is somewhat larger and has a three-segmented rather than two-segmented antennal club. Attacks are made on dying trees through the entrance holes of larger bark beetles. The galleries are wholly within the bark.

Dryocoetes (Bright 1963) contains seven species in North America, six of them in the West. All but one attack conifers. Usually they breed in dying, dead, and down trees, but one species is recorded as a significant tree-killer. The adults are shiny, brown to black, cylindrical beetles ranging from 2 to 5 mm long. The thorax is evenly convex above and the elytra are abruptly rounded and unarmed behind. Several egg galleries radiate from a central nuptial chamber (fig. 226).

Dryocoetes affaber (Mannerheim) occurs in spruce forests from Alaska to New Mexico and the east coast. It attacks the bole of dying and down Sitka, Engelmann, and other spruces and also has been recorded from *Abies*, *Larix*, *Pinus*, and *Pseudotsuga menziesii*. The adult is 2.5 to 3.3 mm long, reddish brown to black, and abundantly clothed with long yellow hairs.

Dryocoetes autographus (Ratzeburg) (= *pseudotsugae* Swaine) (Bright 1963) occurs in coniferous forests of Europe, Asia, and North America. In the West it ranges from Alaska to California and New Mexico. Species of *Picea* are the principal hosts. *Pseudotsuga menziesii*, *Tsuga*, *Larix*, and *Abies* also are attacked.

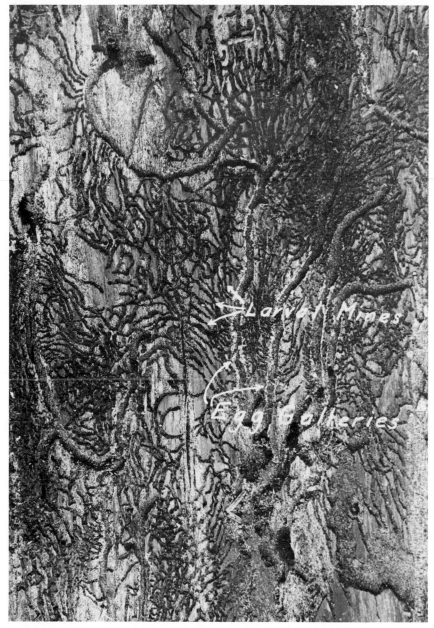

F–523479

FIGURE 226.—*Dryocoetes* egg galleries radiating from a central nuptial chamber, with larval galleries visible.

The adult is 3.4 to 5.0 mm long and similar in appearance to *D. confusus*. Attacks are made in the base and root crown of dying and recently dead standing trees and along the bole of down trees.

In Douglas-fir, the adults construct short, irregular egg galleries in the cambium region, seldom scoring the wood. The young adults gather in considerably larger galleries in the bark to pass the winter. Adults emerge early in the spring. Trees attacked in the spring produce mature beetles by August. There is one generation and probably a partial second each year. The biology in spruce is not recorded.

The **birch bark beetle,** *Dryocoetes betulae* Hopkins, is a secondary enemy of birch from coast to coast and the only species in the genus breeding in hardwoods. In the West, *D. betulae* is recorded from Montana, Washington, and British Columbia.

Dryocoetes caryi Hopkins and *D. sechelti* Swaine are little-known species of similar appearance and habits. They breed in the bole of small, suppressed trees. Both are reddish brown and somewhat less than 3 mm long. *D. caryi* attacks spruces from coast to coast. In the West it is recorded from Alberta, British Columbia, and Wyoming. *D. sechelti* attacks *Abies lasiocarpa* from British Columbia to Oregon and eastward to Colorado.

The **western balsam bark beetle,** *Dryocoetes confusus* Swaine (Bright 1963), is the most destructive species in the genus. In combination with *Ceratocystis dryocoetidis* Kend. and Moln. and other woodstaining, pathogenic fungi, *D. confusus* kills *Abies lasiocarpa* extensively in British Columbia and in Western States southward to Arizona and New Mexico (Molnar 1965). Other *Abies, Picea engelmannii,* and *Pinus contorta* are occasional hosts. The adults are 3.4 to 4.3 mm long. They resemble *D. autographus* except that the declivity is flattened rather than evenly rounded, and the front of the head of the female is densely rather than sparsely hairy. The egg galleries commonly but lightly etch the surface of the wood. Little is published regarding the biology of this species. A 1- to 2-year life cycle is indicated.

Six of the seven North American species of *Gnathotrichus* (Blackman 1931a) are western. The adults are small, cylindrical, dark brown or black beetles of the size and shape of a short piece of pencil lead (fig. 227A). They attack nearly all species of conifers in the West; one species works in alder and poplar and one in oak. Their primary tunnel penetrates the sapwood, and at intervals along this tunnel, secondary tunnels branch horizontally, the branches more or less following the annual rings (fig. 227B). The tunnels are of the compound type, in that larval cradles are constructed at regular intervals, both above and below the primary and secondary galleries (fig. 227C).

In the coastal forests of British Columbia, where damage by ambrosia beetles has been most serious, *G. retusus* (LeConte)

380

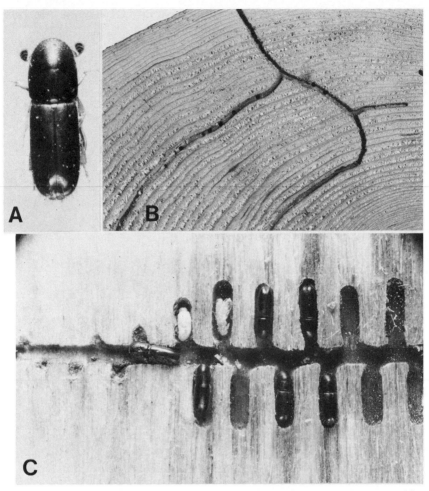

FIGURE 227.—*Gnathotrichus sulcatus*: *A*, Adult, 3.5 mm long; *B*, primary and secondary tunnels; *C*, adults and larvae in larval cradles.

and *G. sulcatus* (LeConte) (= *aciculatus* Blackman) together are a distant second in importance to *Trypodendron lineatum*. Their galleries are smaller in diameter, less stained, and usually fewer than those of *T. lineatum*. *G. sulcatus* attacks from April through November, principally in the spring and late summer (Prebble and Graham 1957). All stages overwinter in the wood. *G. retusus* has similar habits. The borings of *Gnathotrichus* are comma-shaped and uniform in size (fig. 209C). The symbiotic fungi *Ambrosiella sulcati* Funk and *Raffaelea sulcati* Funk are stored and disseminated by the male of *G. sulcatus*. Hosts and distribution of western *Gnathotrichus* are as follows:

Species	Hosts	Distribution
G. alni Blackman	*Alnus* and *Populus*	Western Oreg. and Wash.
G. denticulatus Blackman	*Pinus* and *Abies*	S. Dakota, and Utah to Mexico
G. imitans Wood	*Pinus*	Ariz. and Mexico
G. nimifrons Wood	*Quercus*	Ariz. and Mexico
G. perniciosus Wood	*Pinus*	Ariz. and Mexico
G. retusus (LeConte)	*Pseudotsuga menziesii, Tsuga,* and *Pinus*; rarely *Abies* and *Picea*	Pacific Coast and Northern Rocky Mountains
G. sulcatus (LeConte)	*Picea, Tsuga, Pseudotsuga menziesii, Abies,* and sometimes *Pinus, Sequoia, Thuja,* and other conifers	Western States

Hylocurus, Micracis, Micracisella, Thysanoes, and *Pseudothysanoes* belong to a group of small bark beetles formerly recognized as a subfamily but now considered to be a subdivision of the Scolytinae (Arnett 1960). Predominantly they breed in the branches and small stems of broad-leaved trees and shrubs. The larvae of some mine in the wood somewhat as do powderpost beetles. One species occasionally is a pest.

Hylocurus (Blackman 1928a) contains about three dozen species, mostly eastern and Mexican.

The **shrub bark beetle**, *H.* [*Micracis*] *hirtellus* (LeConte) (Struble and Hall 1954), occurs in California, Oregon, and Washington. It mines in the dead, dry wood of the limbs and stems of many broad-leaved trees and shrubs, including species of *Salix, Alnus, Arbutus,* and *Umbellularia.* The larval galleries contain powdery frass. This species has damaged lead-covered and plastic-covered telephone cables in California, but causes no economic damage to its natural hosts. The adults are 2.4 to 3.0 mm long. The elytra are parallel on the sides and pointed behind.

H. parkinsoniae Blackman is a somewhat smaller species that occurs in California and Arizona, attacking *Cercidium.*

The species of *Micracis* (Blackman 1928a) occur principally in Eastern States and Mexico. *M. carinulatus* Wood is a little-known species that breeds in the wood of *Salix* in Arizona. The adults are 2.0 to 2.4 mm long. They resemble *Hylocurus* in appearance and habits. *M. lignator* Blackman bores in *Quercus* in Arizona and Mexico.

Micracisella contains five species in the United States. They closely resemble *Micracis.* Two of them, *M. knulli* (Blackman) and

*M. subnitid*a Blackman, bore in the pith of oak twigs in Arizona and Mexico.

Pseudothysanoes (Bruck 1936) contains 13 species in North America, several of them in the West. The adults resemble those of *Thysanoes. P. hopkinsi* Blackman breeds in *Fremontia californica* and *Salix* in California. *P. sedulus* Blackman (= *gambetti* Blackman) breeds in branches of *Quercus* in Arizona and New Mexico. *P. phoradendri* Blackman breeds in oak mistletoe, *Phoradendron*, in Arizona and California.

Thysanoes contains seven species in North America. They are brown to black, about 2 mm long, and resemble *Hylocurus*, except that their elytra are rounded rather than pointed in back. *T. xylophagus* Blackman is recorded on oak in Arizona and New Mexico. Its name suggests that it mines in wood.

Among the western bark beetles, *Ips* is second in destructiveness only to *Dendroctonus*. Twenty-five species are currently recognized in the West. Predominantly, they attack pines and spruces (table 14). In this manual they are discussed in 11 groups basically as proposed by Hopping (1963b), and subsequently modified by Lanier (1970a, 1970b, 1972, and in correspondence). The adults are reddish-brown to black, often shiny, cylindrical bark beetles ranging from about 3.0 to 6.5 mm long. A distinguishing feature of the genus is the pronounced concavity at the rear end (declivity) of the elytra of the adult, which is margined on each side with three to six toothlike spines (fig. 228). The number and character of these spines are major means for identifying the species. For that purpose, the spines are numbered from top to bottom (fig. 228A). The kind of host, geographic location, and gallery pattern are other practical aids in identification.

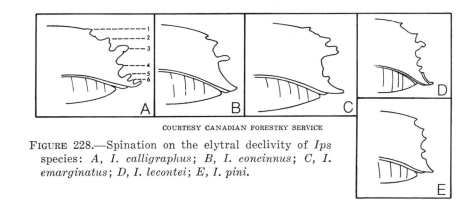

FIGURE 228.—Spination on the elytral declivity of *Ips* species: *A, I. calligraphus; B, I. concinnus; C, I. emarginatus; D, I. lecontei; E, I. pini.*

Table 14.—*Hosts and distribution of western species of* Ips

Group and species	Hosts	Distribution
Group 0		
I. latidens (LeConte)	*Pinus ponderosa, P. contorta, P. lambertiana, P. jeffreyi, P. monticola,* and *P. coulteri*	Pine region of Western Canada; south to Calif. and N. Mex.
I. spinifer (Eichhoff)	*Pinus sabiniana;* also *P. ponderosa, P. jeffreyi,* and *P. attenuata*	Calif. and Mexico
Group I		
I. concinnus (Mannerheim)	*Picea sitchensis*	Alaska to northern Calif.
I. mexicanus (Hopkins)	*Pinus contorta, P. radiata, P. albicaulis, P. attenuata, P. flexilis, P. muricata,* and other pines	Alaska to Mexico; eastward to Alberta, Wyo., and Colo.
Group II		
I. emarginatus (LeConte)	*Pinus ponderosa;* also *P. contorta, P. jeffreyi, P. lambertiana,* and *P. monticola*	British Columbia, Idaho, Mont., Wash., Oreg., and Calif.
I. knausi Swaine	*Pinus ponderosa, P. contorta,* and other pines	Ariz., N. Mex., and Colo.
Group III		
I. integer (Eichhoff)	*Pinus ponderosa;* also *P. contorta,* other pines, and *Picea*	British Columbia to Calif., Mont., Colo., Utah, Ariz., N. Mex., and Mexico
I. plastographus (LeConte)	*Pinus contorta, P. muricata,* and *P. radiata*	British Columbia, Oreg., Calif., Idaho, Mont., and Wyo.
Group IV		
I. bonanseai (Hopkins)	*Pinus ponderosa* and *P. flexilis*	Ariz. and Mexico
I. pini (Say)	*Pinus ponderosa, P. contorta, P. flexilis, P. jeffreyi,* and other pines; also *Picea*	Transcontinental, Western Provinces, and Western States including Alaska
Group V		
I. perroti Swaine	*Pinus banksiana* and *P. contorta*	Manitoba, Saskatchewan, and Alberta
Group VI		
I. hunteri Swaine	*Picea engelmannii* and *P. pungens*	Ariz. and Colo.
I. perturbatus (Eichhoff)	*Picea glauca, P. engelmannii,* and *P. sitchensis*	Western Provinces and Territories, Alaska, and Mont.

Table 14.—*Hosts and distribution of western species of* Ips—Continued

Group and species	Hosts	Distribution
I. woodi Thatcher	*Pinus flexilis*	Alberta, Mont., Wyo., Colo., Idaho, Utah, Nev., Ariz., Calif., and N. Mex.
Group VII		
I. borealis Swaine	*Picea glauca* and *P. engelmannii*	Transcontinental, Western Provinces and Territories, Alaska, and S. Dak.
Group VIII		
I. pilifrons Swaine	*Picea engelmannii* and *P. pungens*	Idaho, Wyo., Utah, Colo., Calif., Nev., Ariz., and N. Mex.
I. tridens (Mannerheim)	*Picea engelmannii, P. glauca,* and *P. sitchensis*	Alaska, Northwest Territories, British Columbia, Alberta, Idaho, Mont., Wyo., Oreg., and Calif.
Group IX		
I. confusus (LeConte)	*Pinus edulis, P. monophylla,* and occasionally other pines	Ariz., N. Mex., Colo., Utah, Nev., and Calif.
I. cribricollis (Eichhoff)	*Pinus ponderosa* and other pines	N. Mex. and Mexico
I. hoppingi Lanier	*Pinus cembroides*	Ariz. and Mexico
I. lecontei Swaine	*Pinus ponderosa* and some Mexican pines	Ariz., N. Mex., and Mexico
I. montanus (Eichhoff)	*Pinus monticola* and *P. contorta*	British Columbia, Wash., Oreg., Idaho, and Mont.
I. paraconfusus Lanier	*Pinus ponderosa, P. attenuata, P. contorta, P. coulteri, P. lambertiana, P. monticola, P. muricata, P. radiata,* and *P. sabiniana*	Oreg. and Calif.
Group X		
I. calligraphus (Germar)	*Pinus ponderosa, P. attenuata, P. flexilis,* and other pines	Transcontinental, Mont., Wyo., S. Dak., Nebr., Colo., Ariz., N. Mex., and Calif.
I. interstitialis (Eichhoff)	*Pinus ponderosa* and other pines	N. Mex. and Mexico

The first evidence of attack by *Ips* beetles is yellow or reddish boring dust in bark crevices or little piles of such dust around the entrance holes or on the ground beneath. Pitch tubes are seldom formed, and the boring dust is usually dry and free from pitch. Rapidly in summer and more slowly in fall and winter, the color of the foliage changes progressively from green to yellow, sorrel, and reddish brown. Upon removal of the infested bark, the tunnels of the beetles will be found grooving the inner bark surface and, where the phloem is thin, lightly to deeply grooving the sapwood. The egg galleries differ from those of the *Dendroctonus* beetles in that instead of being tightly packed with boring dust they are open runways in which the adult beetles are free to travel the entire length. A second difference is their polygamous social habit of constructing a central nuptial chamber from which fork or radiate several egg galleries.

Attacks are made by these bark beetles with the coming of warm weather in the spring. An adult male bores through the bark and constructs a small cell or nuptial chamber in the inner bark. Several females then join in the work and each constructs an egg gallery in which eggs are laid in niches along the sides. The larvae, upon hatching, feed in the inner bark and work away from the egg galleries, leaving gradually widening, excrement-packed tunnels behind them. When their feeding is completed, oval pupal cells are formed in which the transformations from larvae to pupae and then to adults take place. The period from the time of attack to the emergence of the new brood is ordinarily about $1\frac{1}{2}$ to 2 months. From two to five generations of these beetles may develop during the summer, depending on the altitude, latitude, and species, there being considerable overlapping of generations. The winter is usually spent in the adult stage, although occasionally eggs, larvae, and pupae are found. Some species congregate in large groups under the bark of standing trees and feed on the inner bark. Others emerge and hibernate under the bark of old stumps, among the bark scales, or in crevices and litter at the base of old brood trees.

Ips beetles have a number of predaceous and parasitic enemies, but apparently these do not affect the numbers of the beetles so much as does the lack of suitable host material. Given a quantity of freshly cut slash or windfalls, a large beetle population is almost certain to be produced, but it will not long survive after the supply of this material is exhausted.

Since outbreaks in standing, healthy trees are sporadic and of short duration, the application of direct control measures seldom contributes much to reducing the damage. Efforts should be directed toward preventing outbreaks of destructive species by eliminating situations favorable to the development of excessive progeny. Thus, slash should be piled and burned before the *Ips* beetles emerge, or should be scattered in the open where the sun will dry it out and make it unsuitable as a breeding medium. These precautions are most needed with slash created during the spring and early summer, particularly in times of below normal precipitation. Prompt salvage of windthrown and storm-damaged trees will help lessen the likelihood of *Ips* outbreaks. At times direct control by felling and burning infested trees or by treating with chemicals may be needed on intensive use areas, as around homes and on recreation areas.

Species in Group 0 (Hopping 1963a, Wood 1966) are intermediate between *Ips* and *Orthotomicus* and have been recorded in both genera. The adults, about 3.0 to 3.5 mm long, are the smallest western *Ips*. The elytral declivity is nearly vertical and is armed with three slender spines on each side. Pines are the only hosts.

Ips latidens (LeConte) (= *guildi* Blackman) attacks weakened or dying pines (table 14), usually in the tops and limbs of mature trees and in the bole of pole-sized trees. Under favorable conditions it has demonstrated its ability to kill trees, particularly those weakened by dwarf mistletoe or drought, and in some instances, apparently healthy trees of small diameter. During the severe drought of the 1930's, *I. latidens* was one of several bark beetles that bred in the top of "high risk" ponderosa pines in Oregon. During epidemics of mountain pine beetle in lodgepole pine, it sometimes develops in such numbers as to attack and kill many small trees. Its typical work consists of from two to five rather short, sometimes curved, egg galleries radiating from the central nuptial chamber.

Ips spinifer (Eichhoff) (= *sabinianae* (Hopping)) (table 14) closely resembles *I. latidens* but is appreciably more aggressive. It attacks the bole and larger branches of its principal host, *Pinus sabiniana,* frequently killing large trees, especially those damaged by fire or weakened by drought.

Species in Group I (Hopping 1963c) are about 3.5 to 4 mm long. The elytral declivity is nearly vertical and is armed with three spines (fig. 228B) as in Group 0. The egg galleries often form on overall "S" or "E" pattern and are unique among *Ips* in that two to five, usually four, eggs are laid in each egg niche. Spruces and pines are hosts.

The **Sitka spruce ips,** *Ips concinnus* (Mannerheim), commonly attacks the bole of injured, dying, and down Sitka spruce throughout its range (table 14), causing no appreciable economic damage. It closely resembles *I. mexicanus,* but differs in host.

The **Monterey pine ips,** *Ips mexicanus* (Hopkins) (= *radiatae*

Hopkins) (Struble 1961), attacks the bole of living, injured, dying, and recently down pines (table 14). Usually it is a secondary species and is associated with other bark beetles in its attack. In California it sometimes is a significant pest of Monterey pine, especially in plantations. Outbreaks are most likely where weakened trees are growing near accumulations of fresh slash which are favorite breeding grounds for the beetle. Inland, *I. mexicanus* commonly attacks lodgepole pine but does not become a pest. Up to three generations per year occur in coastal California. One generation may be the rule in the upper portions of its range. In areas where *I. mexicanus* is a problem, prompt disposal of slash larger than 80 mm in diameter is recommended.

Group II (Hopping 1963d) contains two species. Ranging from about 4.5 to 6.5 mm long, they are the largest western *Ips*. They usually have four spines on each side of the declivity, although the fourth one is quite small or sometimes missing. These species are unique in having the third spine emarginate at the apex (fig. 228C). Only pines are attacked.

The **emarginate ips** *(I. emarginatus* (LeConte)) (table 14) is most frequently found associated with the mountain pine beetle in its attacks on the bole of ponderosa, lodgepole, and western white pines, and with the Jeffrey pine beetle in Jeffrey pine, but occasionally kills trees by itself. The adults are dark brown, shiny, cylindrical bark beetles. Their work is characterized by the long, straight, nearly parallel egg galleries from 0.6 to 1.2 m (2 to 4 ft) long, which run up and down the tree and connect at different points (fig. 229). Owing to the similarity in length and width of the egg galleries, their work is often confused with that of the mountain pine beetle, with which they are so often associated. However, the presence of a nuptial chamber and the absence of packed boring dust distinguish the *Ips* galleries. In the northern part of its range this species has two complete generations a year, but in the southern part there are a number of summer generations with considerable overlapping of broods. This species has been included in control projects directed against *Dendroctonus*, but on its own has never required control.

Ips knausi Swaine (table 14) usually is a secondary species associated with tree-killing *Dendroctonus*. In its habits, the character of work, and appearance it closely resembles its near relative, *I. emarginatus*, and may be considered the southern Rocky Mountain form of this beetle.

The two species in Group III (Hopping 1963d, Lanier 1970a) are the only four-spined *Ips* with the sutures of the antennal club strongly and acutely angled at the middle. They are structurally very similar, hence difficult to distinguish. Pines are the principal but not exclusive hosts.

FIGURE 229.—Galleries and pupal cells of the emarginate ips (*Ips emarginatus*) on the inner bark surface of ponderosa pine.

Ips integer (Eichhoff) (Lanier 1970a) occurs widely in the West, but is most common in the Rocky Mountain Region (table 14). It breeds in the large portion of the bole of weakened and felled trees, principally ponderosa pine. It often attacks in combination with other bark beetles, such as *Ips pini,* and seldom if ever is primary. The adults are 4.5 to 6.2 mm long and have a prominent vertical ridge on the front of the head. This species constructs three or four straight longitudinal egg galleries that fork from the common entrance or nuptial chamber. The egg niches are so thickly and evenly spaced along the sides of the egg galleries as to give these a sawtoothed appearance—a distinctive feature of this species' work.

Ips plastographus (LeConte) (Lanier 1970a) (table 14) consists of two named subspecies. On the average, this species is slightly smaller than *I. integer* and the frontal ridge is lacking or inconspicuous. The galleries are constructed under the bark of the main bole and the pattern is very similar to that of *I. paraconfusus.* The typical pattern consists of three egg galleries from 10 to 35 cm long issuing from the nuptial chamber. *I. plastographus maritimus* Lanier occurs along the California coast in Monterey pine, Bishop's pine and the shore form of lodgepole pine (Trimble 1924). It is not often primary in its attacks, usually being associated with *I. mexicanus* and *Dendroctronus valens* in the killing of trees weakened by fire or other causes. This subspecies may have up to five generations annually. The typical species, *I. plastographus plastographus* (LeConte), occurs in the Sierra, Cascade, and northern Rocky Mountains, principally in lodgepole pine (Bright and Stark 1973). It is a secondary and often is associated with *I. pini* and *Pityogenes.* Some new adults emerge in the fall and construct irregular feeding galleries in fresh material. No eggs are laid in these galleries which may penetrate the sapwood 6 to 12 mm.

Group IV (Hopping 1964) contains two species in the West. They are four-spined *Ips* (fig. 228E). The spines of the female are about equal in size; the second and third are connected at the base by a curved ridge. Pines are the principal but not exclusive hosts.

Ips bonanseai (Hopkins) is a Mexican species that occurs northward into southern Arizona and New Mexico (table 14). In appearance and habits it closely resembles *I. pini.*

The **pine engraver,** *Ips pini* (Say) (Sartwell et al. 1971), is a transcontinental species, one of the commonest bark beetles in North America, and at times a serious pest. Long known as *I. oregonis* (Eichhoff) in the West, it is distributed extensively in the interior forests of the Western States and Provinces where it breeds in almost any species of pine (table 14). It is most commonly found attacking and killing ponderosa, Jeffrey, and lodgepole pines. Large numbers develop in such host material as windfalls, freshly cut logs, pieces of slash over 5 cm (2 in) in diameter, and in the tops and limbs of trees killed by *Dendroctonus* beetles. When suitable host material is plentiful, they frequently develop in such numbers as to become aggressive in their attacks on healthy living trees. Damage often follows droughty spring weather. Outbreaks are usually of short duration and seldom last more than one season. The most frequent damage is in the killing of young replacement trees from 5.0 to 20 cm (2 to 8 in) in diameter and the top-killing of older trees. During outbreaks, group-killing becomes widespread (fig. 230). In ponderosa pine the groups resemble those killed by *Dendroctonus ponderosae*. The gallery pattern beneath the bark identifies the culprit.

The adults are reddish brown to nearly black and from 3.5 to 4.2 mm long (fig. 231A). A typical sample of their work shows three or four egg galleries forking from a central nuptial chamber and running more or less longitudinally with the grain of the wood for a distance of 13 to 25 cm (5 to 10 in) (fig. 231B). There may be anywhere from one to seven females to each male, with as many egg galleries radiating from one nuptial chamber. There are

F-520749

FIGURE 230.—Ponderosa pines killed or top-killed by the pine engraver (*Ips pini*).

391

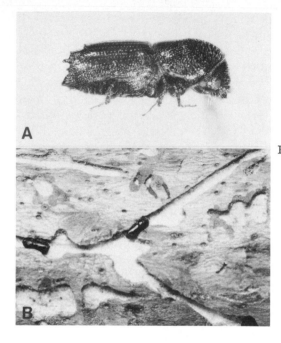

F–520750, F–523481

FIGURE 231.—Pine engraver (*Ips pini*): *A*, Adult, 3.7 mm long; *B*, egg galleries engraving the sapwood of ponderosa pine.

from one to five generations of this species a year, depending on the locality and the length of season. The parent adults often emerge and make a second and even a third attack, a habit that results in a confusing overlapping of broods. During late summer large numbers of beetles may attack and mine extensively under the bark without producing brood. The resulting galleries are mazelike. The winter is spent almost exclusively in the adult stage, either under the bark or in forest litter. Preventing these beetles from becoming too numerous through timely slash disposal and thinning of dense immature stands will do more to prevent damage than the application of control measures after damage has occurred.

Group V (Hopping 1964) contains one species. It is four-spined and unique in that the sutures of the antennal club are straight and transverse. Pines are the only hosts.

Ips perroti Swaine (Reid 1955) extends westward to northern Alberta on pines (table 14). It is not recorded in the Western United States. In lodgepole pine slash in Alberta, this species has one generation with two broods annually. The larvae have the unusual habit of developing in heavily blue-stained pockets adjacent to the egg galleries.

Group VI (Hopping 1965a) are four-spined *Ips* with the third declivital spine being enlarged and conical at the outer end in both sexes. The species are 3.5 to 5.2 mm long and are stouter than most *Ips*. The front of the head is not swollen as in Group VIII. Two species attack spruce; one, pine.

Ips hunteri Swaine is recorded from spruce in the Southwestern United States (table 14). The adult is 3.5 to 3.9 mm long and resembles the male of *I. pilifrons*. The gallery system usually consists of two egg tunnels extending in opposite directions from the entrance and is oriented at random. The biology is not reported.

Ips perturbatus (Eichhoff) (= *hudsonicus* (LeConte), = *interpunctus* (Eichhoff)) (Gobeil 1936) is abundant in northern coniferous forests. White spruce is its principal host (table 14). *I. perturbatus* breeds abundantly in logging and right-of-way slash and in tops of *Dendroctonus*-killed trees. In Alberta and British Columbia it sometimes kills trees in seed strips adjacent to logging operations. In Eastern Canada there is one generation annually. The females construct two sets of egg galleries the first year and sometimes a third set the following year. Winter is spent exclusively as adults in forest litter.

Ips woodi Thatcher apparently occurs throughout the range of limber pine, its only host (table 14). The biology is not recorded.

The species of Group VII (Hopping 1965b) are four-spined *Ips* that differ from all others in that the front of the head of the female is smooth, polished, and practically without punctures.

Ips borealis Swaine (= *swainei* R. Hopping) is commonly associated with *I. perturbatus* in white spruce, its principal host (table 14). The egg galleries are narrower than most other *Ips* within its range. Apparently this is a secondary species.

Group VIII (Hopping 1965c) until recently was ranked as the most confusing group of *Ips*. Discovery that females of the "species" in this group are of several types (Lanier and Oliver 1966) dispelled the confusion and reduced the named western species from 10 to 2 (Lanier in correspondence). They are spruce-infesting, four-spined *Ips* (table 14). The lower portion of the front of the head of the female usually is swollen and often bears a brush of hairs.

Ips pilifrons Swaine (= *sulcifrons* Wood, = *utahensis* Wood) (table 14) is reported to be the most abundant species of *Ips* in Engelmann spruce in Colorado. There it attacks recently down trees, and has been credited with depriving *Dendroctonus rufipennis* of favorable breeding places in windthrown timber, thereby reducing the threat of a spruce beetle outbreak. In Arizona it has caused scattered top-killing of mature spruce.

Ips tridens (Mannerheim) (= *amiskwiensis* G. Hopping, = *engelmanni* Swaine, = *dubius* Swaine, = *interruptus* (Mannerheim), = *semirostris* G. Hopping, = *yohoensis* Swaine)

(Bright and Stark 1973) (table 14) is notable principally for its many aliases. They came about because the females are of several forms. *I. tridens* attacks only weakened and down trees, hence is not economically important.

Group IX (Hopping 1965d, Lanier 1970b) contains seven species, six of which are western. All attack only pines. Three of the western species are serious pests. The members of the group are unique in being five-spined (fig. 228D). Usually the third and largest spine is notched on the lower side. The adults range in size from about 3.0 to 5.5. mm long.

The **piñon ips,** *Ips confusus* (Leconte) is appropriately named. Because of taxonomic confusion, most of the published information regarding *"I. confusus"* in California and Oregon actually concerns *I. paraconfusus.* The real *I. confusus* breeds primarily in pinyon pines (table 14) and at times kills them extensively in Southwestern States. Such outbreaks commonly and quickly develop in trees that are injured or uprooted as in land clearing for range improvement. Damage is most significant in National Parks and Monuments, around homes, and on other areas of intensive use. Three and sometimes four generations are produced annually. From November through March the adults hibernate en masse under the bark of standing trees, mostly in the basal portion of the bole (fig. 232) (Chansler 1964). Prompt disposal of slash to prevent population buildups is highly desirable where pinyon occurs extensively.

Ips cribricollis (Eichhoff) (= *cloudcrofti* Swaine) is a secondary enemy of ponderosa pine in New Mexico. Southward it attacks various other pines in Mexico. Ranging in length from 3.1 to 3.9 mm, it is a smaller replica of *I. confusus.*

Ips hoppingi Lanier (Lanier 1970b) occurs on Mexican pinyon in southern Arizona and southward in Mexico. Its habits are not recorded.

The **Arizona fivespined ips,** *Ips lecontei* Swaine (fig. 233A) (Massey 1971), closely resembles *I. confusus* but differs in that the first and second teeth on the declivity are more widely separated. Ponderosa pine is the principal host of *I. lecontei* (table 14). It is ranked as the most destructive pine bark beetle in central and southern Arizona where it frequently kills sapling and pole-sized ponderosa pine extensively in groups up to 100 or more. This species has the reputation of being strongly attracted to freshly cut pine, even pine lumber, and attacking trees nearby.

Males are polygamous; there is an average of three galleries per nuptial chamber (fig. 233B). The upper bole is attacked first; then the lower bole is filled in either by this or other species of *Ips* or by *Dendroctonus.* There are three generations annually. The

394

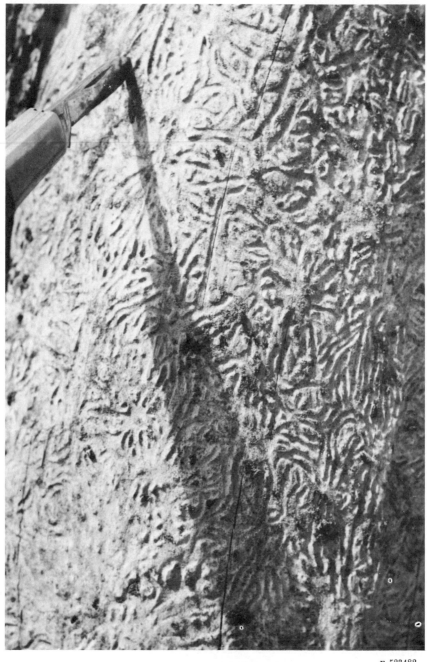

FIGURE 232.—Winter feeding sites of the piñon ips (*Ips confusus*), resulting in etching of the xylem.

395

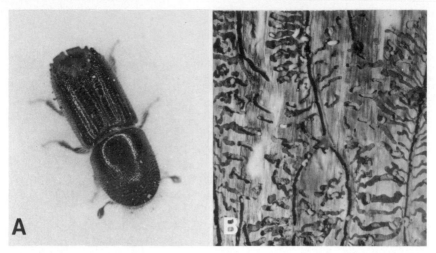

FIGURE 233.—Arizona fivespined ips (*Ips lecontei*): *A*, Adult, about 4 mm long; *B*, egg and larval galleries in the inner bark of ponderosa pine.

adults overwinter in colonies forming irregular galleries under the bark of the bole and usually occurring in greatest numbers between 1.5 and 3.0 m (5 and 10 ft) above ground level. Outbreaks are of short duration, hence it is more practical to prevent them than to try to control them. Prompt disposal or treatment of slash over 7.6 cm (3 in) in diameter produced in spring or early sumer is necessary to prevent outbreaks of this beetle.

Ips montanus (Eichhoff) (= *vancouveri* Swaine) resembles *I. confusus*, but it is slightly larger and considerably less aggressive. *I. montanus* usually attacks decadent, weakened, and down western white pine, its principal host (table 14), and commonly occurs in association with *Dendroctonus ponderosae*. The gallery pattern is a radiating, longitudinal type with three to five short egg galleries extending up and down the tree from the nuptial chamber. Two generations per year apparently are the rule.

The **California fivespined ips,** *Ips paraconfusus* Lanier (Bright and Stark 1973, Lanier 1970b, Struble 1966, Struble and Hall 1955), closely resembles *I. confusus*. They differ in hosts and range. Most of the published information concerning *I. paraconfusus* will be found under the name of its look-alike kin. The California fivespined ips occurs from southern Oregon to southern California west of the summit of the Cascade and Sierra Nevada Mountains. All species of pines within this range may be attacked (table 14). In the central Sierras, ponderosa pine is especially susceptible. This bark beetle kills saplings, poles, young trees up to about 65 cm (26 in) in diameter and the tops of even larger trees. During spring it breeds in fresh slash and recently down trees. During summer the broods that develop in such material often emerge and kill nearby living trees. Outbreaks characteristically build up and subside in 1 year. At times young ponderosa pine is killed extensively in groups up to 500 or more trees. Top-killing by *I. paraconfusus* sometimes stimulates attacks by *Dendroctonus brevicomis* and thus contributes to outbreaks of this destructive beetle.

The egg galleries comprise from three to five nearly straight tunnels radiating from a central entrance chamber. The typical pattern consists of three galleries in the form of a tuning fork or an inverted "Y." Males attack first. When an attack is successful, a potent attractant is produced which leads to mass attack and characteristic group-killing. Attacks are started early in the spring and from two to five generations of beetles may develop during the summer.

In the northern part of the range, at an elevation of about 1000 m, there are usually two summer generations which develop in fallen logs and a third, or overwintering generation, which develops in standing trees. At lower altitudes and in the southern part of the range there are from three to five summer generations. Most of the beetles overwinter in the adult stage under the bark of recently killed trees. In midsummer and fall, saplings and poles may be attacked and the phloem extensively fed upon by adults that produce no brood.

Some attempts have been made to control outbreaks of this beetle by salvage logging, burning, or chemically treating infested trees during the winter and early spring. Usually such methods are not warranted, as outbreaks are brief and sporadic and can be avoided if roadway, powerline, or other slash created in late winter to early summer is burned or lopped and scattered where it will be fully exposed to the sun. Such precautions are especially important in years showing a marked deficiency in spring precipitation.

Group X (Hopping 1965e) stands apart as the only six-spined *Ips* (fig. 228A). It contains two species, both of which occur in the West on pines. Neither is economically important in the West. The adults range from about 4.0 to 6.5 mm long.

The **sixspined ips,** *Ips calligraphus* (Germar) (Ciesla 1973, Lanier 1972), is a transcontinental species, consisting of two subspecies. The typical form, *I. calligraphus calligraphus* (Germar) (Wood and Stark 1968), occurs principally in the East but also in California where it presumably was introduced. In California it is a secondary enemy of ponderosa pine, attacking trees that are down or those dying from attacks of more destructive insects such as *Dendroctonus brevicomis, Melanophila californica,* and *Ips paraconfusus.* The thick-barked portions of the bole are preferred. The gallery pattern consists of two to six egg galleries extending 25 to 38 mm up and down the tree from the nuptial chamber. Though the pattern is similar to that of *I. pini,* the galleries are wider and etch the wood deeper. In California there are four generations annually. The subspecies, *I. calligraphus ponderosae* Swaine, occurs extensively in the West, principally on ponderosa pine (table 14). It is somewhat larger than the typical form of the species. The biology is not recorded.

Ips interstitialis (Eichhoff) is a southwestern species that closely resembles *I. calligraphus* in appearance and presumably in habits (table 14).

The species of *Monarthrum* are small, elongate, cylindrical, dark-brown ambrosia beetles that resemble *Gnathotrichus.* They work in the wood of dead and seriously weakened oak and various other hardwoods. After the beetles have entered the wood, they excavate a central nuptial chamber from which secondary tunnels branch in three or four directions. The larval cradles are excavated at right angles from the secondary branches and parallel to the grain of the wood.

The **oak ambrosia beetle**, *M. scutellare* (LeConte) (Doane and Gilliland 1929), 3.5 to 4 mm long, bores in various oaks from British Columbia to southern California. *Ambrosiella brunnea* (Verrall) Batra (Batra 1967), the fungus upon which the beetle feeds, is stored and disseminated by the female (Farris 1965). *M. huachucae* Wood is a similar species that attacks oaks in Arizona. *M. dentiger* (LeConte) is a smaller species in oaks in California and Arizona.

Myeloborus (Blackman 1928b) contains eight species in North America; six of them are western. All breed in the needle-bearing portion of twigs of pine. The egg tunnels are constructed principally in the pith. The larvae mine out the infested twigs, thus killing them. As twig pruners, the species are mildly beneficial. In appearance, the adults are intermediate between *Pityophthorus* and *Conophthorus.* Representative species are *M. amplus* Blackman in *Pinus ponderosa* in Arizona and New Mexico and *M. boycei* (Swaine) in *P. ponderosa* and *P. contorta* in California, Oregon, Wyoming, and Colorado.

Orthotomicus resembles *Pityokteines* and some small species of *Ips* (Hopping 1963a). *Orthotomicus* contains one species in North America.

Orthotomicus caelatus (Eichhoff) (= *vicinus* LeConte) (Reid 1955) is transcontinental, occurring extensively in the Western Provinces and States, including Alaska. Southward it ranges into

398

Colorado and northern California. Some of its principal hosts are *Pinus contorta, P. monticola, Picea engelmannii, P. glauca, P. sitchensis,* and *Larix occidentalis.* It is a secondary species. Attacks are made in fresh stumps and the lower bole of large standing trees, often in combination with other bark beetles. The gallery pattern is radiate, similar to that of *Ips,* but smaller. In Alberta one generation and two broods annually are the rule.

Pityoborus (Wood 1958a) contains seven species, mostly Mexican. One occurs in the West.

Pityoborus secundus Blackman breeds in small, shaded-out branches on living *Pinus ponderosa* in the La Sal Mountains of Utah, and in Arizona and Mexico. The adult is dark reddish brown and is about 2.5 mm long. The female has a velvetlike, yellowish patch on each side toward the front of the pronotum. The gallery system etches the wood and consists of a nuptial chamber, two transverse egg galleries, and up to five feeding tunnels. The short larval mines resemble larval cradles of ambrosia beetles.

Pityogenes (Chamberlin 1939) contains six species in North America. Three of them occur extensively and abundantly in the West. Pines are their principal hosts. They usually are of secondary importance and attack the tops and limbs of weakened, dying, and newly felled trees; but under favorable conditions they may develop in sufficiently large numbers to attack and kill small trees growing near their breeding place. The biology of *P. hopkinsi* Swaine, an eastern species, was reported in detail by Blackman (1915). The biology of the western species is less thoroughly documented.

The adults are slender, dark brown beetles, 2 to 3.5 mm long. Varying by species, they have two or three spinelike teeth on the sloping rear end (declivity) of each wing cover. The teeth are much larger in the males, with the upper pair often developed into prominent curved spines. The females have a hole in the front of the head. Several egg galleries, each containing a female, radiate from the nuptial chamber containing one male. The galleries score the sapwood and generally resemble those of *Pityophthorus.*

Records indicate that significant damage by *Pityogenes* rarely occurs. Prompt slash disposal on areas of potential hazard should forestall any possible outbreaks.

Pityogenes carinulatus (LeConte) (Bright and Stark 1973) breeds principally in ponderosa pine, much less frequently in Jeffrey, whitebark, lodgepole, and other pines. It occurs in most Western States and British Columbia, occasionally causing economic damage. For example, in 1967 in New Mexico thousands of young ponderosa pines were killed by an epidemic of this beetle that developed in thinning and logging slash. The females have three spines on the elytral declivity, the males two. The hole in the head of the female is large and undivided. Two generations per year are reported as probable in California.

Pityogenes fossifrons (LeConte) breeds principally in western white pine. It also attacks whitebark, limber, foxtail, bristlecone, Jeffrey, and lodgepole pines, and Engelmann spruce. It ranges from British Columbia and Idaho to California and Utah. Its attacks are seldom primary, although it sometimes attacks western white pine reproduction. The adults have three very small spines along each margin of the elytral declivity, somewhat larger in the males. The hole in the head of the female is large and undivided.

Pityogenes knechteli Swaine (Reid 1955) occurs principally in lodgepole pine. Other recorded hosts are pinyon, ponderosa, and western white pines. It occurs in Alberta, British Columbia, and California, and presumably throughout the range of lodgepole pine. Small-diameter slash and thin-bark portions of the bole of trees killed by *Dendroctonus* and *Ips* are normal breeding places for *P. knechteli*. Sometimes it multiplies greatly and spills over into green trees, thus killing small patches of lodgepole pine reproduction. In slash in Alberta it has one generation with two broods annually. The hole in the head of the female is vertically divided into two parts.

Pityokteines [*Orthotomicus, Orthotomides*] (Bright and Stark 1973) contains six species in North America. The five western species are secondaries. The adults resemble *Orthotomicus*. They are 1.5 to 2.5 mm long and the front of the head of females usually bears long yellow hairs. *P. ornatus* (Swaine) breeds in *Pinus ponderosa*, *P. jeffreyi*, and *P. contorta*. Attacks are made near the base under thick bark, often in association with *Dendroctonus* and other bark beetles. The egg galleries radiate from the central chamber in a pattern similar to those of *Pityogenes*. Hosts and distribution of other western species of *Pityokteines* are:

Species	Hosts	Distribution
P. elegans Swaine	Abies and Pseudotsuga menziesii	British Columbia and Idaho to Calif.
P. lasiocarpa (Swaine)	Abies lasiocarpa	British Columbia to Utah
P. minutus (Swaine)	Abies lasiocarpa	Alberta and British Columbia to Calif. and N. Mex.
P. mystacinus Wood	Abies grandis	Wash.

Pityotrichus [*Pityophilus*] (Bright 1971) contains two species, both of them in Arizona and New Mexico. *P. barbatus* (Blackman) occurs on *Pinus edulis* and *P. ponderosa,* and *P. hesperius* Bright on *P. flexilis* and *P. strobiformis.* Habits are not recorded. The adults are slightly less than 2 mm long and resemble *Pityophthorus* except that the under portion (gula) of the head of the females of *Pityotrichus* is bearded with long yellow hairs.

Pityophthorus (Blackman 1928b), with upwards of 120 species, is the largest genus of bark beetles in North America. Many species are western. None is economically important. As a group, they are mildly beneficial in the process of natural pruning. With few exceptions, they breed in conifers, principally pines. More than 20 species occur on *Pinus ponderosa,* and numerous species occur on each of several other trees. Relatively few attack more than one genus of tree. Injured, dying, dead, and down trees are attacked. Generally they breed in twigs and small branches, hence are among the several genera of Scolytidae known as **twig beetles.** Some attack larger branches and the thin-barked portions of the bole, often in association with other bark beetles.

Identification is for experts and for students of taxonomy. The most comprehensive key is by Blackman (1928b), but it does not include numerous recently described species. Adult *Pityophthorus* range from about 1.5 to 3.0 mm long. The typical work consists of a central nuptial chamber under the bark, from which radiate several egg galleries each occupied by a female beetle (fig. 234).

F–523483

FIGURE 234.—Typical galleries of a twig beetle *Pityophthorus pseudotsugae.*

Eggs are placed in large niches along the side of these egg galleries, and the larvae, on hatching, work through the cambium of the twig and, on reaching full growth, pupate at the end of the larval mines, often in the wood or pith of small twigs. There are usually two or more generations of the beetles each year, the number varying with the locality.

Pityophthorus confertus Swaine and *P. confinis* LeConte have been recorded as killing the tips of apparently healthy ponderosa pine in California (Salman 1938) but it is likely that the trees actually were suffering from prolonged drought. Both of these species are widespread on pines in the West. Like others in the genus, they must be rated as secondaries.

P. pseudotsugae Swaine (fig. 234) occurs extensively in the West on Douglas-fir and various true firs. Hemlock also is a recorded host. *P. nitidulus* (Mannerheim) which attacks pines and spruces from Alaska to California is another of the relatively few *Pityophthorus* that attack more than one genus of trees.

P. orarius Bright (Hedlin and Ruth 1970) in British Columbia kills Douglas-fir twigs by mining in the pith much as do the species of *Myeloborus*. This type of twig-killing also reduces the cone crop. *P. juglandis* Blackman in Arizona and California on *Juglans* is one of the few western species attacking a nonconifer.

Pseudopityophthorus (Blackman 1931b) contains 11 species in North America, 6 of them in the West. The western species occur principally in oaks, hence are known as **oak bark beetles**. *Lithocarpus densiflorus* and *Umbellularia californica* also are recorded hosts. These beetles sometimes finish off seriously weakened trees. Typically they infest the bole and branches of injured, felled, or recently dead trees, or the dead branches of otherwise healthy trees. They often are a nuisance in houses by emerging in great numbers from cordwood. In the East, species of *Pseudopityophthorus* are among the suspected insect vectors of oak wilt, *Ceratocystis fagacearum* (Bretz) Hunt (Jones and Phelps 1972).

The adults of western species are cylindrical, brownish beetles about 2 mm long. The elytra are clothed with short, sometimes scalelike hairs. The egg galleries (fig. 235) are mostly in the inner bark and are free of frass. They consist of two transverse arms, one on each side of the entrance tunnel. The larval mines run longitudinally with the trunk or limb. In California two or more generations per year are reported.

The **western oak bark beetle**, *P. pubipennis* (LeConte), is the most common species from British Columbia to southern California. *P. agrifoliae* Blackman occurs in central and southern Cali-

402

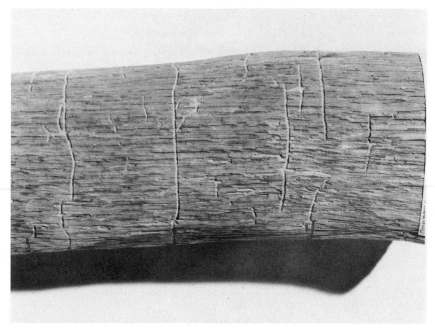

FIGURE 235.—Egg galleries of the western oak bark beetle
(*Pseudopityophthorus pubipennis*).

fornia and in Arizona. *P. yavapii* Blackman apparently is the most
prevalent of the four species in Southwestern States.

Scolytus (Blackman 1934, Edson 1967) contains an array of 18
species in the West (table 15). Many are quite similar in appearance and consequently are difficult to identify. One species

Table 15.—*Hosts and distribution of western species of* Scolytus

Species	Hosts	Distribution
S. abietis Blackman	*Abies grandis, A. concolor*; occasionally other *Abies* and *Tsuga*	Wash. and Idaho to Calif.
S. dentatus Bright	*Abies bracteata*	Calif.
S. fiskei Blackman	*Pseudotsuga menziesii* and *Abies grandis*	British Columbia and Wash. through Rocky Mountains to Ariz. and N. Mex.
S. laricis Blackman **larch engraver**	*Larix occidentalis* and *L. lyallii*	British Columbia, Wash., Oreg., Idaho, and Mont.
S. multistriatus (Marsham) **smaller European elm bark beetle**	*Ulmus*	Introduced from Europe, now recorded in most Western States and Provinces.

Table 15.—*Hosts and distribution of western species of* Scolytus—Cont.

Species	Hosts	Distribution
S. *obelus* Wood	*Abies concolor* and *A. lasiocarpa*	Nev., Utah, Colo., Ariz., and N. Mex.
S. *opacus* Blackman	*Abies lasiocarpa*, occasionally other *Abies*, *Pseudotsuga menziesii*, and *Picea*	Idaho, Mont., Wyo., Utah, and Colo.
S. *oregoni* Blackman	*Pseudotsuga menziesii*, *P. macrocarpa*, and *Abies concolor*	Wash. to Calif.
S. *piceae* (Swaine) **spruce engraver**	Most species of *Picea*; occasionally *Abies* and *Larix*	Transcontinental, Alaska to Calif., Wyo., Colo., and Utah
S. *praeceps* LeConte	*Abies concolor*, *A. magnifica*; occasionally other *Abies*, *Pseudotsuga menziesii*, and *Tsuga*	Wash. to Calif.
S. *reflexus* Blackman	*Pseudotsuga menziesii*	Ariz.
S. *robustus* Blackman	*Abies concolor*, *A. grandis*, *A. lasiocarpa*; and *Pseudotsuga menziesii*	Nev., Utah, Colo., Ariz., and N. Mex.
S. *rugulosus* (Ratzeburg) **shothole borer**	Apple, cherry, plum, pear, and other fruit trees; also mountain-mahogany	Introduced from Europe; now occurs in most orchard areas of West.
S. *subscaber* LeConte	*Abies concolor*, *A. magnifica*, and *A. grandis*	British Columbia and Idaho to Calif.
S. *tsugae* (Swaine) **hemlock engraver**	*Tsuga heterophylla*, *T. mertensiana*, and *Pseudotsuga menziesii*; occasionally *Pinus monticola*, *Abies*, and *Larix*	British Columbia to Calif., Idaho, Mont., and Wyo.
S. *unispinosus* LeConte **Douglas fir engraver**	*Pseudotsuga menziesii*, occasionally *Abies* and *Tsuga*	British Columbia to Calif., Idaho, and Mont.
S. *ventralis* LeConte **fir engraver**	*Abies concolor*, *A. grandis*, and *A. magnifica*; occasionally other *Abies*, *Pseudotsuga menziesii*, *Tsuga*, and *Picea*	British Columbia to Calif., Wyo., Colo., Ariz., and N. Mex.
S. *wickhami* Blackman	*Pseudotsuga menziesii*; occasionally *Abies* and *Pinus*	Idaho, Colo., Utah, Nev., Ariz., and N. Mex.

(*ventralis*) is a wideranging tree killer of major pest significance in the management of western forests. Another (*multistriatus*) is important as a carrier of Dutch elm disease. The others are secondaries, some of which flare up occasionally and kill trees locally. Most western species breed in conifers, especially true firs and Douglas-fir. Two introduced species are exceptions in that they attack hardwoods.

Members of the genus *Scolytus* are shiny, dark brown to black bark beetles, 2 to 5 mm long. They are easily recognized by the "sawed-off," sometimes concave, rear end of the abdomen (fig. 236). The structure of the abdomen and the presence or absence of spines and tubercles on it aid in determination of species. The female makes the initial attack and later is joined by one male. Attacks are made on the bole and larger limbs. The typical egg gallery system consists of a small nuptial chamber from which two galleries extend in opposite directions, either longitudinal with or transverse to the grain, depending upon the species. The longitudinal type of egg galleries usually are somewhat offset at the nuptial chamber, resulting in an alignment similar to that of a bayonet attached to a gun barrel. *Scolytus* galleries resemble those of *Pseudohylesinus* but tend to be more regular in pattern and to etch the wood more deeply.

F–523485

FIGURE 236. Adult of *Scolytus multistriatus*, 2.7 mm long; note "sawed-off" abdomen.

Scolytus abietis Blackman and *S. opacus* Blackman are closely related species varying from about 2 to 3 mm long. They differ in range and principal host (table 15). Both attack the limbs and upper bole of living trees and also fresh slash. Their gallery pattern is transverse, often forming a very wide "V."

Scolytus dentatus Bright (Bright 1964) attacks the bole and larger limbs of bristlecone fir in the Santa Lucia Mountains of California. It is slightly smaller than *S. subscaber*. The egg gallery extends vertically above and below the entrance hole, and each of the two arms ends in a pronounced hook.

The **larch engraver**, *Scolytus laricis* Blackman (Blackman 1934), resembles *S. unispinosus*, but differs from this and most other species of *Scolytus* in that it breeds only in larch (table 15). *S. laricis* attacks distressed trees of pole size, suppressed limbs on larger trees, and also slash.

The **smaller European elm bark beetle**, *Scolytus multistriatus* (Marsham) (Baker 1972), is the principal vector of the Dutch elm disease fungus, *Ceratocystis ulmi* (Buisman) C. Moreau, in

405

North America. It is an introduced species now widespread in the West (table 15). The Dutch elm disease has accompanied its carrier into Colorado, Wyoming, Idaho, and Oregon and further spread of this destructive disease of shade trees seems inevitable.

The adult (fig. 236) is 2.2 to 3.0 mm long. Presence of a prominent spine on the second abdominal segment of *S. multistriatus* readily separates this species from *S. rugulosus* which is unarmed and is the only other hardwood-infesting western *Scolytus*. Newly emerged adults bore into the crotches of twigs on living trees to feed and thereby inoculate the wood with fungus spores carried on their bodies. After feeding, they attack the limbs and bole of injured or weakened standing or recently down trees. The egg gallery is longitudinal with the grain and the larval galleries fan out on both sides, often in a strikingly regular pattern. In southern California there are two complete generations and a partial third annually (Brown and Eads 1966). There the brood overwinters as larvae, pupae, and adults.

Losses caused by Dutch elm disease can be minimized by eliminating favorable breeding material, by spraying to prevent beetles from feeding on healthy elms, and by planting trees resistant to or nonsusceptible to the disease (Schreiber and Peacock 1974).

The **spruce engraver**, *Scolytus piceae* (Swaine) (Edson 1967), occurs in northern forests from coast to coast, principally in spruce (table 15). The second abdominal segment is armed with a spine in both sexes. It differs from all other spined *Scolytus*, except *multistriatus*, in that the spine is separated at the base from the margin of the segment on which it stands. The gallery pattern usually is the bayonet type. Reportedly this species breeds in broken limbs and tops.

Scolytus praeceps LeConte (Struble 1957b) (table 15) commonly fills in the top and branches of fir trees attacked by *S. ventralis*, and sometimes independently kills severely distressed saplings. *S. praeceps* also attacks fresh slash. It varies from 2.2 to 3.0 mm long. The second abdominal segment sometimes bears a low, vertical ridge on its underside. The egg galleries are transverse and generally resemble those of *S. ventralis*, but are shorter, narrower, and less regular. One generation is produced each year. *S. obelus* Wood, *S. oregoni* Blackman, and *S. robustus* Blackman are similar but little-known species (table 15).

The **shothole borer**, *Scolytus rugulosus* (Ratzeburg) (Bright and Stark 1973, Smith 1932), was introduced from Europe and now occurs in most fruit-growing areas of the United States and Canada. It breeds principally in distressed fruit trees and broadleaved ornamental trees (table 15). *S. rugulosus* varies from about 2.0 to 3.0 mm long. It differs from *S. multistriatus* in that the abdomen slopes up gradually and is unarmed rather than being steep and armed with a spine. Adults of the shothole borer kill small twigs by feeding at the base of buds. Brood galleries are constructed in the limbs and bole, often killing them through repeated attacks. The mature larvae commonly bore into the wood to pupate.

Scolytus subscaber LeConte (table 15) attacks suppressed branches of true firs, hence may be mildly beneficial. The adults, up to 4.9 mm long, are the largest western species. The egg gallery, unique for the genus, resembles a rounded capital "E," less than 25 mm across (fig. 237). These galleries are deeply etched in the wood and remain imprinted and identifiable for years on fallen branches.

F-523486

FIGURE 237.—Egg galleries of *Scolytus subscaber;* note E-shaped form.

The **hemlock engraver,** *Scolytus tsugae* (Swaine) (= *monticolae* Swaine) (McMullen and Atkins 1959), is of minor economic importance. Normally it attacks tops, limbs, and logging slash of Douglas-fir, hemlock, and several other conifers (table 15). Occasionally it kills sapling and pole-size trees. An example of such killing of Douglas-fir, presumably weakened by drought, occurred in 1956 in Wyoming near Yellowstone National Park.

The adults are about 3.0 to 3.5 mm long, and the abdominal segments are unarmed in both sexes. On Douglas-fir in interior

British Columbia the egg galleries are the longitudinal, bayonet type (McMullen and Atkins 1959). The galleries of *S. tsugae* (fig. 238) resemble those of *S. unispinosus* and *Pseudohylesinus nebulosus*, but differ from the former in being wider and from the latter in conspicuously etching the wood. In British Columbia the life cycle is 1 year.

FIGURE 238.—Egg and larval galleries of *Scolytus tsugae*.

S. reflexus Blackman and *S. wickhami* Blackman closely resemble *S. tsugae* in body size and structure. They attack principally Douglas-fir (table 15).

The **Douglas fir engraver,** *Scolytus unispinosus* LeConte (McMullen and Atkins 1962), commonly attacks weakened, injured, dying, and recently dead young Douglas-fir (table 15), often in association with *S. tsugae*. It also attacks slash and the tops and limbs of trees killed by *Dendroctonus pseudotsugae*. During periods of drought, large populations sometimes breed in slash and then kill nearby young Douglas-fir. Such outbreaks are sporadic and of short duration. Examples occurred in northwestern California in 1958 and 1959, in Oregon in 1959, and in Washington in 1961.

The adults are variable in size, but average somewhat less than 3 mm long. The male has a prominent spine projecting from the middle of the nearly vertical second segment of the abdomen. The female has only a tubercle in that location. The gallery is longitudinal and quite similar to that of *Pseudohylesinus nebulosus*, but differs in having a well-defined nuptial chamber that etches the wood. The larvae work out at right angles to the egg gallery and then turn either up or down. In interior British Columbia, attacks occur in May, June, and July, depending upon the weather; larvae overwinter; and there is one generation per year. In California there are two generations per year.

S. fiskei Blackman is a very similar species that somewhat overlaps the range of *S. unispinosus* but occurs principally in the Rocky Mountain Region.

The **fir engraver**, *Scolytus ventralis* LeConte (Stevens 1956, Struble 1957b), is a major pest of true firs in western forests (table 3). It attacks trees from pole-size to full maturity, causing a yearly kill estimated to be 450 million fbm in California alone. Periodic epidemics cause even greater mortality. Such outbreaks often occur during and following periods of drought. Trees infected with *Fomes annosus*, a root-rot fungus, are especially subject to attack (Cobb et al. 1974). Trees defoliated by the Douglas fir tussock moth also are likely to be attacked by *S. ventralis*. It also breeds in slash and windthrown trees.

Attacks are made on the bole from the base to the top where *S. praeceps*, *S. robustus*, *S. obelus*, and other bark beetles take over. On the lower bole, *Tetropium abietis* is a frequent associate. Trees may be killed outright, may be top-killed, or may survive repeated attacks for many years. Broods often develop and emerge without destroying enough of the cambium to kill the tree. The patch of dead cambium heals over and leaves a brown pitch pocket in the wood to mark the place of injury. Some wood sections have shown as many as seven attacks during the life of a tree. The usual external evidence of such attacks is roughened patches of bark or scattered dead branches girdled at the base by the egg galleries. The beetles transmit a brown-staining fungus, *Trichosporium symbioticum* Wright, that apparently is essential for successful brood development.

The adults average about 4.0 mm long and are among the largest species of *Scolytus*. The second abdominal segment of the male has a sharp, median tubercle on its underside; that of the female has only a faint tubercle, or none at all. The egg galleries (fig. 239A) are excavated in the inner bark and cut transversely across the grain of the wood, which they score rather deeply for a distance of 5 to 15 cm (2 to 6 in) on both sides of a central entrance chamber.

Deep scoring of the wood differentiates their attacks from those of *Pseudohylesinus* and *Dryocoetes*. Eggs are laid in niches along both sides of these galleries and the larvae, on hatching, work up

F-523488, F-480681

FIGURE 239.—Fir engraver (*Scolytus ventralis*): *A*, Old egg galleries engraved on the sapwood of grand fir; *B*, larval galleries radiating from an egg gallery.

and down the bole (fig. 239B), extending their individual larval mines for a distance of 13 to 18 cm (5 to 7 in). Pupation occurs in the inner bark at the end of the larval mines, and the new adults bore directly to the surface of the bark when ready to emerge. These beetles have one generation annually in much of their range, but in the colder portions may require 2 years to complete the life cycle. Because of the sporadic character of outbreaks and the prevalence of healthy broods in living trees, direct control measures are generally impractical. On intensive use areas, prompt removal or treatment of infested trees may help protect remaining trees for a time, but the principal effort should be on measures to minimize soil compaction, excess exposure, and other adversities to tree vigor. In the forest, stand sanitation and improvement measures to keep the trees in healthy, vigorous condition are the most practical means for minimizing losses caused by the fir engraver.

The genus *Trypodendron* (Wood 1957) contains five species in North America, four of which occur in the West. Entomologists know them as **ambrosia beetles** because the larvae feed upon a special kind of fungus. Log scalers and lumber graders know them as **pinhole borers** because the defect caused by their galleries usually consists of small holes surrounded by dark brown or black stain (fig. 240A). The adults are stubby, generally shiny, dark-colored beetles, often with lighter colored longitudinal stripes (fig. 240B). They range from about 3 to 4.5 mm long. The head and thorax of the female are rounded in front. The head of the male is dished out and the thorax is straight across its front. Males average smaller than females. These beetles bore in the wood of many conifers and some broad-leaved trees. Their galleries are of the compound type with larval cradles arranged in series both above and below the main tunnels, which branch in a horizontal plane and cut across the grain of the wood (fig. 240C). The brood live in these cradles and feed on the ambrosia fungus. The fungus, *Ambrosiella ferruginea* (Math-Kaarik) Batra, is disseminated by the female which stores it in cells (mycangia) in the thorax (Batra 1967).

The **striped ambrosia beetle**, *Trypodendron lineatum* (Olivier) (Wood 1957), recorded variously in the literature as *T. bivittatum* Provancher, *T. borealis* Swaine, and *T. cavifrons* Mannerheim, is holarctic. In the West it ranges from New Mexico and southern California to the northern limits of tree growth. Commercially, it is most significant on *Abies, Picea, Pseudotsuga,* and *Tsuga.* In some areas it also normally attacks species of *Larix* and *Pinus.* It

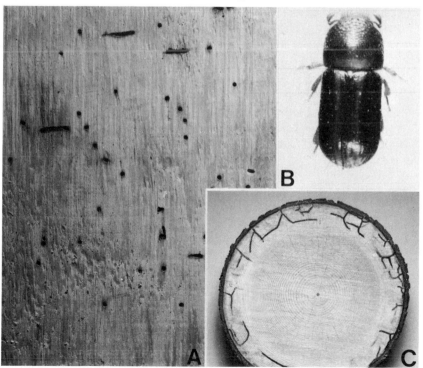

FIGURE 240.—Striped ambrosia beetle (*Trypodendron lineatum*): *A,* Pinhole defect, with staining; *B,* adult, 4.0 mm long; *C,* galleries.

411

is the most damaging ambrosia beetle in the West, reaching peak destructiveness in coastal British Columbia (Dyer and Wright 1967).

The adults are dark brown to black with two lighter longitudinal stripes on each elytron. There is one generation annually in coastal forests, although a small percentage of adults reemerge and establish a second brood. In coastal Oregon, attacks begin in March, reach a peak in May and continue into August (Rudinsky and Daterman 1964). Entrances to the galleries are marked by piles of fine, granular, white boring dust in the bark crevices (fig. 209B). Development from egg to adult requires about 6 to 8 weeks. The new adults emerge in July, August, and September and go into hibernation in duff and litter on the forest floor.

Populations build up in windthrown and fire-killed trees, bases of bark-beetle-killed trees, in logging slash, and in logs stored for long periods. Logs cut in autumn and early winter are most susceptible to attack. Attacks can be prevented by spraying with chemicals, but this sometimes has created environmental problems. Prompt harvesting of logs prior to and during the flight period will minimize attacks. Logs should be promptly utilized or stored in areas remote from beetle concentrations.

Trypodendron retusum (LeConte) (Wood 1957) is somewhat larger than *T. lineatum* and the female is uniformly black when mature. It attacks aspen and poplar. In the West it evidently occurs throughout the range of its host trees.

Trypodendron betulae Swaine (Wood 1957) is an eastern species that breeds principally in species of *Betula,* occasionally in *Alnus.* It ranges westward into the Black Hills of South Dakota. Each wing cover of both sexes is marked with one broad yellowish stripe.

Trypodendron rufitarsis (Kirby) (= *ponderosae* Swaine) (Wood 1957) is similar to *T. lineatum,* but there is only one yellowish marking on each wing cover and the surface of the elytra is dull and finely reticulate rather than smooth and shining. *T. rufitarsis* occurs in the coniferous forests of Canada and the Western States, including Alaska. Species of *Picea* and *Pinus contorta* are the principal hosts in the West.

Xyleborus [*Xyleborinus*] (Bright 1968) is a large and destructive genus in the tropics, but it is of minor economic importance in North America where there are 17 species, 3 of which are western. All are ambrosia beetles and bore in the wood. Females far outnumber the males, which are smaller and do not fly. The mature brood overwinters in the galleries.

The **European shothole borer,** *Xyleborus dispar* (F.) (= *Anisandrus pyri* Peck) (Mathers 1940), was introduced from Europe.

It occurs extensively in the Western States and Canada, where it attacks devitalized fruit trees and many other deciduous trees. The adult female is black and about 3.0 to 3.5 mm long.

Xyleborus saxeseni (Ratzeburg) (Bright 1968) is a transcontinental species and has been recorded under various names including *X. arbuti* Hopkins, *X. libocedri* Swaine, and *X. tsugae* Swaine. In the West, it occurs in British Columbia, Washington, Oregon, California, Arizona, and Utah. It attacks many kinds of hardwoods, such as *Acer* and *Arbutus*, also *Pseudotsuga, Tsuga, Abies, Pinus,* and *Libocedrus,* but is not economically damaging. The tiny-gauge tunnels, ending in enlarged brood chambers, readily distinguish the work of this species from the larger tunnels of other ambrosia beetles in western conifers. The brood moves freely in the galleries, feeding upon the ambrosia fungus, *Ambrosiella saxeseni* (Batra 1967). The adult female is shiny dark brown, about 2 mm long, and thinly hairy.

Xyleborus intrusus Blandford (= *scopulorum* Hopkins) (Bright 1968) is similar to *X. saxeseni* but somewhat larger. In the West, *X. intrusus* attacks various conifers, including *Pinus* and *Pseudotsuga.*

ORDER DIPTERA—FLIES

The Diptera (Stone et al. 1965) are **flies,** typified by the **house fly,** but including such things as midges, gnats, and mosquitoes. The great majority have one pair of functional wings and a rudimentary hind pair that resemble two stalked knobs. Some are wingless or have only rudimentary wings. The larvae are legless and commonly known as maggots. There are more than 16,000 species of Diptera in North America of which more than 8,000 western species are discussed by Cole (1969). In western forests, many flies are beneficial by parasitizing pest insects, some are food for fish and aquatic birds (Usinger et al. 1963), some damage trees, and some are a nuisance or are outright harmful to man and animals. As a group, the Diptera contain few species that are seriously destructive to forest trees.

Species discussed in this manual are grouped under three suborders—Nematocera, Brachycera, and Cyclorrhapha. For keys to these higher categories see Cole (1969).

SUBORDER NEMATOCERA

SUPERFAMILY TIPULOIDEA

The Tipulidae predominate this superfamily (Stone et al. 1965).

FAMILY TIPULIDAE—CRANE FLIES

The **crane flies** (Cole 1969) comprise the largest family of Diptera. The adults are small to large, slender, long-legged, brown or gray flies that resemble mosquitoes but fortunately do not bite. Probably the huge mosquitoes of legend are crane flies mixed with some real mosquitoes. Crane fly larvae develop in moist situations and are seldom seen by foresters, except for species such as *Ctenophora vittata* Meigen which bores in wet rotten wood from California to British Columbia.

SUPERFAMILY CULICOIDEA

Nine families comprise this superfamily in North America (Stone et al. 1965). The species of greatest concern in wooded areas are the ones that torment man and animals by feeding upon their blood.

FAMILY CERATOPOGONIDAE—BITING MIDGES

The **biting midges** (Wirth 1952), often called "no-see-ums" because of their tiny size, are troublesome in wooded areas, especially in the morning and evening when they attack in clouds. They have a fiery bite out of proportion to their size. More than 100 species are recorded in California. *Culicoides obsoletus* (Meigen) occurs extensively in the West and often is troublesome to campers and fishermen.

FAMILY CHAOBORIDAE—PHANTOM MIDGES

The **phantom midges** (Cole 1969) closely resemble mosquitoes but do not feed on blood. The gilled, nearly transparent larvae live in water, often deep below the surface. Some species, such as the **Clear Lake gnat,** *Chaoborus astictopus* Dyar and Shannon, are a nuisance in lakeshore resort areas because of the fantastic abundance of the adults. Chemical control has proven difficult because of adverse effects upon other organisms.

FAMILY CULICIDAE—MOSQUITOES

The **mosquitoes** (Stage et al. 1952) can make life miserable in spring and summer for the woodsman or recreationist caught without a supply of repellent. The female does the biting. The larvae, known as "wigglers," develop in shallow quiet water such as the edges of log ponds and in pools of melted snow water. Species of *Aedes* and *Culex* are the principal nuisance mosquitoes. *C. tarsalis* Coquillett, a very common northwestern species, is a vector of encephalitis in man. *Anopheles freeborni* Aiken, a vector of malaria, occurs widely in the Northwest.

FAMILY SIMULIIDAE—BLACK FLIES

The **black flies** (Sommerman et al. 1955) vie with mosquitoes for the role of most pestiferous biting insects in the "North

414

Woods." The adults descend on man, animals, and birds in swarms in spring and early summer. In Alaska there are 38 species, but fortunately only a few feed on humans. Repellents afford relief. Southward they generally are less abundant, especially in dry areas. The adults are humpbacked, chunky insects, somewhat shorter than a small mosquito. The larvae develop in running water. One generation per year is typical but some species have two or more.

SUPERFAMILY MYCETOPHILOIDEA

The Cecidomyiidae (Stone et al. 1965) is the only one of the five families in this superfamily that is of consequence to foresters.

FAMILY CECIDOMYIIDAE (ITONIDIDAE)—GALL MIDGES

The **gall midges** (Cole 1969) comprise a large family of flies of diverse habits. Most species feed on higher plants, including many forest trees, and often cause galls. Others feed on fungi. Some are predaceous on mites and other insects. The adults are small delicate flies that resemble mosquitoes. Their antennae are long and beaded, necklace fashion. The larvae usually are orange, pink, or yellow. When mature, larvae of many species have a dark spadelike structure, "breastbone," on the thorax. Classification is based upon microscopic examination of slide-mounted adults. Practical identification requires a knowledge of the host and type of gall produced (Felt 1940). Almost any part of a tree may be affected, but most galls are formed on the needles or leaves, in the cones or seeds, or in the bark of twigs. Some gall midges are economically damaging to forest trees but none is a major forest pest.

Alassomyia [*Allomyia*] *juniperi* (Felt) produces on Utah juniper a prickly, burrlike bud gall with numerous short, straight leaves and none reflexed.

The species of *Aphidoletes* (Stone et al. 1965) prey upon aphids and related insects. *A. thompsoni* Möhn (Mitchell and Wright 1967) (fig. 241) from Europe has been established as a predator of *Adelges piceae* in Oregon, Washington, and British Columbia.

Camptomyia pseudotsugae Hedlin and Johnson (Hedlin and Johnson 1968) occurs in Douglas-fir cones infested with the gall midge, *Contarinia washingtonensis*. The relationship has not been determined.

The western species of *Cecidomyia* [*Retinodiplosis*] (Vockeroth 1960) develop in pines and are known as **pitch midges** or **resin midges**. They form pits in the outer layers of new twigs or live in exuded resin masses.

The **gouty pitch midge,** *Cecidomyia piniinopis* Osten Sacken

415

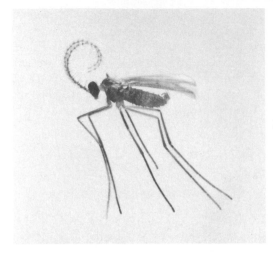

F–523490

FIGURE 241.—A typical gall midge adult, *Aphidoletes thompsoni.*

(Eaton and Yuill 1971), occurs from coast to coast. In the West on its principal host, ponderosa pine, it is known as the **bird's-eye pine midge** or **ponderosa pine resin midge**. Mistakenly, it has been reported to cause the "bird's-eye" figure in pine lumber. In California, Oregon, Washington, Idaho, and Montana, it commonly infests young, open-grown pines, especially in plantations. It attacks only the current year's shoots, often deforming and sometimes killing them (fig. 242A). Attacks are heaviest on trees with sticky twigs and lightest on trees with dry, powdery twigs (Austin et al. 1945). Severe attacks retard tree growth and repeated attacks sometimes kill trees. The damage is first noticeable very early in the summer when the new shoots fade, droop, and gradually turn yellow and die. On some trees nearly every new shoot is affected. When the bark is removed, the infested tips will be found to be pitted with small resinous pockets in which are small bright red maggots (fig. 242B). If the pockets are not numerous enough to kill the terminal, the injury heals over, but for several years the annual rings are distorted into a peculiar whorl until the pocket is completely covered. *C. piniinopis* has one generation per year. The larvae overwinter in pits under the bark. Populations fluctuate widely from year to year due to natural control.

Cecidomyia reeksi Vockeroth (Reeks 1960) is the more common of two species of *Cecidomyia* on *Pinus banksiana* in Manitoba and Saskatchewan. The larvae develop and feed in pitch masses on the shoots. Sometimes the shoots die. Occasionally young trees are killed outright. There is one generation annually.

The **Monterey pine resin midge**, *Cecidomyia resinicoloides* Williams, inhabits the resin exudations of Monterey pine but apparently is not injurious to the trees.

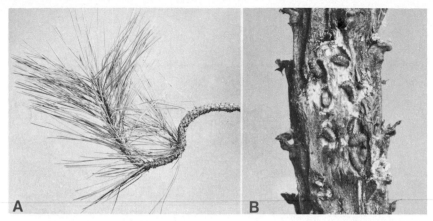

FIGURE 242.—Gouty pitch midge (*Cecidomyia piniinopis*) : *A*, Stunting and twisting of growth of ponderosa pine, caused by repeated attacks; *B*, maggots, 4 to 5 mm long, embedded in woody tissue of new growth.

Contarinia (Gagné 1967, 1973) contains nearly 60 species in North America, several of which are significant forest pests. All are host specific.

Contarinia [*Thecodiplosis*] *cockerelli* (Felt) causes galls at the base of needles of *Pinus edulis*.

The **pine budgall midge**, *Contarinia coloradensis* Felt, forms apical budlike swellings on twigs of ponderosa pine in Colorado.

The **Douglas fir cone midge**, *Contarinia oregonensis* Foote (Hedlin 1961), is one of several insects that destroy seeds of Douglas-fir. In some years and some places it is the most destructive species (Johnson and Heikkenen 1958). It occurs in California, Oregon, Washington, and British Columbia. The larvae form single or aggregate galls in the seed coat thus destroying the seed outright or making it impractical to extract (fig. 243). Eggs are laid in female conelets during the brief period they are open for pollination. There is one generation annually, but diapause for 1 or more years is common. When the infested cones become wet in the fall, the mature larvae, orange in color, drop to the ground and overwinter in litter.

The **cone scale midge**, *Contarinia washingtonensis* Johnson (Hedlin and Johnson 1963), damages seeds of Douglas-fir in Oregon, Washington, and British Columbia. It resembles *C. oregonensis* but feeds in the cone scales without causing galls and lays its eggs in half- to full-grown cones.

Three species of *Contarinia* develop in the new needles of Douglas-fir, causing characteristic galls (fig. 244). *C. pseudotsugae* Condrashoff (Condrashoff 1962a) is the most abundant of the three. It is a significant pest of Christmas trees, particularly in dry-belt, open-grown, interior forests (Condrashoff 1962b). It

417

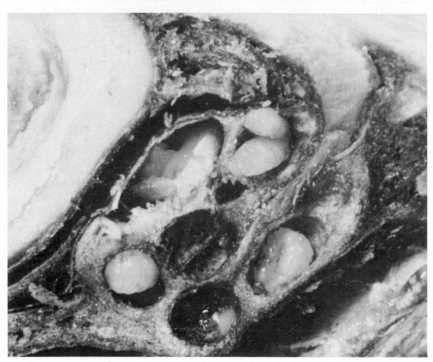

FIGURE 243.—Section of cone damaged by Douglas fir cone midge (*Contarinia oregonensis*) ; note numerous larvae and destruction of seed.

occurs in California, Oregon, Washington, British Columbia, Idaho, and Montana. There is one generation annually. Adults emerge from the soil early in May and lay their eggs on the needles. The usually yellowish larvae feed in the needles, often several per needle. In late fall and early winter they drop to the ground where they hibernate. Pupae form in the spring. Heavy infestations cause much of the foliage to drop and sometimes kill twigs. Populations fluctuate widely from year to year. The other two species, *C. constricta* Condrashoff and *C. cuniculator* Condrashoff, are similar but much less abundant. Both occur in British Columbia and Montana, and the former is also in California.

Dasineura (Stone et al. 1965) has nearly 100 species, mostly eastern. Three of the western species feed in cones of conifers but cause little damage (Keen 1958).

Dasineura rachiphaga Tripp (Keen 1958) develops in the axis of the cones of *Picea glauca* across North America into Alaska. It probably is the most abundant insect in white spruce cones in British Columbia (Hedlin 1973). It also attacks cones of *P.*

418

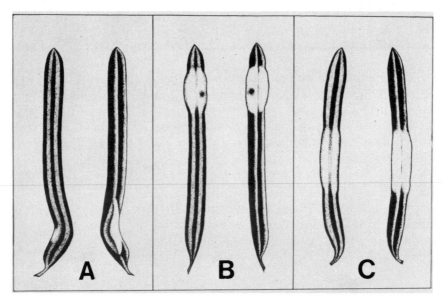

FIGURE 244.—Needle galls on Douglas-fir caused by: *A, Contarinia cuniculator*; *B, C. constricta*; *C, C. pseudotsugae*.

engelmannii, P. mariana, and *P. sitchensis. D. canadensis* Felt forms a small gall in the cone scales of the same four species of spruce and is common in British Columbia. *D. abiesemia* Foote forms galls on seeds and cone scales of various species of *Abies* in the Western States.

The **piñon stunt needle midge,** *Janetiella* sp. near *coloradensis* Felt (Brewer 1971), stunts the needles of *Pinus edulis* in Colorado. It attacks the developing needles at the base causing a small basal gall and premature shedding. This insect is a serious pest of ornamentals but causes little damage in the forest. Eggs are laid in May and June. The larvae are orange. Usually only two develop to maturity in each needle fascicle. The larvae overwinter in the needles. There is one generation a year.

Janetiella siskiyou Felt (Keen 1958) damages seeds of *Chamaecyparis lawsoniana* in Oregon.

Mayetiola (Stone et al. 1965) contains 34 species, many of which were described in *Phytophaga* and *Oligotrophus.* Most are gall formers, principally on trees and shrubs. Several are western.

The **spruce gall midge,** *Mayetiola piceae* (Felt) (Smith 1952), forms hemispherical galls in clusters on the current year's shoots of *Picea glauca* in Manitoba, Alberta, and Yukon. Heavily infested shoots become twisted and frequently die.

Mayetiola thujae (Hedlin) (Hedlin 1964) seriously damages

419

seeds of *Thuja plicata* in Oregon, Washington, and British Columbia. The free-feeding, orange larvae spend their lives in the cones and pupate there in papery cocoons. There is one generation annually.

The **juniper tip midge**, *Oligotrophus betheli* Felt (Tonks 1974), forms reddish, apical, conical galls on *Juniperus* in Colorado, Utah, and British Columbia.

Pinyonia contains one species, the **piñon spindle gall midge,** *P. edulicola* Gagné (Houseweart and Brewer 1972), principally a pest of ornamentals. It occurs in Colorado and presumably other Western States. The larvae mine in the current year's needles causing a spindle-shaped gall near the base (fig. 245) and premature shedding. The galls average about 11 mm long and contain from 5 to 40 of the orange larvae. The larvae overwinter in the galls. There is one generation annually.

FIGURE 245.—Needle galls on pinyon, caused by piñon spindle gall midge (*Pinyonia edulicola*).

Rhabdophaga (Stone et al. 1965), a sizable genus, contains one or two species of some interest to western foresters.

The **spruce bud midge,** *Rhabdophaga swainei* Felt (Clark 1952), occurs in Alberta, Yukon, Northwest Territories, and eastward.

It mines the vegetative buds of *Picea glauca* and *P. mariana* causing multiple branching. This species, or a similar one, attacks young *Picea sitchensis* in coastal British Columbia.

Rhopalomyia sabinae Patterson attacks juniper in Colorado and Utah and produces thick-walled, purplish, apical bud galls which split open in four sections when the midges emerge.

The **Monterey pine midge**, *Thecodiplosis piniradiatae* (Snow and Mills), works at the base of the newly formed needles of Monterey pine and other pines in central California and causes them to become swollen and shortened (fig. 246). Sometimes heavily infested twigs are killed and the ornamental value of the trees is impaired.

EPQ-8749A

FIGURE 246.—Basal needle galls on Monterey pine caused by Monterey pine midge (*Thecodiplosis piniradiatae*).

The species of *Walshomyia* (Gagné 1969) form galls on *Juniperus*, *Cupressus*, and *Libocedrus*. They are closely related to *Oligotrophus*. *W. insignis* Felt causes oval, apical bud galls on *Juniperus scopulorum*. *W. juniperina* Felt occurs in the fruit of *Juniperus osteosperma*.

421

SUBORDER BRACHYCERA

SUPERFAMILY TABANOIDEA

Seven families comprise this superfamily (Stone et al. 1965). Two of them, the Rhagionidae and Tabanidae, contain biting flies that often are troublesome to man and animals in the forest.

FAMILY RHAGIONIDAE—SNIPE FLIES

The **snipe flies** (Leonard 1930) are predaceous, moderate- to large-sized flies with a tapering abdomen and without bristles. The genus *Symphoromyia* (Aldrich 1916b) contains several species that are annoying and painful biters of man, domestic animals, and wildlife. Predominantly western, the flies of this genus generally are blackish and from 5 to 9 mm long. These silent-winged, docile, hard-biting flies are most frequently encountered in mountainous areas and seem most troublesome in northern forests, although California is home for most species. The larval habits are little known.

FAMILY TABANIDAE—DEER AND HORSE FLIES

The **deer flies** and **horse flies** (Cole 1969) are a large family containing the largest of the blood-sucking flies. The adults are stout, bristleless, big-eyed flies. They are strong fliers, persistent in attack, and vicious biters. As with mosquitoes, the females do all the biting. They lurk in the edge of forest openings and are most active on clear days. The larvae of most species are aquatic or semi-aquatic. Good control measures apparently are lacking. The horse flies, *Tabanus* (Stone 1938) and allied genera, are generally brownish or black flies that are commonly 12 to 20 mm long or longer. They are most often encountered around horses. The deer flies, *Chrysops* and allies, rarely over 12 mm long, have mottled wings and have spurs on the hind tibiae whereas *Tabanus* does not. Deer flies often occur in wooded situations far from livestock.

SUPERFAMILY ASILOIDEA

The Asilidae and the Bombyliidae, two of the eight families in this superfamily (Stone et al. 1965), rank as mildly beneficial in the forest.

FAMILY ASILIDAE—ROBBER FLIES

The **robber flies** (Hull 1962) are one of the largest families of insects. About 4,760 species are known. The adults are hairy, generally long-bodied, fast fliers that prey on many kinds of insects and are often seen in openings in and near the forest. Larvae of many asilids live in soil; some live in rotting wood. In general, the asilids are minor elements in the natural control of forest insects.

The larvae of *Laphria gilva* (L.) are associated with cerambycid larvae in wood and have been stated to prey upon them. *L. gilva* adults were observed to destroy about 1 percent of emerging *Dendroctonus ponderosae* in the Black Hills of South Dakota (Schmid 1969).

FAMILY BOMBYLIIDAE—BEE FLIES

The Bombyliidae (Cole 1969) share with some Syrphidae and Asilidae a similarity to bees. Adult bombyliids are fuzzy, compact, medium- to large-sized flies ranging from brown and black to silver and gold. The wings often are clouded and the mouth parts much elongated. In flight they hover hummingbird style. This large family is prevalent in dry areas, scarce in wet areas. The larvae of most species are parasitic or predaceous on Lepidoptera, Hymenoptera, and Diptera. In the forest they apparently are of minor importance. One or more species have been reared from *Neodiprion* sawfly cocoons.

SUPERFAMILY EMPIDOIDEA

The two families in this superfamily are of little interest to foresters except for *Medetera,* a genus of predators in the Dolichopodidae (Stone et al. 1965).

FAMILY DOLICHOPODIDAE—LONGLEGGED FLIES

The Dolichopodidae (Cole 1969) is a large family of small, long-legged flies many of which are predaceous both as larvae and as adults. The larvae of *Medetera* feed on immature stages of bark- and wood-boring insects, principally scolytids. *M. aldrichii* Wheeler (Johnsey et al. 1965), a widely distributed western species, is an important predator of *Dendroctonus ponderosae, D. pseudotsugae* and *D. rufipennis.* The adult is somber gray and about 4 mm long. The full-grown larva is white, cylindrical, pointed at the head end, and about 8.5 mm long (fig. 247).

SUBORDER CYCLORRHAPHA

SUPERFAMILY SYRPHOIDEA

This superfamily contains three families in North America. Only the Syrphidae is significant to foresters.

FAMILY SYRPHIDAE—FLOWER FLIES

The **flower flies** (Stone et al. 1965) are a large family, many of which are beneficial as predators of other insects or as pollinators.

F-523493

FIGURE 247.—Nearly mature larva, about 8 mm long, of *Medetera aldrichii* in a spruce beetle gallery.

The adults are medium- to large-sized flies, strong and quick in flight, and often strikingly marked with black and yellow in mimicry of bees and wasps (fig. 248A). Larvae vary greatly in form and habits. Larvae of species that feed upon aphids have fleshy pseudopods, are usually pale brown to pale green in color, and move freely among their prey (fig. 248B).

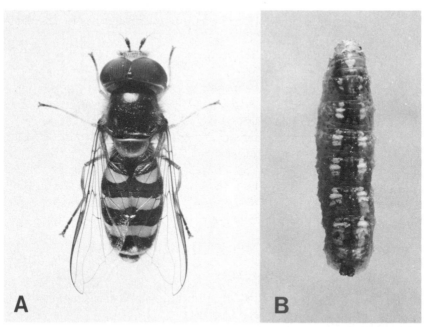

F-523494, F-523495

FIGURE 248.—Examples of flower flies predaceous on balsam woolly aphid: *A*, Adult of *Syrphus opinator* Osten Sacken; *B*, larva of *S. vitripennis*. Both, about 10 mm long.

424

Syrphus vitripennis Meigen is one of five native insects recorded as preying upon the balsam woolly aphid in Oregon and Washington (Mitchell 1962).

Cheilosia is a large genus, the larvae of which mine in plants (Cole 1969). Some species, known as **bark maggots**, mine in the cambium region of conifers. They cause defects consisting of dark brown or blackish resinous scars surrounded by curled, thickened wood (fig. 249B). This type of defect is prevalent in western hemlock growing in western Washington and Oregon at elevations below 550 m and is called the "black check" of hemlock. These defects do not impair the wood for structural purposes but degrade it for interior finishing and other special uses.

The **hemlock bark maggot**, *Cheilosia burkei* Shannon, was studied in detail by Burke (1905) who reported it as *C. alaskensis* Hunter, an Alaskan species. The small dark blue adults presumably lay their eggs on or in resin in wounds caused by *Pseudohylesinus*. The maggots enter the bark through the beetle-caused wounds, enlarge them, and feed on the sap and soft tissues causing a flow of resin at the surface (fig. 249A). The larvae, when full grown,

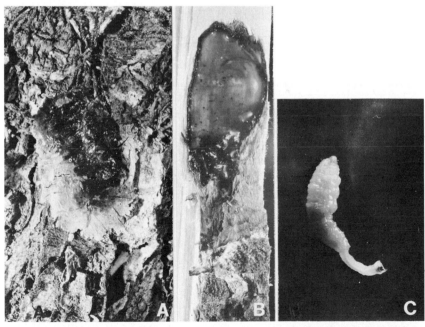

F–523496, F–523497, F–523498

FIGURE 249.—Hemlock bark maggot (*Cheilosia burkei*): *A*, Resin flow on bark of western hemlock caused by feeding of maggot; *B*, defect caused on face of sapwood; *C*, larva, about 10 mm long.

are white maggots 15 to 20 mm long, with the forepart of the body thickened and with a long, telescopic, protractile tail that extends out through the resin for breathing (fig. 249C). Feeding continues for several years, then in the spring puparia are formed in the resin at the entrance of the wound, and the adult flies emerge in April and May. This species occurs in California, Oregon, and Washington. Damage of the same type occurs on hemlock in Alaska.

The **fir bark maggot**, *C. hoodiana* (Bigot), does similar work in white fir and grand fir. It occurs along the Pacific coast and eastward to New Mexico. The adult is greenish black. Other species of *Cheilosia* of little-known habits feed in subalpine fir, Sitka spruce, and probably other western conifers.

SUPERFAMILY LAUXANIOIDEA

This superfamily contains three families, one of which, Chamaemyiidae, contains predators of aphids, scales, and mealybugs.

FAMILY CHAMAEMYIIDAE

The Chamaemyiidae (Cole 1969) are small, chunky, dusty-gray flies. The larvae of some species prey upon aphids, scales, and mealybugs. *Leucopis obscura* Haliday and *Cremifania nigrocellulata* Czerny have been colonized in Oregon from Europe against *Adelges piceae* but are not exerting effective control (Mitchell and Wright 1967).

SUPERFAMILY PALLOPTEROIDEA

This superfamily contains five families, of which only the Lonchaeidae is of concern to foresters.

FAMILY LONCHAEIDAE

The Lonchaeidae (Cole 1969) are small, shiny, black flies (fig. 250A). The female ovipositor is elongate and sword-shaped. Two genera are frequently encountered by foresters: *Earomyia*, in cones, and *Lonchaea*, under bark of trees.

Earomyia (McAlpine 1956) (fig. 250) in North America contains eight species, most of which infest cones. In older literature, the cone-infesting species were listed as belonging to *Lonchaea*. The maggots are among the most abundant and important destroyers of fir seeds (Keen 1958). *E. barbara* McAlpine is most cosmopolitan in its hosts, which include species of *Abies*, *Picea*, *Pinus*, *Pseudotsuga*, and *Tsuga*. It occurs from California to British Columbia, Alberta, and Colorado. *E. abietum* McAlpine attacks cones of several species of *Abies* from California to British Columbia.

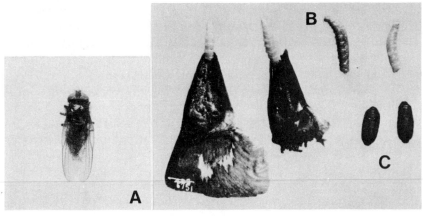

EPQ–2077, EPQ–5751

FIGURE 250.—A cone maggot, *Earomyia* species, on white fir: *A*, Adult, 4.5 mm long; *B*, larvae, 8 mm long; *C*, puparia, 5 mm long.

The genus *Lonchaea* (McAlpine 1964) contains about 60 species, several of which are associated with western bark beetles and weevils. Although some species have been reported as significant predators, there is uncertainty regarding their actual role. The adults are quite similar, hence there is confusion in the literature regarding their identification. The cone-infesting species have been transferred to *Earomyia*. *L. furnissi* McAlpine occurs in galleries of *Dendroctonus pseudotsugae* in Douglas-fir in Oregon, Washington, Idaho, and British Columbia. It is considered to be a scavenger rather than a predator (Johnsey et al. 1965). *L. reidi* McAlpine is associated with *Dendroctonus ponderosae* in pine from California to British Columbia and Idaho. A species of *Lonchaea* often is abundant in galleries of *Pissodes strobi* in spruce in the West and is reported to be an important predator of this weevil (Evans and Dyer 1952).

UNPLACED AS TO SUPERFAMILY

FAMILY AGROMYZIDAE—LEAFMINER FLIES

The **leafminer flies** (Frick 1959, Spencer 1969) are a large family of small to minute black or yellow flies. The larvae are soft, white, headless, and legless, and have paired, hooklike mouth parts. Most species mine leaves of plants, including broad-leaved trees and shrubs. Some are stem miners. Agromyzids usually mine one or only a few related species of plants. The nature of the mine together with the species of host plant often are sufficient evidence for identifying the species of leafminer.

427

A few of the many species of *Agromyza* mine tree leaves. The adults are black, often with yellowish markings and white halteres. *A. albitarsis* Meigen forms a large blotch mine in leaves of *Populus trichocarpa* in British Columbia. It also occurs in Europe and has been reported in Washington and California.

Phytobia contains species that mine in the cambium region of broad-leaved trees and shrubs. *P. pruinosa* (Coquillett) (Greene 1914) is an example. It attacks apparently healthy birch as far west as Colorado, causing a lumber defect known as pitch-ray fleck.

The **holly leafminer,** *Phytomyza ilicis* Curtis (Weigel and Baumhofer 1948), is an import from Europe that has become a pest of ornamental holly from California to British Columbia. The mines, visible on the upper leaf surface, are at first narrow and winding, later blotchlike. There is one generation annually. The larvae overwinter in the mines and the flies emerge in May.

SUPERFAMILY MUSCOIDEA

In North America, this superfamily includes two large and closely related families, the Anthomyiidae and Muscidae, and four small families of ectoparasites (Stone et al. 1965).

FAMILY ANTHOMYIIDAE—ANTHOMYIID FLIES

The Anthomyiidae (Cole 1969) resemble the Muscidae and at times have been considered as part of that family. They are medium-sized, generally grayish or brownish flies. The larvae of most species feed in plant tissues, often the roots. Some are scavengers and a few are predators.

Hylemya (Stone et al. 1965) contains many species, several of which are very destructive to agricultural crops. A few are forest pests.

Hylemya abietis Huckett (Keen 1958), is a spiny, black fly, 8 to 9 mm long. The larvae are white and compressed and have two large hooks at the head end. They bore through the cones of *Abies concolor* and probably other true firs in California and Oregon, destroying up to 30 percent of the seed. *H. anthracina* (Czerny) (Hedlin 1973), a similar but smaller species, damages seeds of *Picea engelmannii*, *P. glauca*, *P. mariana*, *P. sitchensis*, and *Tsuga mertensiana*.

The **seedcorn maggot,** *Hylemya platura* (Meigen) (= *cilicrura* Rondani) (Breakey et al. 1945), a cosmopolitan pest that attacks young plants and planted seeds of numerous agricultural crops, also kills seedling conifers. In 1944 it killed about 20 percent of the Douglas-fir seedlings in one nursery in western Washington. More recently it has caused considerable damage to Douglas-fir in a forest tree nursery in western Oregon. Sitka spruce also is killed. Maximum damage is done early in the spring on cold, wet sites where the soil has an abundance of organic matter. Nurseries near heavily infested agricultural crops apparently suffer most from this insect.

The seedcorn maggot passes the winter in the prepupal or pupal stage within a brown puparium, about the size of a grain of wheat, at a depth of 15 to 18 cm in the soil. In April the ash-gray flies (fig. 251A), about 5 mm long, emerge and lay their eggs in the soil just as the ground begins to crack above the germinating seed. At rest, the two wings are folded back so the outer edges are nearly parallel. The full-grown maggots are legless, about 6 mm long, yellowish white, tough-skinned, sharply pointed at the head end, and blunt and strongly tuberculate at the rear. The maggots feed below ground level, gouging the lowermost part of the stem and the upper part of the taproot. The effect (fig. 251B) resembles damping-off. Adults emerge late in July or early in August. There are two or more generations a year.

Insecticides applied just prior to adult flight have given satisfactory control. Exact timing is essential.

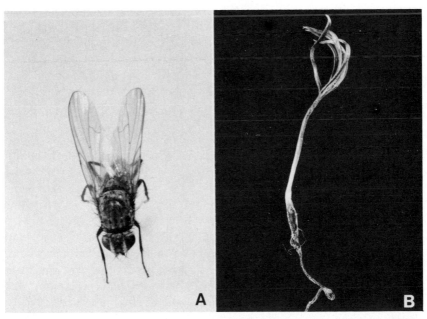

F–523499, F–523500

FIGURE 251.—Seedcorn maggot (*Hylemya platura*): A, Adult, 5 mm long; B, damaged Douglas-fir seedling.

FAMILY MUSCIDAE—HOUSE FLIES, STABLE FLIES, AND ALLIES

The family Muscidae owes its name and much of its reputation to the **house fly,** *Musca domestica* L. a cosmopolitan pest and carrier of diseases. It breeds in manure, garbage, and other filth. Sanitary measures in campgrounds and other forest recreation areas are necessary to keep this insect in check. The adults are 6 to 7 mm long, about medium size among the flies discussed in this manual.

SUPERFAMILY OESTROIDEA

This superfamily contains five families, of which the Calliphoridae, Sarcophagidae, and Tachinidae are most likely to be encountered by foresters. In large part, the species in western forests are beneficial. Some major insect enemies of man and animals are among the exceptions.

FAMILY CALLIPHORIDAE—BLOW FLIES

The **blow flies** (Hall 1948) are medium- to large-sized, usually metallic-colored flies that breed in garbage, carrion, manure, and in wounds of animals. The **greenbottle flies,** such as *Phaenicia,* and the **bluebottle flies,** such as *Calliphora,* are examples. It is a continuing struggle in forest camps to protect meat from them. The **screwworm,** *Cochliomyia hominivorax* (Coquerel) is widely known because of its destructiveness to stock and wildlife in Southern States and because of the sterile male technique developed to eradicate it. Blow flies are beneficial in that they are part of the natural recycling of animal wastes and remains.

FAMILY SARCOPHAGIDAE—FLESH FLIES

The **flesh flies** (Cole 1969, Aldrich 1916a) are a large family. The larvae of most species are scavengers on animal wastes. Some are parasites of insects. Adults give birth to larvae rather than laying eggs. Adults are characterized by the antennal arista being featherlike at the base. The abdomen is checkerboarded gray and black.

Agria housei Shewell (*Pseudosarcophaga affinis* (Fallén)) (Shewell 1971) is a pupal parasite of various lepidopterous pests of forest and shade trees in the West. It is ranked as important in natural control of *Choristoneura occidentalis* (Carolin and Coulter 1959) and *Orgyia pseudotsugata* (Wickman et al. 1973b). It also attacks *Acleris gloverana, Choristoneura conflictana, Malacosoma, Neophasia menapia, Nepytia, Leucoma salicis,* and other western forest defoliators.

The genus *Sarcophaga* (Cole 1969) contains about 80 species in North America. The larvae of some are parasites of insects; others feed on dead animals and animal wastes. *S. aldrichi* Parker parasitizes *Malacosoma* prepupal larvae and pupae and at times is important in the natural control of these insects in the West (Brown and Stevenson 1964). It also is a scavenger feeding on dead insects. The adults transmit a virus and thus may speed the development of epizootics that often decimate tent caterpillar populations (Stairs 1966).

FAMILY TACHINIDAE—TACHINA FLIES

The Tachinidae (Cole 1969, Stone et al. 1965) are a very large family. The larvae are internal parasites of other insects, chiefly Lepidoptera, but also Coleoptera, Hemiptera, Orthoptera, Hymenoptera, and others. The adults are small- to large-sized flies that resemble the house fly but are much more spiny (fig. 252). Many species are important in natural control of insect pests of forest and shade trees. A few have been used in biological control efforts (Dowden 1962, McGugan and Coppel 1962). Identification to species usually can be done only by experts working with reliably named specimens for reference. Generic names are in a state of flux. Only a few examples of the many species that parasitize forest insects are included in this manual. Some tachina flies have only one host species; others have many. Most drop to the ground to pupate. See Clausen (1940) for a detailed account of the role and biology of the Tachinidae.

Carcelia yalensis Sellers oviposits on larvae and subsequently kills pupae of the Douglas fir tussock moth. It sometimes hastens the decline of an outbreak.

Ceromasia auricaudata Townsend is an important parasite of *Choristoneura occidentalis* (Carolin and Coulter 1959). The adult, a medium-sized fly with a golden head and tail, deposits small black eggs on foliage in the vicinity of feeding host larvae. Eggs are ingested by the host larva and hatch shortly thereafter. The tiny maggots do not feed appreciably until the host pupates. The full-grown maggot exits from the host pupa and drops to the ground, enters the soil, and pupates. The adult emerges the same season and must find an alternate host to carry its progeny over the winter.

Chaetophlepsis nasellensis Reinhard (Carolin and Thompson 1967) is an important parasite of larvae of the western hemlock looper. It attacks nearly full-grown host larvae, from which the maggot issues, dropping to the litter to pupate. There is normally one generation a year.

Compsilura concinnata (Meigen) (Culver 1919) is a European species effectively introduced into eastern North America to com-

F–523501

Figure 252.—*Ceromasia auri-*
caudata adult, an example
of a tachina fly which attacks forest insects.

bat the gypsy and browntail moths. In the West it was introduced
against the satin moth. It is the most cosmopolitan of the tachinids
in number of hosts. Continent-wide, it has spread to more than
200 native Lepidoptera. Adults average 7.5 mm long, slightly
larger than a house fly. The female deposits a tiny maggot into
the host larva. The full-grown parasite maggot issues from the
pupa or late-stage larva of the host to pupate. Winter is spent as
a maggot in another host. About a month is required to complete
one generation.

Most of the several species formerly included in *Exorista* (Cole
1969) are now in other genera. One that remains is *E. mella*
(Walker), a transcontinental species that parasitizes larvae of
Orgyia pseudotsugata, *Leucoma salicis*, *Malacosoma*, and probably other forest insects in the West.

Madremyia contains one species, *M. saundersii* (Williston)
(Stone et al. 1965). It is transcontinental. In the West it commonly parasitizes larvae of *Choristoneura occidentalis*, *Acleris*
gloverana, *Lambdina fiscellaria lugubrosa*, *Archips*, *Dioryctria*,
and other forest defoliators. The adult deposits a small whitish
egg, which hatches quickly, in the skin of its host. The maggot
develops rapidly and, when full-grown, issues from either the
host larva or pupa, dropping to the ground to pupate. The adult

emerges the same season and must find an alternate host in which to overwinter.

Omotoma contains one described species, *O. fumiferanae* (Tothill) (Stone et al. 1965). It occurs from coast to coast on various Geometridae, Noctuidae, and Tortricidae. In the West it is an important parasite of *Choristoneura occidentalis* (Carolin and Coulter 1959). The adult fly deposits a large, flattened white egg on the skin of the host larva. The maggot develops within the egg and penetrates the host as it becomes a pupa. The full-grown maggot issues from the host pupa, drops to the ground, and pupates in the soil, where it overwinters. There is one generation a year.

The genus *Tachinomyia* (Webber 1941) contains 10 species of moderately large flies that parasitize lepidopterous larvae. The abdomen of the adult male is decidedly elongate; that of the female shorter and stouter. *T. similis* (Williston) is a western species that parasitizes *Orgyia vetusta, Halisidota argentata,* and *Leucoma salicis.*

Winthemia (Reinhard 1931) contains 24 species in North America, of which several commonly parasitize larvae of forest Lepidoptera. The adults have densely hairy eyes and frequently red markings on the abdomen, hence they sometimes are called "red-tailed tachinids."

ORDER HYMENOPTERA—ANTS, BEES, SAWFLIES, WASPS, AND ALLIES

The Hymenoptera (Muesebeck et al. 1951–67), with about 15,000 species in North America, is outnumbered in this area only by the Coleoptera and Diptera. Some Hymenoptera are in the front ranks of forest pests. Others are among the most beneficial insects in the forest. There are two suborders, the Symphyta and the Apocrita.

SUBORDER SYMPHYTA—SAWFLIES AND HORNTAILS

The suborder Symphyta comprises the sawflies and horntails, among which are the principal forest pests in the Hymenoptera. In this suborder, the abdomen of the adult is broadly joined to the thorax and the ovipositor is sawlike for laying eggs in plant tissue.

There are three superfamilies in the Symphyta—Megalodontoidea, containing the sawfly families Pamphiliidae and Xyelidae; Tenthredinoidea, containing all other sawflies; and Siricoidea, containing the horntails and their relatives.

SUPERFAMILY MEGALODONTOIDEA

FAMILY PAMPHILIIDAE—WEBSPINNING SAWFLIES

This family contains four genera in North America. *Acantholyda* [*Itycorsia*] and *Cephalcia* (Eidt 1969, Middlekauff 1958) feed upon conifers. *Neurotoma* and *Pamphilius* feed on broad-leaved plants. Most pamphilids are of little importance, but some of the conifer-infesting species are pests of ornamental trees, and some are considered potentially important in forest plantations.

The adults have long, slender, many-segmented antennae. The larvae (figs. 253B, 254A) resemble larvae of the free-feeding sawflies, but differ in having a pair of three-segmented appendages on the last segment of the body and by not having any leglike appendages on the abdomen. The larvae feed gregariously or singly. The gregarious ones, sometimes called **false webworms**, spin and feed in silken nests which become filled with discarded food, cast skins, and frass (fig. 253A). The solitary ones build silk-tube shelters along the branchlets (fig. 254B). The nesting habit of the larvae and their wrinkled, rear-tapered appearance aid identification. Pupation is in an earthen cell in the ground. There is one generation per year, but diapause for 2 or more years is common.

Acantholyda contains about 20 species in the West (Middlekauff 1958). Some are gregarious; others are solitary. *Acantholyda burkei* Middlekauff and *A. verticalis* (Cresson) are con-

F-523502, F-523503

FIGURE 253.—A false webworm, *Acantholyda* species, on ponderosa pine: *A*, Nest, showing accumulated frass; *B*, mature larva, 22 mm long.

F–523504, F–523505

FIGURE 254.—Solitary web-spinning sawfly, *Acantholyda* species, on grand fir:
A, Mature larva, 18 mm long; *B*, silk tube shelter on branchlet.

sidered to be important pests of Monterey pine in California.
Hosts and distribution of some of the more widely distributed
species are:

Species	Hosts	Distribution
A. *albomarginata* (Cresson)	*Pinus ponderosa* [1] and *P. muricata* [1]	Alaska, British Columbia, Wash., Oreg., Calif., and Mont.
A. *atrata* (Cresson)	*Tsuga heterophylla* and *Abies concolor*	British Columbia, Wash., Oreg., Calif., and Idaho
A. *balanata* (MacGillivray)	*Pseudotsuga menziesii*, *Picea sitchensis*, *Abies*, and *Tsuga*	Alaska, British Columbia, and Calif.
A. *brunnicans* (Norton)	*Pinus contorta*,[1] *P. sabiniana*,[1] *P. ponderosa*,[1] and *P. radiata* [1]	British Columbia, Oreg., Calif., Mont., Wyo., and Nev.
A. *bucephala* (Cresson)	*Pseudotsuga menziesii* and *Abies concolor*	British Columbia, Wash., Oreg., Calif., and Mont., Calif.
A. *burkei* Middlekauff	*Pinus radiata*	
A. *verticalis* (Cresson)	*Pinus radiata*, *P. contorta*,[1] *P. ponderosa*,[1] and *P. monticola* [1]	British Columbia, Alberta, Wash., Oreg., Calif., Mont., Wyo., Colo., and Nebr.

[1] Recorded as a probable host.

435

Cephalcia contains 10 species in North America (Eidt 1969). *C. californica* Middlekauff and *C. hopkinsi* (Rohwer) are western; *C. provancheri* (Huard) and *C. fascipennis* (Cresson) are transcontinental. The eggs are laid on the needles with a small knoblike part inserted into the host tissue. *C. provancheri* larvae are solitary. *C. californica* and *C. fascipennis* are gregarious. These three eat the previous year's foliage and pupate in unlined cells in the soil. Little is known of *C. hopkinsi*. Hosts and distribution of these four species are as follows:

Species	Hosts	Distribution
C. californica	*Pinus ponderosa* and *P. contorta*	Calif., Mont., Wyo., and British Columbia
C. fascipennis	*Picea engelmannii, P. glauca,* and *P. pungens*	British Columbia
C. hopkinsi	*Pinus ponderosa*	Ariz.
C. provancheri	*Picea engelmannii, P. glauca, P. mariana,* and *P. sitchensis*	Alaska, Yukon Territory, Alberta, British Columbia, Idaho, Oreg., Calif., Utah, Colo., Wyo., Manitoba, and Saskatchewan

FAMILY XYELIDAE

The Xyelidae (Burdick 1961, Smith 1967a) are primitive sawflies. Three of the five North American genera feed on western conifers. None is reported to be economically important. The adults are characterized by antennae having an elongate third segment topped by a many-segmented thread. The larvae are creamy-white, slightly curled, and with weakly developed thoracic legs and prolegs reduced to swellings.

Adult *Xyela* are in flight a short time. They feed on pollen of willow, alder, maple, oak, grasses, and other plants. *Xyela* larvae feed in staminate cones of pines. *Pleroneura* and *Xyelecia* larvae bore in the buds and developing shoots of firs. Actual and presumed hosts of western species (Burdick 1961, Smith 1964, Smith 1967b) are shown in table 16.

The larvae are often encountered but seldom identified to species because they are difficult to rear. The mature larvae of *Xyela* drop to the ground where they remain 2 years before pupating. During the period of larval drop, people camped under pines sometimes report an invasion of these worms.

SUPERFAMILY TENTHREDINOIDEA

The sawflies of this superfamily have diverse habits. Most of them feed openly on the foliage; others feed in nests, mine in leaves, or form galls. In this superfamily the sawflies are discussed alphabetically by family regardless of habit. For classifica-

436

tion of adults see Ross (1937), for larvae see Yuasa (1922) ; and
for distribution see Benson (1962a).

Some of the free-feeding sawflies are among the most destructive forest insects. They weaken and kill trees by defoliating them.
In the Eastern States and Provinces, introduced sawflies have

Table 16.—*Hosts, actual and presumed, and western distribution
of species of* Xyelidae

Species	Hosts	Distribution
Pleroneura brunneicornis Rohwer **balsam shootboring sawfly**	*Abies balsamea*	Alberta
P. californica (Ashmead)	*Abies*	Idaho, Oreg., Calif., and Utah
P. koebelei Rohwer	Unknown	Oreg.
P. lutea Rohwer	Unknown	Oreg.
Xyela alberta (Curran)	*Pinus contorta*	Alberta, Mont., and Wyo.
X. alpigena (Strobl) (= *brunneiceps* Rohwer)	Unknown	Colo.
X. bakeri Konow	*Pinus ponderosa* and *P. sabiniana*	Alberta, British Columbia, Wyo., Colo., Ariz., Nev., Calif., Oreg., and Idaho
X. californica Rohwer	Unknown	Calif., Oreg., Idaho, and Utah
X. cheloma Burdick	*Pinus ponderosa*	British Columbia, Idaho, Wash., Oreg., Calif., and Nev.
X. concava Burdick	*Pinus monophylla*	Calif. and Nev.
X. deserti Burdick	*Pinus monophylla*	Calif.
X. linsleyi Burdick	*Pinus ponderosa*	Calif., Wash., and Idaho
X. lunata Burdick	*Pinus coulteri* and *P. sabiniana*	Calif.
X. minor Norton	*Pinus coulteri*, *P. muricata*, *P. ponderosa*, and *P. sabiniana*	British Columbia, Wash., Idaho, Wyo., Utah, Colo., Ariz., Calif., and Oreg.
X. obscura (Strobl) (= *pini* Rohwer)	*Pinus ponderosa*	British Columbia, Alberta, Northwest Territories, Wash., Idaho, Mont., Colo., and Calif.
X. priceae Burdick	*Pinus coulteri*	Calif.
X. radiatae Burdick	*Pinus radiata*	Calif.
X. serrata Burdick	*Pinus muricata*	Calif.
Xylecia nearctica Ross	*Abies concolor* and possibly *Pinus contorta*	Idaho, Wash., Oreg., and Calif.

been particularly destructive to spruce, larch, and pine. In the West, where introduced sawflies are fewer, native species occasionally cause extensive heavy defoliation in natural forests, killing some trees and reducing the growth and vigor of others, thus subjecting them to attack by other insects. In forest plantations, on Christmas tree areas, and on ornamentals, sawflies sometimes are a persistent problem.

Adults have a thick body with the head, thorax, and base of the abdomen nearly equal in width. The wings are membranous with a conspicuous network of veins. The front pair of wings is larger and more heavily veined than the hind pair. Body color is varied but tends to match the color of bark and foliage surfaces—inconspicuous greens, browns, and black. The adults range in length from about 6 mm to over 25 mm, with most of them being less than 12 mm. The female has a sawlike attachment at the end of the abdomen that she uses to cut slits in plant tissues in which she lays eggs.

Larvae resemble hairless caterpillars except that most of them have seven or eight pairs of leglike appendages on the abdomen. True caterpillars have fewer. The larvae of many sawflies spin capsulelike, papery cocoons in which to pupate. Some species spin their cocoons in the soil and forest litter, others on the foliage. The cocoons may aid in identification (Wong 1951). Some sawflies pupate in earthen cells in the ground.

Sawflies typically have one generation a year; however, some of the brood of many species go into diapause in the cocoon and require 2 to several years to complete development. Sometimes a large percentage of a sawfly population goes into extended diapause. Another characteristic of many sawflies is that outbreaks occur sporadically at long intervals. Outbreaks usually subside quickly. Between outbreaks, populations characteristically are very low.

Many sawflies have a large complement of insect parasites. Others are decimated by disease. Those that pupate on the ground often are heavily preyed upon by small mammals.

Parasites have been imported and colonized with considerable success for biological control of introduced sawflies. Application of viruses for control has shown promise. Chemicals for control have been applied principally in plantations and on ornamentals.

FAMILY ARGIDAE—ARGID SAWFLIES

Adults of the family Argidae may be identified by their three-segmented antennae. The genus *Arge* contains about 12 species, mostly eastern, some of which feed on forest trees. The **birch sawfly**, *A. pectoralis* (Leach) (Schwarz 1909), ranges westward from the Atlantic States and Eastern Provinces to British Columbia on birch. It also feeds on alder and willow. Eggs are laid in rows in the edges of a leaf. The full-grown larva is about 20 mm long; the head is reddish yellow with black eyespots; the abdomen is yellowish with several longitudinal rows of black spots. Occasionally this sawfly causes conspicuous defoliation locally but it is not a serious pest. *A. clavicornis* (F.) is a transcontinental species of similar habits. Color of the adults is widely varied. Willow, birch, and alder are hosts.

FAMILY CIMBICIDAE—CIMBICID SAWFLIES

The family Cimbicidae contains our largest sawflies. Larvae of the genus *Cimbex* are solitary feeders on broad-leaved trees. They are conspicuous because of their size, but are seldom abundant; hence they are of little economic importance. Two species occur in the West.

The **elm sawfly**, *C. americana* Leach, ranges west to Oregon and British Columbia. Hosts are willow, elm, poplar, alder, birch, and other broad-leaved trees. The adults are robust, about 20 mm long, and have short knobbed antennae and smoky wings. They vary in color, typical ones being steel blue to black. The typical female has three or four pairs of yellow spots on the dorsum of the abdomen; the abdomen of the male is black. The larvae are hairless, transversely wrinkled, and yellowish to greenish white with a median black stripe down the back and black spots around the spiracles. When at rest, the larvae usually are coiled.

Adults of the elm sawfly may kill twigs by gnawing on the bark, especially in the tops of trees. Larvae feed on the leaves. Eggs are laid in the leaves. Cocoons are spun in the litter and topsoil. The winter is spent as prepupal larvae in cocoons. There is one generation per year. Extended diapause is common.

Adults of the variety *C. americana pacifica* Cresson, which occurs on willow in the Pacific coast region, are brownish red. *C. rubida* Cresson, also reddish, occurs on willow in California and Nevada.

Trichiosoma adults are similar to those of *Cimbex* but are conspicuously more hairy and the larvae lack the median black stripe. *T. triangulum* Kirby (Wong 1954), a transcontinental species, feeds on willow, poplar, alder, birch, and cherry.

FAMILY DIPRIONIDAE—CONIFER SAWFLIES

The **conifer sawflies**, Diprionidae, include many destructive species, all but one of which feed openly on the foliage of conifers. The western species all are natives. The **European spruce sawfly**, *Diprion hercyniae* (Hartig), the **introduced pine sawfly**, *D. similis*

(Hartig), and the **European pine sawfly**, *Neodiprion sertifer* (Geoffroy), introduced into the Eastern States and Provinces from Europe, are potential invaders that western foresters should be alert to detect. The former now occurs in southeastern Manitoba (Wong 1972).

The adults are 6 to 12 mm long, usually yellowish brown to black and with yellowish legs. The antennae have 13 to 26 segments which are serrate in the female and plumelike in the male. The male is smaller and often darker. The full-grown larva is 18 to 25 mm long and usually is yellowish or greenish with longitudinal stripes. The body is cylindrical and tapers gradually to the rear. The abdomen has eight pairs of leglike appendages. Eggs are laid in pockets excavated singly or more often in rows in living needles. The young larvae feed gregariously, several to a needle, all headed outward from the twig. Older larvae wrap the rear end of the body around the needle on which they are feeding.

Augomonoctenus libocedrii Rohwer sometimes infests cones of incense-cedar in California and Oregon, causing damage resembling that of cone-feeding caterpillars. The adult sawflies are 6 to 10 mm long, shining blue black, with the first five segments of the abdomen brick red.

Of all the sawflies, the species of *Neodiprion* are of greatest concern to western foresters. Some attack young trees, particularly open-growing ones, hence are significant and increasingly important pests in plantations. Others attack trees of all ages. *Neodiprion* sawflies may develop to outbreak numbers either locally or extensively. They feed on old foliage, generally weakening the affected trees and slowing down their growth rather than killing them outright. Teamed with insects that feed on new foliage, these sawflies are a special threat. Outbreaks typically are of short duration.

The species of *Neodiprion* are similar in habits and appearance. According to Ross (1955) there are about 16 species in the West, but some of them appear to be complexes of several closely related species, races, or physiological strains. Some species may be masquerading under two or more names (Ross 1955). Identification is correspondingly difficult and uncertain, even for taxonomists.

The females lay batches of eggs in nearby needles; eggs are placed in niches cut into the edge of a needle, often several per needle (fig. 255A). Upon hatching, the larvae tend to feed in colonies (fig. 255B) until nearly mature, when they feed singly (fig. 255C). Most cocoons are formed in the duff and upper layer of soil; some are formed on foliage, bark, and other surfaces (fig. 255D). Extended diapause is common. Male and female adults (fig. 255E and F) differ, as described for the family.

440

F-523506, F-519389, F-523507, COURTESY CANADIAN FORESTRY SERVICE, F-523508, F-523509

FIGURE 255.—Life stages of conifer sawflies, *Neodiprion* spp.: *A*, Egg niches on pine needles; *B*, small larvae, 8 mm long, feeding as a colony; *C*, mature larva, 18 mm long; *D*, cocoon, 7 mm long; *E*, female adult, 8 mm long; *F*, male adult, 6 mm long.

Normally these sawflies occur in small numbers, escaping attention year after year. Occasionally some species become widely epidemic, causing spectacular defoliation for a year or two. Outbreaks subside abruptly due to natural causes. The need for control has not been fully evaluated, but it appears that plantations, Christmas tree areas, and perhaps recreation areas are most likely to require control.

One or more undetermined species of *Neodiprion* commonly feed on Douglas-fir. Occasionally, as in 1960 in southern Idaho, there are conspicuous local outbreaks that quickly subside without doing much damage.

The **balsam fir sawfly**, *Neodiprion abietis* (Harris), is reported to attack balsam fir and spruce in the East and to range west at

441

least to Alberta, where it is a pest of shelterbelts and ornamental plantings. There appear to be several forms or species closely related to *N. abietis* on *Abies, Picea, Pseudotsuga,* and *Tsuga* in the West. In California from 1951 to 1955, widely scattered outbreaks of one of these species drastically reduced growth of heavily defoliated trees and killed some suppressed trees (Struble 1957a). Epidemic populations developed in dense stands predominantly of white fir. Feeding was heaviest on understory trees and the lower parts of crowns of all infested trees. Many insect parasites and predators were associated with the sawfly in the California outbreaks, but their control effectiveness was not determined. Natural control was attributed to nucleopolyhedrosis virus. Aerial spraying was demonstrated to be effective in California but may seldom be necessary.

Adult males average 5 to 6 mm long and females 6 to 8 mm. The body color is yellowish brown to dark brown. The larvae change from dark olive green in the early instars to yellowish green at maturity. The mature larvae have two darker lateral stripes. The species in California has a 1-year life cycle and overwinters in the egg stage, except for a small percentage in diapause in the cocoon.

The **lodgepole sawfly,** *Neodiprion burkei* Middleton (Burke 1932), attacks lodgepole pine in Montana and Wyoming. During the years 1921 to 1925, this sawfly and the needletier moth were concurrently epidemic on 80,000 acres in the upper drainage of the Madison River in these two States. The sawfly prefers old foliage; the needletier prefers new foliage. In combination they killed practically all trees on 12,000 acres and severely damaged the forest on an additional 20,000 acres.

The adults are 6 to 8 mm long. The females are brownish, the males black. The mature larva is about 24 mm long, hairless and wrinkled, and greenish or grayish with lighter stripes on the sides and back. The head is dark brown. This sawfly has one generation per year, but part of each brood remains as prepupal larvae in the cocoons for 2 to 4 years. The winter is spent as prepupal larvae in the cocoons in the litter on the ground.

On the basis of the one recorded outbreak, the lodgepole sawfly is a potential economic pest. Aerial spraying should be effective, if natural controls fail.

The **piñon sawfly,** *Neodiprion edulicolus* Ross (McGregor and Sandin 1969), attacks *Pinus monophylla* and *P. edulis.* It is recorded from Colorado, New Mexico, Utah, and Nevada. In outbreaks in Nevada in 1959 and again in 1965, trees of all ages and sizes were attacked. Smaller trees were most seriously defoliated; some were killed and many were made unfit for Christmas trees. Parasites and weather were considered to be effective in natural control. No practical method of direct control is known.

442

The adult female is 6 to 8 mm long, with a golden-brown body. The male is 5 to 7 mm long, with a greenish-black body. The mature feeding larva is pale green with a dark green stripe on each side and a greenish-white stripe down the back. There is one generation a year. Eggs overwinter in the needles. Feeding is complete by July. Cocoons are formed in the soil. The cocoon stage lasts from June or July to September or October. Eggs are laid in October and November in needles of the current year.

Pine-infesting sawflies resembling *Neodiprion fulviceps* (Cresson) are widely distributed in the West. Ponderosa, Jeffrey, sugar, western white, and Monterey pines are attacked. These sawflies may be several related species or one variable species. Their biology indicates several. The damage they cause has not been evaluated, but obviously it is considerable on trees that are completely defoliated. Natural enemies, including a variety of insect parasites and predators, seem to be generally effective.

Based on a form studied by Dahlsten (1966) in California, the female adults are 6 to 9 mm long and predominantly brownish; males are 5 to 7 mm long and shiny black. The color and markings of larvae vary by instar, the younger instars being generally dark green and the older ones having dark green and light green longitudinal stripes. The nonfeeding prepupal larva is brownish.

The sawfly studied by Dahlsten has one generation per year. Eggs are laid in October and November, averaging about 18 per needle, mostly in current foliage. The eggs overwinter. The larvae feed on foliage of the previous year or older. They mature in the spring. Cocoons are spun in the litter and soil from May to July. Pupation occurs in the fall. Duration of diapause is not recorded.

Neodiprion nanulus contortae Ross, the western form of *N. nanulus*, has been confused with *N. burkei*. Both feed on lodgepole pine and are similar in appearance. *N. nanulus contortae* has been recorded in Oregon, Idaho, and Alberta. It was epidemic on lodgepole pine on pumice soils in Oregon during 1941–45 and 1952–53. Some trees were killed outright; some were weakened and succumbed to other insects; most recovered but were slowed in growth.

Female adults are 7 to 8 mm long and generally yellowish brown; males are 5 to 6 mm long and predominantly black. The mature larvae are longitudinally striped, being generally olive green above and greenish white below.

In Oregon there is one generation a year. Eggs are laid in the fall and overwinter in the needles. The larvae feed on foliage of the previous year or earlier. Cocoons are spun in the litter and upper layers of soil. At times a large percentage of the larval population goes into extended diapause, spending 2 or more years in the cocoons.

The **hemlock sawfly**, *Neodiprion tsugae* Middleton (Schmiege 1970), is an important defoliator of western hemlock in the coastal forests of Oregon, Washington, British Columbia, and Alaska. It also occurs in interior forests of British Columbia, Idaho, and Montana. More than one species may be involved. *Tsuga mertensiana* and *Abies amabilis* also are recorded hosts. Extensive outbreaks on western hemlock have been recorded in natural forests in Oregon, British Columbia, and Alaska. The larvae feed principally on the old needles, hence tend to reduce growth rather than kill trees outright.

The adults and larvae resemble those of other *Neodiprion*. Characteristically, there is one generation a year, but some larvae hold over in the cocoons, taking 2 or more years to complete a life cycle. Eggs are laid in the fall and overwinter. They are laid in needles of the current year's growth, usually one per needle. Larval feeding is in the late spring and early summer. Cocoons are spun mostly in the duff but also on the needles and other surfaces.

There are many insect parasites which presumably keep this sawfly under control most of the time. Direct control measures have not been developed.

Hosts and distribution of other western species are:

Species	Hosts	Distribution
N. *deleoni* Ross	*Abies grandis*	Wash.
N. *demoides* Ross	*Pinus albicaulis*	Calif.
N. *gillettei* (Rohwer)	*Pinus ponderosa*	Colo., N. Mex., and Ariz.
N. *mundus* Rohwer	*Pinus ponderosa*	Calif. and Oreg.
N. *pratti banksianae* Rohwer jack pine sawfly	*Pinus banksiana*	Saskatchewan
N. *scutellatus* Rohwer	*Pseudotsuga menziesii*	Wash. and Idaho
N. *ventralis* Ross	*Pinus ponderosa*	Colo.
N. *werneri* Ross	Unrecorded	Ariz.

There are three species of *Zadiprion*, two of which feed on pines in Western United States (Smith 1971b). They resemble *Neodiprion* in appearance and habits. *Z. rohweri* (Middleton) (Brown and Eads 1967) occurs in California, Nevada, Utah, Colorado, and New Mexico. Hosts are *Pinus monophylla* and *P. edulis*. It is a minor pest. The larvae feed on old needles sometimes completely defoliating small trees. Female adults are about 10 mm long and yellowish. Males are smaller and predominantly black. The young larvae are yellow. Mature larvae are yellowish with dark brown spots down each side. Reportedly there are two generations a year except for individuals that go into diapause. *Z. townsendi* (Cockerell) (= *grandis* (Rohwer)) feeds on *Pinus ponderosa* in Nebraska, South Dakota, Utah, Colorado, Arizona,

444

and New Mexico. The mature larvae are nearly black except for the whitish underside. This species is a potential pest of plantations.

FAMILY TENTHREDINIDAE—SAWFLIES

The Tenthredinidae is a large family of diverse appearance and habits (Ross 1937). Most species feed openly. Some are leafminers and some are gallformers. Broad-leaved plants, including trees and shrubs, are the principal hosts. Conifers are fed upon by relatively few. One serious forest pest and several of occasional importance are members of this family.

The species of *Anoplonyx* are native sawflies that feed on larch foliage. *A. canadensis* Harrington and *A. luteipes* (Cresson) are predominantly eastern species but range westward into British Columbia and Yukon Territory. The **western larch sawfly**, *A. occidens* Ross and the **twolined larch sawfly**, *A. laricivorus* (Rohwer and Middleton) feed on western larch in British Columbia, Washington, Idaho, and Montana. In 1921 an outbreak of the latter two species occurred extensively in larch stands of northern Idaho and western Montana. From countless numbers in 1921 the population had practically disappeared by 1922. This is the only recorded outbreak of either of these sawflies. So far, they are of minor economic importance.

Adults of the western larch sawfly are black and a little less than 6 mm long. The folded wings have a blue-green metallic sheen. The larvae are about 10 mm long when full grown. The head is brown and the body is gray black with a narrow green stripe down the center of the back (Wong 1955). The larvae do their heaviest feeding from mid-July to late August. When mature, the larvae leave the trees and spin cocoons in the duff. The winter is passed in the cocoon, and the new adults emerge the following spring about the time the larch foliage appears.

Adults of the twolined larch sawfly closely resemble those of the western larch sawfly, but the larvae are green with two olive stripes on each side and without a stripe down the back.

One of the four North American species of *Croesus* (Smith 1972) occurs in the West. The **dusky birch sawfly**, *C. latitarsus* Norton, is common but causes little damage on *Betula* in Alaska, Utah, Saskatchewan, and Manitoba. The larvae are yellowish green with three dark brown spots on each body segment. They feed gregariously in S-curved posture on the edge of the leaf (Wong 1954). Females average 9 mm long and have a black abdomen; males average 7 mm and have a red-banded abdomen.

The **alder woolly sawfly**, *Eriocampa ovata* (L.) (Borden and Dean 1971), is a European species now established in British Columbia on *Alnus rubra*. The larvae, except in the last instar, are covered with a white, woolly secretion. They skeletonize the lower leaves on young alders. They overwinter as prepupae in cocoons in the soil. There are two generations per year.

Euura is a genus of small sawflies related to *Nematus* (Smith 1968). They cause closed galls on the buds, leaf petioles, and stems of willow (fig. 256). The species causing stem galls are by far the most abundant. *E. exiguae* E. L. Smith is very common on *Salix exigua* in California and probably occurs throughout the Great Basin. It causes an elongate brownish stem gall containing one to four larvae. Pupation is in the gall. Emergence and egg laying is in March and April in California. *E. mucronata* (Hartig) is a circumboreal species that causes bud galls on willow from Manitoba to Alaska.

Fenusa contains three species in North America, two of which are in the West (Smith 1971a). All three are leafminers. The **birch leafminer**, *F. pusilla* (Lepeletier) (= *pumila* (Klug)), was introduced from Europe (Friend 1933). In the West, it is recorded from Oregon, Washington, and Alberta as a pest of ornamental birch. Eggs are laid on the surface of the leaf and larvae feed in the leaves causing irregular blotches which wrinkle and turn brown. Heaviest feeding is in tender foliage near the tips of branches. Similar leaf damage (fig. 257) is caused by the **amber-marked birch leafminer**, *Profenusa thomsoni* (Konow). This presumably introduced species has spread westward into the Prairie Provinces.

Full-grown larvae of *F. pusilla* are flattened, about 6 mm long, white to pale green, and marked with black spots on the lower side of the thorax and the first abdominal segment. Pupation is in

COURTESY E. L. SMITH (1970B)

FIGURE 256.—Damage to willow caused by *Euura* sawflies: *A*, Bud gall; *B*, petiole and midrib gall; *C*, stem gall.

446

the ground. Adults are black and about 3 mm long. Males are common. There are two or more generations a year. The winter is spent in a cocoon in the soil.

FIGURE 257.—Paper birch leaf damaged by larval feeding of the amber-marked leafminer (*Profenusa thomsoni*).

The **European alder leafminer,** *F. dohrnii* (Tischbein), is transcontinental and holarctic. The larvae mine in leaves of alder causing blisterlike damage. Habits and appearance are similar to *F. pusilla*. The male is unknown.

The **striped alder sawfly,** *Hemichroa crocea* (Fourcroy), is a transcontinental species that feeds upon various alders. It also occurs in Europe. Periodically it is abundant in British Columbia, Washington, and Oregon on *Alnus rubra*, virtually stripping the foliage from extensive stands. It also occurs in coastal Alaska. Presumably heavy defoliation slows growth of attacked trees, but no actual impact data are available.

In British Columbia there are two generations per year (Hopping 1937). The eggs are laid in the midrib of the leaf on the underside. The larvae are gregarious. Recently emerged larvae commence feeding by eating holes through the leaf from the underside, giving it a characteristic riddled appearance. Feeding continues on a leaf until only the coarser midrib remains. When feeding or disturbed, the larvae often assume a fishhook posture with the tail end curled under and upward (fig. 258). Prepupal

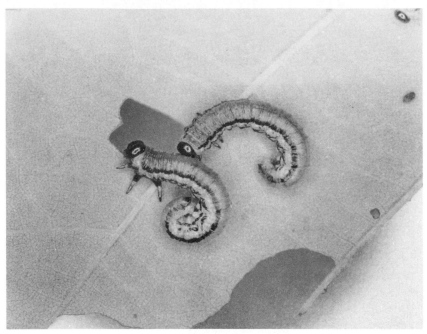

F-523510

FIGURE 258.—Striped alder sawfly (*Hemichroa crocea*) mature larvae, 20 mm long, feeding on alder leaf.

larvae overwinter in cocoons in the soil. The full-grown larva is about 20 mm long and has a shining black head and a yellow-amber body marked by dark brown lateral stripes one above and two below the spiracles.

Nematus is a large genus of small- to medium-sized sawflies, the larvae of which feed freely on the leaves of *Salix, Populus, Alnus, Betula,* and other hardwoods (Ross 1937, Yuasa 1922). *Nematus* larvae are about 10 mm long, cylindrical, hairless, and uniform in diameter except for the tapered rear end. Some species become abundant enough to warrant control on ornamentals, but none is a significant forest pest. *N. oligospilus* Foerster feeds on willow from coast to coast. *N. currani* Ross feeds on *Populus trichocarpa* in British Columbia.

Nineteen species of *Periclista* (Stannard 1949) occur in North America. Nine are western. *P. linea* Stannard feeds in the buds and on the foliage, at times causing damage to ornamental *Quercus agrifolia* severe enough to warrant control. Eggs are laid in the leaf buds a week or so before the buds open. The larvae repose on the lower surface of the leaves. Pupation is in cocoons 25 to 50 mm deep in the soil. The adults fly in late February and early

March in central coastal California. Adults have been collected in April at Corvallis, Oregon. The fifth-instar larva has four rows of bifurcate spines down the back and three rows on each side. The skin of the sixth-instar is entirely smooth (Beer 1955).

The species of *Phyllocolpa* (Smith 1970b) are small sawflies that, during oviposition, inject a fluid that causes open galls on leaf margins of willow and poplar (fig. 259A). The larvae resemble those of *Nematus* and other free-living Nematinae in robustness and green coloration (fig. 259B). There is one generation a year. The **poplar leaffolding sawfly**, *P. bozemani* (Cooley), in British Columbia is representative for the genus. In general the identity of the species is in question.

In North America there are three species of *Pikonema,* all of which range across the continent in the northern spruce forests. The **yellowheaded spruce sawfly**, *P. alaskensis* (Rohwer) (Wilson 1971c), damages and sometimes kills open-growing spruce, especially trees in ornamental and shelterbelt plantings. So far it has not been a serious pest under forest conditions in the West. Hosts include *Picea engelmannii, P. glauca, P. mariana,* and *P. pungens.* It occurs in Wyoming, Idaho, British Columbia, and Alaska. The full-grown larvae are shiny and about 20 mm long. Their head is chestnut brown to reddish yellow and their body is olive green

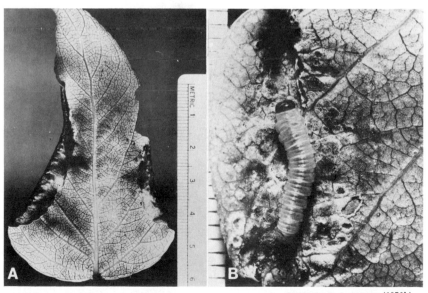

COURTESY E. L. SMITH (1970b)

FIGURE 259.—Poplar leaffolding sawfly (*Phyllocolpa bozemani*) : *A,* Open gall on leaf margin of black cottonwood; *B,* mature larva, 10 mm long, in opened leaf roll.

above and lighter green below. A light green stripe on the side separates darker green stripes above and below (fig. 260A). The adults are about 10 mm long and range in color from straw yellow to nearly black. There is one generation a year. Eggs are laid in the current season's needles or occasionally in the tender bark. The larvae feed first on the new needles and then on the old (fig. 260B). In July they drop to the ground and spin cocoons in the duff or topsoil. They overwinter as prepupae.

The **greenheaded spruce sawfly**, *P. dimmockii* (Cresson), commonly occurs with the yellowheaded spruce sawfly but is considerably less damaging. *P. ruralis* (Cresson) is a little-known species.

Pontania, sometimes considered to be a subgenus of *Nematus*, causes a variety of closed galls on leaves of willow. *P. pacifica* Marlatt (Caltagirone 1964) attacks only *Salix lasiolepis*. The adults are about 4.5 mm long and black with yellowish or light brown markings. The full-grown larva is about 10 mm long. Its body is creamy yellow and its head light brown. Pupation is in the soil. There are several generations per year.

There are 24 species of *Pristiphora* in North America, two of which feed on larch and are the only ones of significance in forestry. The **larch sawfly**, *P. erichsonii* (Hartig) (Drooz 1960, 1971), is a holarctic species consisting of several strains, two of which were introduced from Europe, and two apparently are native (Turnock 1972, Wong 1974). In North America, the larch sawfly was first recorded in 1880 in Massachusetts. Subsequent firsts were: 1910—Saskatchewan, 1923—Alberta, 1930—British Columbia, 1935—Montana, 1964—Oregon, and 1965—Alaska. It is the most destructive insect enemy of *Larix laricina*. On *L. occidentalis*

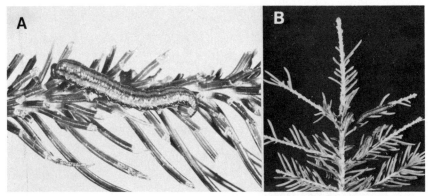

FIGURE 260.—Yellowheaded spruce sawfly (*Pikonema alaskensis*): *A*, Mature larva, 20 mm long; *B*, defoliation of spruce tips.

450

it occurs in Montana, Idaho, Washington, Oregon, and British Columbia and on *L. lyallii* in Alberta. It also attacks exotic larch. It has been most destructive in the Lake States where it has killed large amounts of tamarack. On western larch it has slowed tree growth by repeated defoliation but has not killed trees extensively except in stands under stress from other factors.

The adults are 6 to 9 mm long and are characterized by having an orange band around the abdomen. The mature larva is about 16 mm long, has a jet black head, and is whitish beneath and gray green along the back (fig. 261A).

Reproduction is parthenogenetic. There is one generation a year. Eggs are laid in new shoots causing them to curl characteristically (fig. 261B). The newly hatched larvae feed first along the edges of the needles of the new shoots but soon move back to feed on needle clusters on older twigs. They tend to feed in groups, stripping a branch before moving to another (fig. 261C). When mature they drop to the ground, crawl into the duff, and spin cocoons in which they overwinter as prepupal larvae. Normally the life cycle is completed in 1 year but some individuals remain in cocoons for two or three winters.

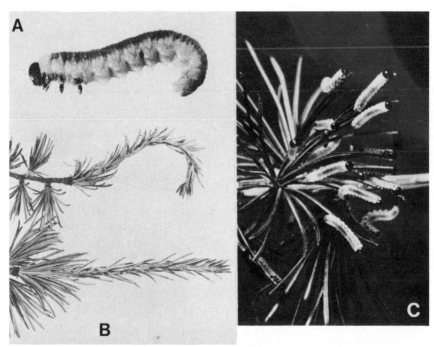

F–523511 (A), COURTESY CANADIAN FORESTRY SERVICE (B,C)

FIGURE 261.—Larch sawfly (*Pristiphora erichsonii*): *A*, Mature larva, 16 mm long; *B*, comparison of curled shoot damaged by sawfly oviposition, and normal shoot; *C*, small larvae, 8 mm long, feeding on western larch foliage.

Parasites, predators, disease organisms, weather, flooding, and competition are among the factors that regulate abundance of the larch sawfly. Insect parasites have been introduced and distributed extensively for biological control. The introduced ichneumonid, *Mesoleius tenthredinis* Morley, became widely established, but initial promise was partially frustrated because one introduced strain of the sawfly is resistant to the parasite. No practical silvicultural or chemical measures to counter the sawfly in the forest have been developed. Prospects for control through stand management are limited because the sawfly appears to attack all types and ages of larch.

Pristiphora leechi Wong and Ross feeds on the foliage of *Larix occidentalis* in Montana, Idaho, Washington, and British Columbia. Little is known of its habits or of its potential importance. In comparison with *P. erichsonii*, the adult of *P. leechi* is much smaller and the abdomen is black above and yellow below rather than banded. The larva of *P. leechi* has a green head and legs in contrast to the black head and legs of *P. erichsonii*. The body of the larva of *P. leechi* is light green with three darker green longitudinal stripes.

Strongylogaster (Smith 1969b) contains 11 species in North America, 3 of which are western. *S. distans* Norton and *S. tibialis* Cresson have pale green larvae that feed on bracken. Occasionally they bore into the outer bark at the base of nearby trees, specifically ponderosa pine and Douglas-fir. Because of their abundance, they sometimes cause concern to woodsmen, but they cause no damage to trees.

There are seven species of *Susana* (Smith 1969a), all western. The **cypress sawfly**, *S. cupressi* Rohwer and Middleton (Brown and Eads 1967), feeds on the foliage of *Cupressus*, and presumably on *Juniperus* and *Thuja*, in southern California, at times being a serious pest of ornamentals. The adults are 6 to 8 mm long with threadlike antennae. The male is black with a yellow band around the middle of the abdomen. The female is similar but has yellow marks on the thorax. The larva at maturity is 16 to 20 mm long, grayish green with longitudinal rows of white spots. The winter is spent as a prepupa in a cocoon in the soil. There is one generation a year. *S. annulata* Smith feeds on *Cupressus macrocarpa* in California, *S. fuscala* Wong and Milliron on *Juniperus scopulorum* in British Columbia, and *S. oregonensis* Smith on *Juniperus* in Oregon.

Trichiocampus viminalis (Fallén) (Downes 1925) from Europe was first recorded in British Columbia in 1917 but has not become a significant pest. It feeds openly and gregariously throughout its development on leaves of poplar and willow. The mature larva is about 20 mm long, has a black head and a yellow body marked on each side with a row of black spots and is sparsely clothed with white hairs. There is one generation a year on Vancouver Island, B.C., where this sawfly is a pest of ornamental Lombardy poplar.

SUPERFAMILY SIRICOIDEA

The superfamily Siricoidea (Muesebeck et al. 1951–67) contains the horntails and relatives. All except the Orussidae are wood borers.

FAMILY ORUSSIDAE

Members of the family Orussidae are unique among the siricids by being parasitic. Two species of *Orussus* are recorded in the West—*O. occidentalis* Cresson and *O. thoracicus* Ashmead. Little is recorded regarding the habits of these species. *O. occidentalis* (Burke 1917b), which occurs in Colorado, Nevada, California, Oregon, Washington, and British Columbia, parasitizes *Buprestis* and presumably other wood-boring beetles, but evidently it is not very abundant. The adults are 8 to 14 mm long, and black with the rearmost six abdominal segments shining ferruginous. The larvae are creamy white, legless, somewhat flattened, and with the body swollen behind the middle, tapered toward both ends, and upturned toward the rear.

FAMILY SIRICIDAE—HORNTAILS

In Western North America, the **horntails,** Siricidae (Middlekauff 1960), number 12 species in 4 genera—*Xeris, Sirex, Urocerus,* and *Tremex.* All except one of the western species attack conifers, and most attack a variety of hosts. Recorded hosts are as follows:

Species	Hosts
Sirex areolatus (Cresson)	*Abies concolor, Cupressus macrocarpa, Juniperus occidentalis,* Libocedrus decurrens, Pinus contorta, P. jeffreyi, P. lambertiana, P. radiata, Pseudotsuga menziesii,* and *Sequoia sempervirens*
S. behrensii (Cresson)	*Cupressus macrocarpa, Pinus jeffreyi, P. lambertiana, P. ponderosa,* and *P. radiata*
S. cyaneus F.	*Abies concolor, A. lasiocarpa, Picea engelmannii, P. glauca, Pinus ponderosa,* and *Pseudotsuga menziesii*
S. juvencus (L.)	*Abies lasiocarpa, Cupressus macrocarpa, Larix occidentalis, Picea sitchensis, Pinus contorta, P. jeffreyi, P. ponderosa, P. radiata,* and *Pseudotsuga menziesii*
S. longicauda Middlekauff	*Abies concolor* and *A. magnifica*
Tremex columba (L.)	*Acer, Betula, Platanus, Quercus, Ulmus,* and other deciduous trees
Urocerus albicornis (F.)	*Abies amabilis, A. lasiocarpa, Larix occidentalis, Picea, Pinus, Pseudotsuga menziesii, Thuja plicata,* and *Tsuga heterophylla*

Species	Hosts
U. *californicus* Norton	*Abies concolor, A. lasiocarpa, A. magnifica, Larix occidentalis, Libocedrus decurrens, Pinus contorta, P. monticola, P. ponderosa, Pseudotsuga menziesii,* and *Tsuga heterophylla*
U. *gigas flavicornis* (F.)	*Abies, Abies concolor, Larix occidentalis, Picea, P. glauca, Pinus,* and *Pseudotsuga menziesii*
Xeris morrisoni (Cresson)	*Abies concolor, A. grandis, A. lasiocarpa, A. magnifica* (?), *Larix occidentalis, Libocedrus decurrens, Picea pungens, P. sitchensis, Pinus contorta* (?), *P. ponderosa* (?), *Pseudotsuga menziesii,* and *Tsuga heterophylla*
X. spectrum (L.)	*Abies concolor, A. grandis, A. lasiocarpa, Larix occidentalis, Picea engelmannii, P. pungens, P. sitchensis, Pinus contorta, P. ponderosa, Pseudotsuga menziesii,* and *Tsuga heterophylla*
X. tarsalis Cresson	*Cupressus macrocarpa, Juniperus occidentalis,* and *Thuja plicata* (?)

Horntails develop in trees that are damaged or killed by fire, wind, insects, diseases, smog, and mechanical operations. Their mines degrade lumber cut from infested trees, but normally these insects attract attention only when lumber from burns and windthrows is marketed in large amounts. In the first year or so after construction of a house, adult horntails may emerge from previously infested timbers, causing holes in walls, floors, and ceilings. Kiln-drying would prevent this type of damage but would seldom be warranted for this purpose alone. These insects do not attack dry, finished wood products. In New Zealand, young pine trees in plantations are killed by *Sirex noctilio* F. and its associated fungus, *Amylostereum areolatum* (Fries) Boidin (Rawlings 1948). This type of damage by horntails is not recorded in Western North America.

The adults are large, thick-waisted cylindrical insects (fig. 262A, B). Both sexes have a short hornlike process (cornus) at the end of the body. Females have a long stingerlike ovipositor that extends straight back when not in use. The adults come in bold colors—dark blue, black, and reddish brown, often with metallic reflections and marked with ivory, yellows, and reds. Size and color vary widely, even within species. Identification of the males is especially difficult.

The biology of the North American species is known only in broad outline. The females insert their long flexible ovipositors deeply into the wood, often 25 mm or more, and lay their eggs. Sometimes they are unable to extract their ovipositors from the wood and die in this position. The larvae are cylindrical and yellowish white, with a small spine at the posterior end of the body. In profile their body resembles a shallow letter "S" (fig. 262C).

454

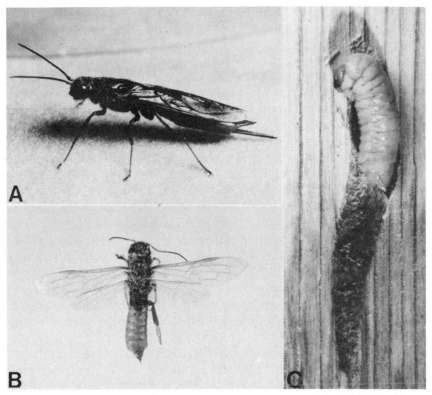

FIGURE 262.—Examples of horntail life stages: *A*, Adult female of *Sirex behrensii*, 22 mm long; *B*, adult male of a *Sirex* species, 18 mm long; *C*, mature larva of *S. longicauda*, 22 mm long.

They mine entirely within the wood, packing their circular holes with fine boring dust. It takes one, two, or more seasons for them to complete their development. Pupal cells are constructed near the surface of the wood, and when the adults mature, they bore round, clean-cut emergence holes to the surface through which they escape.

Symbiotic fungi, *Amylostereum* [*Stereum*], are associated with several species of *Sirex* and *Urocerus*. The larvae are reported to feed upon the fungi rather than the wood (Morgan 1968). Food requirements and host relationships need further study.

Ibalia and *Megarhyssa* are characteristic parasites of horntails (Cameron 1965).

Sirex (Cameron 1967) contains five species in the West. The adults differ from those of *Urocerus* and *Xeris* by not having pale areas on the head above and behind the eyes. The ovipositor of

455

Sirex is shorter than the forewing, except for *S. areolatus* and *S. longicauda.*

Sirex areolatus (Cresson), occurs from California to British Columbia and eastward to Colorado, New Mexico, and Arizona. The adult female is metallic blue black with uniformly smoky wings. The male is similar but smaller and the terminal segments of the abdomen are yellowish orange. Cedarlike trees are most commonly attacked.

Sirex behrensii (Cresson) is a small species, about 15 to 23 mm long, with head, thorax and base of abdomen blue black and apical segments of the abdomen reddish brown. It occurs in California, Nevada, and Washington, usually on pines.

The **blue horntail**, *Sirex cyaneus* F., is a circumboreal species, occurring on the west coast from California to British Columbia and in the Rocky Mountain States and Provinces. The body is bluish black and the legs are mostly reddish brown. This species resembles *S. juvencus.*

Sirex juvencus (L.) (= *varipes* Walker) (Benson 1962b) is a holarctic species with several named varieties. *S. juvencus californicus* (Ashmead) (= *obesus* Bradley) occurs in the Pacific Coast States and is one of the insects attacking smog-killed ponderosa pine in California (Cameron 1968). The female body and legs are metallic blue black, wings smoky, and ovipositor short. The male body is metallic greenish black except the terminal segments of the abdomen which are reddish brown.

Sirex longicauda Middlekauff is a California species that closely resembles *S. areolatus* but the wings are smoky only along the veins. It breeds abundantly in fire-killed and damaged fir and causes degrade of lumber salvaged from such trees.

The **pigeon tremex**, *Tremex columba* (L.), is the only western horntail that does not develop in conifers. It attacks weakened or dead deciduous trees, including birch, elm, maple, oak, and sycamore and is not economically important. In contrast with the long, threadlike antennae of *Sirex*, *Urocerus*, and *Xeris*, the antennae of *T. columba* are short and slightly swollen in the middle. The forms of this insect in Colorado, New Mexico, Arizona, and California may have a yellow abdomen with black markings and golden-yellow wings or an entirely yellowish-brown abdomen and dark reddish-brown wings. The biology has not been studied in detail.

Urocerus (Middlekauff 1960) contains the largest of the horntails. There are three species in the West. Like *Xeris*, the species of *Urocerus* have a pale spot behind the eye, but the head lacks a lateral ridge and the hind tibiae have two apical spurs rather than one. The females are wasplike in appearance and actions but harmless to man.

Urocerus albicornis (F.) is a transcontinental species widely distributed in the West but most abundant in the Canadian Life Zone. The female's wings are smoky brown and the male's nearly clear. The body and legs of the female are black, usually with white markings. The abdomen of the male is mostly black, but the third to sixth segments are yellow. This species has numerous hosts. In Washington it has been reared abundantly from Pacific silver fir killed by *Pseudohylesinus* bark beetles.

Urocerus californicus Norton is the largest of the western horn-tails. It occurs from California to British Columbia, Colorado, and New Mexico, tending to be more abundant southward than *U. albicornis*. The wings of both sexes are golden yellow. The female body and legs are black except for yellow markings on the legs. The male body and legs are reddish brown.

Urocerus gigas flavicornis (F.) has a range similar to *U. albicornis* but apparently is less common. It is somewhat smaller than *U. californicus*. The abdomen of the female is partially yellow.

Xeris (Middlekauff 1960) contains three species in the West. They are slender and resemble *Sirex* but differ in having a white spot behind the eye and a generally longer ovipositor.

Xeris morrisoni (Cresson) and *X. tarsalis* Cresson (= *macgillivrayi* Bradley) are quite similar. Both have a reddish abdomen. *X. morrisoni* occurs in California, Oregon, Washington, Utah, and Colorado on numerous hosts, perhaps most abundantly on firs and lodgepole pine. *X. tarsalis* occurs from California to Washington and is positively recorded on *Juniperus* and *Cupressus*.

Xeris spectrum (L.) is a circumboreal species that occurs extensively in the Western States and British Columbia, attacking numerous hosts. The abdomen is entirely black.

FAMILY SYNTEXIDAE

The family Syntexidae, containing one genus and one species, resembles the Xiphydriidae. The **incensecedar wood wasp**, *Syntexis libocedrii* Rohwer (Wickman 1967), bores in the sapwood of fire-scorched incense-cedar in California, western juniper and probably western redcedar in Oregon. It is more a curiosity than a pest. The life cycle is completed in 1 to 2 years. Adult females range from 8 to 16 mm long and males from 6 to 11 mm. The larva is white and cylindrical and has small spines at the rear (Middlekauff 1974). Its head is recessed in the thorax.

FAMILY XIPHYDRIIDAE

Larvae of the Xiphydriidae (Muesebeck et al. 1951–67) bore in partially decayed wood of various broad-leaved trees, hence are not economically important. In North America there are six species, all in the genus *Xiphydria*. Two occur in the West—*X. mellipes* Harris in birch and alder and *X. maculata* Say in maple. The adults are 12 to 20 mm long and resemble horntails. The full-grown larvae are 20 mm long, yellowish white, and with the thorax and terminal segments of the abdomen swollen. The abdomen is without leglike appendages and ends in a hornlike projection.

SUBORDER APOCRITA

The suborder Apocrita contains all else than the sawflies and horntails in the Hymenoptera, notably the ants, bees, wasps, and parasites, grouped in several superfamilies, seven of which are included in this manual. A few of the species damage the forest. Many are beneficial, notably among the parasites. The base of the abdomen of the adult is strongly constricted and waistlike. The constricted portion is called the pedicel.

SUPERFAMILY ICHNEUMONOIDEA

The superfamily Ichneumonoidea consists principally of the Braconidae and Ichneumonidae, two of the largest and more important families of parasites. Many of the species are parasitic on forest insects, often exerting strong natural control.

FAMILY BRACONIDAE—BRACONIDS

The Braconidae is a large family of parasites, mostly primary, many of which attack forest insects. Marsh (1971) keys the nearctic genera. Braconids are related to the ichneumonids and have similar habits but generally are much smaller.

Agathis contains numerous small species some of which parasitize forest Lepidoptera such as *Coleophora, Coleotechnites,* and *Epinotia. A. pumila* (Ratzeburg) attacks only the larvae of the larch casebearer. In the late 1920's and 1930's it was colonized from Europe into the Eastern States and Provinces where it became widely dispersed and effective. In 1960 it was colonized against the casebearer in Idaho where it has become well established and exerts considerable control locally but has spread slowly (Denton 1972). It has also been released in Montana, Oregon, Washington, and British Columbia but not enough time has elapsed to evaluate its effectiveness in those areas.

There are nearly 200 species of *Apanteles* (Muesebeck 1920) in North America. Most are 2 to 4 mm long and predominantly black. All are parasitic on larvae of Lepidoptera, including many tree-infesting species of diverse size and habit. Some *Apanteles* are solitary; others develop gregariously in the host larva. All species form characteristic small white cocoons on the host remains (fig. 263) or nearby.

FIGURE 263.—Cocoons of a gregarious species of *Apanteles* on dead larva of the pandora moth.

Apanteles aristoteliae Viereck ranges from coast to coast attacking species of *Aroga, Argyrotaenia, Choristoneura, Dioryctria,* and other genera.

Apanteles californicus Muesebeck is an important parasite of *Coleotechnites milleri* on lodgepole pine in California (Telford 1961). It ranges northward to British Columbia and Alberta, where it attacks *C. starki,* but is much less abundant on that host than *A. starki* Mason (Stark 1961).

Apanteles fumiferanae Viereck is an important parasite of the immature larvae of *Choristoneura occidentalis* and *C. fumiferana.* The biology on the latter host is reported by Brown (1946).

Apanteles solitarius (Ratzeburg) (Jones et al. 1938, Lejeune and Silver 1961) was colonized from Europe into Washington in 1932 and into British Columbia in 1933 against the satin moth. The parasite quickly spread and exerted strong control.

Aphidius [*Incubus*] (Smith 1944) contains about 50 species that parasitize aphids including *Cinara* and *Lachnus.* These parasites are small, slender-bodied, long-legged insects. Upon maturity, the adult parasite emerges through a circular hole it cuts in the back of the mummified aphid.

Atanycolus (Shenefelt 1943) contains 36 species in North America; about half of them are western. They resemble *Coeloides* but are larger. The females range from 6 to 13 mm long, are shiny black to red, and have dusky wings. They parasitize larvae of wood-boring Cerambycidae and Buprestidae. Their cocoon resembles an elongate-oval, flattened, brownish pillbox. *A. longifemoralis* Shenefelt, occurring from California to British Columbia and eastward to Montana, attacks *Melanophila drummondi,* and *M. gentilis. A. anocomidis* Cushman occurs extensively in the West and attacks both buprestids and cerambycids.

There are about 90 species of *Bracon* [*Microbracon*] (Muesebeck 1925) in North America. These small parasites attack the large larvae of many Lepidoptera and Coleoptera and a few Hymenoptera, including a wide variety of forest insects. Some species have widely different hosts but are of similar habit. *B. politiventris* (Cushman) attacks lepidopterous species in *Archips, Argyrotaenia, Choristoneura, Dioryctria,* and *Rhyacionia.* McKnight (1971) reports its biology on *C. occidentalis.*

Two species of *Coeloides* are important parasites of the larvae of western bark beetles. *C. brunneri* Viereck (Ryan and Rudinsky 1962) (fig. 264) occurs from British Columbia to California and eastward to Colorado. It parasitizes *Dendroctonus pseudotsugae* and *Scolytus ventralis.* In Oregon it has three generations annu-

F–523514, F–523515

FIGURE 264.—The bark beetle parasite, *Coeloides brunneri*: *A,* Adult, 4.5 mm long, ovipositing in bark of Douglas-fir; *B,* cocoons formed in larval galleries of the Douglas fir beetle.

ally. A portion of each generation enters diapause and over-winters in the fifth instar. The adults are shiny, somewhat antlike insects, 3 to 6 mm long, with globular heads, prominent eyes, and smoky, minutely hairy wings. *C. dendroctoni* Cushman (DeLeon 1935) is a similar species with a similar range. It parasitizes *Dendroctonus ponderosae, D. rufipennis, Ips pini, I. perturbatus, I. montanus, I. emarginatus,* and *Orthotomicus caelatus.*

Eubadizon contains 18 species in North America, about half of them in the West. Hosts include a wide range of Lepidoptera and Coleoptera. *E. gracile* Provancher, a transcontinental species, is one of the most important parasites of *Acleris gloverana*. It also attacks *Choristoneura occidentalis, Coleotechnites milleri, C. starki,* and other Lepidoptera. The adult is testaceous, 5 to 7 mm long, and the ovipositor is slender and about the length of the body. The cocoon is brown and torpedo-shaped.

There are about 40 species of *Meteorus* (Muesebeck 1923). Most are internal parasites of lepidopterous larvae; a few parasitize Coleoptera. The cocoon often hangs suspended by a thread.

Meteorus versicolor (Wesmael) (Jones et al. 1938) from Europe was colonized in 1932–34 in Washington against *Leucoma salicis* and soon exerted considerable control. *M. hyphantriae* Riley is transcontinental attacking *Hyphantria cunea* and species of *Malacosoma, Halisidota, Hemileuca, Alsophila, Orgyia, Nepytia,* and other Lepidoptera. *M. hypophlaei* Cushman (DeLeon 1933) parasitizes larvae of *Corticeus*, a genus of tenebrionids often abundant in galleries of bark beetles.

FAMILY ICHNEUMONIDAE—ICHNEUMONS

The Ichneumonidae (Muesebeck et al. 1951–67, Townes 1944–45) is a family of parasites estimated to contain 10,000 species in North America, of which some 2,500 have been described. They range in size from small to the largest of the parasitic wasps. The adults are slender-bodied and most species have a long ovipositor. The white legless larvae usually feed internally in their hosts, mostly insects and especially Lepidoptera. Many are parasites of forest insects and some are among the most effective agents in natural control of forest pests. Several ichneumons have been imported and released against foreign insect pests in North American forests (Dowden 1962). Of the imports, only *Mesoleius tenthredinis* Morley has given appreciable control in the West. Of the hundreds of native ichneumons in western forests, the following are a few representative examples.

Apechthis [*Ephialtes*] *ontario* (Cresson), a transcontinental species, parasitizes the pupae of *Choristoneura occidentalis* and other lepidopterous defoliators, including species of *Lambdina*, *Acleris*, *Dioryctria*, and *Nepytia* (fig. 265). The adults are 7 to 12 mm long and black except for white markings on the head of the male.

FIGURE 265.—Adult of the parasite, *Apechthis ontario*, 10 mm long, ovipositing in a moth pupa.

Glypta (Muesebeck et al. 1951–67) contains about 50 species. They parasitize caterpillars in twigs, rolled leaves, and similar situations.

Glypta fumiferanae (Viereck) (Dodge 1961) is a transcontinental species and a common parasite of several budworms in the genus *Choristoneura*, including *C. occidentalis*. The brownish-black adults, 7.5 to 8.0 mm long, fly in midsummer. Using their ovipositors, they probe bark scales and lichens (fig. 266) and insert eggs into the small hibernating host larvae. The eggs hatch quickly and the parasite larvae overwinter within their hosts. Parasite larvae develop in spring, kill their host larvae as the latter mature, and form conspicuous transparent cocoons nearby. *G. fumiferanae* occasionally attacks those species of *Dioryctria* which overwinter as small larvae.

Itoplectis (Muesebeck et al. 1951–67) contains nine species in North America, most of which parasitize forest Lepidoptera. These parasites closely resemble *Apechthis*.

FIGURE 266.—Adult of the parasite, *Glypta fumiferanae*, 8 mm long, ovipositing in overwintering western spruce budworm larva concealed in twig scar.

Itoplectis quadricingulatus (Provancher) parasitizes numerous destructive defoliators in the West, including *Choristoneura occidentalis, Lambdina fiscellaria lugubrosa, Orgyia pseudotsugata, Neodiprion tsugae,* and many lesser ones. Experimentally this parasite has been released to control the European pine shoot moth (Ryan and Medley 1970).

The four North American species of *Megarhyssa* (Michener 1939) are parasites of Siricidae. They are large, colorful insects with very long ovipositors. Only one is western.

Megarhyssa nortoni (Cresson) is 25 to 38 mm long with an ovipositor about twice the body length (fig. 267). The color is black marked with red and yellow. It parasitizes species of *Sirex* and *Xeris* extensively in the West.

Mesoleius (Muesebeck et al. 1951–67) contains upward of 50 species, many in the West. They parasitize sawfly larvae.

Mesoleius tenthredinis Morley (McGugan and Coppel 1962), a primary larval parasite, was introduced into Canada from England beginning in 1910, to control *Pristiphora erichsonii.* In Manitoba this parasite at first gave effective control but later it encountered resistant strains. In British Columbia *M. tenthredinis* continues effective.

Phytodietus (Muesebeck et al. 1951–67) is a small genus the species of which parasitize smaller Lepidoptera.

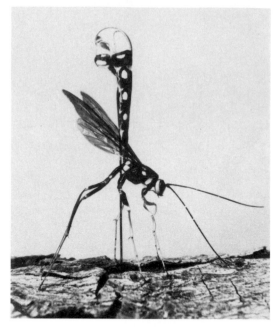

COURTESY K. L. TAYLOR (1967)

FIGURE 267.—Adult of the parasite, *Megarhyssa nortoni*, 32 mm long, ovipositing through bark and wood into the body of a concealed horntail larva.

Phytodietus fumiferanae Rohwer (Wilkes et al. 1948) is one of the more important of the 50 or so insect parasites of *Choristoneura occidentalis*. It develops externally on late-stage larvae (fig. 268).

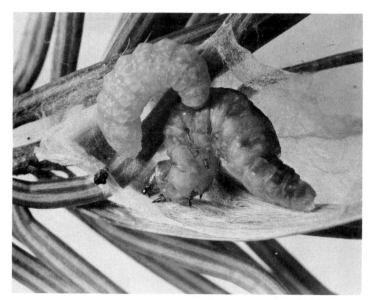

F-494227

FIGURE 268.—Mature larva, 8 mm long, of an external parasite, *Phytodietus fumiferanae*, killing its host, a western spruce budworm larva.

The species of *Rhyssa* (Townes and Townes 1960) resemble those of *Megarhyssa* but are smaller. Five of the six North American species are western. They parasitize wood borers including Cerambycidae, Siricidae, and Melandryidae. *R. lineolata* (Kirby) and *R. persuasoria* (L.) have been introduced into New Zealand from North America in an attempt to control *Sirex noctilio* Fabricius.

Theronia atalantae (Poda) is the only western species in this genus. It is transcontinental and parasitizes the pupae of many forest Lepidoptera including species of *Choristoneura, Malacosoma, Orgyia, Leucoma,* and *Nymphalis*. It is reported to have been effective in reducing outbreaks of *Neophasia menapia* in Idaho.

SUPERFAMILY CHALCIDOIDEA

This very large superfamily (Peck 1963) contains thousands of species. Six of the 21 North American families are included in this manual—Encyrtidae, Eulophidae, Eurytomidae, Pteromalidae, Torymidae, and Trichogrammatidae. The adults are small to tiny and have elbowed antennae. The forewings are veined only near the front margin and do not have closed cells. Most species are parasitic on insects; some feed upon plants. Forest chalcids generally are beneficial; a few are minor pests.

FAMILY ENCYRTIDAE

The Encyrtidae (Clausen 1940) is a sizable family of small parasites many of which attack scale insects and the eggs and larvae of Lepidoptera. Some that lay their eggs in the embryo of the host egg have polyembryonic development, and a single egg may produce hundreds, even thousands of adults. *Copidosoma deceptor* Miller, an example of polyembryonic development, parasitizes many forest Lepidoptera, particularly *Coleotechnites* and other leafminers. *Blastothrix sericea* (Dalman), an example of single-embryonic development, was introduced from England in 1928, and is reported to have controlled *Lecanium corni* effectively in British Columbia (Turnbull and Chant 1961).

FAMILY EULOPHIDAE

The Eulophidae (Peck 1963) are tiny parasites that attack many forest insects. *Tetrastichus* is a large and representative genus. Perhaps the best known species is *T. minutus* (Howard), usually designated as *T. blepyri* Ashmead, in the West. It parasitizes aphids and scales principally but also coccinellids and other insects. *T. malacosomae* Girault parasitizes the eggs of various western *Malacosoma*. *Aphelinus mali* (Haldeman) is an important parasite of *Eriosoma lanigerum*, and *Chrysocharis laricinellae* (Ratzeburg) has been introduced for control of the larch casebearer. Species of *Prospaltella* attack scales and whiteflies. *P. near aurantii* (Howard) is the most important factor in natural control of the scale, *Nuculaspis californica* (Edmunds 1973).

FAMILY EURYTOMIDAE—EURYTOMIDS, JOINTWORMS, AND SEED CHALCIDS

Some members of the family Eurytomidae are phytophagous; others are parasitic. As a group, they are of minor importance in forestry. Typically, the adults are shining black, heavily-punctured, humpbacked in profile, and sharply tapered to the rear. The larvae are legless, white, and tapered to both ends.

Eurytoma contains upward of 80 species in North America (Bugbee 1967). They are reported to attack many kinds of insects and plants. Some commonly occur in galls caused by cynipids on oak. *E. pini* Bugbee is reported to parasitize larvae of *Rhyacionia buoliana* previously paralyzed by primary parasites (Arthur 1961).

E. tumoris Bugbee causes a characteristic swelling and pitting of terminal and lateral branches of Scotch pine in Christmas tree plantings in California (Stark and Koehler 1964). *E. calycis* Bugbee causes galls on the current shoots of jack pine reproduction in Saskatchewan (Drouin and Wong 1962). Unidentified *Eurytoma* have been recorded on *Pinus coulteri, P. ponderosa,* and *P. jeffreyi* in California and on *P. ponderosa* in Oregon (fig. 269). The one in Oregon attacks 2- and 3-year-old growth and presumably has a 1-year life cycle.

FAMILY PTEROMALIDAE

The Pteromalidae (Peck 1963) are numerous in western forests, attacking a wide variety of insects including other parasites. The adults are dark colored, usually black and shiny, often with metallic reflections. The abdomen tapers strongly to the rear. The life cycle is short, usually less than a month.

Dibrachys cavus (Walker) parasitizes many destructive forest Lepidoptera and sawflies and also many of their primary parasites. Several to many individuals develop from a single host. *Tritneptis klugii* (Ratzeburg) is of similar appearance and habits. It parasitizes various *Neodiprion* in the cocoon and also is a hyperparasite.

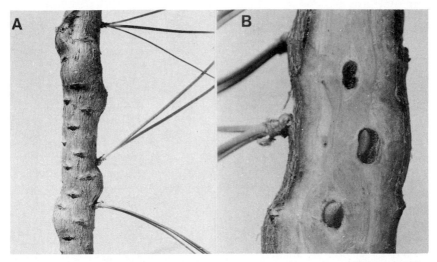

F–523517, F–523518

FIGURE 269.—*Eurytoma* species: *A*, Swellings caused on branches of ponderosa pine; *B*, sectioned branch, showing larval galleries.

FAMILY TORYMIDAE—TORYMIDS

In the family Torymidae, formerly Callimomidae (Peck 1963), the many species of *Torymus* [*Callimome*] are largely parasites of cynipid and cecidomyiid gall formers. Species in other genera parasitize Lepidoptera and other insects. Some destroy tree seeds.

In North America there are 23 species of *Megastigmus* (Milliron 1949). All these species are phytophagous. About half of them, mostly western, feed in seeds of conifers (Keen 1958). The others are known or presumed to feed in seeds of rosaceous plants.

The adults are antlike, 2.5 to 6.5 mm long, and range from black to brown or yellowish. The females are larger and have a subglobose abdomen with a long, curved ovipositor with which they drill through the young green cones to lay their eggs in the immature seeds (fig. 270A). The small, white, legless larvae feed on and destroy the tissue within the seeds (fig. 270B). The outer shell forms normally and the surface shows no evidence that the seed is infested. In the following spring the larvae mature and the adults form and emerge, leaving a smooth round emergence hole in the seed coat. Some hold over and emerge 2 or even 3 years later. At times these insects cause a high percentage of cull in commercially processed tree seed.

The **Douglas fir seed chalcid**, *Megastigmus spermotrophus* Wachtl (Keen 1958), the most thoroughly known species, occurs on *Pseudotsuga menziesii* and *P. macrocarpa* in Western United States and Canada and is an introduced pest in Europe. Generally rated as

FIGURE 270.—The Douglas fir seed chalcid (*Megastigmus spermotrophus*): *A*, Adult ovipositing in Douglas-fir cone; *B*, larvae, 2 mm long, inside seeds.

less destructive than *Barbara* and *Contarinia*, it is at times quite damaging. Preventive control is still experimental. If seeds are to be shipped to other countries, it is desirable to fumigate them before shipment.

Hosts and distribution of other species of *Megastigmus* that infest conifers in the West are:

Species	Hosts	Distribution
M. albifrons Walker pine seed chalcid	*Pinus ponderosa*	Calif., Ariz., and N. Mex.
M. lasiocarpae Crosby	*Abies amabilis* and *A. lasiocarpa*	Colo., Wash., and British Columbia
M. milleri Milliron	*Abies grandis* and *A. magnifica shastensis*	Calif. and British Columbia
M. piceae Rohwer spruce seed chalcid	*Picea engelmannii*, *P. glauca*, *P. pungens*, and *P. sitchensis*	Calif., Oreg., Alaska, Mont., Colo., and N. Mex.
M. pinus Parfitt fir seed chalcid	*Abies amabilis*, *A. concolor*, *A. grandis*, *A. lasiocarpa*, *A. magnifica*, and *A. magnifica shastensis*	Calif., Oreg., Wash., Nev., Colo., Idaho, and British Columbia
M. rafni Hoffmeyer	*Abies concolor*, *A. grandis*, *A. magnifica*, and *A. magnifica shastensis*	Calif., Oreg., Idaho, Colo., N. Mex., and British Columbia
M. tsugae Crosby	*Tsuga heterophylla* and *T. mertensiana*	Oreg. and Wash.

468

Among the parasitic torymids, *Roptrocerus eccoptogastri* (Ratzeburg) commonly parasitizes the larvae of various *Dendroctonus, Ips,* and other scolytids.

FAMILY TRICHOGRAMMATIDAE—MINUTE EGG PARASITES

The **minute egg parasites**, Trichogrammatidae (Peck 1963), are internal parasites in the eggs of other insects.

Trichogramma minutum Riley is a light yellow, fragile species, about 0.3 mm long. It parasitizes the eggs of more than 150 species of insects in several orders, but mostly Lepidoptera. Parasitized eggs become brown to black, and are readily recognized (fig. 271). Hosts include many forest pests in genera such as *Choristoneura, Acleris, Rhyacionia, Lambdina,* and *Malacosoma.* Under optimum conditions, the life cycle of *T. minutum* requires little more than a week. Countless millions have been reared to control agricultural pests. It apparently is not very effective against forest pests.

F–523519

FIGURE 271.—Black unhatched eggs in egg mass of western spruce budworm are parasitized by *Trichogramma minutum.*

SUPERFAMILY CYNIPOIDEA

The superfamily Cynipoidea (Muesebeck et al. 1951–67) contains four families in North America but is of interest to foresters chiefly because of the Cynipidae and to a lesser extent the Ibaliidae.

FAMILY CYNIPIDAE—CYNIPIDS OR GALL WASPS

Most Cynipidae (Felt 1940, Weld 1957) are gallformers; some live in galls formed by others; a few are parasites. A great variety of galls are formed on trees, predominantly on oaks. Most of the galls are on the leaves and branches but some occur on flowers, acorns, and roots. The galls may be large, round and shiny, irregular in shape, spiny, or tiny swellings (fig. 272). The larvae that inhabit these galls are white, legless, and without a distinct head. The adults are somber-colored yellow to brown or black, antlike insects, 1 to 6 mm long. Over 200 species are known to occur in the

469

West. Several genera produce alternately a female-only generation and a bisexual generation. These generations differ markedly in appearance, both the adults and the galls (Evans 1972). Mostly, the cynipids are innocuous. A few are considered pests of ornamentals and even fewer are mildly beneficial (Kinsey 1935).

Andricus (Muesebeck et al. 1951–67) contains about 100 species in North America; about half of them are western. All develop on *Quercus. A. californicus* Ashmead is one of the best known because of the large, persistent, applelike galls it causes on twigs of white oaks in California, Oregon, and Washington (fig. 272A). Only the female is known.

Bassettia ligni Kinsey (Evans 1972) occurs from California to British Columbia. The female-only generation causes seedlike galls under the bark of branches of *Quercus garryana* and *Q. douglasii*

F–523520, COURTESY CANADIAN FORESTRY SERVICE (B,C), F–523521

FIGURE 272.—Examples of oak galls caused by Cynipidae: *A, Andricus californicus* apple-size galls on branch stem; *B, Bassetia ligni* emergence holes from galls under bark of branch; *C, Besbicus mirabilis* spherical galls on underside of leaves; *D, Neuroterus saltatorius* small seed-size galls on underside of leaf.

(fig. 272B). The bark over the galls ruptures, often girdling and killing the branches. The resulting clusters of dead leaves sometimes are quite abundant and conspicuous on open-grown trees. The bisexual generation causes inconspicuous blisterlike swellings between veins on the leaves.

Besbicus mirabilis (Kinsey) (Evans 1967) occurs on *Quercus garryana* in California, Oregon, Washington, and British Columbia. The female-only generation causes mottled, spherical galls on the underside of the leaves (fig. 272C). The bisexual generation causes small ovoid galls among the leaf buds. It is noneconomic.

Callirhytis (Muesebeck et al. 1951–67) contains about 100 species in North America, mostly eastern. All develop on *Quercus. C. perdens* (Kinsey) causes slender, elongate stem galls on black oaks in California and Oregon. Kinsey (1935) rates it as one of the few economically damaging oak gall wasps.

Neuroterus contains about 50 species in North America, somewhat less than half of them western. All develop on *Quercus. N. saltatorius* (H. Edwards) (Brown and Eads 1965a) forms ovoid, mustardseedlike galls about 1 mm long on the lower surface of leaves of white oaks in California, Arizona, and Oregon (fig. 272D). Often abundant, these galls cause no appreciable damage. They arouse interest in the fall when they drop to the ground and jump about in the fashion of Mexican jumping beans.

FAMILY IBALIIDAE

This family contains one genus, *Ibalia* (Weld 1952), the members of which are parasites of horntails. The females range in length from 8 to 18 mm. The abdomen is smooth, shining, and almost sessile; that of the female is compressed laterally and is very thin like a knife blade. The thorax is very much roughened. The adults are often seen around horntail-infested logs and trees.

Ibalia ensiger Norton has been associated with and presumed parasitic upon *Sirex areolatus* in fire-killed incense-cedar in California (Wickman 1964b). This species also has been sent to Australia in an attempt to control *Sirex noctilio* (Cameron 1965).

SUPERFAMILY EVANIOIDEA

The superfamily Evanioidea contains several families of small parasites, only a few of which are significant in forestry. The smaller ones resemble chalcids; the larger ones, ichneumons. Some are wingless.

FAMILY GASTERUPTIIDAE

The Gasteruptiidae are slender, ichneumonlike parasites with long ovipositors.

The genus *Pristaulacus* (Townes 1950) contains about 20 species, most of which occur in the West. They parasitize wood borers, principally Cerambycidae and Buprestidae. The forewings of most species are spotted to overall brownish. *P. rufitarsis* (Cresson), a parasite of *Melanophila* and *Saperda,* is transcontinental. *P. editus* (Cresson) on *Paratimia* and *Chrysophana, P. minor* (Cresson) on *Melanophila* and *Semanotus,* and *P. montanus* (Cresson) on *Chrysobothris* and *Xylotrechus* are common species on the Pacific slope.

FAMILY SCELIONIDAE

The species in the family Scelionidae parasitize the eggs of other insects, including several forest pests. Species of *Telenomus* (Muesebeck et al. 1951–67) are common parasites of *Orgyia* and *Malacosoma.*

SUPERFAMILY SCOLIOIDEA

The superfamily Scolioidea (Muesebeck et al. in 1951–67) contains seven families in North America but is significant in western forestry almost exclusively because of the ants, Formicidae.

FAMILY FORMICIDAE—ANTS

"An ant is an ant" characterizes the Formicidae (Creighton 1950, Wheeler 1926, Wheeler and Wheeler 1963) sufficiently for most people. Technically **ants** are a group of social insects with winged reproductives, unwinged workers, elbowed antennae, and with the abdominal pedicel consisting of one or two segments. Of the 600 or so species and subspecies recognized in North America, a few damage forest trees or wood products. Still fewer may be of use in biological control of harmful forest insects.

Ants belonging to the genus *Camponotus* are called **carpenter ants** because they tunnel in the wood of stumps, logs, dead standing trees, the dead interior of living trees, and the wooden portions of buildings. These black or black and red ants are 7 to 15 mm long—our biggest ants. They excavate cavities for nests in which to rear their young. The wood is not eaten by the ants, but cast out to make room for the nests, causing piles of wood fibers to collect below the entrance holes. Their excavations in wood are frequently so extensive as to seriously impair its structural value (fig. 273). *Camponotus* is at home in the forests of the West, except in very shady, wet places. They are general feeders, including in their fare both animal food and sweets, their preferred items of food appearing to be caterpillars of certain lycaenid butterflies and the honeydew excreted by aphids. They have even been known to shelter the aphid eggs in their nest during the winter and carry them out and place them on plants to develop in the spring.

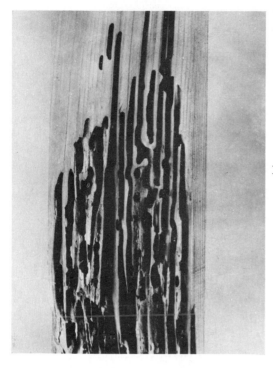

FIGURE 273.—Damage caused by carpenter ants, *Camponotus* spp., to structural wood.

Camponotus differs from some of the other ant species in that the queen carpenter ant works alone in founding a colony. An interesting feature is that, from the time the queen builds her cell and begins to lay eggs until a brood of workers mature, no food is taken into the cell. This covers a period of about 10 days from the laying of the egg to the larval stage and perhaps 30 days more until the workers are mature and begin to carry in food. It is generally supposed that the queen carries enough food within her body to feed the growing workers, apparently by regurgitation.

In the Pacific Northwest, carpenter ant damage to buildings is more prevalent than that done by termites. In this region *C. herculeanus modoc* W. M. Wheeler, *C. laevigatus* (F. Smith), and *C. vicinus* Mayr are the species commonly found in houses. Carpenter ants cause some deterioration and breakage by mining in the base of fire-scarred and butt-rotted standing trees, especially western redcedar, and including giant sequoia, Douglas-fir,

473

pines, and true firs. They also damage young conifers by gnawing and girdling them in the root collar zone while tending *Cinara* aphids. The most serious damage is done on 4- to 8-year-old trees, although older trees also are attacked. This type of damage has caused the death of both planted and wild seedlings in various parts of the Pacific Northwest. *C. noveboracensis* (Fitch) has been found injuring and killing Douglas-fir and western hemlock reproduction at several places in western Washington (fig. 274). In southeastern Oregon, *C. herculeanus modoc* has been found doing similar damage to small white firs.

F–523523

FIGURE 274.—Damage by a carpenter ant, *Camponotus noveboracensis*, to the root collar of a young Douglas-fir tree.

Control of carpenter ants in houses requires skill and patience (Furniss and Every 1964). Sometimes they are in out-of-the-way places that are difficult to treat. Sometimes they move their entire colony when treatment is applied. Dead and down trees and waste wood are likely to harbor colonies, hence should be cleared away from buildings. Clean sound construction will minimize but not entirely prevent invasion by carpenter ants. The hazard is greatest near wooded areas.

Formica (Muesebeck et al. 1951–67) is a large genus of ants some of which nest in rotting wood and some in the soil. They feed principally on honeydew and other insects. Like *Camponotus*, some tend aphids on trees. An eastern species kills small trees in clearing its nesting site.

Foresters in the pine areas of the West know well the red pugnacious *Formica rufa* Linnaeus. It builds large nesting mounds of pine needles, twigs, and other debris, bites viciously, but is not reported to damage trees. A related species of *Formica* has been colonized extensively in European forests to control harmful forest insects, but the effectiveness has been questioned (Adlung 1966).

Lasius [*Donisthorpea*] (Wilson 1955) is a genus of small, non-descript, brownish ants that live in the soil or in rotten wood. *L. sitkaensis* Pergande is a transcontinental species occurring extensively in the West from Alaska to California and New Mexico. Normally it lives in wooded areas but often infests houses. Usually it nests in moist, very rotten wood; hence its presence in a house strongly indicates a structural defect that should be corrected. Sound wood is not attacked. The workers are 3.0 to 4.5 mm long and the females about 8.5 mm. Both are reddish brown.

The **harvester ants** of the genus *Pogonomyrmex* (Cole 1968) comprise some 60 species, of which 22 occur in North America, mostly in arid parts of Western United States. They feed principally upon seeds but also upon dead insects, pollen, and other dry, high-protein material. They nest in the ground, build conical mounds of pebbles, and clear the vegetation from the surrounding area. Their clearings reduce the capacity of the range to support stock and wildlife. The effects are greatest on already depleted ranges. The workers are red, conspicuously sculptured, medium-sized, pugnacious ants with a painful sting. Control by baiting is considered effective.

The **western harvester ant**, *Pogonomyrmex occidentalis* (Cresson) (Sharp and Barr 1960), and the **Owyhee harvester ant**, *P. owyheei* Cole (Willard and Crowell 1965), occupy much of the western range from southern Arizona and New Mexico into Saskatchewan, Alberta, and British Columbia. *P. owyheei* occurs to the northwest and *P. occidentalis* to the southeast of a line running from northeastern Montana to northeastern California. The **red harvester ant**, *P. barbatus* (F. Smith), and the **California harvester ant**, *P. californicus* (Buckley), are southwestern species of importance on cultivated land. All these ants are similar in appearance and habits.

FAMILY MUTILLIDAE—VELVET ANTS

The **velvet ants** (Mickel 1928) are a large family of medium- to large-sized, brightly colored, solitary parasites of wasps and bees. The females are wingless and have an effective stinger. The males are winged. Both sexes are prominently hairy, hence their common name. These insects are mentioned because of their striking appearance and abundance in southwestern woodlands.

SUPERFAMILY VESPOIDEA

The superfamily Vespoidea (Muesebeck et al. 1951–67) contains two families in North America. Neither is of much concern to foresters.

FAMILY POMPILIDAE (PSAMMOCHARIDAE)—SPIDER WASPS

The spider wasps are medium-sized to very large, black, metallic-blue, or reddish wasps that parasitize spiders. They are especially abundant in the Southwest.

FAMILY VESPIDAE—HORNETS, YELLOW JACKETS, AND POTTER WASPS

There are many species of Vespidae, well known and widely respected because of their stinging habits. Generally black marked with yellow or white, they usually build gray paperlike nests and defend them vigorously against all who come too near. They stock the nests with insects of many kinds, hence are mildly beneficial. They are of interest to foresters chiefly because of their nuisance value in recreation areas. Baits specific for **yellow jackets** have given protection to people in camps and picnic grounds (Davis et al. 1968).

SUPERFAMILY APOIDEA

The superfamily Apoidea (Muesebeck et al. 1951–67) contains six families and many hundreds of species in North America. Hairs on the head and thorax are branched or plumelike. Most species have a stinger. The **honey bee**, *Apis mellifera* L., is the best-known example. A few of the many species of Apidae and Megachilidae are of some significance to foresters.

FAMILY APIDAE—BUMBLE, CARPENTER, HONEY, AND STINGLESS BEES

The Apidae (Muesebeck et al. 1951–67), a large and diverse family of bees containing hundreds of species, is of little concern to most foresters. The honey bee is occasionally pastured in fireweed on recent burns and thus produces a secondary crop from forest land. Bees as pollinators evidently are of little consequence in the forest. None damages the growing forest.

Carpenter bees of the genus *Xylocopa* (Hurd 1955), formerly in a separate family, are rated as pests of wood products. They are large robust bees that resemble **bumblebees** but they have a naked rather than a hairy abdomen (fig. 275A). Also, they lack the yellow and red markings of bumblebees. The color usually is metallic blue black with green or purplish reflections. Five species occur in the West, principally in California and other Southwestern States. They excavate tunnels in bark and wood in which to rear their young. Their work differs from that of the carpenter ants in that the burrows are partitioned into larval cells by chips of wood cemented together to form circular or spiral discs (fig. 275B). *X. tabaniformis* Smith is the principal species nesting in structural timbers. It frequently mines in exposed wood in buildings, bridges, tanks, poles, and posts. Damage is rarely extensive.

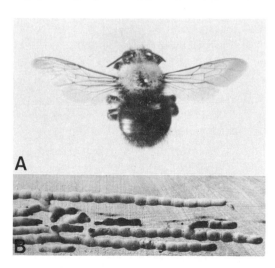

FIGURE 275.—Carpenter bee: A, Typical adult; B, nesting burrows and larval cells of *Xylocopa tabaniformis*.

FAMILY MEGACHILIDAE—LEAFCUTTING BEES

The **leafcutting bees** are small- to medium-sized. They range in color from black, brown, and gray, to metallic blue or green.

Their name relates to their habit of cutting discs from the leaves of various plants to line their cell-like nests. There are many species in the West (Muesebeck et al. 1951–67). Some are important pollinators of agricultural plants. *Megachile,* a large and representative genus, is reported as injuring shade trees in Montana and as common on shelterbelt plantings in the northern Great Plains (Wilson 1962).

Part III
Glossary, Literature Cited, and Indexes

GLOSSARY

Abdomen—the third and rearmost region of the insect body.

Ampulla (pl., **ampullae**)—a blisterlike structure, as on abdominal segments of larvae of some Cerambycidae.

Antenna (pl., **antennae**)—a pair of segmented appendages on the head above the mouth parts, often called "feelers."

Antennal club—the enlarged segments at the outer end of an antenna.

Arista—a large bristle, usually dorsal, on the apical antennal segment of Diptera.

Asperate—roughened or rasplike; refers to surfaces.

Bifurcate—divided into two forks or branches.

Biotic—of or pertaining to living organisms.

Bipectinate—having comblike projections on each side of the antennal segments, as with some Hymenoptera and Lepidoptera.

Boreal—northern; pertaining to the Boreal Region.

Boreal Region—in the Nearctic Realm, a faunal region that extends from the Polar Sea southward to near the northern boundary of the United States and farther south occupies a narrow strip along the Pacific coast and the higher parts of the Sierra-Cascade, Rocky, and Alleghany Mountain Ranges.

Brood—all the individuals that hatch at one time from eggs laid by one series of parents, and normally mature at about the same time.

Caudal—of or pertaining to the rear end of the insect body.

Circumboreal—throughout the Boreal Region.

Cornicles—paired, tubelike structures on the upper side of the fifth or sixth abdominal segments of aphids.

Crawler—the active first-instar larva of a scale insect.

Declivity—sloping rear end of the elytra of Coleoptera, especially Scolytidae.

Degrade—reduction in log grade, lumber grade, or both, resulting from defect or damage.

Diapause—a condition of suspended animation or arrested development during the life cycle of an insect.

Dimorphism—a condition of having two distinct forms in the same species.

Dorsum—the upper surface of the insect body.

Elytron (pl., **elytra**)—leathery forewings, as in Coleoptera. They may be fused and shell-like or may be divided to permit use of the hindwings for flying.

Endemic—pertaining to insect populations that are limited to economically insignificant numbers by environmental restraints.

Epidemic—pertaining to insect populations that expand to a level causing disturbances of the normal relationships in the forest association, often to the point of causing economic loss.

Epizootic—pertaining to temporary prevalence of a disease in an insect (animal) population.

Exuviae—the cast-off nymphal or larval skins resulting from molting.

Femur (pl., **femora**)—upper part or division of the insect leg, consisting of one, usually stout, elongated segment.

Flagging—occurrence of conspicuous dead branches, with the foliage still present and discolored.

Forest plantation—a stand resulting from the planting of nursery-grown seedlings or transplants.

Frass—solid larval excrement as in defoliators; wood fragments made by a wood-boring insect, usually mixed with excrement.

Gall—a pronounced swelling on a plant part, caused by insects, mites, fungi, bacteria, or nematodes.

Generation—period of time to complete the life cycle of an insect.

Genitalia—the sexual organs and associated structures.

Girdling—destruction or removal of living tissue in a ring around a stem, branch, or root.

Glabrous—smooth, without hairs.

Globose—nearly spherical.

Gouting—tumorlike swellings on bole, branches, or twigs, caused by feeding of sucking insects.

Granular—covered with minute grainlike elevations.

Head—the first region of the insect body bearing the eyes, antennae, and mouth parts.

Hibernaculum (pl., **hibernacula**)—silken shelter in which larvae of some Lepidoptera hibernate.

Holarctic—pertaining to the Holarctic Realm.

Holarctic Realm—all of Europe, North Africa to the Sahara, Asia down to the Himalaya Mountains, and North America south to Mexico.

Honeydew—a sweetish excretion produced by sucking insects, particularly aphids and scales.

Host—the plant or animal upon which an insect feeds.

Hyperparasite—a parasite whose host is another parasite.

Instar—the period or stage between molts in the larva, numbered to designate the various periods: e.g., the first instar is the stage between the egg and first larval molt.

Interspace—in Coleoptera, the surface of the elytra in between longitudinal impressed lines (striae).

Larva (pl., larvae)—a young insect differing fundamentally in form from the adult, typical of insects that undergo complete metamorphosis, as in Coleoptera, Hymenoptera, and Diptera.

Maggot—a legless larva without a well-defined head, as in the Diptera and some of the parasitic Hymenoptera.

Mandibles—the first pair of jaws of insects, usually stout and toothlike, as in larvae of wood borers.

Margined bounded by a narrow raised border; often refers to thorax of an insect.

Mesothorax—the middle or second segment of the thorax. It bears the first pair of wings and middle pair of legs.

Metamorphosis—series of changes through which an insect passes in developing from egg to adult.

Metathorax—hind portion of thorax of insects, bearing the second pair of wings and the hindlegs.

Mycangia—pouchlike structures in insects for storing fungi, as in Scolytidae and Platypodidae.

Nearctic—pertaining to the Nearctic Realm.

Nearctic Realm—that part of the Holarctic Realm occupying the North American continent, including Greenland, south to Mexico.

Nuptial chamber—a cavelike opening made by bark beetles in the inner bark beneath the entrance hole and from which the egg tunnels originate.

Nymph—young stage of insects having incomplete metamorphosis, as in Hemiptera.

Ovipositor—tubular or valvelike structure at the rear end of the insect, used to place eggs on or in suitable material.

Parasite—an organism living in or on, and nourished by another living organism.

Parasitism—the act or process of a parasitic organism living on or at the expense of another organism.

Parthenogenesis—reproduction without male fertilization.

Pathogen—an organism that causes a disease.

Pectinate—comblike; term applied to structures, especially antennae, having regularly-spaced protuberances or hairs.

Pedicel—the much-narrowed basal one or two segments of the abdomen of ants and some other Hymenoptera.

Pheromones—insect-produced chemicals that stimulate a specific reaction by the receiving individuals; i.e., sex attractants.

Phoretic—carried on an insect or other animal, but not feeding on it.

Pitch tube—a tubelike accumulation of pitch around a bark beetle entrance hole on the bark of a tree.

Polyembryonic—pertaining to the production of several to many embryos from one egg.

Polygamy—the condition of a single male having three or more female mates.

Polymorphism—the condition of having several different forms in the same species; it may be seasonal, sexual, genetic, or geographic.

Predator—any animal that preys on other animals.

Predation—the act or process in which an animal feeds on other animals.

Prepupa (pl., **prepupae**)—nonfeeding, usually inactive larval stage before transformation to the pupal stage.

Proboscis—any extended mouth structure; usually applied to the extensile mouth of Diptera, the beak of Hemiptera, and the tongue of Lepidoptera.

Proleg—false leg; any appendage that serves the purpose of a leg, as with the abdominal "legs" of caterpillars and sawflies.

Pronotum—upper surface of the prothorax.

Prothoracic shield—a hardened area, usually brownish or blackish, extending transversely across the first thoracic segment.

Prothorax—first thoracic segment; it bears the first pair of legs but no wings. In Coleoptera, it usually is referred to as "thorax."

Pseudopod—soft, footlike appendage of larvae of many Diptera.

Pubescence—short, fine, soft hair.

Pupa (pl., **pupae**)—the intermediate stage between the larva and the adult.

Puparium (pl., **puparia**)—in higher Diptera, a barrellike case formed from the last larval skin and within which the pupa is formed.

Quadripectinate—having twice-divided, comblike projections on each side of the antennal segments, as with some Lepidoptera.

Reproductives—a caste of termites that performs the reproductive function for the entire colony.

Scale—a flat outgrowth of the body wall of some insects; flattened and modified hairs on the wings of Lepidoptera.

Scales—scale insects, one of the major groups (a superfamily) of the Homoptera.

Scavenger—an animal that feeds on dead plants or animals, on decaying materials, or on animal wastes.

Segment—a subdivision of an animal body or appendage.

Serrate—notched like the teeth of a saw.

Sessile—closely seated or broadly attached; without a pedicel.

Seta (pl., **setae**)—bristlelike hair.

Spiracles—breathing pores located along the sides of the insect body.

Striae—parallel, fine longitudinal impressed lines as on the elytra of many Coleoptera.

Sulcate—furrowed or grooved; refers to surfaces.

Suture—an external linelike groove separating parts of the body wall.

Symbiosis—the living together of organisms of different species without disadvantage to either and often to mutual benefit.

Tarsus (pl., **tarsi**)—the foot; the outermost jointed division of the insect leg.

Taxon—a category used in biological classifications and based on natural relationships; for example, a species of insect.

Testaceous—brownish yellow.

Thorax—the second region of the insect body, bearing true legs and wings. See also prothorax.

Tibia (pl., **tibiae**)—a single-segmented division of the insect leg between the femur and the tarsus.

Trachea (pl., **tracheae**)—a tube of the respiratory system ending externally at a spiracle and internally with fine branching tubes.

Tree seed orchard—a forest plantation of presumed genetically superior trees, managed for seed production.

Tubercle—a small rounded projection from a surface.

Vector—carrier of a disease-producing organism.

Venation—the complete system of veins of a wing.

Venter—the under surface of the insect body.

Vertex—top of the head between the eyes.

LITERATURE CITED

Adlung, Karl G.
    1966. A critical evaluation of the European research on use of
        red wood ants (*Formica rufa* group) for the protection of
        forests against harmful insects. Z. angew. Entomol. 57(2):
        167–189.
Aldrich, J. M.
    1916a. *Sarcophaga* and allies in North America. Thomas Say
        Found., vol. I, 301 p. + plates. Murphy-Bivins Co., LaFayette,
        Ind.
Aldrich, J. M.
    1916b. The dipterous genus *Symphoromyia* in North America.
        U.S. Natl. Mus. Proc. 49:113–142.
Allen, T. C., R. V. Smythe, and H. C. Coppel.
    1964. Response of twenty-one termite species to aqueous ex-
        tracts of wood invaded by the fungus *Lenzites trabea* Pers.
        ex. Fri. J. Econ. Entomol. 57(6):1009–1011.
Anderson, D. M.
    1975. Common names of insects (1975 revision) approved by
        The Entomological Society of America. Entomol. Soc. Am.
        Spec. Pub. 75–1, 37 p.
Anderson, N. H.
    1962. Anthocoridae of the Pacific Northwest with notes on
        distributions, life histories, and habits (Heteroptera). Can.
        Entomol. 94(12):1325–1334.
Andison, H.
    1937. The juniper webworm (*Dichomeris marginella* Fabr.).
        Entomol. Soc. B. C. Proc. 33:3–5.
Annand, P. N.
    1928. A contribution toward a monograph of the Adelginae
        (Phylloxeridae) of North America. Stanford Univ. Series
        Biol. Sci. 6(1):1–146.
Arnett, Ross H., Jr.
    1951. A revision of the Nearctic Oedemeridae. Am. Midl. Nat.
        45:257–391.
Arnett, Ross H., Jr.
    1960. The beetles of the United States. 1112 p. Cathol. Univ.
        Am. Press, Washington, D.C.
Arnott, David A.
    1957. Occurrence of *Trirhabda pilosa* Blake (Coleoptera: Chryso-
        melidae) on sagebrush in British Columbia, with notes on
        life-history. Entomol. Soc. B. C. Proc. 53:14–15.

Arthur, A. P.
1961. The cleptoparasitic habits and the immature stages of *Eurytoma pini* Bugbee (Hymenoptera: Chalcidae), a parasite of the European pine shoot moth, *Rhyacionia buoliana* (Schiff.) (Lepidoptera: Olethreutidae). Can. Entomol. 93(8): 655–660.

Atkins, M. D.
1957. An interesting attractant for *Priacma serrata* (Lec.), (Cupesidae: Coleoptera). Can. Entomol. 89(5):214–219.

Atkins, M. D.
1963. The Cupedidae of the world.
Can. Entomol. 95(2): 140–162.

Austin, L., J. S. Yuill, and K. G. Brecheen.
1945. Use of shoot characters in selecting ponderosa pines resistant to resin midge. Ecology 26(3):288–296.

Bailey, S. F.
1957. The thrips of California, Part I: Suborder Terebrantia. Calif. Insect Surv. Bull. 4(5):143–220. Univ. Calif. Press, Berkeley and Los Angeles.

Baker, A. C., and W. M. Davidson.
1916. Woolly pear aphis. J. Agric. Res. 6(10):351–360.

Baker, A. C., and W. M. Davidson.
1917. A further contribution to the study of *Eriosoma pyricola*, the woolly pear aphis. J. Agric. Res. 10(2):65–74.

Baker, Edward W., and G. W. Wharton.
1952. An introduction to Acarology. 465 p. Macmillan Co., New York.

Baker, J. M.
1963. Ambrosia beetles and their fungi, with particular reference to *Platypus cylindrus* Fab., *In* Symbiotic Associations. Soc. Gen. Microbiol. 13th Symp. p. 232–265. Univ. Press, London.

Baker, Whiteford L.
1972. Eastern forest insects. U.S. Dep. Agric., Misc. Publ. 1175. 642 p.

Balch, R. E.
1937. Notes on the wharf borer (*Nacerda melanura* L.). Can. Entomol. 69(1):1–5.

Balch, R. E.
1960. The approach to biological control in forest entomology. Can. Entomol. 92(4):297–310.

Balch, R. E., and G. R. Underwood.
1950. The life-history of *Pineus pinifoliae* (Fitch) (Homoptera: Phylloxeridae) and its effect on white pine. Can. Entomol. 82(6):117–123.

Banham, F. L.
1961. Distribution of *Trirhabda pilosa* Blake (Coleoptera: Chrysomelidae), attacking big sagebrush in the Interior of British Columbia. Entomol. Soc. B. C. Proc. 58:38–40.

Barber, H. S.
1936. Some species of *Colaspis* from the Brunnea confusion (Coleoptera: Chrysomelidae). Entomol. Soc. Wash. Proc. 38(9):198–204.

Barcia, Dorothy R., and Edward P. Merkel.
1972. Bibliography on insects destructive to flowers, cones, and seeds of North American conifers. USDA For. Serv. Res. Pap. SE–92, 80 p. Southeast. For. Exp. Stn., Asheville, N.C.

Barnes, William S. B., and J. H. McDunnough.
1911. Revision of the Cossidae of North America. *In* History of the Lepidoptera of North America. 1(1):35 p. 7 plates.

Barr, W. F.
1949. A revision of the species of the genus *Polycesta* occurring in the United States (Coleoptera, Buprestidae). Am. Mus. Novit. No. 1432. 42 p.

Barr, W. F.
1962. A key to the genera and a classification of the North American Cleridae (Coleoptera). Coleopt. Bull. 16(4):121–127.

Barr, W. F.
1971. Family Buprestidae; *In* Melvin H. Hatch, The beetles of the Pacific Northwest, Part 5. p. 55–89. Univ. Wash. Press, Seattle and London.

Barr, W. F., and E. G. Linsley.
1947. Distributional and biological notes on the species of the subgenus *Melanophila* occurring in western North America (Coleoptera: Buprestidae). Pan-Pac. Entomol. 23(4):162–166.

Barron, J. R.
1971. A revision of the Trogositidae of America north of Mexico (Coleoptera: Cleroidea). Entomol. Soc. Can. Mem. 75, 143 p.

Barstow, Darrel A., and A. R. Gittens.
1971. Life history studies on a willow leaf beetle *Altica bimarginata* Say in North Idaho (Coleoptera: Chrysomelidae). Idaho Coll. Agric. Res. Bull. 80, 19 p. Moscow, Idaho.

Basham, J. T., and R. M. Belyea.
1960. Death and deterioration of balsam fir weakened by spruce budworm defoliation in Ontario. Part III. The deterioration of dead trees. For. Sci. 6(1):78–96.

Batra, Lekh R.

1967. Ambrosia fungi: A taxonomic revision, and nutritional studies of some species. Mycologia 56(6):976–1017.

Batzer, Harold O., and Imants Millers.

1970. Jack-pine budworm. U.S. Dep. Agric., For. Pest Leafl. 7, 4 p.

Bauman, N. G., and B. A. Sugden.

1968. Juniper webworm in British Columbia. Can. For. Serv., For. Insect and Dis. Surv. For. Pest Leafl. 8, 3 p. For. Res. Lab., Victoria, B.C.

Beal, J. A.

1943. Relation between tree growth and outbreaks of the Black Hills beetle. J. For. 41(5):359–366.

Beal, J. A.

1957. The outlook for selecting and breeding trees resistant to insects. Soc. Am. For. Meet. Proc., Nov. 10–13, p. 52–54.

Bean, J. L., and D. G. Mott.

1972. Spruce budworm in eastern United States. U.S. Dep. Agric., For. Pest Leafl. 58, 8 p.

Beck, S. D.

1968. Insect photoperiodism. 288 p. Academic Press, New York and London.

Beckwith, Roy C.

1973. The large aspen tortrix. U.S. Dep. Agric., For. Pest Leafl. 139, 5 p.

Beckwith, Roy C.

1976. Influence of host foliage on the Douglas-fir tussock moth. Environ. Entomol. 5(1):73–77.

Bedard, W. D.

1938. An annotated list of the insect fauna of Douglas-fir (*Pseudotsuga mucronata* Rafinesque) in the northern Rocky Mountain Region. Can. Entomol. 70(9):188–197.

Bedard, William D.

1968. The sugar pine cone beetle. U.S. Dep. Agric., For. Pest Leafl. 112, 6 p.

Beer, R. E.

1954. A revision of the Tarsonemidae of the western hemisphere. Univ. Kans. Sci. Bull. 36, 2(16):1091–1387.

Beer, R. E.

1955. Biological studies in the genus *Periclista* (Hymenoptera, Tenthredinidae, Blennocampinae). J. Kans. Entomol. Soc. 28(1):19–26.

Beirne, Bryan P.

1955. Collecting, preparing and preserving insects. Can. Dep. Agric., Sci. Serv., Entomol. Div. Publ. 932, 133 p.

Beirne, Bryan P.
1956. Leafhoppers (Homoptera: Cicadellidae) of Canada and Alaska. Can. Entomol. 88, Suppl. 2. 180 p.

Beirne, Bryan P.
1962. Trends in applied biological control of insects. Annu. Rev. Entomol. 7:387–400.

Bejer-Petersen, B.
1962. Peak years and regulation of numbers in the aphid *Neomyzaphis abietina* Walker. OIKOS 13(1) :155–168.

Benesh, Bernard.
1946. A systematic revision of the holarctic genus *Platycerus* Geoffroy (Coleoptera: Lucanidae). Am. Entomol. Soc. Trans. 72: 139–202 + plates.

Bennett, William H., and W. M. Ciesla.
1971. Southern pine beetle. U.S. Dep. Agric., For. Pest Leafl. 49, 8 p.

Benson, Robert B.
1962a. Holarctic sawflies (Hymenoptera: Symphyta). Brit. Mus. (Nat. Hist.) Bull. 12(8) :381–409.

Benson, Robert B.
1962b. A character gradient in *Sirex juvencus* L. (Hym., Siricidae). Entomol. Mon. Mag. 98(1180–1183) :252–253.

Berry, Ralph E., and Robert R. Robinson.
1974. Biology and control of the garden symphylan. Oreg. State Ext. Circ. 845, 9 p.

Berryman, Alan A.
1966. Studies on the behavior and development of *Enoclerus lecontei* (Wolcott), a predator of the western pine beetle. Can. Entomol. 98(5) :519–526.

Berryman, Alan A.
1967. Preservation and augmentation of insect predators of the western pine beetle. J. For. 65(4): 260–262.

Bickley, W. E., and E. G. MacLeod.
1956. A synopsis of the nearctic Chrysopidae with a key to the genera. Entomol. Soc. Wash. Proc. 58(4) :177–202.

Birch, Martin E.
1974. Pheromones. 495 p. Am. Elsevier Publ. Co., New York; North Holland Publ. Co., Amsterdam and London.

Bitz, W. E., and D. A. Ross.
1958. Population trends of some common loopers (Geometridae) on Douglas-fir, 1949–1956, in the Okanogan-Shuswap area. Can. Dep. Agric. Sci. Serv., For. Biol. Div. Bimon. Prog. Rep. 14(5) :2–3.

Blackman, M. W.

1915. Observations on the life history and habits of *Pityogenes hopkinsi* Swaine. N.Y. State Coll. For., Syracuse Univ., Tech. Publ. 2, 11–66 + 6 plates.

Blackman, M. W.

1928a. Notes on Micracinae, with description of twelve new species. N.Y. State Coll. For., Syracuse Univ., Bull. 1(3b). Tech. Publ. 25, p. 185–212.

Blackman, M. W.

1928b. The genus *Pityophthorus* Eichh. in North America: a revisional study of the Pityophthori, with descriptions of two new genera and seventy-one new species. N.Y. State Coll. For., Syracuse Univ., Bull. 1(3b). Tech. Publ. 25, p. 1–184.

Blackman, M. W.

1931a. A revisional study of the genus *Gnathotrichus* Eichhoff in North America. J. Wash. Acad. Sci. 21(12):264–276.

Blackman, M. W.

1931b. A revisional study of the genus *Pseudopityophthorus* Sw. in North America. J. Wash. Acad. Sci. 21(10):223–236.

Blackman, M. W.

1931c. The Black Hills beetle, *Dendroctonus ponderosae* Hopk. N.Y. State Coll. For., Syracuse Univ., Bull. 4(4). Tech. Publ. 36, 97 p.

Blackman, M. W.

1934. A revisional study of the genus *Scolytus* Geoffroy (*Eccoptogaster* Herbst) in North America. U.S. Dep. Agric., Tech. Bull. 431, 30 p.

Blackman, M. W.

1938. The genus *Chramesus* LeConte in North America (Coleoptera: Scolytidae). J. Wash. Acad. Sci. 28(12):534–545.

Blackman, M. W.

1940. The Scolytid beetles of the genus *Renocis* Casey, with descriptions of nine new species. U.S. Natl. Mus. Proc. 88 (3084):373–401.

Blackman, M. W.

1941. Bark beetles of the genus *Hylastes* Erichson in North America. U.S. Dep. Agric., Misc. Publ. 417. 27 p.

Blackman, M. W.

1942. Revision of the genus *Phloeosinus* Chapuis in North America (Coleoptera, Scolytidae). U.S. Natl. Mus. Proc. 92(3154):397–474 + 4 plates.

Blackwelder, Richard E.

1939. Fourth supplement, 1933 to 1938 (inclusive), to The Leng Catalogue of Coleoptera of America, north of Mexico. 146 p. John D. Sherman, Jr., Mount Vernon, N.Y.

Blackwelder, Richard E., and Ruth M. Blackwelder.
 1948. Fifth supplement, 1939 to 1947 (inclusive), to The Leng
 Catalogue of Coleoptera of America, north of Mexico. 87 p.
 John D. Sherman, Jr., Mount Vernon, N.Y.
Blais, J. R.
 1961. Notes on the biology of *Griselda radicana* (Wlshm.)
 (Lepidoptera: Olethreutidae). Can. Entomol. 93(8):648–653.
Blake, Doris H.
 1931. Revision of the species of beetles of the genus *Trirhabda*
 north of Mexico. U.S. Natl. Mus. Proc. 79(2):1–36 + plates.
Blake, Doris H.
 1936. *Altica bimarginata* Say, with descriptions of new species
 and varieties (Coleoptera). Entomol. Soc. Wash. Proc.
 38(2):13–23.
Blake, Doris H.
 1967. Revision of the beetles of genus *Glyptoscelis* (Coleoptera:
 Chrysomelidae). U.S. Natl. Mus. Proc. 123(3604):1–53.
Bodenheimer, F. S.
 1951. Insects as human food. 352 p. Dr. W. Junk, Publ., The
 Hague.
Bongberg, J. W.
 1958. Forest insect surveys in the United States. 10th Int.
 Congr. Entomol. Proc., Montreal, August 17–25, 1956,
 4:193–200.
Borden, John H.
 1969. Observations on the life history and habits of *Alniphagus
 aspericollis* (Coleoptera: Scolytidae) in southwestern British
 Columbia. Can. Entomol. 101(8):870–878.
Borden, John H.
 1974. Chapter 8: Aggregation pheromones in the Scolytidae. *In*
 Pheromones, p. 135–160. Martin C. Birch, ed. Am. Elsevier
 Publ. Co., Inc., New York.
Borden, J. H., and W. F. Dean.
 1971. Observations on *Eriocampa ovata* L. (Hymenoptera:
 Tenthredinidae) infesting red alder in southwestern British
 Columbia, J. Entomol. Soc. B. C. 68:26–28.
Borror, Donald J., and Dwight M. DeLong.
 1954. An introduction to the study of insects. 1030 p. Rinehart
 and Co., New York.
Borror, Donald J., and Richard E. White.
 1970. A field guide to the insects of America north of Mexico.
 The Peterson Field Guide Series, Field Guide No. 19, 404 p.
 Houghton Mifflin Co., Boston.

Boss, Gary D., and T. O. Thatcher.

1970. Mites associated with *Ips* and *Dendroctonus* in Southern Rocky Mountains, with special reference to *Iponemus truncatus* (Acarina: Tarsonemidae). USDA For. Serv. Res. Note RM–171, 7 p. Rocky Mt. For. and Range Exp. Stn., Fort Collins, Colo.

Böving, Adam G.

1927. The larva of *Nevermannia dorcatomoides* Fisher with comments on the classification of the Anobiidae according to their larvae (Coleoptera:). Entomol. Soc. Wash. Proc. 29(3):51–62.

Böving, Adam G., and A. B. Champlain.

1920. Larvae of North American beetles of the family Cleridae. U.S. Natl. Mus. Proc. 57(2323):575–649 + plates.

Böving, Adam G., and F. C. Craighead.

1931. An illustrated synopsis of the principal larval forms of the order Coleoptera. Brooklyn Entomol. Soc., 351 p.

Bradley, G. A.

1961. A study of the systematics and biology of aphids of the genus *Cinara* Curtis in Canada. Ph.D. thesis on file at McGill Univ., Montreal. 86 p.

Bramhall, G.

1966. Marine borers and wooden piling in British Columbia waters, Can. Dep. For. Publ. 1138, 68 p. For. Prod. Lab., Vancouver.

Braun, Annctte F.

1908. Revision of the North American species of the genus *Lithocolletis* Hübner. Am. Entomol. Soc. Trans. 34:269–357.

Breakey, E. P.

1967. Insect pests of rhododendrons and azaleas. Rhododendron Inf., p. 185–198. Am. Rhododendron Soc., Sherwood, Oreg.

Breakey, E. P., C. J. Gould, and C. E. Reynolds.

1945. Seed-corn maggots as pests of coniferous seedlings in western Washington. J. Econ. Entomol. 38(1):121.

Brewer, J. W.

1971. Biology of the pinyon stunt needle midge. Ann. Entomol. Soc. Am. 65(5):1099–1102.

Bridwell, J. C.

1946. The genera of beetles of the family Bruchidae in America north of Mexico. J. Wash. Acad. Sci. 36(2):52–57.

Bright, Donald E., Jr.

1963. Bark beetles of the genus *Dryocoetes* (Coleoptera: Scolytidae) in North America. Ann. Entomol. Soc. Am. 56(1):103–115.

491

Bright, Donald E., Jr.
  1964. Descriptions of three new species and new distribution records of California bark beetles (Coleoptera: Scolytidae). Pan-Pac. Entomol. 40(3):165–170.
Bright, Donald E., Jr.
  1967. A review of the genus *Cactopinus*, with descriptions of two species and a new genus (Coleoptera: Scolytidae). Can. Entomol. 99(9):917–925.
Bright, Donald E., Jr.
  1968. Review of the tribe Xyleborini in America north of Mexico (Coleoptera: Scolytidae). Can. Entomol. 100(12):1288–1323.
Bright, Donald E., Jr.
  1969. Biology and taxonomy of bark beetle species in the genus *Pseudohylesinus* Swaine (Coleoptera: Scolytidae). Univ. Calif. Publ. Entomol. 54, 46 p. + plates.
Bright, Donald E., Jr.
  1971. New species, new synonomies, and new records of bark beetles from Arizona and California (Coleoptera: Scolytidae). Pan-Pac. Entomol. 47(1):63–70.
Bright, Donald E., Jr., and R. W. Stark.
  1973. The bark and ambrosia beetles of California (Coleoptera: Scolytidae and Platypodidae). Calif. Insect Surv. Bull. 16, 169 p. Univ. Calif. Press, Berkeley.
Brown, A. W. A.
  1941. Foliage insects of spruce in Canada. Can. Dep. Agric., Tech. Bull. 31, 29 p.
Brown, C. E.
  1962. The life history and dispersal of the Bruce spanworm, *Operophtera bruceata* (Hulst), (Lepidoptera: Geometridae). Can. Entomol. 94(10):1103–1107.
Brown, C. E.
  1965. Mass transport of forest tent caterpillar moths, *Malacosoma disstria* Hübner, by a cold front. Can. Entomol. 97(10):1073–1075.
Brown, C. E.
  1966. Habits and control of the forest tent caterpillar, *Malacosoma disstria* Hbn., 6 p. Can. Dep. For., Ottawa.
Brown, C. E., and R. E. Stevenson.
  1964. Forest insect conditions, Province of Alberta. *In* Annu. Rep. For. Insect and Dis. Surv. 1963, p. 96–101. Can. Dep. For., Ottawa.
Brown, C. E., and R. E. Stevenson.
  1965. Forest insect conditions, Province of Alberta, *In* Annu. Rep. For. Insect and Dis. Surv. 1964, p. 97–102. Can. Dep. For., Ottawa.

Brown, Leland R., and Clark O. Eads.

1965a. A technical study of insects affecting the oak tree in southern California. Calif. Agric. Exp. Stn. Bull. 810, 105 p. Berkeley.

Brown, Leland R., and Clark O. Eads.

1965b. A technical study of insects affecting the sycamore tree in southern California. Calif. Agric. Exp. Stn. Bull. 818, 38 p. Berkeley.

Brown, Leland R., and Clark O. Eads.

1966. A technical study of insects affecting the elm tree in southern California. Calif. Agric. Exp. Stn. Bull. 821, 24 p. Berkeley.

Brown, Leland R., and Clark O. Eads.

1967. Insects affecting ornamental conifers in southern California. Calif. Agric. Exp. Stn. Bull. 834, 72 p. Berkeley.

Brown, Leland R., and Clark O. Eads.

1969. Unnamed and little-known insects attacking cottonwood in southern California. J. Econ. Entomol. 62(3):667–674.

Brown, N. R.

1946. Studies on parasites of the spruce budworm, *Archips fumiferana* (Clem.). I. Life history of *Apanteles fumiferanae* Viereck (Hymenoptera, Braconidae). Can. Entomol. 78(6): 121–129.

Brown, W. J.

1942. The American species of *Phytodecta* Kby. (Coleoptera, Chrysomelidae). Can. Entomol. 74(6):99–105.

Brown, W. J.

1951. The American species of *Phratora* Chev. (Coleoptera: Chrysomelidae). Can. Entomol. 83(5):121–130.

Brown, W. J.

1956. The New World species of *Chrysomela* L. (Coleoptera: Chrysomelidae). Can. Entomol. 88, suppl. 3, 54 p.

Brown, W. J.

1962. The American species of *Chrysolina* Mots. (Coleoptera: Chrysomelidae). Can. Entomol. 94(1):58–74.

Brown, W. J.

1966a. Chrysomelinae and Curculionidae (Coleoptera); descriptions and notes. Can. Entomol. 98(8):855–859.

Brown, W. J.

1966b. The species of *Steremnius* Schoenherr (Coleoptera: Curculionidae). Can. Entomol. 98(6):586–587.

Browne, F. G.

1968. Pests and diseases of forest plantation trees; an annotated list of the principal species occurring in the British Commonwealth. 1130 p. Oxford Univ. Press, New York.

Bruck, C. R.
  1936. New Scolytidae (Coleoptera) of southern California with a key to the species of *Pseudothysanoes* Blackman. South. Calif. Acad. Sci. Bull. 35(1) :30–38.
Brues, C. T., A. L. Melander, and F. M. Carpenter.
  1954. Classification of insects. Mus. Comp. Zool. Bull. 108, 917 p.
Bryan, Douglas E., and Ray F. Smith.
  1956. The *Frankliniella occidentalis* (Pergande) complex in California (Thysanoptera: Thripidae). Univ. Calif. Publ. Entomol. 10:359–410.
Buchanan, L. L.
  1929. A new *Agronus* from Canada (Coleoptera: Otiorhynchidae). Entomol. Soc. Wash. Proc. 31(5) :102–104.
Buchanan, L. L.
  1936. The genus *Panscopus* Schoenherr (Coleoptera: Curculionidae). Smithson. Misc. Collect. 94(16) :1–18.
Buchanan, L. L.
  1940. Three new species of the *longulus* group of *Cylindrocopturus* (Coleoptera: Curculionidae). Entomol. Soc. Wash. Proc. 42(8) :177–181.
Buchanan, L. L.
  1946. Notes on American *Rhyncolus*, with description of a new species (Coleoptera, Curculionidae). Brooklyn Entomol. Soc. Bull. 41(4) :129–136.
Buckhorn, W. J., and P. W. Orr.
  1961. Forest insect conditions in the Pacific Northwest during 1960. 40 p. Pac. Northwest For. and Range Exp. Stn., Portland. Oreg.
Buckner, Charles H.
  1959. The assessment of larch sawfly cocoon predation by small mammals. Can. Entomol. 91(5) :275–282.
Buckner, Charles H.
  1966. The role of vertebrate predators in the biological control of forest insects. Annu. Rev. Entomol. 11:449–470.
Bugbee, Robert E.
  1967. Revision of chalcid wasps of genus *Eurytoma* in America north of Mexico. U.S. Natl. Mus. Proc. 3533(118) :433–552.
Bullard, William E., Donald R. Hopkins, Benton Howard, and others.
  1964. Status report, 1963 Willapa hemlock looper infestation control project. Wash. State Dep. Nat. Resour., 74 p.
Burdick, Donald J.
  1961. A taxonomic and biological study of the genus *Xyela* Dalman in North America. Univ. Calif. Publ. Entomol. 17(3) : 285–355.

Burdick, D. J., and J. E. Powell.

    1960. Studies on the early stages of two California moths which feed in the staminate cones of digger pine (Lepidoptera: Gelechiidae). Can. Entomol. 92(4):310–320.

Burges, A., and F. Raw, eds.

    1967. Soil biology. 532 p. Academic Press, London and New York.

Burges, H. D., and N. W. Hussey.

    1971. Microbial control of insects and mites. 861 p. Academic Press, London and New York.

Burgess, A. F., and C. W. Collins.

    1917. The genus *Calosoma*. U.S. Dep. Agric. Bull. 417, 124 p.

Burke, H. E.

    1905. Black check in western helmlock. U.S. Dep. Agric. Circ. 61, 10 p.

Burke, H. E.

    1917a. Flat-headed borers affecting forest trees in the United States. U.S. Dep. Agric. Bull. 437. [Contrib. from Bur. Entomol.] 8 p.

Burke, H. E.

    1917b. *Oryssus* is parasitic. Entomol. Soc. Wash. Proc. 19(1–4): 87–89.

Burke, H. E.

    1919. Notes on a cocoon making colydiid (Coleopt.) Entomol. Soc. Wash. Proc. 21(6):123–124.

Burke, II. E.

    1921. Biological notes on *Desmocerus*, a genus of roundheaded borers, the species of which infest various elders. J. Econ. Entomol. 14(5):450–452.

Burke, H. E.

    1928. The western cedar pole borer or powder worm. U.S. Dep. Agric., Tech. Bull. 48, 16 p.

Burke, H. E.

    1929. The Pacific flathead borer. U.S. Dep. Agric., Tech. Bull. 83, 36 p.

Burke, H. E.

    1932. Two destructive defoliators of lodgepole pine in the Yellowstone National Park. U.S. Dep. Agric. Circ. 224, 20 p.

Burke, H. E.

    1937. Important insect enemies of the Monterey pine. 4th West. Shade Tree Conf. Proc., p. 21–30. Santa Barbara, Calif.

Burke, H. E., R. D. Hartman, and T. E. Snyder.

    1922. The lead-cable borer or "short-circuit beetle" in California. U.S. Dept. Agric. Bull. 1107, 56 p. + 10 plates.

Butler, George D., Jr., and Floyd G. Werner.
  1961. The distribution and host plants of May beetles in Arizona. Ariz. Agric. Exp. Stn. Bull. 147:1–19.
Callaham, R. Z., and M. Shifrine.
  1960. The yeasts associated with bark beetles. For. Sci. 6(2): 146–154.
Caltagirone, L. E.
  1964. Notes on the biology, parasites, and inquilines of *Pontania pacifica* (Hymenoptera: Tenthredinidae), a leaf-gall incitant on *Salix lasiolepis*. Ann. Entomol. Soc. Am. 57(3):279–291.
Cameron, E. A.
  1965. The Siricinae (Hymenoptera: Siricidae) and their parasites. Commonw. Inst. Biol. Control Tech. Bull. 5, 31 p. Fontana, Calif.
Cameron, E. A.
  1967. Notes on *Sirex juvencus californicus* (Hymenoptera: Siricidae) with a description of the male and a key to the California species of *Sirex*. Can. Entomol. 99(1):18–24.
Cameron, E. A.
  1968. *Sirex juvencus californicus* in smog-killed trees in southern California (Hymenoptera: Siricidae). Pan-Pac. Entomol. 44(2):168.
Capizzi, Joseph, and Robert R. Robinson.
  1975. Oregon insect control handbook. 221 p. Oreg. State Univ. Bookstores, Inc., Corvallis.
Capps, Hahn W.
  1943. Some American geometrid moths of the subfamily Ennominae heretofore associated with or closely related to *Ellopia* Treitschke. U.S. Natl. Mus. Proc. 93(3159):115–151.
Carolin, V. M., Jr.
  1971. Extended diapause in *Coloradia pandora* Blake (Lepidoptera: Saturniidae). Pan-Pac. Entomol. 47(1):19–23.
Carolin, V. M., Jr., and W. K. Coulter.
  1959. The occurrence of insect parasites of *Choristoneura fumiferana* (Clem.) in Oregon. J. Econ. Entomol. 52(4):550–555.
Carolin, V. M., Jr., and W. K. Coulter.
  1972a. Sampling populations of western spruce budworm and predicting defoliation on Douglas-fir in eastern Oregon. USDA For. Serv. Res. Pap. PNW–149, 38 p. Pac. Northwest For. and Range Exp. Stn., Portland, Oreg.
Carolin, V. M., Jr., and F. W. Honing.
  1972b. Western spruce budworm. U.S. Dep. Agric., For. Pest Leafl. 53, 8 p.

Carolin, V. M., Jr., and J. A. E. Knopf.
  1968. The pandora moth. U.S. Dep. Agric., For. Pest Leafl.
    114, 7 p.
Carolin, V. M., Jr., and C. G. Thompson.
  1967. Field testing of *Bacillus thuringiensis* for control of
    western hemlock looper. USDA For. Serv. Res. Pap. PNW–
    38, 24 p. Pac. Northwest For. and Range Exp. Stn., Portland,
    Oreg.
Carpenter, F. M.
  1936. Revision of the Nearctic Raphidiodea (recent and fossil).
    Am. Acad. Arts and Sci. Proc. 71(2):89–157.
Carpenter, F. M.
  1940. Revision of Nearctic Hemerobiidae. Am. Acad. Arts and
    Sci. Proc. 74(7):193–280.
Carter, C. I.
  1971. Conifer woolly aphids (Adelgidae) in Britain. For. Comm.
    Bull. 42, 51 p. Her Majesty's Stationery Office, London.
Castle, Gordon B.
  1934. The damp-wood termites of western United States, genus
    Zootermopsis (formerly *Termopsis*). I. General biology and
    ecology. *In* Termites and termite control, 2d ed. p. 273–291,
    Charles Kofoid et al., eds. Univ. Calif. Press, Berkeley.
Cazier, Mont A.
  1940. The species of *Polyphylla* in America, north of Mexico
    (Coleoptera: Scarabaeidae). Entomol. News 51(5):134–139.
Cerezke, H. F.
  1970. Biology and control of Warren's collar weevil, *Hylobius
    warreni* Wood, in Alberta. Can. Dep. Fish. and For., For.
    Serv. Int. Rep. A–27, 28 p. For. Res. Lab., Calgary, Alberta.
Chamberlin, W. J.
  1920. Notes on two little-known wood-boring beetles, *Chryso-
    bothris sylvania* Fall and *Melasis rufipennis* Horn (Bupres-
    tidae, Elateridae). J. N.Y. Entomol. Soc. 28(2):151–157.
Chamberlin, W. J.
  1939. The bark and timber beetles of North America. 513 p.
    Oreg. State Coll. Coop. Assoc., Corvallis.
Chamberlin, W. J.
  1953. Insects affecting forest products and other materials.
    159 p. Oreg. State Coll. Coop. Assoc., Corvallis.
Chamberlin, W. J.
  1958. The Scolytoidea of the Northwest: Oregon, Washington,
    Idaho, and British Columbia. Oreg. State Monogr. Stud.
    Entomol. No. 2, 208 p. Corvallis.

Chansler, J. F.
  1964. Overwintering habits of *Ips lecontei* Sw. and *Ips confusus* (Lec.) in Arizona and New Mexico. USDA For. Serv. Res. Note RM–27, 4 p. Rocky Mt. For. and Range Exp. Stn., Fort Collins, Colo.
Chansler, J. F.
  1967. Biology and life history of *Dendroctonus adjunctus* (Coleoptera: Scolytidae). Ann. Entomol. Soc. Am. 60(4): 760–767.
Chant, D. A.
  1959. Phytoseiid mites (Acarina: Phytoseiidae). Part I. Bionomics of seven species in southeastern England. Part II. A taxonomic review of the family Phytoseiidae, with descriptions of 38 new species. Can. Entomol. 91, suppl. 12, 166 p.
Chapin, Edward A.
  1946. Review of the New World species of *Hippodamia* Dejean (Coleoptera: Coccinellidae). Smithson. Inst. Misc. Collect. 106(11):1–39 + plates.
Chapman, Paul J.
  1930. Corrodentia of the United States of America: I. Suborder Isotecnomera. J. N. Y. Entomol. Soc. 38(3):219–290. (4): 319–403.
Chemsak, John A., and E. G. Linsley.
  1971. Some aspects of adult assembly and sexual behavior of *Rosalia funebris* Motschulsky under artificial conditions (Coleoptera: Cerambycidae). Pan-Pac. Entomol. 47(2):149–154.
Chrystal, R. N.
  1916. The life history of *Chermes cooleyi* Gillette in Stanley Park, Vancouver, B.C. 46th Annu. Rep. Entomol. Soc. Ont. 36, p. 123–130.
Ciesla, W. M.
  1973. Six-spined engraver beetle. U.S. Dep. Agric., For. Pest Leafl. 141, 6 p.
Clapp, W. F., and R. Kenk.
  1963. Marine borers; an annotated bibliography. U.S. Dep. Navy, Off. Nav. Res. ACR–74, 1136 p.
Clark, J.
  1952. The spruce bud midge, *Rhabdophaga swainei* Felt (Cecidomyiidae: Diptera). Can. Entomol. 84(3):87–89.
Clausen, Curtis P.
  1940. Entomophagous insects. 688 p. McGraw-Hill Book Co., New York.
Clausen, Curtis P.
  1958. Biological control of insect pests. Annu. Rev. Entomol. 3:291–310.

Cobb, F. W., Jr., J. R. Parmeter, D. L. Wood, and R. W. Stark.
1974. Root pathogens as agents predisposing ponderosa pine and white fir to bark beetles. Int. Union For. Res. Organ., 4th Int. *Fomes annosus* Conf. Proc. (Sect. 24) p. 8–15. U.S. Dep. Agric., For. Serv., Asheville, N.C.

Cole, A. C., Jr.
1968. *Pogonomyrmex* harvester ants. A study of the genus in North America. 222 p. Univ. Tenn. Press, Knoxville.

Cole, Frank R.
1969. The flies of western North America. 693 p. Univ. Calif. Press, Berkeley and Los Angeles.

Cole, W. E.
1971. Pine butterfly. U.S. Dep. Agric., For. Pest Leafl. 66, 3 p.

Collis, D. G.
1970. A hemlock needle miner in British Columbia. Can. For. Serv., For. Insect and Dis. Surv. For. Pest Leafl. 30, 3 p. For. Res. Lab., Victoria, B.C.

Common, I. F. B.
1971. Lepidoptera. *In* The insects of Australia, p. 785–866. I. M. Mackerras, ed. Melbourne Univ. Press, Canberra, Aust.

Comstock, J. H.
1948. The spider book. 729 p. Comstock Publ. Assoc., Div. of Cornell Univ. Press, Ithaca, N.Y.

Condrashoff, S. F.
1962a. Bionomics of three closely related species of *Contarinia* Rond. (Diptera: Cecidomyiidae) from Douglas-fir needles. Can. Entomol. 94(4):376–394.

Condrashoff, S. F.
1962b. Douglas-fir needle midges—pests of Christmas trees in British Columbia. Can. Dep. For. 5 p. Ottawa.

Condrashoff, S. F.
1964. Bionomics of the aspen leaf miner, *Phyllocnistis populiella* Cham. (Lepidoptera: Gracillariidae). Can. Entomol. 96(6): 857–874.

Condrashoff, S. F.
1966a. A description of the immature stages of *Steremnius carinatus* (Boheman) (Coleoptera: Curculionidae). Can. Entomol. 98(6):663–667.

Condrashoff, S. F.
1966b. Larval descriptions of *Zeiraphera pacifica* Freeman and *Epinotia hopkinsana* (Kearfott) (Lepidoptera: Olethreutidae). Can. Entomol. 98(7):703–706.

Condrashoff, S. F.
1968. Biology of *Steremnius carinatus* (Coleoptera: Curculionidae), a reforestation pest in coastal British Columbia. Can. Entomol. 100(4):386–394.

Cooley, R. A.
   1932. The Rocky Mountain wood tick. Mont. Agric. Exp. Stn. Bull. 268, 58 p. Bozeman.
Cornelius, R. O.
   1955. How forest pests upset management plans in the Douglas-fir region. J. For. 53(10):711–713.
Cornell, James Fraser, Jr.
   1972. A taxonomic review of the beetle genus *Dichelonyx* Harris in North America (Scarabaeidae: Melolonthinae). Ph.D. thesis. Oreg. State Univ., Corvallis. 253 p.
Cott, H. E.
   1956. Systematics of the suborder Tubulifera (Thysanoptera) in California. Univ. Calif. Publ. Entomol. 13:1–216.
Craighead, F. C.
   1915. Larvae of the Prioninae. Contributions toward a classification and biology of the North American Cerambycidae. U.S. Dep. Agric. Rep. 108. 24 p. + 8 plates.
Craighead, F. C.
   1923. North American cerambycid larvae, a classification and the biology of North American cerambycid larvae. Can. Dep. Agric. Bull. 27 (New Ser.), 239 p. incl. plates.
Craighead, F. C.
   1941. The influence of insects on the development of forest protection and forest management. Smithson. Inst. Rep. 1941. Pub. 3665:367–392.
Craighead, F. C., and George Hofer.
   1921. Protection of mesquite cordwood and posts from borers. U.S. Dep. Agric., Farmers' Bull. 1197. 22 p.
Craighead, F. C., and W. Middleton.
   1930. An annotated list of the important North American forest insects. U.S. Dep. Agric., Misc. Publ. 74, 30 p.
Creighton, William Steel.
   1950. The ants of North America. Mus. Comp. Zool. Bull. 104, 585 p. + plates. The Cosmos Press, Inc., Cambridge, Mass.
Cross, Earle E.
   1965. The generic relationships of the family Pyemotidae (Acarina, Trombidiformes). Univ. Kans. Sci. Bull. 45(2):29–275.
Cross, Earle E., and John C. Moser.
   1975. A new dimorphic species of *Pyemotes* and a key to previously described forms. Ann. Entomol. Soc. Am. 68(4):723–732.
Crumb, S. E.
   1956. The larvae of the Phalaenidae. U.S. Dep. Agric., Tech. Bull. 1135, 356 p.

500

Culver, Julian J.

1919. A study of *Compsilura concinnata,* an imported tachinid parasite of the gypsy moth and the brown-tail moth. U.S. Dep. Agric. Bull. 766, 27 p.

Cumming, Margaret E. P.

1953. Notes on the life history and seasonal development of the pine needle scale, *Phenacaspis pinifoliae* (Fitch) Diaspididae: Homoptera). Can. Entomol. 85(9):347–352.

Cumming, Margaret E. P.

1954. Notes on the spruce needle miner, *Taniva albolineana* Kft. (Olethreutidae: Lepidoptera). Can. Entomol. 86(10):457–460.

Cumming, Margaret E. P.

1959. The biology of *Adelges cooleyi* (Gill.) (Homoptera: Phylloxeridae). Can. Entomol. 91(10):601–617.

Cumming, Margaret E. P.

1962a. The biology of *Pineus similis* (Gill.) (Homoptera: Phylloxeridae) on spruce. Can. Entomol. 94(4):395–408.

Cumming, Margaret E. P.

1962b. A monomorphic cycle of *Adelges cooleyi* (Gill.) (Homoptera: Phylloxeridae) living only on spruce. Can. Entomol. 94(11):1190–1195.

Cumming, Margaret E. P.

1968. The life history and morphology of *Adelges lariciatus* (Homoptera: Phylloxeridae). Can. Entomol. 100(2):113–126.

Dahlsten, Donald L.

1966. Some biological attributes of sawflies in the *Neodiprion fulviceps* complex in a brushfield pine plantation (Hymenoptera: Diprionidae). Can. Entomol. 98(10):1055–1083.

Dahlsten, Donald L.

1967. Preliminary life tables for pine sawflies in the *Neodiprion fulviceps* complex (Hymenoptera: Diprionidae). Ecology 48(2):275–289.

Dahlsten, Donald L.

1970. Parasites, predators, and associated organisms reared from western pine beetle infested bark samples. *In:* Studies on the population dynamics of the western pine beetle, *Dendroctonus brevicomis* LeConte (Coleoptera: Scolytidae). p. 75–79. R. W. Stark and D. L. Dahlsten, eds. Univ. Calif., Berkeley.

Daterman, G. E., and V. M. Carolin, Jr.

1973. Survival of European pine shoot moth, *Rhyacionia buoliana* (Lepidoptera: Olethreutidae) under caged conditions in a ponderosa pine forest. Can. Entomol. 105(7):929–940.

501

David, W. A. L.
  1975. The status of viruses pathogenic for insects and mites. Annu. Rev. Entomol. 20:97–117.
Davidson, A. G., and R. M. Prentice, eds.
  1967. Important forest insects and diseases of mutual concern to Canada, the United States, and Mexico. 248 p. Can. Dep. For. and Rural Dev., Ottawa.
Davis, D. R.
  1964. Bagworm moths of the western hemisphere (Lepidoptera: Psychidae). U.S. Natl. Mus. Bull. 244, 233 p.
Davis, Harry G., T. P. McGovern, Gaines W. Eddy, and others.
  1968. New chemical attractants for yellow jackets (*Vespula* spp.) J. Econ. Entomol. 61(2):459–462.
Dawson, Allan F.
  1970. Green-striped forest looper in British Columbia. Can. For. Serv., For. Insect and Dis. Surv. For. Pest Leafl. 22, 5 p. For. Res. Lab., Victoria, B.C.
Dawson, Allan F.
  1971. Balsam twig aphid in British Columbia. Can. For. Serv., For. Insect and Dis. Surv. For. Pest Leafl. 36, 3 p. For. Res. Cent., Victoria, B.C.
de Bach, Paul, ed.
  1964. Biological control of insect pests and weeds. 844 p. Chapman and Hall Ltd., London.
DeBarr, G. L.
  1969. The damage potential of a flower thrips in slash pine seed orchards. J. For. 67(5):326–327.
De Leon, Donald.
  1933. Notes on the biology of *Meteorus hypophloei* Cushm. (Hymenoptera-Braconidae.). Brooklyn Entomol. Soc. Bull. 28(1):32–36.
De Leon, Donald.
  1934. An annotated list of the parasites, predators, and other associated fauna of the mountain pine beetle in western white pine and lodgepole pine. Can. Entomol. 66:51–61.
De Leon, Donald.
  1935. The biology of *Coeloides dendroctoni* Cushman (Hymenoptera-Braconidae), an important parasite of the mountain pine beetle (*Dendroctonus monticolae* Hopk.). Ann. Entomol. Soc. Am. 28(4):411–424.
De Leon, Donald.
  1952. Insects associated with *Sequoia sempervirens* and *Sequoia gigantea* in California. Pan-Pac. Entomol. 28(2):75–91.

Denton, Robert E.
  1972. Establishment of *Agathis pumila* (Ratz.) for control of larch casebearer, and notes on native parasitism and predation in Idaho. USDA For. Serv. Res. Note INT–164, 6 p. Intermt. For. and Range Exp. Stn., Moscow, Idaho.

Denton, Robert E., and Scott Tunnock.
  1972. Larch casebearer in western larch forests. U.S. Dep. Agric., For. Pest Leafl. 96, 8 p.

Dewey, Jerald E.
  1975. Pine looper. U.S. Dep. Agric., For. Pest Leafl. 151, 5 p.

Dillon, L. S.
  1956. The nearctic components of the tribe Acanthocinini (Coleoptera: Cerambycidae). Part 2. Ann. Entomol. Soc. Am. 49(3):207–235.

Dillon, Lawrence S., and Elizabeth S. Dillon.
  1941. The tribe Monochamini in the Western Hemisphere (Coleoptera: Cerambycidae). Reading Mus. Sci. Publ. 1. p. 1–135 + 5 plates.

Dimond, John B., and Robert H. Bishop.
  1968. Susceptibility and vulnerability of forests to the pine leaf aphid, *Pineus pinifoliae* (Fitch) (Adelgidae). Maine Agric. Exp. Stn. Bull. 658, 16 p. Orono.

Dixon, J. C., and E. A. Osgood.
  1961. Southern pine beetle. A review of knowledge. USDA, South. For. Exp. Stn. Paper 128. 34 p. New Orleans, La.

Doane, R. W., and O. J. Gilliland.
  1929. Three California ambrosia beetles. J. Econ. Entomol. 22(6):915–921.

Doane, R. W., E. C. VanDyke, W. J. Chamberlin, and H. E. Burke.
  1936. Forest insects. 463 p. McGraw-Hill Book Co., New York.

Dodge, Harold R.
  1961. Parasitism of spruce budworm by *Glypta* and *Apanteles* at different crown heights in Montana. Can. Entomol. 93(3): 222–228.

Doering, Kathleen C.
  1928. The genus *Clastoptera* in America North of Mexico. Univ. Kans. Sci. Bull. 18(1):5–153.

Doering, Kathleen C.
  1930. Synopsis of the family Cercopidae (Homoptera) in North America. J. Kans. Entomol. Soc. 3(3):53–64 and 3(4):81–108.

Dohanian, S. M.
  1940. *Melissopus latiferreanus* as a pest of filberts in the Northwest. J. Econ. Entomol. 33(6):852–856.

Dohanian, S. M.
  1944. Control of the filbert worm and filbert weevil by orchard sanitation. J. Econ. Entomol. 37(6) :764–766.

Doidge, D. F., and V. G. Marshall.
  1971. Spruce spider mite in British Columbia. Can. For. Serv., For. Insect and Dis. Surv. Pest Leafl. 33, 3 p. For. Res. Lab., Victoria, B.C.

Dominick, R. B., ed.
  1971. The moths of America north of Mexico. E. W. Classey Ltd. and R. B. D. Publications Inc., London. [a continuing series of fascicles].

Donley, David E., and Denver P. Burns.
  1971. The tuliptree scale. U.S. Dep. Agric., For. Pest Leafl. 92, 7 p.

Dorsey, C. K., and J. G. Leach.
  1956. The bionomics of certain insects associated with oak wilt with particular reference to the Nitidulidae. J. Econ. Entomol. 49(2) :219–230.

Doutt, Richard L.
  1967, Biological control. In Pest Control—biological, physical, and selected control methods. p. 1–30. Wendell W. Kilgore and Richard L. Doutt, eds. Academic Press, London and New York.

Dowden, P. B.
  1959. What about biological control? J. For. 57(4) :267–270.

Dowden, P. B.
  1962. Parasites and predators of forest insects liberated in the United States through 1960. U.S. Dep. Agric., Agric. Handb. 226, 70 p.

Downes, W.
  1925. The poplar sawfly (Trichiocampus viminalis (Fallen)). Entomol. Soc. B. C. Proc. 22, p. 26–32.

Downes, W., and H. Andison.
  1941. Notes on the life history of the June beetle Polyphylla perversa Casey. Entomol. Soc. B. C. Proc. 37:5–8.

Drake, C. J., and F. A. Ruhoff.
  1965. Lacebugs of the world, a catalog (Hemiptera: Tingidae). U.S. Natl. Mus. Bull. 243, 634 p.

Drooz, A. T.
  1960. The larch sawfly, its biology and control. U.S. Dep. Agric., Tech. Bull. 1212, 52 p.

Drooz, A. T.
  1971. The larch sawfly. U.S. Dep. Agric., For. Pest Leafl. 8, 4 p.

Drouin, J. A., C. R. Sullivan, and S. G. Smith.

1963. Occurrence of *Pissodes terminalis* Hopk. (Coleoptera: Curculionidae) in Canada: Life history, behavior, and cytogenetic identification. Can. Entomol. 95 (1) :70–76.

Drouin, J. A., and H. R. Wong.

1962. *Eurytoma calycis* Bugbee in Saskatchewan. Can. Dep. For. Bimon. Prog. Rep. 18 (2) :3.

Dyer, E. D. A. and K. H. Wright.

1967. Striped ambrosia beetle, *Trypodendron lineatum* (Oliv.). *In* Important forest insects and diseases of mutual concern to Canada, the United States, and Mexico. p. 27–30. A. G. Davidson and R. M. Prentice, eds. Can. Dep. For. and Rural Dev. Ottawa.

Eaton, C. B.

1942. Biology of the weevil *Cylindrocopturus eatoni* Buchanan, injurious to ponderosa and Jeffrey pine reproduction. J. Econ. Entomol. 35 (1) :20–25.

Eaton, C. B.

1962. Entomological considerations in the economics of forest pest control. J. For. 60 (5) :309–311.

Eaton, C. B., and R. R. Lara.

1967. Red turpentine beetle, *Dendroctonus valens* LeConte. *In* Important forest insects and diseases of mutual concern to Canada, the United States, and Mexico. p. 21–24. A. G. Davidson and R. M. Prentice, eds. Can. Dep. For. and Rural Dev. Ottawa.

Eaton, C. B., and R. L. Lyon.

1955. *Arhopalus productus* (Lec.) a borer in new buildings. USDA For. Serv., Calif. For. and Range Exp. Stn. Tech. Paper 11, 11 p. Berkeley.

Eaton, C. B., and J. S. Yuill.

1971. Gouty pitch midge. U.S. Dep. Agric., For. Pest Leafl. 46, 8 p.

Ebeling, W.

1968. Termites, identification, biology, and control of termites attacking buildings. Calif. Agric. Exp. Stn. Ext. Serv. Manual 38, 74 p. Los Angeles.

Edmunds, George F., Jr.

1973. Ecology of black pineleaf scale (Homoptera: Diaspididae). Environ. Entomol. 2 (5) :765–777.

Edson, Lewis J.

1967. An annotated and illustrated key to the species of the genus *Scolytus* (Coleoptera, Scolytidae) attacking coniferous trees of the nearctic region. M. A. thesis. Humbolt State Coll., Arcata, Calif. 62 p.

Edwards, J. Gordon.
1952. Species of the genus *Syneta* of the world (Coleoptera: Chrysomeloidea). Wasmann J. Biol. 11(1):23–82.

Edwards, W. D., and Don C. Mote.
1936. Omnivorous leaf tier, *Cnephasia longana* Haw., a relatively new pest of strawberries, iris, and other crops in Oregon. J. Econ. Entomol. 29(6):1118–1123.

Eidt, D. C.
1969. The life histories, distribution, and immature forms of the North American sawflies of the genus *Cephalcia* (Hymenoptera: Pamphiliidae). Entomol. Soc. Can. Mem. 59, 56 p.

Eide, Paul M.
1966. The life history and control of *Nemocestes incomptus* (Horn), a native root weevil attacking strawberries in western Washington, J. Econ. Entomol. 59(4):1004–1005.

Ellertson, F. E., and P.O. Ritcher.
1959. Biology of rain beetles, *Pleocoma* spp., associated with fruit trees in Wasco and Hood River Counties. Oreg. Agric. Exp. Stn. Tech. Bull. 44, 42 p. Corvallis.

Engelhardt, G. P.
1946. The North America clear-wing moths of the family Aegeriidae. U.S. Natl. Mus. Bull. 190, 222 p.

Engelhardt, N. T.
1957. Pathological deterioration of looper-killed western hemlock on southern Vancouver Island. For. Sci. 3(2):125–136.

Esselbaugh, Charles O.
1946. A study of the eggs of the Pentatomidae (Hemiptera). Ann. Entomol. Soc. Am. 39(4):667–691.

Essig, E. O.
1926. Insects of western North America. 1035 p. The Macmillan Co., New York.

Essig, E. O.
1948. Mounting aphids and other small insects on microscopic slides. Pan-Pac. Entomol. 24(1):9–22.

Essig, E. O., and Frieda Abernathy.
1952. The aphid genus *Periphyllus*. A systematic, biological, and ecological study. 166 p. Univ. Calif. Press, Berkeley and Los Angeles.

Evans, David.
1957. A revision of the genus *Poecilonota* in America north of Mexico (Coleoptera: Buprestidae). Ann. Entomol. Soc. Am. 50(1):21–37.

Evans, David.
1958. Two-year life cycle of *Pseudohazis eglanterina* (Boisduval) (Lepidoptera: Saturniidae). Can. Entomol. 90(2):125–127.

Evans, David.
1960. A revision of the genus *Enypia* (Lepidoptera: Geometridae). Ann. Entomol. Soc. Am. 53(5):560–574.

Evans, David.
1962. Descriptions and life history of *Melanolophia imitata* (Walker) (Lepidoptera: Geometridae). Can. Entomol. 94(6): 594–605.

Evans, David.
1967. The bisexual and agamic generations of *Besbicus mirabilis* (Hymenoptera: Cynipidae), and their associate insects. Can. Entomol. 99(2):187–196.

Evans, David.
1969. *Laspeyresia pseudotsugae* n. sp. (Lepidoptera: Olethreutidae), a bark miner in Douglas-fir. Can. Entomol. 101(9): 955–963.

Evans, David.
1970. Life history and immature stages of *Pandemis cerasana* (Lepidoptera: Tortricidae). Can. Entomol. 102(12):1597–1603.

Evans, David.
1972. Alternate generations of gall cynipids (Hymenoptera: Cynipidae) on Garry oak. Can. Entomol. 104(11):1805–1818.

Evans, D., and E. D. A. Dyer.
1952. Important insects—British Columbia, Coastal Forests. *In* Annu. Rep. Can. Dep. Agric., For. Insect and Dis. Surv., p. 129–131. Ottawa.

Evenden, James C., W. D. Bedard, and G. R. Struble.
1943. The mountain pine beetle, an important enemy of western pines. U.S. Dep. Agric., Circ. 664, 25 p.

Every, R. W.
1968. Control of root weevils on ornamentals and in homes. Oreg. State Univ. Ext. Circ. 738, 5 p. Corvallis.

Every, R. W., and J. A. Rudinsky.
1962. The golden Buprestid, a wood-boring beetle. Oreg. State Univ. Ext. Circ. 713, 4 p.

Fall, H. C.
1913. A brief review of our species of *Magdalis* with notes and descriptions of other North American Rhynchophora. Trans. Am. Entomol. Soc. 39(1):23–72.

Farris, S. H.
1965. Repositories of symbiotic fungus in the ambrosia beetle *Monarthrum scutellare* Lec. (Coleoptera: Scolytidae). Entomol. Soc. B. C. Proc. 62:30–33.

Fellin, David G.
  1966. Biology and feeding habits of *Pleocoma* larvae (Coleoptera: Scarabaeidae) in western Oregon coniferous forests. Ph.D. thesis. Oreg. State Univ., Corvallis, 172 p.

Fellin, David G.
  1968. Mites collected from Douglas-fir foliage in Montana. J. Econ. Entomol. 61(3):877-878.

Fellin, David G.
  1973. Weevils attracted to thinned lodgepole pine stands in Montana. USDA For. Serv. Res. Pap. INT-136, 20 p. Intermt. For. and Range Exp. Stn., Moscow, Idaho.

Fellin, David G., and P. O. Ritcher.
  1967. Distribution of *Pleocoma* species in Oregon with notes on the habitat of *P. simi* and *P. carinata*. Pan-Pac. Entomol. 43(4):251-263.

Felt, Ephraim Porter.
  1940. Plant galls and gall makers. 364 p. Comstock Publ. Co., Inc., Ithaca, N.Y.

Fenton, F. A.
  1917. Observations on *Lecanium corni* Bouche, and *Physokermes piceae* Schr. Can. Entomol. 49(9):309-320.

Fenton, F. A.
  1942. The flatheaded apple tree borer (*Chrysobothris femorata* (Olivier)). Okla. Agric. Exp. Stn. Bull. B-259, 31 p. Stillwater.

Ferguson, Douglas C.
  1972. Bombycoidea: Saturniidae. *In* The moths of America north of Mexico. Fascicle 20.2A and 20.2B. 275 p., 22 color plates. R. B. Domminick, ed. E. W. Classey Ltd. and R. B. D. Publications Inc., London.

Ferguson, Douglas C.
  1974. Moths of the *Semiothisa signaria* complex (Lepidoptera: Geometridae). Can. Entomol. 106(6):569-621.

Ferguson, R. B., M. M. Furniss, and J. V. Basile.
  1963. Insects destructive to bitterbrush flowers and seeds in southwestern Idaho. J. Econ. Entomol. 56(4):459-462.

Ferris, G. F.
  1937-61. Atlas of the scale insects of North America: Ser. 1-5 and vols. 6-7. 1782 p. Stanford Univ. Press, Stanford, Calif.

Fisher, R. C., G. H. Thompson, and W. E. Webb.
  1954. Ambrosia beetles in forest and sawmill, their biology, economic importance and control. Part 2. Prevention and control. For. Abstr. 15(1):3-15.

Fisher, W. S.
   1928. A revision of the North American species of Buprestid beetles belonging to the genus *Agrilus*. Smithson. Inst., U.S. Natl. Mus. Bull. 145, 345 p.

Fisher, W. S.
   1942. A revision of the North American species of Buprestid beetles belonging to the tribe Chrysobothrini. U.S. Dep. Agric., Misc. Publ. 470, 275 p.

Fisher, W. S.
   1950. A revision of the North American species of beetles belonging to the family Bostrichidae. U.S. Dep. Agric., Misc. Publ. 698, 157 p.

Fitzgerald, T. D., and J. B. Simeone.
   1971. Serpentine miner *Marmara fraxinicola* (Lepidoptera: Gracillariidae) in stems of white ash. Ann. Entomol. Soc. Am. 64(4):770–773.

Flake, Harold W., Jr., and Robert L. Lyon.
   1967. Insecticide tests against larvae of *Hemerocampa* new species, a tussock moth that defoliates boxelder in New Mexico. J. Econ. Entomol. 60(2):607–608.

Fleming, Walter E.
   1962. The Japanese beetle in the United States. U.S. Dep. Agric., Agric. Handb. 236, 30 p.

Florence, Laura.
   1917. The Pacific Coast species of *Xylococcus* (scale insects). Ann. Entomol. Soc. Am. 10(2):147–162 + 4 plates.

Forbes, A. R., B. D. Frazer, and H. R. MacCarthy.
   1973. The aphids (Homoptera: Aphididae) of British Columbia. 1. A basic taxonomic list. J Entomol. Soc. B. C. 70:43–57.

Forbes, William T. M.
   1923. The Lepidoptera of New York and neighboring states. Cornell Univ. Agric. Exp. Stn. Mem. 68, 792 p. Ithaca, N.Y.

Force, D. C.
   1967. Genetics in the colonization of natural enemies for biological control. Ann. Entomol. Soc. Am. 60(4):722–729.

Fowells, H. A.
   1940. Cutworm damage to seedlings in California pine stands. J. For. 38(7):590–591.

Franclemont, John G.
   1973. Mimallonoidea: Mimallonidae, and Bombycoidea: Apatelodidae, Bombycidae, Lasiocampidae. *In* The moths of America north of Mexico. Fasc. 20.1. 86 p., 11 color plates. R. B. Dominick, ed. E. W. Classey Ltd. and R. B. D. Publications Inc., London.

Frankie, Gordon W., and C. S. Koehler.
  1971. Studies on the biology and seasonal history of the cypress bark moth, *Laspeyresia cupressana* (Lepidoptera: Olethreutidae). Can. Entomol. 103(7):947–961.
Franz, J. M.
  1961. Biological control of pest insects in Europe. Annu. Rev. Entomol. 6:183–200.
Freeman, T. N.
  1958. The Archipinae of North America (Lepidoptera: Tortricidae). Can. Entomol. 90, Suppl. 7, 89 p.
Freeman, T. N.
  1960. Needle-mining Lepidoptera of pine in North America. Can. Entomol. 92, suppl. 16, 51 p.
Freeman, T. N.
  1967a. Annotated keys to some nearctic leaf-mining Lepidoptera on conifers. Can. Entomol. 99(4):419–435.
Freeman, T. N.
  1967b. On coniferophagous species of *Choristoneura* (Lepidoptera: Tortricidae) in North America. 1. Some new forms of *Choristoneura* allied to *C. fumiferana*. Can. Entomol. 99(5): 449–455.
Freeman, T. N.
  1972. The coniferous feeding species of *Argyresthia* in Canada (Lepidoptera: Yponomeutidae). Can. Entomol. 104(5):687–697.
Frick, Kenneth E.
  1959. Synopsis of the species of agromyzid leaf miners described from North America (Diptera). U.S. Natl. Mus. Proc. 108(3407):347–365.
Friend, Roger B.
  1933. The birch leaf-mining sawfly *Fenusa pumila* Klug. Conn. Agric. Exp. Stn. Bull. 348:291–364 New Haven.
Funk, A.
  1965. The symbiotic fungi of certain ambrosia beetles in British Columbia. Can. J. Bot. 43(8):929–932.
Funk, A.
  1970. Fungal symbionts of the ambrosia beetle *Gnathotrichus sulcatus*. Can. J. Bot. 48(7):1445–1448.
Furniss, M. M.
  1965. Susceptibility of fire-injured Douglas-fir to bark beetle attack in southern Idaho. J. For. 63(1):8–11.
Furniss, M. M.
  1972a. A preliminary list of insects and mites that infest some important browse plants of western big game. USDA For. Serv. Res. Note INT–155, 16 p. Intermt. For. and Range Exp. Stn., Moscow, Idaho.

Furniss, M. M.
　1972b. Poplar-and-willow borer. U.S. Dep. Agric., For. Pest Leafl. 121, 5 p.

Furniss, M. M.
　1976. Controlled breeding, comparative anatomy, and bionomics of *Dendroctonus simplex* LeConte and *Dendroctonus pseudotsugae* Hopkins (Coleoptera: Scolytidae). *In* Univ. Idaho, Dep. Entomol. Anniv. Publ. W. F. Barr ed. p. 109–120. Moscow.

Furniss, Malcolm M., and William F. Barr.
　1967. Bionomics of *Anacamptodes profanata* (Lepidoptera: Geometridae) on mountain mahogany in Idaho. Univ. Idaho Agric. Exp. Stn. Bull. 73, 24 p. Moscow.

Furniss, Malcolm M., and William F. Barr.
　1975. Insects affecting important native shrubs of the northwestern United States. USDA For. Serv. Gen. Tech. Rep. INT–19, 64 p. Intermt. For. and Range Exp. Stn., Ogden, Utah.

Furniss, M. M., G. E. Daterman, L. N. Kline, and others.
　1974. Effectiveness of the Douglas fir beetle antiaggregative pheromone methylcyclohexenone at three concentrations and spacings around felled host trees. Can. Entomol. 106(4):381–392.

Furniss, Malcolm M., and Robert L. Furniss.
　1972. Scolytids (Coleoptera) on snowfields above timberline in Oregon and Washington. Can. Entomol. 104(9):1471–1478.

Furniss, Malcolm M., and J. A. E. Knopf.
　1971. Western tussock moth. U.S. Dep. Agric., For. Pest Leafl. 120, 4 p.

Furniss, Malcolm M., and P. W. Orr.
　1970. Douglas-fir beetle. U.S. Dep. Agric., For. Pest Leafl. 5, 4 p.

Furniss, R. L.
　1941. Fire and insects in the Douglas-fir region. Fire Control Notes 5(4):211–213.

Furniss, R. L.
　1942. Biology of *Cylindrocopturus furnissi* Buchanan on Douglas-fir. J. Econ. Entomol. 35(6):853–859.

Furniss, R. L., and R. W. Every.
　1964. Carpenter ant control. Oreg. State Univ. Coop. Ext. Serv., Ext. Circ. 627, 5 p. Corvallis.

Gagné, Raymond J.
　1967. Notes on the genus *Thecodiplosis* Kieffer in North America, and some generic reassignments (Diptera: Cecidomyiidae). Entomol. Soc. Wash. Proc. 69(4):338–339.

Gagné, Raymond J.
   1969. A review of the genus *Walshomyia* including a new species reared from *Cupressus* galls in California (Diptera: Cecidomyiidae). Pan-Pac. Entomol. 45(1) :16–19.
Gagné, Raymond J.
   1973. A generic synopsis of the Nearctic Cecidomyiidi (Diptera: Cecidomyiidae: Cecidomyiinae). Ann. Entomol. Soc. Am. 66(4) :857–889.
Gardiner, L. M.
   1970. Biological notes on some Nearctic Lepturinae. Pan-Pac. Entomol. 46(4) :284–288.
Gerberg, E. J.
   1957. A revision of the new world species of powder-post beetles belonging to the family Lyctidae. U.S. Dep. Agric., Tech. Bull. 1157, 55 p. + 14 plates.
Gerhold, H. D., E. J. Schreiner, R. E. McDermott, and J. A. Winieski.
   1964. Breeding pest-resistant trees. Proc. NATO and NSF Adv. Study Inst. on Genet. Impr. for Dis. and Insect Resist. For. Trees. 505 p. Pergamon Press, New York.
Gertsch, W. J.
   1949. American spiders. 285 p. D. Van Nostrand Co., Inc.: Toronto, New York, London.
Gibson, Arthur.
   1917. A little known cutworm. *Euxoa excellens* Grt. Can. Entomol. 49(12) :401–403.
Gibson, Lester P.
   1969. Monograph of the genus *Curculio* in the New World (Coleoptera: Curculionidae). Part 1. United States and Canada. *In* Entomol. Soc. Am. Misc. Publ. 6(5) :241–285.
Gidaspow, T.
   1959. North American caterpillar hunters of the genera *Calosoma* and *Callisthenes* (Coleoptera: Carabidae). Bull. Am. Mus. Natl. Hist. 116(3) :225–344.
Gobeil, A. R.
   1936. The biology of *Ips perturbatus* Eichhoff. Can. J. Res. 14(12) :181–204.
Godfrey, George L.
   1972. A review and reclassification of larvae of the subfamily Hadeninae (Lepidoptera, Noctuidae) of American north of Mexico. U.S. Dep. Agric., Tech. Bull. 1450, 265 p.
Godwin, P. A.
   1972. Gypsy moth. U.S. Dep. Agric., For. Pest Leafl. 41, 5 p.

Goulding, R. L., and R. W. Every.
    1964. Dampwood termite control. Oreg. State Univ. Ext. Circ.
    700, 4 p. Corvallis.
Graham, K.
    1954. Notes on a polyhedral disease of black-headed budworm.
    Can. Entomol. 86(12):546–548.
Graham, K.
    1963. Concepts of forest entomology. 388 p. Reinhold Publ.
    Corp., New York.
Graham, K.
    1967. Fungal-insect mutualism in trees and timber. Annu. Rev.
    Entomol. 12:105–122.
Graham, S. A., and F. B. Knight.
    1965. Principles of forest entomology. 417 p. McGraw-Hill
    Book Co., New York.
Greeley, A. W., K. H. Wright, and R. B. Pope.
    1953. Final report on the 1952 blowdown and bark beetle sur-
    vey in the Douglas-fir region of Oregon and Washington.
    USDA For. Serv., Pac. Northwest For. and Range Exp.
    Stn., and Bur. of Entomol. and Plant Quar. 33 p + maps.
Greene, Charles T.
    1914. The cambium miner in river birch. J. Agric. Res. 1(6):
    471–474.
Grisdale, Dail.
    1970. An improved laboratory method for rearing large num-
    bers of spruce budworm, *Choristoneura fumiferana* (Lepi-
    doptera: Tortricidae). Can. Entomol. 102(9):1111–1117.
Griswold, Grace Hall.
    1925. A study of the oyster-shell scale. *Lepidosaphes ulmi*,
    (L.), and one of its parasites, *Aphelinus mytilaspidis* Le B.
    Part 1. Biology and morphology of the two forms of the
    oyster-shell scale. Part 2. Biology of a parasite of the oyster-
    shell scale. Cornell Univ. Agric. Exp. Stn. Mem. 93, 67 p.
    Ithaca, N.Y.
Grobler, Johan H.
    1962. The life history and ecology of the woolly pine needle
    aphid, *Schizolachnus pini-radiatae* (Davidson) (Homoptera:
    Aphididae). Can. Entomol. 94(1):35–45.

Hagen, K. S.
    1962. Biology and ecology of predaceous Coccinellidae. Annu.
    Rev. Entomol. 7:289–326.
Hagen, K. S., and R. van den Bosch.
    1968. Impact of pathogens, parasites, and predators on aphids.
    Annu. Rev. Entomol. 13:325–384.

Hagenstein, W. D., and R. L. Furniss.
  1956. Cooperation speeds salvage of windthrown and beetle-killed timber in Oregon and Washington. Soc. Am. For. Proc. 1955, p. 167–168.

Hall, David G.
  1948. The blowflies of North America. Thomas Say Found., 477 p. Monumental Print. Co., Baltimore, Md.

Hall, David G.
  1952. How to get further information on insects. U.S. Dep. Agric., Yearb. Agric. 1952, p. 737–743.

Hall, Ralph C.
  1962. California. *In* Forest insect conditions in the United States, 1961. J. W. Bongberg, ed. U.S. Dep. Agric., For. Serv., Washington, D.C.

Hall, Ralph C.
  1965. Sagebrush defoliator outbreak in northern California. USDA For. Serv. Res. Note PSW–75, 12 p. Pac. Southwest For. and Range Exp. Stn., Berkeley, Calif.

Hard, J. S.
  1967. Identification of destructive Alaska forest insects. USDA For. Serv. Pac. Northwest For. and Range Exp. Stn., Inst. North. For., 19 p.

Hardy, George A.
  1945. Notes on the life history of the vapourer moth (*Notolophus antiqua badia*) on Vancouver Island (Lepidoptera, Liparidae). Entomol. Soc. B. C. Proc. 42:3–6.

Hardy, George A.
  1962. Notes on life histories of one butterfly and three moths from Vancouver Island (Lepidoptera: Lycaenidae, Phalaenidae, and Geometridae). Entomol. Soc. B. C. Proc. 59:35–38.

Harper, A. M.
  1959. Gall aphids on poplar in Alberta. I. Descriptions of galls and distributions of aphids. Can. Entomol. 91(8):489–496.

Harris, J. W. E.
  1963. Sampling the egg stages of the two-year cycle spruce budworm near Babine Lake, British Columbia. For. Chron. 39:199–204.

Harris, J. W. E.
  1968. Poplar-and-willow borer in British Columbia. Can. For. Serv., For. Insect and Dis. Surv. For. Pest Leafl. 7, 4 p. For. Res. Lab., Victoria, B.C.

Harris, J. W. E., and H. C. Coppel.
  1967. The poplar-and-willow borer, *Sternochetus* (= *Cryptorhynchus*) *lapathi* (Coleoptera: Curculionidae), in British Columbia. Can. Entomol. 99(4):411–418.

Harris, P.
  1958. Life-history and natural control in British Columbia of
    Ocnerostoma piniariella Zell. (Lepidoptera: Yponomeutidae),
    a needle miner on white pine. Can. Entomol. 90(10):627–631.
Harris, P.
  1962. Effect of temperature on fecundity and survival of *Chry-
    solina quadrigemina* (Suffr.) and *C. hyperici* (Forst.) (Coleop-
    tera: Chrysomelidae). Can. Entomol. 94(7):774–780.
Harvey, P. A.
  1934. Life history of *Kalotermes minor. In* Termites and termite
    control, 2d ed. p. 217–233. Charles Kofoid et al., eds. Univ.
    Calif. Press, Berkeley.
Hatch, Melville H.
  1947. The Chelifera and Isopoda of Washington and adjacent
    regions. Univ. Wash. Publ. Biol. 10:157–274.
Hatch, Melville H.
  1953. The beetles of the Pacific Northwest. Part 1: Introduction
    and Adephaga. Univ. Wash. Publ. Biol. 16(1), 340 p. Univ.
    Wash. Press, Seattle.
Hatch, Melville H.
  1957. The beetles of the Pacific Northwest. Part 2: Staphylini-
    formia. Univ. Wash. Publ. Biol. 16(2), 384 p. Univ. Wash.
    Press, Seattle.
Hatch, Melville H.
  1962. The beetles of the Pacific Northwest. Part 3: Pselaphidae
    and Diversicornia. Univ. Wash. Pub. Biol. 16(3), 503 p. Univ.
    Wash. Press, Seattle.
Hatch, Melville H.
  1965. The beetles of the Pacific Northwest. Part 4: Macro-
    dactyles, Palpicornes, and Heteromera. Univ. Wash. Publ.
    Biol. 16(4), 268 p. Univ. Wash. Press, Seattle.
Hatch, Melville H.
  1971. The beetles of the Pacific Northwest. Part 5: Rhipi-
    ceroidea, Sternoxi, Phytophaga, Rhynchophora, and Lamelli-
    cornia. Univ. Wash. Publ. Biol. 16(5), 662 p. Univ. Wash.
    Press, Seattle.
Hawkes, Robert B.
  1968. The cinnabar moth, *Tyria jacobaeae*, for control of tansy
    ragwort. J. Econ. Entomol. 61(2):499–501.
Hawksworth, F. G.
  1961. Dwarfmistletoe of ponderosa pine in the southwest. U.S.
    Dep. Agric., Tech. Bull. 1246, 112 p.
Hay, C. J., and R. C. Morris.
  1970. Carpenterworm. U.S. Dep. Agric., For. Pest Leafl. 64, 8 p.

Hedlin, A. F.
  1960. On the life history of the Douglas-fir cone moth, *Barbara colfaxiana* (Kft.) (Lepidoptera: Olethreutidae), and one of its parasites, *Glypta evetriae* Cush. (Hymenoptera: Ichneumonidae). Can. Entomol. 92(11):826–834.
Hedlin, A. F.
  1961. The life history and habits of a midge, *Contarinia oregonensis* Foote (Diptera: Cecidomyiidae) in Douglas-fir cones, Can. Entomol. 93(11):952–967.
Hedlin, A. F.
  1964. Life history and habits of a midge, *Phytophaga thujae* Hedlin (Diptera: Cecidomyiidae) in western red cedar cones. Can. Entomol. 96(7):950–957.
Hedlin, A. F.
  1967. The pine seedworm, *Laspeyresia piperana* (Lepidoptera: Olethreutidae), in cones of ponderosa pine. Can. Entomol. 99(3):264–267.
Hedlin, A. F.
  1973. Spruce cone insects in British Columbia and their control. Can. Entomol. 105(1):113–122.
Hedlin, A. F.
  1974. Cone and seed insects of British Columbia. Can. For. Serv. Rep. BC–X–90, 63 p. Pac. For. Res. Cent., Victoria, B.C.
Hedlin, Alan F., and Norman E. Johnson.
  1963. Life history and habits of a midge, *Contarinia washingtonensis* Johnson (Diptera: Cecidomyiidae), in Douglas-fir cones. Can. Entomol. 95(11):1168–1175.
Hedlin, Alan F., and Norman E. Johnson.
  1968. A new species of *Camptomyia* (Diptera: Cecidomyiidae) from Douglas-fir cones. Can. Entomol. 100(5):532–535.
Hedlin, A. F., and D. S. Ruth.
  1970. A Douglas-fir twig mining beetle, *Pityophthorus orarius* (Coleoptera: Scolytidae). Can. Entomol. 102(1):105–108.
Heinrich, Carl.
  1923. Revision of the North American moths of the subfamily Eucosminae of the family Olethreutidae. U.S. Natl. Mus. Bull. 123, 298 p.
Heinrich, Carl.
  1926. Revision of the North American moths of the subfamilies Laspeyresiinae and Olethreutinae. U.S. Natl. Mus. Bull. 132, 216 p.
Heinrich, Carl.
  1956. American moths of the subfamily Phycitinae. U.S. Natl. Mus. Bull. 207, 581 p.

Heinrichs, E. A., and Hugh E. Thompson.
  1968. The biology of *Choristoneura houstonana* (Lepidoptera: Tortricidae), a pest of *Juniperus* species. Can. Entomol. 100(7):750–763.
Helfer, J. R.
  1941. A revision of the genus *Buprestis* of North America, north of Mexico (Coleoptera: Buprestidae). Entomol. Am. 21(3): 123–199.
Helfer, J. R.
  1963. How to know the grasshoppers, cockroaches, and their allies. 353 p. Wm. C. Brown Publ., Dubuque, Iowa.
Henson, W. R.
  1951. Mass flights of the spruce budworm. Can. Entomol. 83(9):240.
Herbert, F. B.
  1920. Cypress bark scale. U.S. Dep. Agric., Dep. Bull. 838, 22 p.
Herbert, F. B.
  1924. The European elm scale in the west. U.S. Dep. Agric., Dep. Bull. 1223, 20 p.
Heron, R. J.
  1955. Studies on the starvation of last-instar larvae of the larch sawfly, *Pristiphora erichsonii* (Htg.) (Hymenoptera: Tenthredinidae). Can. Entomol. 87(10):417–427.
Herrick, G. W.
  1935. Insect enemies of shadetrees. 417 p. Comstock Publ. Co., Ithaca, N.Y.
Hickin, N. E.
  1963. The insect factor in wood decay. 336 p. Hutchison and Co., Ltd., London.
Hicks, S. D.
  1962. The genus *Oberea* Mulsant (Coleoptera: Cerambycidae) with notes on the taxonomy, variation, and host affinities of many of the species. Coleopt. Bull. 16(1):5–12.
High, M. M.
  1915. The huisache girdler. U.S. Dep. Agric. Bull. 184:1–9.
Hildahl, V., and W. A. Reeks.
  1960. Outbreaks of the forest tent caterpillar, *Malacosoma disstria* Hbn., and their effects on stands of trembling aspen in Manitoba and Saskatchewan. Can. Entomol. 92(3):199–209.
Hodges, R. W.
  1962a. A review of the genus *Periploca* with descriptions of nine new species (Lepidoptera: Gelechioidea). Pan-Pac. Entomol. 38(2):83–97.

Hodges, R. W.
  1962b. A revision of the Cosmopterigidae of America north of
    Mexico, with a definition of the Momphidae and Walshiidae
    (Lepidoptera: Gelechioidea). Entomol. Am. 42 (new ser.):
    1–166.
Hodges, R. W.
  1965. Generic names of the *Recurvaria* group (Lepidoptera:
    Gelechiidae). Entomol. News 76:262–264.
Hodges, R. W.
  1971. Sphingoidea, *In* The moths of America north of Mexico.
    Fasc. 21. 158 p. and 14 color plates. R. B. Dominick, ed. E. W.
    Classey Ltd. and R. B. D. Publications Inc., London.
Hofer, George.
  1920. The aspen borer and how to control it. U.S. Dep. Agric.,
    Farmers' Bull. 1154, 11 p.
Holloway, James K.
  1958. The biological control of Klamath weed in California.
    10th Int. Congr. Entomol. Proc. 1956, 4:557–560.
Holms, J., and D. S. Ruth.
  1968. Spruce aphid in British Columbia. Can. For. Serv., For.
    Insect and Dis. Surv. For. Pest Leafl. 16, 4 p. For. Res. Lab.,
    Victoria, B.C.
Hood, J. D.
  1937. On some Thysanoptera from American conifers. Entomol.
    News 48:74–80.
Hopkins, A. D.
  1909. Practical information on the Scolytid beetles of North
    American forests. I. Bark beetles of the genus *Dendroctonus*.
    U.S. Dep. Agric. Bur. Entomol. Bull. 83, 169 p.
Hopkins, A. D.
  1911. Technical papers on miscellaneous forest insects. I. Con-
    tributions toward a monograph of the bark-weevils of the
    genus *Pissodes*. U.S. Dep. Agric. Tech. Ser. 20, Part 1. 68 p.
Hopkins, A. D.
  1915a. A new genus of scolytid beetles (*Conophthorus*), descrip-
    tions of new species. J. Wash. Acad. Sci. 12(5):424–433.
Hopkins, A. D.
  1915b. Contributions toward a monograph of the scolytid
    beetles. II. Preliminary classification of the superfamily
    Scolytoidea. U.S. Dep. Agric., Bur. Entomol. Tech. Ser., Part
    2:165–232.
Hopping, George R.
  1926. A new *Melasis* with a key to the species (Coleoptera).
    Can. Entomol. 58(9):225–228.

Hopping, George R.
  1928. The western cedar borer *(Trachykele blondeli* Mars.).
  The life-history, distribution and means of control, with a
  report on the strength of infested poles. Can. Dep. Agric.
  Entomol. Branch Pam. 94 (new ser.), 17 p.

Hopping, George R.
  1932. A revision of the *Clytini* of Boreal America (Cerambycidae, Coleoptera). Ann. Entomol. Soc. Am. 25(3):529–577.

Hopping, George R.
  1937. Sawfly biologies, No. 2, *Hemichroa crocea* Geoffroy. Can.
  Entomol. 69(11):243–249.

Hopping, George R.
  1962. Insects injurious to lodgepole pine in the Canadian Rocky
  Mountain Region. *In* Lodgepole pine in Alberta. Can. Dep.
  For. Bull. 127, p. 77–87. Ottawa.

Hopping, George R.
  1963a. Generic characters in the tribe Ipini (Coleoptera: Scolytidae) with a new species, a new combination and new synonomy. Can. Entomol. 95(1):61–68.

Hopping, George R.
  1963b. The natural groups of species in the genus *Ips* De Geer
  (Coleoptera: Scolytidae) in North America. Can. Entomol.
  95(5):508–516.

Hopping, George R.
  1963c. The North American species in Group I of *Ips* De Geer
  (Coleoptera: Scolytidae). Can. Entomol. 95(10):1091–1096.

Hopping, George R.
  1963d. The North American species in Groups II and III of
  Ips De Geer (Coleoptera: Scolytidae). Can. Entomol. 95(11):
  1202–1210.

Hopping, George R.
  1964. The North American species in Groups IV and V of *Ips*
  De Geer (Coleoptera: Scolytidae). Can. Entomol. 96(7):970–
  978.

Hopping, George R.
  1965a. The North American species in Group VI of *Ips* De Geer
  (Coleoptera: Scolytidae). Can. Entomol. 97(5):533–541.

Hopping, George R.
  1965b. The North American species in Group VII of *Ips* De
  Geer (Coleoptera: Scolytidae). Can. Entomol. 97(2):193–198.

Hopping, George R.
  1965c. The North American species in Group VIII of *Ips* De
  Geer (Coleoptera: Scolytidae). Can. Entomol. 97(2):159–172.

Hopping, George R.
1965d. The North American species in Group IX of *Ips* De Geer (Coleoptera: Scolytidae). Can. Entomol. 97(4):422–434.

Hopping, George R.
1965e. The North American species in Group X of *Ips* De Geer (Coleoptera: Scolytidae). Can. Entomol. 97(8):803–809.

Hopping, Ralph.
1937. The Lepturini of America north of Mexico, Part 2. Can. Dep. Mines and Resour. Natl. Mus. of Can. Bull. 85, Biol. Ser. 22, 42 p.

Hottes, F. C.
1956. Descriptions of some undescribed forms of *Schizolachnus* with key to species found in the United States (Aphididae). Biol. Soc. Wash. Proc. 69:59–62.

Hottes, F. C.
1957. A synopsis of the genus *Essigella* (Aphididae). Biol. Soc. Wash. Proc. 70:69–110.

Houseweart, Mark W., and J. W. Brewer.
1972. Biology of a pinyon spindle gall midge (Diptera: Cecidomyiidae). Ann. Entomol. Soc. Am. 65(2):331-336.

Hovore, Frank T.
1971. A new *Pleocoma* from southern California with notes on additional species (Coleoptera: Scarabaeidae). Pan-Pac. Entomol. 47(3):193–201.

Hubbard, H. G.
1897. The ambrosia beetles of the U.S. *In* U.S. Dep. Agric. Div. Entomol. Bull. 7 (new ser.), p. 9–30.

Huffaker, C. B., and C. E. Kennett.
1959. A ten-year study of vegetational changes associated with biological control of Klamath weed. J. Range Manage. 12(2): 69-82.

Hughes, K. M.
1957. An annotated list and bibliography of insects reported to have virus diseases. Hilgardia 26:597–629.

Hughes, K. M.
1972. Fine structure and development of two polyhedrosis viruses. J. Invertebr. Pathol. 19:198–207.

Hughes, K. M., and R. B. Addison.
1970. Two nuclear polyhedrosis viruses of the Douglas-fir tussock moth. J. Invertebr. Pathol. 16:196–204.

Hull, Frank M.
1962. Robber flies of the world. The genera of the family Asilidae. U.S. Natl. Mus. Bull. 224, parts 1 and 2, 907 p.

Hunt, G. M.
1926. The forest's enemies in the sea. Am. For. and For. Life 32:655–658, 682.

Hurd, Paul D., Jr.
  1955. The carpenter bees of California (Hymenoptera: Apoidea). Calif. Insect Surv. Bull. 4(2):35–72. Univ. Calif. Press, Berkeley and Los Angeles.
Hurlbutt, Henry W.
  1967. Digamasellid mites associated with bark beetles and litter in North America. Acarologia 9(2):497–534.
Hurtig, H.
  1964. The decision-making process and insect control. Can. Entomol. 96(1–2):221–230.
Hussey, N. W.
  1952. A contribution to the bionomics of green spruce aphid (*Neomyzaphis abietina* Walker). Scott. For. 6(4):121–130.

Ives, W. G. H., and R. M. Prentice.
  1958. A sequential sampling technique for surveys of the larch sawfly. Can. Entomol. 90(6):331-338.

James, Maurice T., and Robert F. Harwood.
  1969. Herms's medical entomology. 6th ed. 484 p. The MacMillan Co., New York.
Jardine, Alvin K.
  1969. Western hemlock looper in British Columbia. Can. For. Serv., For. Insect and Dis. Surv. For. Pest Leafl. 21, 4 p. For. Res. Lab., Victoria, B.C.
Jennings, Daniel T.
  1975. Life history and habits of the southwestern pine tip moth, *Rhyacionia neomexicana* (Dyar) (Lepidoptera: Olethreutidae). Ann. Entomol. Soc. Am. 68(3):597-606.
Jennings, Daniel T., and Herbert Allen Pase, III.
  1975. Spiders preying on *Ips* bark beetles. S.W. Naturalist 20(2):225–229.
Jensen, Frank.
  1971. Reseeding and *Labops*. USDA For. Serv. Range Impr. Notes 16(1):6–9. Intermt. Reg., Ogden, Utah.
Jensen, G. L., and C. S. Koehler.
  1969. Biological studies of *Scythropus californicus* on Monterey pine in northern California. Ann. Entomol. Soc. Am. 62(1):117–120.
Jessen, Eric.
  1964. Life history of the Monterey pine needle miner, *Argyresthia pilatella* (Lepidoptera: Yponomeutidae). Ann. Entomol. Soc. Am. 57(3):332–341.
Jewett, Stanley G., Jr.
  1963. Chapter 6: Plecoptera. *In* Aquatic insects of California. p. 155–181. Robert L. Usinger, ed. Univ. Calif. Press, Berkeley and Los Angeles.

Johnsey, R. L., W. P. Nagel, and J. A. Rudinsky.

    1965. The Diptera *Medetera aldrichii* Wheeler (Dolichopodidae) and *Lonchaea furnissi* McAlpine (Lonchaeidae) associated with the Douglas-fir beetle in western Oregon and Washington. Can. Entomol. 97(5): 521–527.

Johnson, N. E.

    1958. Field identification of ambrosia beetles attacking coniferous timber in the Douglas-fir region. Can. Entomol. 90(4): 236–240.

Johnson, N. E.

    1959. *Pienus* [*Pineus*] infestation on true firs in western Washington. J. Econ. Entomol. 52(5):828–829.

Johnson, N. E.

    1965. Reduced growth associated with infestations of Douglas-fir seedlings by *Cinara* species (Homoptera: Aphidae). Can. Entomol. 97(2):113–119.

Johnson, Norman E., and John W. Duffield.

    1961. Larvae of *Nomophila noctuella* feeding on Douglas-fir nursery seedlings, J. Econ. Entomol. 54(6):1258–1259.

Johnson, Norman E., and H. J. Heikkenen.

    1958. Damage to the seed of Douglas-fir by the Douglas fir cone midge. For. Sci. 4(4):274–282.

Johnson, N. E., W. H. Lawrence, and I. D. Ellis.

    1966. Seasonal occurrence of ground beetles (Coleoptera: Carabidae) in three habitats in southwestern Washington. Ann. Entomol. Soc. Am. 59(6):1055–1059.

Johnson, N. E., Russel G. Mitchell, and Kenneth H. Wright.

    1963. Mortality and damage to Pacific silver fir by the balsam woolly aphid in southwestern Washington. J. For. 61:854–860.

Johnson, N. E., and L. F. Pettinger.

    1961. Douglas-fir beetle attacks in living trees as influenced by the presence of fresh windthrow. Weyerhaeuser Co. For. Res. Note 37, 8 p.

Johnson, P. C.

    1949. Determining the bark beetle hazard of pine stands in northeastern California. J. For. 47(4):277–284.

Johnson, P. C.

    1954. A feeding record of the ten-lined June beetle. J. Econ. Entomol. 47(4):717–718.

Johnson, P. C.

    1958. Spruce spider mite infestations in northern Rocky Mountain Douglas-fir forests. USDA For. Serv. Res. Pap. INT–55, 14 p. Intermt. For. and Range Exp. Stn., Ogden, Utah.

Johnson, P. C.
  1966. Attractiveness of lightning-struck ponderosa pine trees to *Dendroctonus brevicomis* (Coleoptera: Scolytidae). Ann. Entomol. Soc. Am. 59 (3) : 615.
Johnson, P. C., and D. A. Ross.
  1967. Douglas-fir tussock moth, *Hemerocampa (Orgyia) pseudotsugata* McDunnough. *In* Important forest insects and diseases of mutual concern to Canada, the United States and Mexico. p. 105–107. A. G. Davidson and R. M. Prentice, eds. Can. Dep. For. and Rural Dev., Ottawa.
Johnston, H. R.
  1965. Soil insecticides for prevention and control of subterranean termites in buildings. 12th Int. Congr. Entomol. Proc., p. 687.
Johnston, H. R., Virgil K. Smith, and Raymond H. Beal.
  1972. Subterranean termites, their prevention and control in buildings. U.S. Dep. Agric., Home and Gard. Bull. 64, 30 p.
Jones, Thomas W., and William R. Phelps.
  1972. Oak wilt. U.S. Dep. Agric., For. Pest Leafl. 29. 7 p.
Jones, T. H., and J. V. Schaffner, Jr.
  1953. Cankerworms. U.S. Dep. Agric., Leafl. 183, 7 p.
Jones, T. H., R. T. Webber, and P. B. Dowden
  1938. Effectiveness of imported insect enemies of the satin moth. U.S. Dep. Agric., Circ. 459, 24 p.

Kaston, B. J., and E. Kaston.
  1953. How to know the spiders. 220 p. Wm. C. Brown Co., Publ. Dubuque, Iowa.
Kattoulas, Marios E., and C. S. Koehler.
  1965. Studies on the biology of the irregular pine scale. J. Econ. Entomol. 58 (4) :727–730.
Keen, F. P.
  1936. Relative susceptibility of ponderosa pines to bark-beetle attack. J. For. 34 (10) :919–927.
Keen, F. P.
  1937. Climatic cycles in eastern Oregon as indicated by tree rings. Mon. Weather Rev. 65 (5) :175–188.
Keen, F. P.
  1943. Ponderosa pine tree classes redefined. J. For. 41 (4) :249–253.
Keen, F. P.
  1950. The influence of insects on ponderosa pine silviculture. J. For. 48 (3) :186–188.
Keen, F. P.
  1955. The western pine beetle. U.S. Dep. Agric., For. Pest Leafl. 1. 4 p.

Keen, F. P.
   1958. Cone and seed insects of western forest trees. U.S. Dep. Agric., Tech. Bull. 1169, 168 p.
Keen, F. P., and R. L. Furniss.
   1937. Effects of subzero temperatures on populations of western pine beetle, *Dendroctonus brevicomis* Lec. J. Econ. Entomol. 30(3):482–504.
Keifer, H. H.
   1952. The eriophyid mites of California (Acarina: Eriophyidae). Calif. Insect Surv. Bull. 2(1):1–123. Sacramento.
Keifer, H. H.
   1963. Eriophyid studies B–10. Calif. Dept. Agric. Bull. B–10, 20 p. Sacramento.
Keifer, H. H.
   1965. Eriophyid studies B–16. Calif. Dept. Agric. Bull. B–16, 20 p. Sacramento.
Keifer, H. H., and J. L. Saunders.
   1972. *Trisetacus campnodus*, n. sp. (Acarina: Eriophyidae) attacking *Pinus sylvestris*. Ann. Entomol. Soc. Am. 65:46–49.
Kelsey, Harlan P., and William A. Dayton.
   1942. Standardized plant names. 2d ed. 675 p. [For Am. Joint Comm. on Hortic. Nomencl.] J. Horace McFarland Co., Harrisburg, Pa.
Kelson, Walter E.
   1964. The biology of *Aphrophora permutata* and some observations on *Aphrophora canadensis* attacking Monterey pine in California. (Homoptera: Cercopidae). Pan-Pac. Entomol. 40(3):135–146.
Kelton, Leonard A.
   1966. Synopsis of the genus *Tetraphleps* Fieber in North America (Hemiptera: Anthocoridae). Can. Entomol. 98(2):199–204.
Kelton, Leonard A.
   1967. Synopsis of the genus *Lyctocoris* in North America and description of a new species from Quebec (Heteroptera: Anthocoridae). Can. Entomol. 99(8):807–814.
Kevan, D. Keith McE.
   1962. Soil animals. 237 p. Philosophical Lib., Inc., New York.
Kilgore, W. W., and R. L. Doutt.
   1967. Pest control, biological, physical, and selected chemical methods. 477 p. Academic Press, New York and London.
Kimmey, J. W., and R. L. Furniss.
   1943. Deterioration of fire-killed Douglas-fir. U.S. Dep. Agric., Tech. Bull. 851. 61 p.

Kinghorn, J .M.
   1954. The influence of stand composition on the mortality of various conifers, caused by defoliation by the western hemlock looper on Vancouver Island, British Columbia. For. Chron. 30(4) :380–400).

Kingsolver, J. M., and R. E. White.
   1967. A review of the genus *Aulonium* for the United States (Coleoptera: Colydiidae). Entomol. Soc. Wash. Proc. 69(2) : 149–154.

Kinn, D. N.
   1966. A new genus and species of Schizogyniidae (Acarina: Mesostigmata) from North America with a key to the genera. Acarologia 8(4) :576–586.

Kinn, D. N.
   1967. Notes on the life cycle and habits of *Digamasellus quadrisetus* (Mesostigmata: Digamasellidae). Ann. Entomol. Soc. Am. 60(4) :862–865.

Kinn, D. N.
   1971. The life cycle and behavior of *Cercoleipus coelonotus* (Acarina: Mesostigmata) including a survey of phoretic mite associates of California Scolytidae. Univ. Calif. Publ. Entomol. 65:1–66.

Kinsey, Alfred C.
   1935. The economic importance of the Cynipidae. J. Econ. Entomol. 28(1) :86–91.

Kinzer, H. G., B. J. Ridgill, and J. G Watts.
   1970. Biology and cone attack behavior on *Conophthorus ponderosae* in southern New Mexico (Coleoptera: Scolytidae). Ann. Entomol. Soc. Am. 63(3) :795–798.

Kirk, H. B.
   1922. Biological notes on Elateridae and Melasidae (Coleoptera). Entomol. News 33:236–240.

Kissinger, D. G.
   1964. Curculionidae of America north of Mexico. A key to the genera. 143 p. Taxon. Publ., South Lancaster, Mass.

Kitching, R. L.
   1971. The Psyllidae of British Columbia with a key to species. J. Entomol. Soc. B.C. 68:36–43.

Klein, M. G., and H. C. Coppel.
   1969. The pine Chrysomelid, *Glyptoscelis pubescens*, in northwestern Wisconsin. Ann. Entomol. Soc. Am. 62(1):1–7.

Klein, William H., and Maxine W. Minnoch.
   1971. On the occurrence and biology of *Nepytia freemani* (Lepidoptera: Geometridae) in Utah. Can. Entomol. 103(1) : 119–124.

Kline, L. N., and J. A. Rudinsky.
  1964. Predator and parasites of the Douglas-fir beetle: description and identification of the immature stages. Oreg. Agric. Exp. Stn., Tech. Bull. 79, 52 p.
Knight, F. B.
  1958. The effects of woodpeckers on populations of the Engelmann spruce beetle. J. Econ. Entomol. 51(5):603–607.
Knight, F. B.
  1967. Evaluation of forest insect infestations. Annu. Rev. Entomol. 12:207–228.
Knight, Harry H.
  1968. Taxonomic review: Miridae of the Nevada test site and the western United States. Brigham Young Univ. Sci. Bull., Biol. Ser. 9(3):1–282.
Knipling, E. F.
  1960. Use of insects for their own destruction. J. Econ. Entomol. 53(3):415–420.
Koehler, C. S.
  1964. Control of *Asterolecanium* scales and cynipid leaf galls on oak in northern California. J. Econ. Entomol. 57(4): 579–581.
Koehler, C. S., and G. W. Frankie.
  1968. Distribution and seasonal abundance of *Oligonychus subnudus* on Monterey pine. Ann. Entomol. Soc. Am. 61(6): 1500–1506.
Koehler, C. S., and Maurice Tauber.
  1964a. *Periploca nigra*, a major cause of dieback of ornamental juniper in California. J. Econ. Entomol. 57(4):563–566.
Koehler, C. S., and Maurice Tauber.
  1964b. Seasonal activity and control of the Monterey pine tip moth. J. Econ. Entomol. 57(6):825–829.
Koerber, Thomas W.
  1963. *Leptoglossus occidentalis* (Hemiptera, Coreidae), a newly discovered pest of coniferous seed. Ann. Entomol. Soc. Am. 56(2):229–234.
Koerber, Thomas W.
  1967. Studies of the insect complex affecting seed production of ponderosa pine in California. Ph.D. thesis. Univ. Calif., Berkeley. 86 p.
Koerber, Thomas W., and George R. Struble.
  1971. Lodgepole needle miner. U.S. Dep. Agric., For. Pest Leafl. 22, 8 p.
Kofoid, C. A., S. F. Light, A. C. Horner, and others.
  1934. Termites and termite control. 795 p. Univ. Calif. Press, Berkeley.

Krantz, G. W.
   1970. A manual of Acarology. 335 p. Oreg. State Univ. Book Stores, Inc., Corvallis.
Kraus, E. J.
   1912. A revision of the genus *Lasconotus* Er. (Coleoptera: Colydiidae). Entomol. Soc. Wash. Proc. 14:25–44.
Krishna, Kumar.
   1966. Key to eight termite genera. U.S. Dep. Agric. Coop. Econ. Insect Surv. Rep. 16(47):1087–1098.
Krugman, Stanley L., and Thomas W. Koerber.
   1969. Effect of cone feeding by *Leptoglossus occidentalis* on ponderosa pine seed development. For. Sci. 15(1):104–111.
Kusch, D. S.
   1963. Notes on *Itame loricaria julia* Hlst. Can. Dep. For. Bimon. Prog. Rep. 19(4):3.
Kusch, D. S.
   1967. Notes on the biology of *Epinotia criddleana* Kft. Can. Dep. For. and Rural Dev. Bimon. Res. Notes 23(1):3.

Lane, C. E.
   1961. The teredo. Sci. Am. 204(2):132–140.
Lange, W. Harry Jr.
   1936. The biology of the orange tortrix, *Eulia* (*Argyrotaenia*) *citrana* Fern. Calif. Dep. Agric. Bull. 25:283–285, Sacramento.
Lange, W. Harry Jr.
   1937. An annotated list of the insects, mostly Coleoptera, associated with Jeffrey pine in Lassen National Forest, California. Pan-Pac. Entomol. 13(4):172–175.
Lanier, G. N.
   1970a. Biosystematics of the genus *Ips* (Coleoptera: Scolytidae) in North America. Hopping's Group III. Can. Entomol. 102(11):1404–1423.
Lanier, G. N.
   1970b. Biosystematics of North American *Ips* (Coleoptera: Scolytidae). Hopping's Group IX. Can. Entomol. 102(9):1139–1163.
Lanier, G. N.
   1972. Biosystematics of the genus *Ips* in North America. Hopping's Groups IV and X. Can. Entomol. 104(3):361–388.
Lanier, G. N., and J. H. Oliver, Jr.
   1966. "Sex-Ratio" condition: unusual mechanisms in bark beetles. Science 153:208–209.
Lanier, G. N., and D. L. Wood.
   1968. Controlled mating, karology, morphology, and sex-ratios in the *Dendroctonus ponderosae* complex. Ann. Entomol. Soc. Am. 61(2):517–526.

Latta, Randall.
1937. The rhododendron whitefly and its control. U.S. Dep. Agric., Circ. 429, 8 p.

Lavender, D. P., W. P. Nagel, and A. Doerksen.
1967. Eriophyid mite damage on Douglas-fir seedlings. J. Econ. Entomol. 60(2):621–622.

Leech, Hugh B.
1963. *Centrodera spurca* (LeConte) and two new species resembling it, with biological and other notes (Coleoptera: Cerambycidae). Calif. Acad. Sci. Proc. 32(7):149–218.

Lejeune, R. R., and G. T. Silver.
1961. Parasites and hyperparasites of the satin moth, *Stilpnotia salicis* Linnaeus, (Lymantriidae) in British Columbia. Can. Entomol. 93(6):456–467.

Leng, Charles W.
1920. Catalogue of the Coleoptera of America north of Mexico. 470 p. John D. Sherman, Jr., Mount Vernon, N.Y.

Leng, Charles W., and Andrew J. Mutchler.
1927. Supplement, 1919–1924 (inclusive), to Catalogue of the Coleoptera of America, north of Mexico. 78 p. John D. Sherman, Jr., Mount Vernon N.Y.

Leng, Charles W., and Andrew J. Mutchler.
1933. Second and third supplements, 1925 to 1932 (inclusive), to Catalogue of the Coleoptera of America, north of Mexico. 112 p. John D. Sherman, Jr., Mount Vernon, N.Y.

Leonard, M. D.
1930. A revision of the dipterous family Rhagionidae (Leptidae) in the United States and Canada. Am. Entomol. Soc. Mem. 7:1–181.

Leuschner, William A., and Carlton M. Newton.
1974. Benefits of forest insect control. Entomol. Soc. Am. Bull. 20(3):223–227.

Lewis, Trevor.
1973. Thrips, their biology, ecology, and economic importance. 349 p. Academic Press, London and New York.

Light, S. F.
1934a. The desert termites of the genus *Amitermes*. *In* Termites and termite control, 2d ed. p. 199–205. Charles Kofoid et al., eds. Univ. Calif. Press, Berkeley.

Light, S. F.
1934b. Dry-wood termites, their classification and distribution. *In* Termites and termite control, 2d ed. p. 206–209. Charles Kofoid et al., eds. Univ. Calif. Press, Berkeley.

Light, S. F.
1934c. The southern and mountain dry-wood termites, *Kalo-*

termes hubbardi and *Kalotermes marginipennis. In* Termites and termite control, 2d ed. p. 266–268. Charles Kofoid et al., eds. Univ. Calif. Press, Berkeley.

Light, S. F.
1934d. The desert damp-wood termite, *Paraneotermes simplicicornis. In* Termites and termite control, 2d ed. p. 311–313. Charles Kofoid et al., eds. Univ. Calif. Press, Berkeley.

Light, S. F., and A. L. Pickens.
1934. American subterranean termites, their classification and distribution. *In* Termites and termite control, 2d ed. p. 150–156. Charles Kofoid et al., eds. Univ. Calif. Press, Berkeley.

Lindsey, A. W., E. L. Bell, and R. C. Williams.
1931. Hesperioidea of North America. J. Sci. Lab. Denison Univ. 26:1–142.

Lindquist, Evert E.
1969a. Mites and the regulation of bark beetle populations. 2nd Int. Congr. Acarol. Proc. 1967, p. 389–399.

Lindquist, Evert E.
1969b. Review of Holarctic tarsonemid mites (Acarina: Prostigmata) parasitizing eggs of ipine bark beetles. Entomol. Soc. Can. Mem. 60, 111 p.

Lindquist, Evert E.
1970. Relationships between mites and insects in forest habitats. Can. Entomol. 102(8):978–984.

Lindquist, Evert E.
1974. Nomenclatural status and authorship of some family-group names in the Eriophyoidea (Acarina: Prostigmata). Can. Entomol. 106(2):209–212.

Lindquist, Evert E.
1975. *Digamasellus* Berlese, 1905, and *Dendrolaelaps* Halbert, 1915, with descriptions of new taxa of Digamasellidae (Acarina: Mesostigmata). Can. Entomol. 107(1):1–27.

Lindquist, Evert E., and William D. Bedard.
1961. Biology and taxonomy of mites of the genus *Tarsonemoides* (Acarina: Tarsonemidae) parasitizing eggs of bark beetles of the genus *Ips*. Can. Entomol. 93(11):982–999.

Lindquist, O. H., and C. N. Davis.
1971. The biology of a birch leaf beetle, *Phratora hudsonia* (Coleoptera: Chrysomelidae), with a larval key to forest Chrysomelinae in Ontario. Can. Entomol. 103(4):622–626.

Lindquist, O. H., and W. Ingram.
1968. The pill beetle, *Cytilus alternatus* (Coleoptera: Byrrhidae), a nursery pest in Ontario. Can. Entomol. 100(10):1113–1114.

Linsley, E. Gorton.
1935. A revision of the Pogonocherini of North America (Coleoptera, Cerambycidae). Ann. Entomol. Soc. Am. 28(1):73–103.

Linsley, E. Gorton.
1940. Notes on *Oncideres* twig girdlers. J. Econ. Entomol. 33(3):561–563.

Linsley, E. Gorton.
1942. A further note on wood-boring by the drugstore beetle. J. Econ. Entomol. 35(5):701.

Linsley, E. Gorton.
1943a. Attraction of *Melanophila* beetles by fire and smoke. J. Econ. Entomol. 36(2):341–342.

Linsley, E. Gorton.
1943b. The recognition and control of deathwatch, powderpost, and false powderpost beetles. Pests and Their Control, March 1943. 8 p.

Linsley, E. Gorton.
1946. A preliminary key to the species of *Pleocoma* (Coleoptera, Scarabaeidae). Pan-Pac. Entomol. 22(2):61–65.

Linsley, E. Gorton.
1957. Distributional records for some species of *Pleocoma* (Coleoptera, Scarabaeidae). Pan-Pac. Entomol. 33(2):102–104.

Linsley, E. Gorton.
1958. The role of Cerambycidae in forest, urban, and agricultural environments. Pan-Pac. Entomol. 34(3):105–124.

Linsley, E. Gorton.
1959. Ecology of Cerambycidae. Annu. Rev. Entomol. 4:99–138.

Linsley, E. Gorton.
1961. The Cerambycidae of North America. Part 1. Introduction. Univ. Calif. Publ. Entomol. 18. 97 p.

Linsley, E. Gorton.
1962a. The Cerambycidae of North America. Part 2. Taxonomy and classification of the Parandrinae, Prioninae, Spondylinae, and Aseminae. Univ. Calif. Publ. Entomol. 19. 102 p.

Linsley, E. Gorton.
1962b. The Cerambycidae of North America. Part 3. Taxonomy and classification of the subfamily Cerambycinae, tribes Opsimini and Megaderini. Univ. Calif. Publ. Entomol. 20. 188 p.

Linsley, E. Gorton.
1963. The Cerambycidae of North America. Part 4. Taxonomy and classification of the subfamily Cerambycinae, tribes Elaphidionini through Rhinotragini. Univ. Calif. Publ. Entomol. 21. 165 p.

Linsley, E. Gorton.
1964. The Cerambycidae of North America. Part 5. Taxonomy
and classification of the subfamily Cerambycinae, tribes
Callichromini through Ancylocerini. Univ. Calif. Publ.
Entomol. 22. 197 p.

Linsley, E. Gorton, and John A. Chemsak.
1972. The Cerambycidae of North America. Part 6. No. 1,
Taxonomy and classification of the subfamily Lepturinae.
Univ. Calif. Publ. Entomol. 69. 138 p.

Little, E. L.
1943. Common insects on pinyon *(Pinus edulis)*. J. N. Y.
Entomol. Soc. 51(4):239–252.

Little, E. L.
1953. Check list of native and naturalized trees of the United
States (including Alaska). U.S. Dep. Agric., Agric. Handb.
41, 472 p.

Loughton, B. G., C. Derry, and A. S. West.
1963. Spiders and the spruce budworm. *In* The dynamics of
epidemic spruce budworm populations. p. 249–268. R. F.
Morris, ed. Entomol. Soc. Can. Mem. 31, 332 p.

Luginbill, P., Sr., and H. R. Painter.
1953. May beetles of the United States and Canada. U.S. Dep.
Agric., Tech. Bull. 1060, 102 p.

Lyon, Robert L.
1970. California flatheaded borer. U.S. Dep. Agric., For. Pest
Leafl. 24, 8 p.

Lyon R. L., C. E. Richmond, J. L. Robertson, and B. A. Lucas.
1972. Rearing diapause and diapause-free western spruce
budworm *(Choristoneura occidentalis)* (Lepidoptera: Tortricidae) on an artificial diet. Can. Entomol. 104(3) : 417–426.

MacAloney, H. J.
1968. The bronze birch borer. U.S. Dep. Agric., For. Pest Leafl.
111, 4 p.

MacAloney, Harvey J., and Louis F. Wilson
1971. The Saratoga spittlebug. U.S. Dep. Agric., For. Pest
Leafl. 3, 6 p.

McAlpine, J. F.
1956. Cone-infesting lonchaeids of the genus *Earomyia* Zett.,
with descriptions of five new species from western North
America (Diptera: Lonchaeidae). Can. Entomol. 88(4):178–
196.

McAlpine, J. F.
1964. Descriptions of new Lonchaeidae (Diptera) II. Can.
Entomol. 96(5):701–757.

McCambridge, William F.
  1974. Pinyon needle scale. U.S. Dep. Agric., For. Pest. Leafl. 148, 4 p.
McCambridge, William F., and Galen C. Trostle.
  1972. The mountain pine beetle. U.S. Dep. Agric., For. Pest Leafl. 2, 6 p.
McDunnough, J.
  1938. Check list of the Lepidoptera of Canada and the United States of America. Part 1. Macrolepidoptera. South. Calif. Acad. Sci. Mem. 1, 272 p.
McDunnough, J.
  1939. Check list of the Lepidoptera of Canada and the United States of America. Part 2. Microlepidoptera. South. Calif. Acad. Sci. Mem. 2 (1), 171 p.
McGhehey, J. H., and W. P. Nagel.
  1969. The biologies of *Pseudohylesinus tsugae* and *P. grandis* (Coleoptera: Scolytidae) in western hemlock. Can. Entomol. 101 (3) :269–279.
McGregor, Mark D.
  1967. Biology and natural enemies of an aspen leaf tier, *Sciaphila duplex*, in the Intermountain Region. J. Econ. Entomol. 60 (5) :1213–1216.
McGregor, Mark D.
  1970. Biological observations on the life history and habits of *Choristoneura lambertiana* (Lepidoptera: Tortricidae) on lodgepole pine in southeastern Idaho and western Montana. Can. Entomol. 102 (10) :1201–1208.
McGregor, Mark D., and L. Otto Sandin.
  1969. Pinyon sawfly, *Neodiprion edulicolus* Ross. U.S. Dep. Agric., For. Pest Leafl. 117, 4 p.
McGregor, Mark D., and Richard I. Washburn.
  1968. The white-fir needle miner, *Epinotia meritana*, in Utah. J. Econ. Entomol. 61 (6) :1506–1507.
McGuffin, W. C.
  1958. Larvae of the nearctic Larentiinae (Lepidoptera: Geometridae). Can. Entomol. 90, suppl. 8, 104 p.
McGuffin, W. C.
  1967. Guide to the Geometridae of Canada (Lepidoptera). 1. Subfamily Sterrhinae. Entomol. Soc. Can. Mem. 50, 67 p.
McGuffin, W. C.
  1972. Guide to the Geometridae of Canada (Lepidoptera). 2. Subfamily Ennominae. Entomol. Soc. Can. Mem. 86, 159 p.
McGuffin, W. C.
  1973. The Rheumaptera of North America (Lepidoptera: Geometridae). Can. Entomol. 105 (3) :383–398.

McGugan, B. M.
   1958. Forest Lepidoptera of Canada. Vol. 1. Papilionidae to
   Arctiidae. Can. Dep. Agric., For. Biol. Div. Publ. 1034, 76 p.
McGugan, B. M.
   1958. The Canadian forest insect survey. 10th Int. Congr.
   Entomol. Proc., Montreal, Aug. 17–25, 1956. 4: 219–232.
McGugan, B. M., and H. C. Coppel.
   1962. Part 2: Biological control of forest insects, 1910–1958.
   In A review of the biological control attempts against insects
   and weeds in Canada. Commonw. Inst. Biol. Control Tech.
   Commun. 2, p. 35–216. Commonw. Agric. Bur., Farnham
   Royal, Bucks, Engl.
McIntyre, T., and R. A. St. George.
   1961. The old house borer. U.S. Dep. Agric., Leafl. 501, 8 p.
MacKay, Margaret Rae.
   1959. Larvae of the North American Olethreutidae (Lepidoptera). Can. Entomol. 91, suppl. 10, 338. p.
MacKay, Margaret Rae.
   1962. Larvae of the North American Tortricinae (Lepidotera:
   Tortricidae). Can. Entomol. suppl. 28, 182 p.
MacKay, Margaret Rae.
   1968. The North American Aegeriidae (Lepidoptera). A revision based on late-instar larvae. Entomol. Soc. Can. Mem. 58,
   112 p.
McKenzie, Howard L.
   1942a. New species of pine-infesting Margarodidae from California and southwestern United States (Homoptera: Coccoidea; Margarodidae). Microentomology 7(1):1–18.
McKenzie, Howard L.
   1942b. Seasonal history of the margarodid scale, *Matsucoccus
   bisetosus* Morrison, occurring on ponderosa and Jeffrey pines
   in California (Homoptera: Coccoidea; Margarodidae). Microentomology 7(1):19–24.
McKenzie, Howard L.
   1956. The armored scale insects of California. Calif. Insect
   Surv. Bull. 5:1–209.
McKenzie, Howard L.
   1967. Mealybugs of California, with taxonomy, biology and
   control of North American species. 525 p., Univ. Calif. Press,
   Berkeley.
McKenzie, Howard L., L. S. Gill, and Don E. Ellis.
   1948. The Prescott scale (*Matsucoccus vexillorum*) and associated organisms that cause flagging injury to ponderosa pine
   in the southwest. J. Agric. Res. 76(2):33–51.

McKittrick, F. A.
   1964. Evolutionary studies of cockroaches. Cornell Univ. Agric.
   Exp. Stn. Mem. 389, 197 p. Ithaca, N. Y.
McKittrick, F. A.
   1965. A contribution to the understanding of cockroach-termite
   affinities. Ann. Entomol. Soc. Am. 58(1):18–22.
McKnight, Melvin E.
   1968. A literature review of the spruce, western, and 2-year
   cycle budworms *Choristoneura fumiferana, C. occidentalis,*
   and *C. biennis* (Lepidoptera: Tortricidae). USDA For. Serv.
   Res. Pap. RM–44, 35 p. Rocky Mt. For. and Range Exp. Stn.,
   Fort Collins, Colo.
McKnight, Melvin E.
   1970. Sequential plan for western budworm egg mass surveys
   in the central and southern Rocky Mountains. USDA For.
   Serv. Res. Note RM–174, 8 p. Rocky Mt. For. and Range
   Exp. Stn., Fort Collins, Colo.
McKnight, Melvin E.
   1971. Biology and habits of *Bracon politiventris* (Hymenoptera:
   Braconidae). Ann. Entomol. Soc. Am. 64(3):620–624.
McLeod, J. M.
   1962. The adults and immature stages of four species of *Eu-
   cordylea* Dietz (Lepidoptera: Gelechiidae) on spruce in
   Quebec. Can. Entomol. 94(11):1198–1215.
McMullen, L. H., and M. D. Atkins.
   1959. Life-history and habits of *Scolytus tsugae* (Swaine)
   (Coleoptera: Scolytidae) in the interior of British Columbia.
   Can. Entomol. 91(7):416–426.
McMullen, L. H., and M. D. Atkins.
   1962. The life history and habits of *Scolytus unispinosus* Le
   Conte (Coleoptera: Scolytidae) in the interior of British
   Columbia. Can. Entomol. 94(1):17–25.
MacSwain, J. W.
   1945. Notes on the habits of the predator *Cymatodera ovipennis*
   Say with a description of the pupa (Coleoptera, Cleridae).
   Pan-Pac. Entomol. 21(3):97–100.
Mani, M. W.
   1964. The ecology of plant galls. (Monographiae Biologicae)
   434 p. W. Junk, Publ., The Hague.
Marsh, Paul M.
   1971. Keys to the nearctic genera of the families Braconidae,
   Aphidiidae, and Hybrizontidae (Hymenoptera). Ann.
   Entomol. Soc. Am. 64(4):841–850.
Martignoni, Mauro E., and Paul J. Iwai.
   1975. A catalog of viral diseases of insects and mites. USDA

For. Serv. Gen. Tech. Rep. PNW–40, 35 p. Pac. Northwest For. and Range Exp. Stn., Portland, Oreg.

Martignoni, M. E., P. J. Iwai, K. M. Hughes, and R. B. Addison.
1969. A cytoplasmic polyhedrosis of *Hemerocampa pseudo-tsugata*. J. Invertebr. Pathol. 13:15–18.

Martignoni, M. E., and R. L. Langston.
1959. Supplement to an annotated list and bibliography of insects reported to have virus diseases. Hilgardia 30:1–40.

Mason, R. R.
1970. Development of sampling methods for the Douglas-fir tussock moth, *Hemerocampa pseudotsugata* (Lepidoptera: Lymantriidae). Can. Entomol. 102(7):836–845.

Mason, Richard R., and Timothy C. Tigner.
1972. Forest-site relationships within an outbreak of lodgepole needle miner in central Oregon. USDA For. Serv. Res. Pap. PNW–146, 18 p. Pac. Northwest For. and Range Exp. Stn., Portland, Oreg.

Massey, C. L.
1964. The nematode parasites and associates of the fir engraver beetle, *Scolytus ventralis* LeConte, in New Mexico. J. Insect Pathol. 6:133–155.

Massey, Calvin L.
1971. Arizona five-spined ips. U.S. Dep. Agric., For. Pest Leafl. 116, 5 p.

Massey, Calvin L.
1974. Biology and taxonomy of nematode parasites and associates of bark beetles in the United States. U.S. Dep. Agric., Agric. Handb. 446, 233 p.

Massey, C. L., and D. A. Pierce.
1960. *Trirhabda nitidicollis*, a pest of rabbitbrush in New Mexico. J. Range Manage. 13(4):216–217.

Massey, C. L., and N. D. Wygant.
1954. Biology and control of the Engelmann spruce beetle in Colorado. U.S. Dep. Agric., Circ. 944, 35 p.

Mathers, Wm. G.
1935. Time of felling in relation to injury from ambrosia beetles, or pinworms. B. C. Lumberman 19(8):14.

Mathers, Wm. G.
1940. The shot hole borer, *Anisandrus pyri* (Peck), in British Columbia (Coleoptera, Scolytidae). Can. Entomol. 72(10):189–190.

Maynard, Elliott A.
1951. A monograph of the Collembola or springtail insects of New York State. 339 p. Comstock Publ. Co., Inc., Ithaca, N. Y.

Metcalf, C. L., and W. P. Flint.
    1962. Destructive and useful insects, their habits and control.
    1087 p. McGraw-Hill Book Co., Inc., New York.
Metcalf, Z. P. and others.
    1927-71. General catalogue of the Hemiptera; general catalogue
    of the Homoptera. Fascicles I-VIII. 16,783 p. U.S. Dep. Agric.,
    Agric. Res. Serv. and North Cent. Exp. Stn.
Michelbacher, A. E.
    1938. The biology of the garden centipede, *Scutigerella imma-
    culata.* Hilgardia 11(3):55–148.
Michelbacher, A. E.
    1949. The ecology of Symphyla. Pan-Pac. Entomol. 25(1):1–12.
Michelbacher, A. E., and E. Ross.
    1939. The giant palm borer, (Coleoptera Bostrichidae) an
    economic pest in lower California. Calif. Dep. Agric. Bull.
    28(2):166–169.
Michener, Charles D.
    1939. Notes on North American species of *Megarhyssa* (Hy-
    menoptera, Ichneumonidae). Pan-Pac. Entomol. 15(3):126–
    131.
Michener, Charles D.
    1952. The Saturniidae (Lepidoptera) of the western hemisphere.
    Morphology, phylogeny, and classification. Am. Mus. Natl.
    Hist Bull. 98:341–501.
Mickel, C. E.
    1928. Biological and taxonomic investigations on the mutillid
    wasps. U.S. Natl. Mus. Bull. 143, 351 p.
Middlekauff, Woodrow W.
    1958. The North American sawflies of the genera *Acantholyda,
    Cephalcia* and *Neurotoma* (Hymenoptera, Pamphiliidae).
    Univ. Calif. Publ. Entomol. 14(2):51–174 + plates.
Middlekauff, Woodrow W.
    1960. The siricid wood wasps of California (Hymenoptera: Sym-
    phyta). Calif. Insect Surv. Bull. 6(4):59–77. Univ. Calif.
    Press, Berkeley and Los Angeles.
Middlekauff, Woodrow W.
    1974. Larva of the wood-boring sawfly *Syntexis libocedrii*
    Rohwer. Pan-Pac. Entomol. 50(3):288–290.
Mielke, J. L.
    1950. Rate of deterioration of beetle-killed Engelmann spruce.
    J. For. 48(12):882–888.
Miller, Douglass R., and Howard L. McKenzie.
    1973. Seventh taxonomic study of North American mealybugs
    (Homoptera: Coccoidea; Pseudococcidae). Hilgardia 41
    (17):489–542.

Miller, John M.

1915. Cone beetles: injury to sugar pine and western yellow pine. U.S. Dep. Agric. Bull. 243, 12 p.

Miller, John M.

1931. High and low lethal temperatures for the western pine beetle. J. Agric. Res. 43 (4) :303–321.

Miller, John M.

1943. Damage to ponderosa pine lumber and rustic poles by the black-horned pine borer. U.S. Dep. Agric. Bur. Entomol. and Plant Quar. E–599, 9 p.

Miller, J. M., and F. P. Keen.

1960. Biology and control of the western pine beetle. U.S. Dep. Agric., Misc. Publ. 800, 381 p.

Miller, J. M., and J. E. Patterson.

1927. Preliminary studies on the relation of fire injury to bark-beetle attack in western yellow pine. J. Agric. Res. 34 (7) :597–613.

Miller, William E.

1967a. Taxonomic review of the *Rhyacionia frustrana* group of pine-tip moths, with description of a new species (Olethreutidae). Can. Entomol. 99 (6) :590–596.

Miller, William E.

1967b. The European pine shoot moth—ecology and control in the Lake States. For. Sci. Monogr. 14. 72 p.

Miller, William E., Arthur R. Hastings, and Valentine M. Carolin.

1970. European pine shoot moth. U.S. Dep. Agric., For. Pest Leafl. 59, 8 p.

Milliron, H. E.

1949. Taxonomic and biological investigations in the genus *Megastigmus*, with particular reference to the taxonomy of the nearctic species (Hymenoptera: Chalcidoidea; Callimonidae). Am. Midl. Nat. 41 (2) :257–420.

Minnoch, Maxine W., and Douglas L. Parker.

1971. Life history of a looper, *Lambdina punctata*, in Utah (Lepidoptera: Geometridae). Ann. Entomol. Soc. Am. 64 (2) : 386–389.

Mitchell, Russel G.

1962. Balsam woolly aphid predators native to Oregon and Washington. Oreg. Agric. Exp. Stn. Tech. Bull. 62, 63 p. Corvallis.

Mitchell, Russel G.

1965. An experiment in biological control of the balsam woolly aphid in northwestern United States. 12th Int. Congr. Entomol. Proc. p. 703–704.

Mitchell, Russel G.
  1966. Infestation characteristics of the balsam woolly aphid in the Pacific Northwest. USDA For. Serv. Res. Pap. PNW–35, 18 p. Pac. Northwest For. and Range Exp. Stn., Portland, Oreg.
Mitchell, Russel G., G. D. Amman, and W. E. Waters.
  1970. Balsam woolly aphid. U.S. Dep. Agric., For. Pest Leafl. 118, 10 p.
Mitchell, Russel G., and K. H. Wright.
  1967. Foreign predator introductions for control of the balsam woolly aphid in the Pacific Northwest. J. Econ. Entomol. 60(1) :140–147.
Molnar, A. C.
  1965. Pathogenic fungi associated with a bark beetle on alpine fir. Can. J. Bot. 43:563–570.
Molnar, A. C., J. W. E. Harris, and D. A. Ross.
  1967. Forest insect conditions, British Columbia region. *In* Ann. Rep. For. Insect and Dis. Surv., 1966, p. 108–123, Ottawa.
Morgan, C. V. G.
  1948. The biology of *Monchamus notatus morgani* (Coleoptera: Cerambycidae). Entomol. Soc. B.C. Proc. 44:28–30.
Morgan, C. V. G., and A. F. Hedlin.
  1960. Notes on the juniper berry mite, *Trisetacus quadrisetus* (Thomas) (Acarina: Eriophyidae), in British Columbia. Can. Entomol. 92(8) :608–610.
Morgan, F. David.
  1968. Bionomics of Siricidae. Annu. Rev. Entomol. 13:239–256.
Morris, E. V.
  1970. Saddleback looper in British Columbia. Can. For. Serv., For. Insect and Dis. Surv. For. Pest Leafl. 23, 3 p. For. Res. Lab., Victoria, B. C.
Morris, R. F.
  1963. The dynamics of epidemic spruce budworm populations. Can. Entomol. Mem. 31, 332 p.
Morrison, Harold.
  1939. Descriptions of new species of *Matsucoccus* (Hemiptera: Coccidae). Entomol. Soc. Wash. Proc. 41(1) :1–20.
Moser, John C., and Lawrence M. Roton.
  1971. Mites associated with southern pine bark beetles in Allen Parish, Louisiana. Can. Entomol. 103(12) :1775–1798.
Muesebeck, C. F. W.
  1920. A revision of the North American species of ichneumon-flies belonging to the genus *Apanteles*. U.S. Natl. Mus. Proc. 2349, 58:483–576.

Muesebeck, C. F. W.
   1923. A revision of the North American species of ichneumon-flies belonging to the genus *Meteorus* Haliday. U.S. Natl. Mus. Proc. 2470, 93 (2) :1–44.
Muesebeck, C. F. W.
   1925. A revision of the parasitic wasps of the genus *Microbracon* occurring in America north of Mexico. U.S. Natl. Mus. Proc. 2580, 67 (8) :1–85.
Muesebeck, C. F. W., Karl V. Krombein, Henry K. Townes, and others.
   1951–67. Hymenoptera of America north of Mexico, synoptic catalog. U.S. Dep. Agric., Agric. Monogr. 2, 1420 p. First suppl. 305 p., 1958; Second suppl. 584 p., 1967.
Munroe, Eugene.
   1959. Canadian species of *Dioryctria* Zeller (Lepidoptera: Pyralidae). Can. Entomol. 91 (2) :65–72.
Munroe, Eugene.
   1963. A new species of *Nepytia* (Lepidoptera: Geometridae), of economic importance to Douglas-fir in British Columbia. Can. Entomol. 95 (4) :407–413.
Munroe, Eugene.
   1972. Pyraloidea, Pyralidae (Part). *In* The moths of America north of Mexico, Fasc. 13. 1A, 134 p. R. B. Dominick, ed. E. W. Classey Ltd. and R. B. D. Publications Inc., London.
Munroe, Eugene.
   1973. A supposedly cosmopolitan insect: the celery webworm and allies, genus *Nomophila* Hübner. Can. Entomol. 105 (2) : 177–216.
Murtha, P. A.
   1972. A guide to air photo interpretation of forest damage in Canada. Can. For. Serv. Publ. 1292, 63 p. Ottawa.
Mutuura, A., and T. N. Freeman.
   1966. The North American species of the genus *Zeiraphera* Treitschke (Olethreutidae). J. Res. Lepid. 5:153–176.
Mutuura, Akira, and Eugene Munroe.
   1973. American species of *Dioryctria* (Lepidoptera: Pyralidae): 4. The *schuetzeela* group and the taxonomic status of the spruce cone moth. Can. Entomol. 105 (4) :653–668.
Mutuura, Akira, Eugene Munroe, and D. A. Ross.
   1969a. American species of *Dioryctria* (Lepidoptera: Pyralidae) : 1. Western Canadian species of the *zimmermani* group. Can. Entomol. 101 (10) :1009–1023.
Mutuura, Akira, Eugene Munroe, and D. A. Ross.
   1969b. American species of *Dioryctria* (Lepidoptera: Pyralidae) : 2. Western Canadian species of the *baumhoferi* and *ponderosae* groups. Can. Entomol. 101 (10) 1042–1047.

National Academy of Sciences, National Research Council.
  1962. Pest control and wildlife relationships, Part 2. Policy and
  procedures for pest control. Div. Biol. and Agric. Publ. 920–B,
  53 p.
Needham, James G., Stuart W. Frost, and Beatrice H. Tothill.
  1928. Leaf-mining insects, 351 p. The Williams and Wilkins Co.,
  Baltimore.
Newcomer, E. J.
  1918. Some stoneflies injurious to vegetation. J. Agric. Res.
  13(1):37–42.
Newport, C. A.
  1962. Economics of forest pest control. J. For. 60(5):306–308.
Nielson, Mervin W.
  1957. A revision of the genus *Colladonus* (Homoptera,
  Cicadellidae). U.S. Dep. Agric., Tech. Bull. 1156, 52 p. +
  plates.
Nielson, Mervin W.
  1968. The leafhopper vectors of phytopathogenic viruses
  (Homoptera, Cicadellidae): taxonomy, biology, and virus
  transmission. U.S. Dep. Agric., Tech. Bull. 1382, 386 p.
Nord, J. C.
  1968. The life history and behavior of *Saperda inornata* and
  Oberea schaumii (Coleoptera: Cerambycidae) in trembling
  aspen, *Populus tremuloides*. Ph.D. thesis. Univ. Mich. Micro-
  films, Ann Arbor. 272 p.

O'Brien, Charles William.
  1970. A taxonomic revision of the weevil genus *Dorytomus* in
  North America (Coleoptera: Curculionidae). Univ. Calif.
  Publ. Entomol. 60, 68 p.
Ollieu, Max M., and John A. Schenk.
  1966. The biology of *Eucosma rescissoriana* Heinrich in western
  white pine in Idaho (Lepidoptera: Olethreutidae). Can.
  Entomol. 98(3):268–274.
Oman, Paul.
  1971. The leafhopper subfamily Koebeliinae (Homoptera:
  Cicadellidae). *In* Entomol. Essays to Commemorate the
  Retirement of Professor K. Yasumatsu, 129–139. Hokuryukan
  Publ. Co. Ltd., Tokyo.
Oman, Paul Wilson.
  1949. The nearctic leafhoppers (Homoptera: Cicadellidae), a
  generic classification and check list. Entomol. Soc. Wash.
  Mem. 3, 253 p.
Oman, P. W., and A. D. Cushman.
  1948. Collection and preservation of insects. U.S. Dep. Agric.,
  Misc. Publ. 601, 42 p.

O'Neill, K., and R. S. Bigelow.
  1964. The *Taeniothrips* of Canada (Thysanoptera: Thripidae). Can. Entomol. 96(9):1219–1239.

Opler, Paul A.
  1974. Biology, ecology, and host specificity of microlepidoptera associated with *Quercus agrifolia* (Fagaceae). Univ. Calif. Publ. Entomol. 75, 98 p.

Orr, T. J., Jr.
  1942. Reducing pine beetle damage through partial cutting. West Coast Lumberman 69(4):42,44,46,79.

Orr, T. J., Jr.
  1945. Selective marking in ponderosa pine on a Klamath Falls tree farm. J. For. 43(10):738–741.

Palmer, Miriam A.
  1952. Aphids of the Rocky Mountain Region. Thomas Say Found., vol. 5, 452 p. The A. B. Hirschfeld Press, Denver.

Parker, D. L., and D. W. Davis.
  1971. Feeding habits of *Corticeus substriatus* (Coleoptera: Tenebrionidae) associated with mountain pine beetle in lodgepole pine. Ann. Entomol Soc. Am. 64(1):293–294.

Parker, Douglas L., and Maxine W. Moyer.
  1972. Biology of a leafroller, *Archips negundanus*, in Utah (Lepidoptera: Tortricidae). Ann. Entomol. Soc. Am. 65(6): 1415–1418.

Parshley, H. M.
  1921. Essay on the American species of *Aradus* (Hemiptera). Am. Entomol. Soc. Trans. 47:1–106 + plates.

Parsons, Carl T.
  1943. A revision of the nearctic Nitidulidae (Coleoptera). Mus. Comp. Zool. Bull. 92:121–278.

Patterson, J. E.
  1927. The relation of highway slash to infestations by the western pine beetle in standing timber. U.S. Dep. Agric., Tech. Bull. 3, 10 p.

Patterson, J. E.
  1929. The pandora moth, a periodic pest of western pine forests. U.S. Dep. Agric., Tech. Bull. 137, 20 p.

Peck, Oswald.
  1963. A catalogue of the nearctic Chalcidoidea (Insecta: Hymenoptera). Can. Entomol. suppl. 30, 1092 p.

Person, H. L.
  1928. Tree selection by the western pine beetle. J. For. 26:564–578.

Person, H. L.
    1940. The clerid *Thanasimus lecontei* (Wolc.) as a factor in the control of the western pine beetle. J. For. 38(5):390–396.
Peterson, L. O. T.
    1958. The boxelder twig borer, *Proteoteras willingana* (Kearfott), (Olethreutidae). Can. Entomol. 90(11):639–646.
Petrunkevitch, A.
    1911. A synonymic index-catalogue of spiders of North, Central and South America. Am. Mus. Nat. Hist. Bull. 29:1–791.
Pickens, A. L.
    1934a. The biology and economic significance of the western subterranean termite, *Reticulitermes hesperus*. *In* Termites and termite control, 2d ed., p. 157–183. Charles Kofoid et al., eds. Univ. Calif. Press, Berkeley.
Pickens, A. L.
    1934b. The barren-lands subterranean termite, *Reticulitermes tibialis*. *In* Termites and termite control, 2d ed., p. 184–186. Charles Kofoid et al., eds. Univ. Calif. Press, Berkeley.
Pickens, A. L., and S. F. Light.
    1934. The desert subterranean termite, *Heterotermes aureus*. *In* Termites and termite control. 2d ed., p. 196–198. Charles Kofoid et al., eds. Univ. Calif., Press, Berkeley.
Pitman, G. M.
    1971. Trans-verbenol and alpha-pinene: their utility in manipulation of the mountain pine beetle. J. Econ. Entomol. 64(2): 426–430.
Pope, R. B.
    1958. Final report, cooperative evaluation survey of *Chermes* damage, Mt. St. Helens, Washington, 1957. USDA For. Serv., Pac. Northwest For. and Range Exp. Stn., Portland, Oreg. 25 p.
Popham, W. L., and D. G. Hall.
    1958. Insect eradication programs. Annu. Rev. Entomol. 3:335–354.
Potts, S. F.
    1958. Concentrated spray equipment, mixtures, and application methods. 598 p. Dorland Books, Caldwell, N. J.
Powell, J. M.
    1971. The arthropod fauna collected from the comandra blister rust, *Cronartium comandrae*, on lodgepole pine in Alberta. Can. Entomol. 103(6):908–918.
Powell, Jerry A.
    1961. Taxonomic and biological observations on *Pseudexentera habrosana* (Heinrich). Pan-Pac. Entomol. 37(4):203–209.

Powell, Jerry A.
  1962a. Taxonomic studies on the *Acleris gloverana-variana* complex, the black-headed budworms (Lepidoptera: Tortricidae). Can. Entomol. 94(8):833–840.

Powell, Jerry A.
  1962b. Two previously undescribed species of Canadian Archipsini, with a report of the genus *Lozotaenia* Stephens in North America (Lepidoptera: Tortricidae). Can. Entomol. 94(8):841–845.

Powell, Jerry A.
  1963. Observations on larval and pupal habits of the juniper cone moth, *Periploca atrata* Hodges (Lepidoptera: Gelechioidea). Pan-Pac. Entomol. 39(3)177–181.

Powell, Jerry A.
  1964a. A review of *Griselda*, with descriptions of a related new genus and two species (Lepidoptera: Tortricidae). Pan-Pac. Entomol. 40(2):85–97.

Powell, Jerry A.
  1964b. Biological and taxonomic studies on tortricine moths, with reference to the species in California. Univ. Calif. Publ. Entomol. 32, 317 p.

Powell, Jerry A.
  1967. Taxonomic status and descriptions of some fungus feeding Tineidae (Lepidoptera). Pan-Pac. Entomol. 43(4):292–307.

Powell, Jerry A.
  1968. Host associations and taxonomy of nearctic conifer cone moths in the genus *Eucosma* (Lepidoptera: Tortricidae). Hilgardia 39:1–36.

Powers, Robert F., and William E. Sundahl.
  1973. Sequoia pitch moth: A new problem in fuel-break construction. J. For. 71(6):338–339.

Prebble, M. L.
  1933. The biology of *Podisus serieventris* Uhler, in Cape Breton, Nova Scotia. Can. J. Res. 9:1–30.

Prebble, M. L., and K. Graham.
  1945. The current outbreak of defoliating insects in coast hemlock forest of British Columbia. Part 1. Description of outbreak and damage. B. C. Lumberman 29(2):25–27, 42, 44, 46, 48, 50

Prebble, M. L., and K. Graham.
  1957. Studies of attack by ambrosia beetles in softwood logs on Vancouver Island, British Columbia. For. Sci. 3(1):90–112.

Prentice, R. M.
  1955. The life history and some aspects of the ecology of the

large aspen tortrix, *Choristoneura conflictana* (Wlkr.) (n. comb.) (Lepidoptera: Tortricidae). Can. Entomol. 87(11): 461–473.

Prentice, R. M.
  1962. Forest Lepidoptera of Canada. Vol. 2. Nycteolidae, Noctuidae, Notodontidae, Liparidae. p. 77–281. Can. Dep. For., Ottawa.

Prentice, R. M.
  1963. Forest Lepidoptera of Canada. Vol. 3. Lasiocampidae, Thyatiridae, Drepanidae, Geometridae. p. 282–543. Can. Dep. For., Ottawa.

Prentice, R. M.
  1965. Forest Lepidoptera of Canada. Vol. 4. Microlepidoptera. p. 544–840. Can. Dep. For., Ottawa.

Pritchard, A. Earl, and Edward W. Baker.
  1958. The false spider mites (Acarina: Tenuipalpidae). Univ. Calif. Publ. Entomol. 14(3):175–274.

Pritchard, A. Earl, and Robert E. Beer.
  1950. Biology and control of *Asterolecanium* scales on oaks in California. J. Econ. Entomol. 43(4):494–497.

Quaintance, A. L., and E. R. Sasscer.
  1916. The oyster-scale and the scurfy scale. U.S. Dept. Agric., Farmers' Bull. 723, 14 p.

Raske, A. G.
  1966. Bionomics and taxonomy of the genus *Moneilema* (Coleoptera: Cerambycidae). Ph.D. thesis. Univ. Calif., Berkeley. 268 p.

Raske, A. G.
  1973a. *Tetropium parvulum* elevated to species rank and contrasted to *T. cinnamopterum* in morphology and host preference (Coleoptera: Cerambycidae). Can. Entomol. 105(5): 745–755.

Raske, A. G.
  1973b. Notes on the biology of *Tetropium parvulum* (Coleoptera: Cerambycidae) in Alberta. Can. Entomol. 105(5):757–760.

Raske, A. G.
  1973c. Taxonomic relationship between *Monochamus scutellatus* and *M. oregonensis* (Coleoptera: Cerambycidae). Can. Entomol. 105(5):795–806.

Rawlings, G. B.
  1948. Recent observations on the *Sirex noctilio* population in *Pinus radiata* forests in New Zealand. N.Z. J. For. 5:411–421.

Readio, P. A.
1927. Biology of Reduviidae of America north of Mexico. Univ. Kans. Sci. Bull. 17:1–248.

Reeks, W. A.
1960. Observations on the life history, distribution, and abundance of two species of *Cecidomyia* (Diptera, Cecidomyiidae) on jack pine in Manitoba and Saskatchewan. Can. Entomol. 92(2):154–160.

Reid, R. W.
1955. The bark beetle complex associated with lodgepole pine slash in Alberta. Part 1—Notes on the biologies of some Scolytidae attacking lodgepole pine slash. Can. Entomol. 87(7):311–323.

Reid, R. W.
1957. The bark beetle complex associated with lodgepole slash in Alberta. Part 3—Notes on the biologies of several predators with special reference to *Enoclerus sphegeus* Fab. (Coleoptera: Cleridae) and two species of mites. Can. Entomol. 89(3):111–120.

Reinhard, H. J.
1931. Revision of the American parasitic flies belonging to the genus *Winthemia*. U.S. Natl. Mus. Proc. Vol. 79, Artic. 20, No. 2886, 54 p. + plate.

Rice, R. E.
1969. Bionomics of *Enoclerus barri* (Coleoptera: Cleridae). Can. Entomol. 101(4):382–386.

Richards, W. R.
1965. The Callaphidini of Canada (Homoptera: Aphididae). Entomol. Soc. Can. Mem. 44, 149 p.

Richards, W. R.
1968. Generic classification, evolution, and biogeography of the Sminthuridae of the world (Collembola). Can. Entomol. Mem. 53, 54 p.

Richards, W. R.
1972. The Chaitophorinae of Canada (Homoptera: Aphididae). Entomol. Soc. Can. Mem. 87, 109 p.

Richmond, H. A., and R. R. Lejeune.
1945. The deterioration of fire-killed white spruce by wood-boring insects in northern Saskatchewan. For. Chron. 21(3): 168–192.

Rindge, Frederick H.
1964. A revision of the genera *Carphoides*, *Paraphoides*, and *Galenara* (Lepidoptera: Geometridae). Am. Mus. Novit. No. 2189, 53 p.

Rindge, Frederick H.
   1966. A revision of the moth genus *Anacamptodes* (Lepidop-
      tera: Geometridae). Bull. Am. Mus. Nat. Hist. Vol. 132,
      Artic. 3, p. 177–243.
Ritcher, P. O.
   1958. Biology of Scarabaeidae. Annu. Rev. Entomol. 3:311–334.
Ritcher, P. O.
   1966. White grubs and their allies. 219 p. Oreg. State Univ.
      Press, Corvallis.
Rockwood, L. P.
   1952. Notes on coccinellids in the Pacific Northwest (Coleop-
      tera). Pan-Pac. Entomol. 28(3):139–147.
Ross, D. A.
   1967. The western larch borer, *Tetropium velutinum* LeConte,
      in interior British Columbia. J. Entomol. Soc. B. C. 64:25–28.
Ross, D. A.
   1968. Wood- and bark-feeding Coleoptera of felled spruce in
      interior British Columbia. J. Entomol. Soc. B. C. 65:10–12.
Ross, D. A., and D. Evans.
   1954. Annotated list of forest insects of British Columbia. Part
      1—Lasiocampidae, Saturniidae, Liparidae. Entomol. Soc.
      B. C. Proc. 51:40–43.
Ross, D. A., and D. Evans.
   1956. Annotated list of forest insects of British Columbia.
      Part 3—*Eupithecia* spp. (Geometridae). Entomol. Soc. B. C.
      Proc. 52:36–38.
Ross, D. A., and D. Evans.
   1958. Annotated list of forest insects of British Columbia.
      Part 8—*Semiothisa* spp. (Geometridae). Entomol, Soc. B. C.
      Proc. 55:40–41.
Ross, D. A., and D. Evans.
   1959. Annotated list of forest insects of British Columbia.
      Part 9—*Caripeta* spp. (Geometridae). Entomol. Soc. B. C.
      Proc. 56:15.
Ross, D. A., and D. Evans.
   1961. Annotated list of forest insects of British Columbia.
      Part 10—Notodontidae. Entomol. Soc. B. C. Proc. 58:30–32.
Ross, D. A., and H. Vanderwal.
   1969. A spruce borer, *Tetropium cinnamopterum* Kirby, in
      interior British Columbia. J. Entomol. Soc. B. C. 66:10–14.
Ross, Herbert H.
   1937. A generic classification of the nearctic sawflies (Hy-
      menoptera, Symphyta). Univ. Ill. Bull. Vol. 34, No. 94, 173 p.
Ross, Herbert H.
   1955. The taxonomy and evolution of the sawfly genus *Neodi-
      prion*. For. Sci. 1(3):196–209.

Roth, E. R.
  1970. Resistance, a review of the literature on important insects and diseases. USDA For. Serv., Southeast Area State and Priv. For. 59 p.

Ruckes, Herbert.
  1946. Notes and keys on the genus *Brochymena* (Pentatomidae, Heteroptera). Entomol. Am. 26 (4) :143–238.

Ruckes, Herbert Jr.
  1957. A synopsis of the California deathwatch beetles of the genus *Ernobius* Thomson, with descriptions of two new species which attack pine cones (Coleoptera: Anobiidae). Pan-Pac. Entomol. 33 (4) :157–161.

Ruckes, Herbert Jr.
  1958. Observations on two species of pine cone feeding deathwatch beetles in California (Coleoptera: Anobiidae). Ann. Entomol. Soc. Am. 51 (2) :186–188.

Rudinsky, J. A.
  1962. Ecology of Scolytidae. Annu. Rev. Entomol. 7:327–348.

Rudinsky, J. A., and G. E. Daterman.
  1964. Field studies on flight patterns and olfactory responses of ambrosia beetles in Douglas-fir forests of western Oregon. Can. Entomol. 96 (10) :1339–1352.

Rudinsky, J. A., and J. P. Vité.
  1956. Effects of temperature upon the activity and the behavior of the Douglas fir beetle. For. Sci. 2 (4) :258–267.

Russell, Louise M.
  1941. A classification of the scale insect genus *Asterolecanium*. U.S. Dep. Agric., Misc. Publ. 424, 322 p.

Russell, Louise M.
  1948. The North American species of whiteflies of the genus *Trialeurodes*. U.S. Dep. Agric., Misc. Publ. 635, 85 p.

Ryan, Roger B., and Richard D. Medley.
  1970. Test release of *Itoplectis quadricingulatus* against European pine shoot moth in an isolated infestation. J. Econ. Entomol. 63 (5) :1390–1392.

Ryan, Roger B., and Julius A. Rudinsky.
  1962. Biology and habits of the Douglas-fir beetle parasite, *Coeloides brunneri* Viereck (Hymenoptera: Braconidae), in western Oregon. Can. Entomol. 94 (7) :748–763.

Safranyik, L., D. M. Shrimpton, and H. S. Whitney.
  1974. Management of lodgepole pine to reduce losses from the mountain pine beetle. Environ. Can., For. Sci., For. Tech. Rep. 1, 24 p.

Salman, K. A.
  1938. An unusual type of top-kill of ponderosa pine. J. Econ.
    Entomol. 31(5):613–616.
Salman, K. A., and J. W. Bongberg.
  1942. Logging high-risk trees to control insects in the pine
    stands of northeastern California. J. For. 40:533–539.
Sartwell, Charles, R. F. Schmitz, and W. J. Buckhorn.
  1971. Pine engraver, *Ips pini*, in the Western States. U.S. Dep.
    Agric., For. Pest Leafl. 122, 5 p.
Sartwell, Charles, and Robert E. Stevens.
  1975. Mountain pine beetle in ponderosa pine, prospects for
    silvicultural control in second-growth stands. J. For. 73(3):
    136–140.
Saunders, Joseph L.
  1969. Occurrence and control of the balsam twig aphid on *Abies
    grandis* and *A. concolor*. J. Econ. Entomol. 62(5):1106–1109.
Schaefer, C. H.
  1962. Life history of *Conophthorus radiatae* (Coleoptera:
    Scolytidae) and its principal parasite, *Cephalonomia utahensis*
    (Hymenoptera:Bethylidae). Ann. Entomol. Soc. Am. 55(5):
    569–577.
Scheller, H. D. v.
  1963. Zur Biologie und Schadwirkung der Nadelholzspinnmilbe
    Oligonychus ununguis Jacobi und der Sitkafichtenlaus *Lioso-
    maphis abietina* Walker (Hom. Aphid.). Teil 2: *Liosomaphis
    abietina* Walker. Sonderdr. aus Z. ang. Entomol. 51(3):258–
    284.
Schmid, J. M.
  1969. *Laphria gilva* (Diptera: Asilidae), a predator of *Dendroc-
    tonus ponderosae* in the Black Hills of South Dakota. Ann.
    Entomol. Soc. Am. 62(6):1237–1241.
Schmid, J. M., and Roy C. Beckwith.
  1975. The spruce beetle. U.S. Dep. Agric., For. Pest Leafl. 127,
    7 p.
Schmiege, Donald C.
  1970. Hemlock sawfly. U.S. Dep. Agric., For. Pest Leafl. 31, 4 p.
Schmiege, Donald C., and David Crosby.
  1970. Black-headed budworm in Western United States. U.S.
    Dep. Agric., For. Pest Leafl. 45, 4 p.
Schreiber, Lawrence R., and John W. Peacock.
  1974. Dutch elm disease and its control. U.S. Dep. Agric., Agric.
    Inf. Bull. 193, 15 p.
Schuh, Joe, and Don C. Mote.
  1948. Insect pests of nursery and ornamental trees and shrubs
    in Oregon. Oreg. Agric. Exp. Stn. Bull. 449, 164 p. Oreg.
    State Coll., Corvallis.

Schwarz, E. A.
  1909. Illustrations of the life history of a sawfly (*Hylotoma pectoralis* Leach) injurious to willows. [Hymenoptera, Tenthredinidae.] Entomol. Soc. Wash. Proc. 11(3):106–108 + plates.

Scott, H. G.
  1961. Collembola: Pictorial keys to the Nearctic genera. Ann. Entomol. Soc. Am. 54(1):104–113.

Severin, Henry H. P.
  1950. Spittle-insect vectors of Pierce's disease virus. 2. Life history and virus transmission. Hilgardia 19(11):357–376 + 6 plates.

Sharp, Lee A., and William G. Barr.
  1960. Preliminary investigations of harvester ants on southern Idaho rangelands. J. Range Manage. 13(3):131–134.

Shea, K. R., and N. E. Johnson.
  1962. Deterioration of wind-thrown conifers three years after blowdown in southwestern Washington. Weyerhaeuser Co. For. Res. Note 44, 17 p.

Shea, K. R., N. E. Johnson, and S. McKee.
  1962. Deterioration of Pacific silver fir killed by the balsam woolly aphid. J. For. 60(2):104–108.

Shenefelt, Roy D.
  1943. The genus *Atanycolus* Foerster in America north of Mexico. Res. Stud. State Coll. Wash. 11(2):51–163.

Shewell, G. E.
  1971. On the type of *Agria*, with description of a new nearctic species (Diptera: Sarcophagidae). Can. Entomol. 103(8):1179–1191.

Silver, G. T.
  1958. Studies on the silver-spotted tiger moth, *Halisidota argentata* Pack. (Lepidoptera: Arctiidae) in British Columbia. Can. Entomol. 90(2):65–80.

Silver, G. T.
  1960. The relation of weather to population trends of the black-headed budworm, *Acleris variana* (Fern.) (Lepidoptera: Tortricidae). Can. Entomol. 92(6):401–410.

Silver, G. T.
  1961. Notes on the chemical control of *Ectropis crepuscularia* Schiff., at Kitimat, B.C. Entomol. Soc. B.C. Proc. 58:13–16.

Silver, G. T.
  1968. Studies on the Sitka spruce weevil, *Pissodes sitchensis*, in British Columbia, Can. Entomol. 100(1):93–110.

Silver, G. T., and D. A. Ross.
  1961. Forest insect conditions, British Columbia. *In* Annual

report forest insect and disease survey, 1960, p. 93–105. Can. Dep. Agric., Ottawa.

Silver, G. T., and D. A. Ross.
1962. Forest insect conditions, British Columbia. *In* Annual report forest insect and disease survey, 1961, p. 107–119. Can. Dep. For., Ottawa.

Simeone, J. B.
1965. The frass of Northeastern United States powder posting beetles. 12th Int. Congr. Entomol. Proc., p. 707–708.

Simons, John N.
1954. The cicadas of California, Homoptera: Cicadidae. Calif. Insect Surv. Bull. 2(3):153–192.

Sleeper, E. L.
1963. A study of the Zygopinae (Coleoptera: Curculionidae) of America north of Mexico, 1. Bull. South. Calif. Acad. Sci. 62:209–220.

Sloop, K. D.
1937. A revision of the North American Buprestid beetles belonging to the genus *Melanophila* (Coleoptera, Buprestidae). Univ. Calif. Publ. Entomol. 7(1):1–20.

Smirnoff, W. A.
1974. Three years of aerial field experiments with *Bacillus thuringiensis* plus chitinase formulation against the spruce budworm. J. Invertebr. Pathol. 24(3):344–348.

Smith, C. C.
1952. The life-history and galls of a spruce gall midge, *Phytophaga piceae* Felt (Diptera: Cecidomyiidae). Can. Entomol. 84(9):272–275.

Smith, Clyde F.
1944. The Aphidiinae of North America (Braconidae: Hymenoptera). Ohio State Univ. Contrib. Zool. and Entomol. 6, 154 p.

Smith, Clyde F.
1969. Pemphiginae associated with the roots of conifers in North America (Homoptera: Aphididae). Ann. Entomol. Soc. Am. 62(5):1128–1152.

Smith, D. N.
1962. Prolonged larval development in *Buprestis aurulenta* L. (Coleoptera: Buprestidae). A review with new cases. Can. Entomol. 94(6):586–593.

Smith, David R.
1964. Description of the male of *Xyelecia nearctica*, with comments on the genus (Hymenoptera: Xyelidae). Pan-Pac. Entomol. 40(1):54–56.

Smith, David R.
  1967a. A review of the larvae of Xyelidae, with notes on the family classification (Hymenoptera). Ann. Entomol. Soc. Am. 60(2):376–384.
Smith, David R.
  1967b. New Synonymy in *Pleroneura* Konow (Hymenoptera: Xyelidae). Entomol. Soc. Wash. Proc. 69(2):182–183.
Smith, David R.
  1969a. The genus *Susana* Rohwer and Middleton (Hymenoptera: Tenthredinidae). Entomol. Soc. Wash. Proc. 71(1):13–23.
Smith, David R.
  1969b. Nearctic sawflies. 2. Selandriinae: adults (Hymenoptera: Tenthredinidae). U.S. Dep. Agric., Tech. Bull. 1398, 48 p. + plates.
Smith, David R.
  1971a. Nearctic sawflies. 3. Heterarthrinae: adults and larvae (Hymenoptera: Tenthredinidae). U.S. Dep. Agric., Tech. Bull. 1420, 84 p. + plates.
Smith, David R.
  1971b. The genus *Zadiprion* Rohwer (Hymenoptera: Diprionidae). Entomol. Soc. Wash. Proc. 73(2):187–197.
Smith, David R.
  1972. Sawflies of the genus *Croesus* Leach in North America (Hymenoptera: Tenthredinidae). Entomol. Soc. Wash. Proc. 74(2):169–180.
Smith, Edward Laidlaw.
  1968. Biosystematics and morphology of Symphyta. 1. Stem-galling *Euura* of the California region, and a new female genitalic nomenclature. Ann. Entomol. Soc. Am. 61(6):1389–1407.
Smith, Edward Laidlaw.
  1970a. Biology and structure of some California bristletails and silverfish (Apterygota: Microcoryphia, Thysanura). Pan-Pac. Entomol. 46(3):212–225.
Smith, Edward Laidlaw.
  1970b. Biosystematics and morphology of Symphyta. 2. Biology of gall-making nematine sawflies in the California region. Ann. Entomol. Soc. Am. 63(1):36–51.
Smith, K. M.
  1967. Insect virology. 250 p. Academic Press. New York and London.
Smith, Leslie M.
  1932. The shot hole borer. Calif. Agric. Ext. Serv. Circ. 64, 13 p.

Smith, Ray F., and Robert van den Bosch.
    1967. Integrated control. *In* Pest control, biological, physical and selected chemical methods, p. 295–340. Wendell W. Kilgore and Richard L. Doutt, eds. Academic Press, New York and London.

Smith, Richard H.
    1961. Red turpentine beetle. U.S. Dep. Agric., For. Pest Leafl. 55, 8 p.

Smith, Richard H.
    1971. Jeffrey pine beetle. U.S. Dep. Agric., For. Pest Leafl. 11, 7 p.

Smith, Roger C.
    1922. The biology of the Chrysopidae. Cornell Univ. Agric. Exp. Stn. Mem. 58:1287–1372.

Smith, S. G., and B. A. Sugden.
    1969. Host trees and breeding sites of native North American *Pissodes* bark weevils, with a note on synonomy. Ann. Entomol. Soc. Am. 62(1):146–148.

Snyder, T. E.
    1936. Preventing damage by *Lyctus* powder-post beetles. U.S. Dep. Agric., Farmers' Bull. 1477, 14 p.

Snyder, T. E.
    1944. Powder-post beetles and their control. Pests (April):8, 27–31.

Snyder, T. E.
    1949a. Catalog of the termites (Isoptera) of the world. Smithson. Inst. Misc. Collect. 112 (3953):1–490.

Snyder, T. E.
    1949b. Insects in wood products. U.S. Dep. Agric., Yearb. Agric., 1949, p. 432–436. Washington, D.C.

Snyder, T. E.
    1956. Annotated, subject-heading bibliography of termites, 1350 BC to AD 1954. Smithson. Inst. Misc. Collect. 130(4258):1–305.

Snyder, T. E.
    1961. Supplement to the annotated, subject-heading bibliography of termites 1955 to 1960. Smithson. Misc. Collect. 143(3):1–137.

Snyder, T. E.
    1966. Control of nonsubterranean termites. U.S. Dep. Agric., Farmers' Bull. 2018, 16 p.

Søegaard, Bent.
    1964. Breeding for resistance to insect attack in forest trees. Unasylva 18(2–3):82–88.

Solomon, J. D., and C. J. Hay.

   1974. Annotated bibliography of the carpenterworm, *Prionoxystus robiniae*. USDA For. Serv. Gen. Tech. Rep. SO–14, 13 p. South. For. Exp. Stn., New Orleans, La.

Sommerman, K. M., R. I. Sailer, and C. O. Esselbaugh.

   1955. Biology of Alaskan black flies (Simuliidae, Diptera). Ecol. Monogr. 25(4):345–385.

Spencer, Kenneth A.

   1969. The Agromyzidae of Canada and Alaska. Entomol. Soc. Can. Mem. 64, 311 p.

Stage, H. H., C. M. Gjullin, and W. W. Yates.

   1952. Mosquitoes of the Northwestern States. U.S. Dep. Agric., Agric. Handb. 46, 95 p.

Stairs, G. R.

   1966. Transmission of virus in tent caterpillar populations. Can. Entomol. 98(10):1100–1104.

Stairs, Gordon R.

   1972. Pathogenic microorganisms in the regulation of forest insect populations. Annu. Rev. Entomol. 17:355–372.

Stannard, L. J., Jr.

   1949. The nearctic species of the genus *Periclista* (Hymenoptera: Tenthredinidae). Am. Entomol. Soc. Trans. 75:7–42 + plates.

Stark, R. W.

   1954. Distribution and life history of the lodgepole needle miner (*Recurvaria* sp.) in Canadian Rocky Mountain parks. Can. Entomol. 86(1):1–12.

Stark, R. W.

   1959. Population dynamics of the lodgepole needle miner, *Recurvaria starki* Freeman, in Canadian Rocky Mountain parks. Can. J. Zool. 37(6):917–943.

Stark, R. W.

   1961. Notes on the parasite complex of *Evagora* (*Recurvaria*) *starki* Freeman in Canadian Rocky Mountain Parks. Can. J. Zool. 39(6):893–904.

Stark, R. W., and J. H. Borden.

   1965. Life history of *Choristoneura lambertiana subretiana* Obraztsov (Lepidoptera: Tortricidae) attacking lodgepole pine. Can. Entomol. 97(7):684–690.

Stark, R. W., and D. L. Dahlsten, editors.

   1970. Studies on the population dynamics of the western pine beetle, *Dendroctonus brevicomis* LeConte (Coleoptera: Scolytidae). Univ. Calif. Div. Agric. Sci. Publ., 174 p. Berkeley.

Stark, R. W., and C. S. Koehler.

   1964. Biology of the gall wasp, *Eurytoma tumoris*, on Scots pine (Hymenoptera: Eurytomidae). Pan-Pac. Entomol. 40(1): 41–46.

Stark, R. W., P. R. Miller, F. W. Cobb, Jr., and others.
1968. Photochemical oxidant injury and bark beetle (Coleoptera: Scolytidae) infestation of ponderosa pine. 1. Incidence of bark beetle infestation in injured trees. Hilgardia 39(6): 121–126.

Stark, R. W., and D. L. Wood.
1964. The biology of *Pissodes terminalis* Hopping (Coleoptera: Curculionidae) in California. Can. Entomol. 96(9):1208–1218.

Stehr, Frederick W., and Edwin F. Cook.
1968. A revision of the genus *Malacosoma* Hübner in North America (Lepidoptera: Lasiocampidae): Systematics, biology, immatures, and parasites. U.S. Natl. Mus. Bull. 276, 321 p.

Stein, John D., and Patrick C. Kennedy.
1972. Key to shelterbelt insects in the Northern Great Plains. USDA For. Serv. Res. Pap. RM–85, 153 p. Rocky Mt. For. and Range Exp. Stn., Fort Collins, Colo.

Stein, W. I.
1963. *Pleocoma* larvae, root feeders in western forests. Northwest Sci. 37(4):126–143.

Steinhaus, Edward A.
1947. Insect microbiology. 763 p. Comstock Publ. Co., Ithaca, N.Y.

Steinhaus, Edward A.
1963a. Background for the diagnosis of insect diseases. *In* Insect pathology, an advanced treatise, vol. 2. p. 549–589. Edward A. Steinhaus, ed. Academic Press, New York and London.

Steinhaus, Edward A.
1963b. Insect pathology, an advanced treatise. vol. 1. 661 p. Academic Press, New York and London.

Steinhaus, Edward A.
1963c. Insect pathology, an advanced treatise. vol. 2. 689 p. Academic Press, New York and London.

Stelzer, Milton J.
1968. The Great Basin tent caterpillar in New Mexico: life history, parasites, disease, and defoliation. USDA For. Serv. Res. Pap. RM–39, 16 p. Rocky Mt. For. and Range Exp. Stn., Fort Collins, Colo.

Stelzer, Milton J.
1971. Western tent caterpillar. U.S. Dep. Agric., For. Pest Leafl. 119, 5 p.

Stelzer, Milton J., John Neisess, and C. G. Thompson.
1975. Aerial applications of a nucleopolyhedrosis virus and *Bacillus thuringiensis* against the Douglas-fir tussock moth. J. Econ. Entomol. 68(2):269–272.

Stevens, R. E.
1956. Fir engraver beetle. U.S. Dep. Agric., For. Pest Leafl. 13, 7 p.

Stevens, R. E.
1959. Biology and control of the pine needlesheath miner, *Zelleria haimbachi* Busck (Lepidoptera: Hyponomeutidae). USDA For. Serv. Pac. Southwest For. and Range Exp. Stn. Tech. Pap. 30, 20 p. Berkeley, Calif.

Stevens, R. E.
1965. Pine reproduction weevil. U.S. Dep. Agric., For. Pest Leafl. 15, 6 p.

Stevens, R. E.
1966. The ponderosa pine tip moth, *Rhyacionia zozana*, in California (Lepidoptera: Olethreutidae). Ann. Entomol. Soc. Am. 59(1):186–192.

Stevens, R. E.
1969. Occurrence of *Exoteleia burkei* in the Sierra Nevada (Lepidoptera: Gelechiidae). Pan-Pac. Entomol. 45(3):238.

Stevens, R. E.
1971. Ponderosa pine tip moth. U.S. Dep. Agric. For. Pest Leafl. 103, 5 p.

Stevens, Robert E., and Harold W. Flake.
1974. A roundheaded pine beetle outbreak in New Mexico. USDA For. Serv. Res. Note RM–259, 4 p. Rocky Mt. For. and Range Exp. Stn., Fort Collins, Colo.

Stevens, Robert E., and Ronald W. Stark.
1962. Sequential sampling of the lodgepole needle miner, *Evagora milleri*. J. Econ. Entomol. 55(4):491–494.

Stevenson, R. E.
1967. Notes on the biology of the Engelmann spruce weevil, *Pissodes engelmanni* (Curculionidae: Coleoptera) and its parasites and predators. Can. Entomol. 99(2):201–213.

Stewart, K. W.
1965. Observations on the life history and habits of *Scierus annectens* (Coleoptera: Scolytidae). Ann. Entomol. Soc. Am. 58(6):924–927.

Stone, Alan.
1938. The horseflies of the subfamily Tabaninae of the Nearctic Region. U.S. Dep. Agric., Misc. Publ. 305, 172 p.

Stone, Alan, Curtis W. Sabrosky, Willis W. Wirth, and others.
1965. A catalog of the Diptera of America north of Mexico. U.S. Dep. Agric., Agric. Handb. 276, 1696 p.

Stoszek, Karel J.
   1973. Damage to ponderosa pine plantations by the western pine-shoot borer. J. For. 71 (11) :701–705.
Struble, G. R.
   1930. The biology of certain Coleoptera associated with bark beetles in western yellow pine. Univ. Calif. Publ. Entomol. 5(6) :105–134.
Struble, G. R.
   1942a. Biology of two native coleopterous predators of the mountain pine beetle in sugar pine. Pan-Pac. Entomol. 18(3) : 97–107.
Struble, G. R.
   1942b. Laboratory propagation of two predators of the mountain pine beetle. J. Econ. Entomol. 35(6)841–844.
Struble, G. R.
   1957a. Biology and control of the white-fir sawfly. For. Sci. 3(4) :306–313.
Struble, G. R.
   1957b. The fir engraver, a serious enemy of western true firs. USDA For. Serv. Prod. Res. Rep. 11, 18 p.
Struble, G. R.
   1961. Monterey pine ips. U.S. Dep. Agric., For. Pest Leafl. 56, 8 p.
Struble, G. R.
   1966. California five-spined ips. U.S. Dep. Agric., For. Pest Leafl. 102, 4 p.
Struble, G. R.
   1968. Infestations and biology of the white-fir needle miner in California red fir. J. Econ. Entomol. 61(4) :1093–1097.
Struble, G. R.
   1972. Biology, ecology, and control of the lodgepole needle miner. U.S. Dep. Agric., Tech. Bull. 1458, 38 p.
Struble, G. R., and R. C. Hall.
   1954. Telephone cables invaded by shrub bark beetle in Pacific coastal region. J. Econ. Entomol. 47(5) :933–934.
Struble, G. R., and R. C. Hall.
   1955. The California five-spined engraver, its biology and control. U.S. Dep. Agric., Circ. 964, 21 p.
Struble, George R., and Philip C. Johnson.
   1964. Black pine-leaf scale. U.S. Dep. Agric., For. Pest Leafl. 91, 6 p.
Sugden, B. A.
   1964. Annotated list of forest insects of British Columbia. Part 12, Boarmiini and Melanolophiini (Geometridae). Entomol. Soc. B.C. Proc. 61:36–39.

Sugden, B. A.
    1966. Annotated list of forest insects of British Columbia, Part 13, Brephinae, Geometrinae, Sterrhinae, and Larentiinae (Geometridae). J. Entomol. Soc. B.C. 63:4–10.
Sugden, B. A.
    1968. Annotated list of forest insects of British Columbia. Part 14, Ennominae (Geometridae). J. Entomol. Soc. B.C. 65: 24–33.
Sugden, B. A.
    1970. Annotated list of forest insects of British Columbia. Part 14, *Polygonia, Nymphalis*, and *Limenitis* (Nymphalidae). J. Entomol. Soc. B.C. 67:30–31.
Sugden, B. A., and D. A. Ross.
    1963. Annotated list of forest insects of British Columbia. Part 11, *Papilio* spp. (Papilionidae). Entomol. Soc. B.C. Proc. 60: 17–18.
Swaine, J. M.
    1918. Canadian bark beetles. Part 2. A preliminary classification, with an account of the habits and means of control. Can. Dep. Agric. Tech. Bull. 14, 143 p.
Swaine, J. M., and Ralph Hopping.
    1928. The Lepturini of America north of Mexico, Part 1. Can. Dep. Mines. Natl. Mus. Can. Bull. 52, Biol. Ser. No. 14, 95 p.
Sweetman, Harvey L.
    1958. The principles of biological control. 560 p. W. C. Brown Co., Dubuque, Iowa.

Telford, Allan D.
    1961. Lodgepole needle miner parasites: biological control and insecticides. J. Econ. Entomol. 54(2):347–355.
Thomas, G. M., and K. H. Wright.
    1961. Silver fir beetles. U.S. Dep. Agric., For. Pest Leafl. 60, 7 p.
Thomas, J. B.
    1965. The immature stages of Scolytidae: the genus *Dendroctonus* Erichson. Can. Entomol. 97(4):374–400.
Thompson, R. M., and G. M. Buxton.
    1964. An index of the Acridoidea (Orthoptera) of California, with selected references. Calif. Dep. Agric., Bur. Entomol., Occas. Pap. 5, 62 p.
Thompson, W. R.
    1943. A catalogue of the parasites and predators of insect pests. Sect. 1, Part 1. 151 p. Commonw. Agric. Bur., London.
Tinker, Milton E.
    1952. The seasonal behavior and ecology of the boxelder bug *Leptocoris trivittatus* in Minnesota. Ecology 33(3):407–414.

557

Tonks, N. V.
1974. Occurrence of a midge, *Oligotrophus betheli* Felt, on juniper on Vancouver Island, British Columbia (Diptera: Cecidomyiidae). J. Entomol. Soc. B.C. 71:33–34.

Torre-Bueno, J. R. de la.
1939. A synopsis of the Hemiptera-Heteroptera of America north of Mexico. Part 1. Families Scutelleridae, Cydnidae, Pentatomidae, Aradidae, Drysodiidae, Termitaphididae. Entomol. Am. 19(3):141–206.

Torre-Bueno, J. R. de la.
1940. Additions and corrections to "A synopsis of the Hemiptera-Heteroptera of America north of Mexico." Brooklyn Entomol. Soc. Bull. 35(2):51–53.

Torre-Bueno, J. R. de la.
1941. A synopsis of the Hemiptera-Heteroptera of America north of Mexico. Part 2. Families Coreidae, Alydidae, Corizidae, Neididae, Pyrrhocoridae, and Thaumastotheriidae. Entomol. Am. 21(2):41–122.

Torre-Bueno, J. R. de la.
1946. A synopsis of the Hemiptera-Heteroptera of America north of Mexico. Part 3. Family Lygaeidae. Entomol. Am. 26(1):1–40; 26(2):41–88; 26(3):89–141.

Toschi, Catherine A.
1965. The taxonomy, life histories, and mating behavior of the green lacewings of Strawberry Canyon (Neuroptera: Chrysopidae). Hilgardia 36(11):391–433.

Townes, Henry.
1950. The nearctic species of Gasteruptiidae (Hymenoptera). U.S. Natl. Mus. Proc. 100(3259):85–145.

Townes, Henry, and Marjorie Townes.
1960. Ichneumon-flies of America north of Mexico: subfamilies Ephialtinae, Xoridinae, Acaenitinae. U.S. Natl. Mus. Bull. 216, Part 2, 676 p.

Townes, Henry K., Jr.
1944–45. A catalogue and reclassification of the nearctic Ichneumonidae (Hymenoptera). Part 1. The subfamilies Ichneumoninae, Tryphoninae, Cryptinae, Phaeogeninae and Lissonotinae. Am. Entomol. Soc. Mem. 11, Part 1, 477 p. 1944. Part 2. The subfamilies Mesoleiinae, Plectiscinae, Orthocentrinae, Diplazoninae, Metopiinae, Ophioninae, Mesochorinae. Am. Entomol. Soc. Mem. 11, Part 2, 925 p. 1945.

Trimble, F. M.
1924. Life history and habits of two Pacific coast bark beetles. Ann. Entomol. Soc. Am. 17(4):382–391.

Tunnock, S., R. E. Denton, C. E. Carlson, and W. W. Janssen.
  1969. Larch casebearer and other factors involved with deterioration of western larch stands in northern Idaho. USDA For. Serv. Res. Pap. INT–68, 10 p. Intermt. For. and Range Exp. Stn., Ogden, Utah.
Tunnock, Scott
  1966. Northern Rocky Mountains. *In* Forest insect conditions in the United States—1965, p. 19–25. U.S. Dep. Agric., Washington, D.C.
Tunnock, Scott.
  1967. Northern Rocky Mountains. *In* Forest insect conditions in the United States—1966, p. 21–23. U.S. Dep. Agric. Washington, D. C.
Turnbull, A. L., and D. A. Chant.
  1961. The practice and theory of biological control of insects in Canada. Can. J. Zool. 39(5):697–753.
Turner, George T., and David F. Costello.
  1942. Ecological aspects of the pricklypear problem in eastern Colorado and Wyoming. Ecology 23(4):419–426.
Turner, R. D.
  1966. A survey and illustrated catalogue of the Teredinidae (Mollusca: Bivalvia). 265 p. Mus. Comp. Zool.. Harvard Univ., Cambridge, Mass.
Turnock, W. J.
  1953. Some aspects of the life history and ecology of the pitch nodule maker, *Petrova albicapitana* (Busck) (Lepidoptera: Olethreutidae). Can. Entomol. 85(7):233–243.
Turnock, W. J.
  1972. Geographical and historical variability in population patterns and life systems of the larch sawfly (Hymenoptera: Tenthredinidae). Can. Entomol. 104(12): 1883–1900.
Tuthill, Leonard D.
  1943. The *Psyllids* of America, North of Mexico (Psyllidae: Homoptera). Iowa State Coll. J. Sci. 17(4):443–660.
Tuthill, Donald M., and Edward W. Baker.
  1968. Spider mites of Southwestern United States and a revision of the family Tetranychidae. 143 p. Univ. Ariz. Press, Tucson.
Tyson, W. H.
  1970. Cerambycidae of the Panamint Mountains, California (Coleoptera). Pan-Pac. Entomol. 46(4):296–299.

U.S. Department of Agriculture.
  1960. The elm leaf beetle. U.S. Dep. Agric., Leafl. 184, 4 p.
U.S. Department of Agriculture.
  1972. Guidelines for the use of insecticides to control insects affecting crops, livestock, households, stored products, forests,

and forest products. U.S. Dep. Agric., Agric. Handb. 452, 296 p.

U.S. Department of Agriculture, Agricultural Research Service.
1966a. Black grass bug observations in Utah. Coop. Econ. Insect Rep. 16 (25) : 596.

U.S. Department of Agriculture, Agricultural Research Service.
1966b. Wheatgrass bugs (*Labops* spp.). Coop. Econ. Insect Rep. 16 (26) :623–624.

U.S. Department of Agriculture, Bureau of Entomology.
1927. The relation of insects to slash disposal. Dep. Circ. 411, 12 p.

U.S. Department of Agriculture, Forest Service.
1954. Powderpost beetles in buildings, what to do about them. U.S. Dep. Agric., Leafl. 358, 8 p.

U.S. Department of Agriculture, Forest Service.
1958. Timber resources for America's future. For. Resour. Rep. No. 14, 713 p.

U.S. Department of Agriculture, Forest Service.
1967. Forest pest conditions in California—1966. 21 p. Calif. For. Pest Action Counc. Sacramento.

Usinger, R. L.
1945. Biology and control of ash plant bugs in California. J. Econ. Entomol. 38 (5) :585–591.

Usinger, R. L.
1946. Biology and control of the ash lace bug, *Leptoypha minor*. J. Econ. Entomol. 39 (3) :286–289.

Usinger, R. L., W. C. Bentinck, H. G. Chandler, and others.
1963. Aquatic insects of California. 508 p. Univ. Calif. Press, Berkeley and Los Angeles.

Uvarov, B. P.
1931. Insects and climate. Trans. Entomol. Soc. London 79 :1–247.

van den Bosch, R., and V. M. Stern.
1962. The integration of chemical and biological control of arthropod pests. Annu. Rev. Entomol. 7 :367–386.

Van Duzee, Edward P.
1917. Catalogue of the Hemiptera of America north of Mexico excepting the Aphididae, Coccidae and Aleurodidae. Univ. Calif. Publ. Entomol. Tech. Bull. 2 :1–902.

Van Dyke, E. C.
1915. The species of *Cossonus* Clairv. (Coleoptera) of America north of Mexico. Bull. Brooklyn Entomol. Soc. 10 (1) :1–23.

Van Dyke, E. C.
1933. A short review of *Dyslobus* LeConte, a genus of broad-

nosed weevils of the subfamily Otiorhynchinae with descriptions of new species. Pan-Pac. Entomol. 9(1) :31–47.

Van Dyke, E. C.
1936. New species of North American weevils in the family Curculionidae, subfamily Brachyrhininae, 4. Pan-Pac. Entomol. 12(1) :19–32.

Van Haverbeke, David F., Robert E. Roselle, and Gary D. Sexson.
1971. Western pine tip moth reduced in ponderosa pine shelterbelts by systemic insecticides. USDA For. Serv. Res. Note RM–194, 7 p. Rocky Mt. For. and Range Exp. Stn., Fort Collins, Colo.

Vaurie, P.
1958. A revision of the genus *Diplotaxis* (Coleoptera: Scarabaeidae, Melolonthinae). Part 1. Am. Mus. Natl. Hist. Bull. 115(5) :267–396.

Vaurie, P.
1960. A revision of the genus *Diplotaxis* (Coleoptera: Scarabaeidae, Melolonthinae). Part 2. Am. Mus. Natl. Hist. Bull. 120(2) :167–433.

Vaux, H. J.
1954. Some implications of the spruce beetle control and salvage programs in Colorado. J. For. 52(7) :506–510.

Vité, J. P.
1970. Pest management systems using synthetic pheromones. Contrib. Boyce Thompson Inst. 24(13) :343–350.

Vockeroth, J. R.
1960. Taxonomy of the genus *Cecidomyia* (Diptera: Cecidomyiidae) with special reference to the species occurring on *Pinus banksiana* Lamb. Can. Entomol. 92(1) :65–79.

Wagener, Willis W.
1939. The canker of *Cupressus* induced by *Coryneum cardinale* n. sp. J. Agric. Res. 58(1) :1–46.

Wagener, Willis W.
1963. Judging hazard from native trees in California recreational areas—a guide for professional foresters. USDA For. Serv. Res. Pap. PSW–1, 29 p. Pac. Southwest For. and Range Exp. Stn., Berkeley, Calif.

Wakeland, C.
1959. Mormon crickets in North America. U.S. Dep. Agric., Tech. Bull. 1202, 77 p.

Walker, Thomas J.
1962. The taxonomy and calling songs of United States tree crickets (Orthoptera: Gryllidae: Oecanthinae). 1. The genus *Neoxabea* and the *niveus* and *varicornis* groups of the genus *Oecanthus*. Ann. Entomol. Soc. Am. 55(3) :303–322.

Walley, G. Stuart.
  1928. The genus *Aphrophora* in America north of Mexico (Cercopidae, Hemipt.). Can. Entomol. 60(8):184–192.
Walters, J.
  1956. Biology and control of the Douglas-fir beetle in the interior of British Columbia. Can. Dep. Agric. Publ. 975, 11 p.
Walters, J., and L. H. McMullen.
  1956. Life history and habits of *Pseudohylesinus nebulosus* (LeConte) (Coleoptera: Scolytidae) in the interior of British Columbia. Can. Entomol. 88(5):197–202.
Warner, Rose Ella.
  1966. A review of the *Hylobius* of North America, with a new species injurious to slash pine (Coleoptera: Curculionidae). Coleopt. Bull. 20(3):65–81.
Warren, L. O., and M. Tadic.
  1970. The fall webworm, *Hyphantria cunea* (Drury). Arkansas Agric. Exp. Stn. Bull. 759, 106 p. Univ. Arkansas, Fayetteville.
Washburn, R. I.
  1965. Description and bionomics of a new species of *Puto* from Utah (Homoptera: Coccoidea: Pseudococcidae). Ann. Entomol. Soc. Am. 58(3):293–297.
Washburn, Richard I., and Mark D. McGregor.
  1974. White fir needle miner. U.S. Dep. Agric., For. Pest Leafl. 144, 5 p.
Washington State University.
  1971. Chemical insect control handbook. 329 p. Coop. Ext. Serv., Coll. Agric., Wash. State Univ., Pullman.
Wear, J. F., R. B. Pope, and P. W. Orr.
  1966. Aerial photographic techniques for estimating damage by insects in western forests. USDA For. Serv., Pac. Northwest For. and Range Exp. Stn., 79 p. Portland, Oreg.
Weaver, Harold.
  1961. Ecological changes in the ponderosa pine forest of Cedar Valley in southern Washington. Ecology 42:416–420.
Weaver, Harold.
  1967. Fire as a continuing ecological factor in perpetuation of ponderosa pine forests in Western United States. Adv. Front. Plant Sci. 18:137–153.
Webber, Ray T.
  1941. Synopsis of the tachinid flies of the genus *Tachinomyia*, with descriptions of new species. U.S. Natl. Mus. Proc. 90(3108):287–304.
Weesner, F. M.
  1965. The termites of the United States, a handbook. Natl. Pest Control Assoc., 67 p.

Weidman, R. H., and G. T. Robbins.
  1947. Attacks of pitch moth and turpentine beetle on pines in the Eddy Arboretum. J. For. 45(6):428–433.
Weigel, C. A., and L. G. Baumhofer.
  1948. Handbook on insect enemies of flowers and shrubs. U.S. Dep. Agric., Misc. Publ. 626, 115 p.
Weiser, Jaroslav, and John D. Briggs.
  1971. Identification of pathogens. *In* Microbial control of insects and mites. Chapter 2, p. 13–66. H. D. Burges and N. W. Hussey, eds. Academic Press, London and New York.
Weld, Lewis H.
  1952. Cynipoidea (Hym.) 1905–1950, a supplement to the Dalla Torre and Kieffer monograph—the Cynipidae in Das Tierreich, Lieferung 24, 1910. 351 p. Privately printed, Ann Arbor, Mich.
Weld, Lewis H.
  1957. Cynipid galls of the Pacific slope (Hymenoptera, Cynipoidea): an aid to their identification. 64 p. + plates. (For sale by: Robert J. Lyon, Los Angeles City College, 855 North Vermont Ave., Los Angeles, Calif. 90029, or by the author 6613 North Washington Blvd., Arlington, VA. 22205.)
Wellington, W. G.
  1954. Weather and climate in forest entomology. Meteorol. Monogr. 2(8):11–18.
Wene, G. P.
  1968. Biology of the elm leaf beetle in southern Arizona. J. Econ. Entomol. 61(5):1178–1180.
West, A. S., Jr.
  1947. The California flatheaded borer (*Melanophila californica* Van Dyke) in ponderosa pine stands of northeastern California. Can. J. Res. D, 25:97–118.
Wester, Horace V., and R. A. St. George.
  1947. Life history and control of the webworm, *Homadaula albizziae*. J. Econ. Entomol. 40(4):546–553.
Wheeler, George C., and Jeanette Wheeler.
  1963. The ants of North Dakota. 326 p. Univ. North Dakota Press, Grand Forks.
Wheeler, William Morton.
  1926. Ants, their structure, development and behavior. 663 p. Columbia Univ. Press, New York.
White, R. E.
  1962. A new *Xyletinus*, with a key to the North American species (Coleoptera: Anobiidae). Ann. Entomol. Soc. Am. 55(2):251–253.
White, R. E.
  1965. A revision of the genus *Tricorynus* of North America

(Coleoptera: Anobiidae). Entomol. Soc. Am. Misc. Publ. 4(7) : 283–368.

White, R. E.
1966. Six new Anobiidae from North America with keys. Entomol. Soc. Wash. Proc. 68(3) :228–236.

White, R. E.
1971. Key to North American genera of Anobiidae, with phylogenetic and synonymic notes (Coleoptera). Ann. Entomol. Soc. Am. 64(1) :179–191.

Whiteside, J. M.
1958. Spruce budworm control in Oregon and Washington, 1949–1956. 10th Int. Congr. Entomol. Proc., Montreal, Aug. 17–25, 1956, 4:291–302.

Wickman, Boyd E.
1964a. Freshly scorched pines attract large numbers of *Arhopalus asperatus* adults (Coleoptera: Cerambycidae). Pan-Pac. Entomol. 40(1) :59–60.

Wickman, Boyd E.
1964b. Observations on the siricid parasite *Ibalia ensiger* (Hymenoptera: Ibalidae). Pan-Pac. Entomol. 40(1) :19–20.

Wickman, Boyd E.
1965. Insect-caused deterioration of windthrown timber in northern California, 1963–64. USDA For. Serv. Res. Pap. PSW–20, 14 p. Pac. Southwest For. and Range Exp. Stn., Berkeley, Calif.

Wickman, Boyd E.
1967. Life history of the incense-cedar wood wasp. *Syntexis libocedrii* (Hymenoptera: Syntexidae). Ann. Entomol. Soc. Am. 60(6) :1291–1295.

Wickman, Boyd E.
1968. Fir tree borer. U.S. Dep. Agric., For. Pest Leafl. 115, 6 p.

Wickman, Boyd E.
1971. California oakworm. U.S. Dep. Agric., For. Pest Leafl. 72, 4 p.

Wickman, Boyd E., and Richard H. Hunt.
1969. Biology of the phantom hemlock looper on Douglas-fir in California. J. Econ. Entomol. 62(5) :1046–1050.

Wickman, Boyd E., Richard R. Mason, and C. G. Thompson.
1973a. Major outbreaks of the Douglas-fir tussock moth in Oregon and California. USDA For. Serv. Gen. Tech. Rep. PNW–5, 18 p. Pac. Northwest For. and Range Exp. Stn., Portland, Oreg.

Wickman, Boyd E., and Serje G. Seminoff.
1968. Notes on the biology of *Eucrossus villicornis* LeConte (Coleoptera: Cerambycidae). Pan-Pac. Entomol. 44(4) :321–324.

Wickman, Boyd E., Galen G. Trostle, and Paul E. Buffam.
1973b. Douglas-fir tussock moth. U.S. Dep. Agric., For. Pest Leafl. 86, 6 p.

Wilcox, J., D. C. Mote, and L. Childs.
1934. The root-weevils injurious to strawberries in Oregon. Oreg. State Agric. Coll., Agric. Exp. Stn. Bull. 330, 109 p.

Wilcox, John A.
1965. A synopsis of the North American Galerucinae (Coleoptera: Chrysomelidae). N. Y. State Mus. and Sci. Serv. Bull. 400, 226 p.

Wilcox, John A.
1972. A review of the North American Chrysomeline leaf beetles (Coleoptera: Chrysomelidae). N.Y. State Mus. and Sci. Serv. Bull. 421, 37 p.

Wilkes, A., H. C. Coppel, and W. G. Mathers.
1948. Notes on the insect parasites of the spruce budworm *Choristoneura fumiferana* (Clem.) in British Columbia. Can. Entomol. 80(1–12):138–155.

Willard, J. R., and H. H. Crowell.
1965. Biological activities of the harvester ant, *Pogonomyrmex owyheei*, in central Oregon. J. Econ. Entomol. 58(3):484–489.

Williamson, D. L., J. A. Schenk, and W. F. Barr.
1966. The biology of *Conophthorus monticolae* in northern Idaho. For. Sci. 12(2):234–240.

Wilson, E. O.
1955. A monographic revision of the ant genus *Lasius*. Bull. Mus. Comp. Zool. 113:1–205. Harvard Coll., Cambridge, Mass.

Wilson, Louis F.
1962. Forest insects and diseases in the Northern Great Plains. USDA For. Serv. Stn. Pap. 101, 28 p. Lake States For. Exp. Stn., St. Paul, Minn.

Wilson, Louis F.
1964. Walkingstick. U.S. Dep. Agric., For. Pest Leafl. 82, 4 p.

Wilson, Louis F.
1971a. Pine tortoise scale. U.S. Dep. Agric., For. Pest Leafl. 57, 7 p.

Wilson, Louis F.
1971b. Variable oak leaf caterpillar. U.S. Dep. Agric., For. Pest Leafl. 67, 4 p.

Wilson, Louis F.
1971c. Yellow-headed spruce sawfly. U.S. Dep. Agric., For. Pest Leafl. 69, 4 p.

Wilson, Louis F.
1975. White-spotted sawyer. U.S. Dep. Agric., For. Pest Leafl. 74, 8 p.

Wirth, W. W.
  1952. The Heleidae of California. Univ. Calif. Publ. Entomol.
    9(2):95–266.
Woglum, R. S., and E. A. McGregor.
  1959. Observations on the life history and morphology of *Agulla
    astuta* (Banks) (Neuroptera: Raphidiodea: Raphidiidae).
    Ann. Entomol. Soc. Am. 52(5):489–502.
Wollerman, E. H.
  1970. The locust borer. U.S. Dep. Agric., For. Pest Leafl. 71, 8 p.
Wollerman, E. H.
  1971a. Bagworm. U.S. Dep. Agric., For. Pest Leafl. 97, 7 p.
Wollerman, E. H.
  1971b. The boxelder bug. U.S. Dep. Agric., For. Pest Leafl. 95,
    6 p.
Wong, H. R.
  1951. Cocoons of some sawflies that defoliate forest trees in
    Manitoba and Saskatchewan. 82d Annu. Rep. Entomol. Soc.
    Ont., p 61–67.
Wong, H. R.
  1954. Common sawflies feeding on white birch in the forested
    areas of Manitoba and Saskatchewan. Can. Entomol. 86(4):
    154–158.
Wong, H. R.
  1955. Larvae of the nearctic species of *Anoplonyx* (Tenthredi-
    nidae, Hymenoptera). Can. Entomol. 87(5):224–227.
Wong, H. R.
  1960. Preliminary notes on the life history of *Herculia thy-
    metusalis* Wlk. Can. Dep. Agric., For. Biol. Div., Bimon.
    Prog. Rep. 16(1):3.
Wong, H. R.
  1972. The spread of the European spruce sawfly, *Diprion her-
    cyniae* (Hymenoptera: Diprionidae), in Manitoba. Can. En-
    tomol. 104(5):755–756.
Wong, H. R.
  1974. The identification and origin of the strains of the larch
    sawfly, *Pristiphora erichsonii* (Hymenoptera: Tenthredini-
    dae), in North America. Can Entomol. 106(11):1121–1131.
Wong, H. R., and J. C. E. Melvin.
  1967. The leaf roller, *Pseudexentera oregonana* Wlshm. Can.
    Dep. For. and Rural Dev., Bimon. Res. Notes 23(1):3–4.
Wood, D. L., and R. W. Stark.
  1968. The life history of *Ips calligraphus* (Coleoptera: Scolyti-
    dae) with notes on its biology in California. Can. Entomol.
    100(2):145–151.

Wood, G. W., and W. T. A. Neilson.
1956. Notes on the black army cutworm. *Actebia fennica* (Tausch.) (Lepidoptera: Phalaenidae), a pest of low-bush blueberry in New Brunswick. Can. Entomol. 88(3):93–96.

Wood, Stephen L.
1954a. A revision of North American Cryphalini (Scolytidae, Coleoptera). Univ. Kans. Sci. Bull. 36(2):959–1089.

Wood, Stephen L.
1954b. Bark beetles of the genus *Carphoborus* Eichhoff (Coleoptera: Scolytidae) in North America. Can. Entomol. 86(11): 502–526.

Wood, Stephen L.
1957. Ambrosia beetles of the tribe Xyloterini (Coleoptera: Scolytidae) in North America. Can. Entomol. 89(8):337–354.

Wood, Stephen L.
1958a. Bark beetles of the genus *Pityoborus* Blackman (Coleoptera: Scolytidae). Great Basin Nat. 18(2):46–56.

Wood, Stephen L.
1958b. Some virtually unknown North American Platypodidae (Coleoptera). Great Basin Nat. 18(1):37–40.

Wood, Stephen L.
1959. New records and species of Arizona bark beetles (Coleoptera: Scolytidae). Great Basin Nat. 19(2,3):57–62.

Wood, Stephen L.
1961. A key to the North American genera of Scolytidae. Coleopt. Bull. 15(2):41–48.

Wood, Stephen L.
1963. A revision of the bark beetle genus *Dendroctonus* Erichson (Coleoptera: Scolytidae). Great Basin Nat. 23(1–2):1–117.

Wood, Stephen L.
1966. New synonomy in the Platypodidae and Scolytidae (Coleoptera). Great Basin Nat. 26(1–2):17–33.

Wood, Stephen L.
1971a. New species of bark beetles (Scolytidae: Coleoptera) from western North America. Great Basin Nat. 31(2):69–76.

Wood, Stephen L.
1971b. New synonomy in American bark beetles (Scolytidae: Coleoptera). Great Basin Nat. 31(3):140–152.

Wood, Stephen L.
1971c. Family Scolytidae (Ipidae). *In* The beetles of the Pacific Northwest, Part 5. p. 395–428. Melvin H. Hatch. Univ. Press, Seattle and London.

Wood, Stephen L.
1973. On the taxonomic status of Platypodidae and Scolytidae (Coleoptera). Great Basin Nat. 33(2):77–90.

Woodring, J. P.
    1966. North American Tyroglyphidae (Acari): 1. New species
    of *Calvolia* and *Nanacarus* with keys to the species. La. Acad.
    Sci. Proc. 29: 76–84.

Woodring, J. P., and J. C. Moser.
    1970. Six new species of anoetid mites associated with North
    American Scolytidae. Can. Entomol. 102:1237–1257.

Wright, E., W. K. Coulter, and J. J. Gruenfeld.
    1956. Deterioration of beetle-killed Pacific silver fir. J. For.
    54(5):322–325.

Wright, K. H.
    1970. Sitka-spruce weevil. U.S. Dep. Agric., For. Pest Leafl. 47,
    6 p.

Wright, K. H., and G. M. Harvey.
    1967. The deterioration of beetle-killed Douglas-fir in western
    Oregon and Washington. USDA For. Serv. Res. Pap.
    PNW–50, 20 p. Pac. Northwest For. and Range Exp. Stn.,
    Portland, Oreg.

Wygant, N. D.
    1941. An infestation of the pandora moth, *Coloradia pandora*
    Blake, in lodgepole pine in Colorado. J. Econ. Entomol.
    34(5):697–702.

Wygant, N. D.
    1958. Engelmann spruce beetle control in Colorado. 10th Int.
    Congr. Entomol. Proc., Montreal, Aug. 17–25, 1956, 4:181–
    184.

Wygant, N. D., and A. L. Nelson.
    1949. Four billion feet of beetle-killed spruce. U.S. Dep. Agric.,
    Yearb. Agric. 1949, p. 417–422. Washington, D.C.

Wymore, F. H.
    1928. On *Dinapate wrighti* Horn. Pan-Pac. Entomol. 4(3):143.

Yuasa, Hachiro.
    1922. A classification of the larvae of the Tenthredinoidea. Ill.
    Biol. Monogr. 7(4):1–172.

Yuill, J. S.
    1941. Cold hardiness of two species of bark beetles in California
    forests. J. Econ. Entomol. 34(5):702–709.

Zak, B.
    1965. Aphids feeding on mycorrhizae of Douglas-fir. For. Sci.
    11(4):410–411.

Zethner-Moller, O., and J. A. Rudinsky.
    1967. On the biology of *Hylastes nigrinus* (Coleoptera: Scoly-
    tidae) in western Oregon. Can. Entomol. 99(9):897–911.

DIAGNOSTIC HOST INDEX

This index serves in lieu of keys to insects and their damage. It provides a means of narrowing the search for the identity of an insect observed on a particular host.

Primary arrangement of this index is alphabetical by scientific names of trees and shrubs according to Little (1953) supplemented by Kelsey and Dayton (1942); common names are cross-referenced to scientific names. Under a host species, the first grouping is according to part of plant infested. Under the part infested, insects are listed alphabetically by scientific name according to habit or type of insect.

The procedure in using this index thus involves the following steps: (1) Identifying the host tree or shrub, (2) determining the part or parts fed upon, (3) consulting the habit groups to see which one most closely describes the insect, and (4) referring to the text pages on which insects in the selected habit group are discussed in order to decide which description best fits the insect or sample of damage in hand.

Many insects infest more than one tree part. In some, the habit group changes with the tree part; in others it remains the same. With some boring or sucking insects, bark thickness may determine whether the bole or a branch is attacked. The Diagnostic Host Index attempts to cover most of this variation. Designation of plant parts on shrubby host species is as for trees, with bole indicating the stem, and the difference between twigs and branches versus large limbs based on relative size.

Many insects have similar habits and look very much alike. The taxonomic references in this manual will aid in distinguishing closely related species. For positive identification, one should submit specimens to experts.

571

Abies procera (noble fir)—Continued
Foliage, on
Aphid
Adelges nüsslini, 106
Twigs and small branches, on
Aphid
Adelges nüsslini, 106
Twigs and small branches, under bark
Moth, twig
Dioryctria abietivorella, 181
Trunk and large branches, on
Aphid
Adelges nüsslini, 106
Trunk and large branches, under bark
Beetles, bark
Pseudohylesinus dispar, 371
Pseudohylesinus nobilis, 372
Roots, on
Aphid
Prociphilus americanus, 101
Roots, under bark
Weevil, root-collar
Pissodes dubius, 332
Acacia (acacia):
Seeds
Beetles, seed
Bruchidae, 321
Twigs and small branches, in wood
Girdler, twig
Oncideres pustulata, 312
Trunk and large branches, under bark
Borer, flatheaded
Chrysobothris octocola, 260
Trunk and large branches, in wood
Beetle, powderpost
Scobicia declivis, 274
Borer, flatheaded
Chrysobothris octocola, 260
Acacia greggii (catclaw):
Foliage, on
Beetles, scarab
Diplotaxis spp., 247
Acer (maple):
Flowers
Sawflies
Xyela spp., 436
Seeds
Bugs, plant
Leptocoris rubrolineatus, 84
Leptocoris trivittatus, 83
Moths, seed
Holocera sp., 174
Proteoteras aesculana, 152
Foliage, on
Aphids
Drepanaphis acerifoliae, 96
Periphyllus americanus, 100
Periphyllus brevispinosus, 100
Periphyllus californiensis, 100
Periphyllus lyropictus, 100
Periphyllus testudinacea, 101

Acer (maple)—Continued
Foliage, on—Continued
Bugs, plant
Leptocoris rubrolineatus, 84
Leptocoris trivittatus, 83
Caterpillars
Acronicta americana, 231
Antheraea polyphemus, 192
Halisidota maculata, 218
Hemileuca eglanterina, 197
Hyalophora cecropia, 198
Hyalophora gloveri, 198
Orgyia antiqua, 223
Schizura concinna, 236
Leafhopper
Edwardsiana rosae, 93
Leaf skeletonizer
Schizura concinna, 236
Loopers
Alsophila pometaria, 199
Biston cognataria, 202
Erannis tiliaria, 204
Erannis vancouverensis, 204
Iridopsis emasculata, 205
Lambdina punctata, 208
Operophtera bruceata, 213
Operophtera occidentalis, 214
Sawfly
Cimbex americana, 439
Scales
Lecanium corni, 112
Pulvinaria innumerabilis, 113
Webworm
Hyphantria cunea, 219
Twigs and small branches, on
Scales
Lecanium corni, 112
Lepidosaphes ulmi, 116
Pulvinaria innumerabilis, 113
Quadraspidiotus perniciosus, 118
Twigs and small branches, under bark
Borers, flatheaded
Chrysobothris femorata, 260
Chrysobothris mali, 260
Twigs and small branches, in wood
Borer, roundheaded
Phymatodes vulneratus, 303
Trunk and large branches, on
Scale
Quadraspidiotus perniciosus, 118
Trunk and large branches, under bark
Borers, flatheaded
Agrilus politus, 255
Chrysobothris femorata, 260
Chrysobothris mali, 260
Trunk and large branches, in wood
Beetle, ambrosia
Xyleborus saxeseni, 413
Beetles, powderpost
Hemicoelus gibbicollis, 270
Melalgus confertus, 273

Betula occidentalis (water birch)—Con.
  Trunk and large branches, under bark
    Borer, flatheaded
      Agrilus anxius, 255
Birch (*Betula*)
Bitterbrush (*Purshia*)
Blueberry (*Vaccinium*)
Bracken (*Pteridium aquilinum*)
Bursera microphylla (elephant tree):
  Trunk and large branches, in bark
    Beetle, bark
      Cactopinus desertus, 375
  Trunk and large branches, under bark
    Beetle, bark
      Cactopinus desertus, 375

California-laurel (*Umbellularia
  californica*)
California Washington-palm
  (*Washingtonia filifera*)
Camellia (Camellia):
  Foliage, on
    Scale
      Pulvinaria floccifera, 113
  Twigs and small branches, on
    Scale
      Pulvinaria floccifera, 113
Cascara buckthorn (*Rhamnus
  purshiana*)
Castanopsis chrysophylla (golden
  chinkapin):
  Seeds
    Moth, seed
      Melissopus latiferreanus, 150
  Foliage, on
    Caterpillar
      Phryganidia californica, 220
    Mite, spider
      Oligonychus platani, 62
  Twigs and small branches, in wood
    Borer, roundheaded
      Phymatodes aenus, 303
Catclaw (*Acacia greggii*)
Ceanothus (Ceanothus)
  Foliage, on
    Beetle, scarab
      Serica anthracina, 252
    Caterpillars
      Hemileuca eglanterina, 197
      Hyalophora euryalus, 198
      Nymphalis californica, 238
    Caterpillar, tent
      Malacosoma californicum, 188
    Thrips
      Thrips madronii, 79
    Whitefly
      Trialeurodes vaporariorum, 110
  Trunk and large branches, in wood
    Borer, flatheaded
      Dicerca horni, 262

Cedar (*Cedrus, Chamaecyparis,
  Libocedrus, Thuja*)
Cedrus (cedar)
  Foliage, on
    Scale
      Chionaspis pinifoliae, 115
  Twigs and small branches, on
    Aphid
      Cinara curvipes, 96
Celtis (hackberry):
  Twigs and small branches, under bark
    Beetles, bark
      Chramesus spp., 346
Cercidium (paloverde):
  Seeds
    Beetles, seed
      Bruchidae, 321
  Foliage, on
    Caterpillar
      Hemileuca tricolor, 196
  Twigs and small branches, in wood
    Beetle, bark
      Hylocurus parkinsoniae, 382
  Trunk and large branches, under bark
    Beetle, bark
      Chaetophloeus fasciatus, 345
    Borer, flatheaded
      Chrysobothris octocola, 260
  Trunk and large branches, in wood
    Borer, flatheaded
      Chrysobothris octocola, 260
Cercocarpus (cercocarpus, mountain-
  mahogany):
  Foliage, on
    Caterpillar, tent
      Malacosoma californicum, 188
    Leafroller
      Ethmia discostrigella, 175
    Looper
      *Anacamptodes clivinaria
        profanata*, 200
  Trunk and large branches, under bark
    Beetle, bark
      Chaetophloeus heterodoxus, 345
  Trunk and large branches, in wood
    Borers, flatheaded
      Dicerca horni, 262
      Polycesta californica, 265
Cereus giganteus (saguaro):
  Trunk and large branches, under bark
    Beetle, bark
      Cactopinus hubbardi, 375
Chamaecyparis (white-cedar):
  Cones and seeds
    Scale
      Carulaspis juniperi, 115
  Foliage, on
    Leaftier
      Herculia phoezalis, 185
    Mealybug
      Pseudococcus obscurus, 125

587

589

609

Quercus kelloggii (California black oak):
  Twigs and small branches, on
    Scale
      Asterolecanium minus, 112
Quercus lobata (California white oak):
  Foliage, on
    Caterpillar
      Phryganidia californica, 220
  Twigs and small branches, on
    Scales
      Asterolecanium minus, 112
      Kermes cockerelli, 120

Rabbitbrush (*Chrysothamnus*)
Redcedar (*Thuja*)
Redwood (*Sequoia sempervirens*)
Rhamnus purshiana (cascara, buckthorn):
  Twigs and small branches, under bark
    Beetles, bark
      Chramesus spp., 346
Rhododendron (rhododendron, azalea):
  Foliage, on
    Caterpillar
      Phryganidia californica, 220
    Thrips
      Thrips madronii, 79
    Weevils
      Nemocestes incomptus, 328
      Otiorhynchus ovatus, 329
      Otiorhynchus rugosostriatus, 329
      Otiorhynchus sulcatus, 329
      Sciopithes obscurus, 335
    Whitefly
      Dialeurodes chittendeni, 110
  Foliage, in
    Miner
      Lyonetia candida, 137
  Roots, on
    Weevils, root
      Nemocestes incomptus, 328
      Otiorhynchus ovatus, 329
      Otiorhynchus rugosostriatus, 329
      Otiorhynchus sulcatus, 329
      Sciopithes obscurus, 335
Rhus (sumac):
  Trunk and large branches, under bark
    Beetle, bark
      Chaetophloeus penicillatus, 345
Ribes (currant):
  Foliage, on
    Caterpillar
      Xylomyges simplex, 234
    Caterpillar, tent
      Malacosoma californicum, 188
Robinia (locust):
  Seeds
    Beetles, seed
      Bruchidae, 321

Robinia (locust)—Continued
  Twigs and small branches, under bark
    Beetles, bark
      Chramesus spp., 346
Robinia pseudoacacia (black locust):
  Trunk and large branches, in wood
    Borers, roundheaded
      Megacyllene robiniae, 301
      Neoclytus acuminatus, 302
    Carpenterworm
      Prionoxystus robiniae, 132
Rosa (rose):
  Foliage, on
    Caterpillar
      Orgyia vetusta gulosa, 226
    Caterpillar, tent
      Malacosoma californicum, 188
    Leafhopper
      Edwardsiana rosae, 93
Rose (*Rosa*)

Sagebrush (*Artemisia*)
Saguaro (*Cereus giganteus*)
Salal (*Gaultheria shallon*)
Salix (willow):
  Flowers
    Louse, jumping plant
      Psylla americana, 93
    Sawflies
      Xyela spp., 436
    Weevils
      Dorytomus spp., 325
  Foliage, on
    Aphids
      Chaitophorus spp., 94
    Beetles, leaf
      Altica bimarginata, 315
      Altica prasina, 316
      Chrysomela aeneicollis, 317
      Chrysomela scripta, 317
      Gonioctena arctica, 318
      Gonioctena notmani, 318
      Melasomida californica, 318
      Phratora frosti remisa, 319
      Phratora interstitialis, 319
      Phratora purpurea purpurea, 319
      Pyrrhalta decora carbo, 319
      Pyrrhalta decora decora, 319
      Pyrrhalta punctipennis, 319
      Syneta albida, 320
    Beetle
      Buprestis langi, 259
    Beetle, longhorned
      Oberea schaumii, 311
    Bugs, lace
      Corythucha elegans, 83
      Corythucha salicata, 83

Thuja plicata (western redcedar)—Con.
Foliage, on
Beetle
Trachykele blondeli, 265
Caterpillar
Halisidota argentata, 216
Leaftier
Herculia phoezalis, 185
Loopers
Caripeta divisata, 202
Ectropis crepuscularia, 202
Lambdina fiscellaria lugubrosa,
205
Melanolophia imitata, 209
Neoalcis californiaria, 210
Nepytia phantasmaria, 212
Nepytia umbrosaria nigrovenaria,
213
Webworm
Halisidota argentata, 216
Trunk and large branches, under bark
Beetles, bark
Phloeosinus punctatus, 369
Phloeosinus sequoiae, 369
Phloeosinus spp., 366
Borers, roundheaded
Atimia confusa, 292
Semanotus amethystinus, 304
Trunk and large branches, in wood
Beetle, ambrosia
Gnathotrichus sulcatus, 381
Borer, flatheaded
Trachykele blondeli, 265
Horntails
Urocerus albicornis, 457
Xeris tarsalis, 457
Weevils, sapwood
Hexarthrum thujae, 334
Rhyncolus brunneus, 334
Roots, on
Weevils, root
Otiorhynchus spp. 328
Tsuga (hemlock):
Cones and seeds
Looper, cone
Eupithecia spermaphaga, 204
Maggot, cone
Earomyia barbara, 426
Moth, cone
Dioryctria pseudotsugella, 185
Dioryctria reniculelloides, 185
Foliage, on
Beetle, scarab
Polyphylla decemlineata, 250
Budworms
Acleris gloverana, 163
Archippus tsuganus, 165
Dioryctria pseudotsugella, 185
Dioryctria reniculelloides, 185
Loopers
Caripeta aequaliaria, 202

Tsuga (hemlock)—Continued
Foliage, on—Continued
Loopers—Continued
Eupithecia annulata, 204
Eupithecia luteata, 204
Lambdina fiscellaria fiscellaria,
205
Lambdina fiscellaria lugubrosa,
205
Nyctobia limitaria, 213
Mite, spider
Oligonychus ununguis, 61
Sawfly
Neodiprion abietis var., 441
Sawfly, webspinning
Acantholyda balanata, 435
Buds and shoots, in
Budworms
Acleris gloverana, 163
Dioryctria reniculelloides, 185
Twigs and small branches, on
Spittlebug
Aphrophora permutata, 89
Twigs and small branches, under bark
Beetles, bark
Pityophthorus pseudotsugae, 402
Scolytus praeceps, 406
Twigs and small branches, in wood
Moth, tip
Argyresthia tsuga, 142
Trunk and large branches, under bark
Beetles, bark
Dryocoetes autographus, 378
Hylastes nigrinus, 364
Scolytus abietis, 405
Scolytus unispinosus, 408
Scolytus ventralis, 409
Borers, roundheaded
Phymatodes aeneus, 303
Phymatodes dimidiatus, 303
Rhagium inquisitor, 297
Semanotus litigiosus, 305
Weevils, bark
Steremnius carinatus, 336
Steremnius tuberosus, 336
Trunk and large branches, in wood
Beetles, ambrosia
Gnathotrichus retusus, 381
Gnathotrichus sulcatus, 381
Trypodendron lineatum, 411
Xyleborus saxeseni, 413
Beetle, powderpost
Microbregma emarginatum, 270
Borer, flatheaded
Chrysophana placida, 261
Borers, roundheaded
Acmaeops proteus, 295
Anoplodera canadensis, 295
Leptura obliterata, 296
Pachyta armata, 297
Phymatodes dimidiatus, 303

GENERAL INDEX

This index provides the principal access to information in the manual. It has both routine and innovative features.

Principal pages for insect species, taxonomic groups, and subjects of importance are designated by bold-face type. For insect species, the principal pages are the initial page of a text discussion and tables or text tabulations supplementing this discussion. Both the insect scientific name and its common name, if one is available, are given in the text discussion. Elsewhere in the text, use of scientific names and common names is alternated. To provide access for a reader, complete pagination is listed for insects under both scientific and common names. This procedure was also followed in indexing closely related species having a group common name.

In addition, pages with illustrations are marked with an asterisk. Illustrations for an insect are designated under both scientific and common names. If an illustration involves an insect-related condition—e.g., blowdown, insect disease—appropriate pages are designated with an asterisk for both the insect and the subject.

631

647

651

653

☆ US GOVERNMENT PRINTING OFFICE: 1978 O—221—622